Msgr. J.J. O'Brien
Elementary / Jr. High School
99 Bridlewood Road SW
Calgary, AB T2Y 4J5

♡
Love

$(-5)-(-10)=$

SCIENCEFOCUS 7

McGraw-Hill Ryerson SCIENCEFOCUS Program

SCIENCEFOCUS 7

SCIENCEFOCUS 8

Chenelière/McGraw-Hill CONVERGENCES Program

CONVERGENCES 7

CONVERGENCES 8

This program is available directly from Chenelière/McGraw-Hill.

Teacher Support for Each Grade Level

Teacher's Resource, including *Blackline Masters* and *Assessment Checklists* and *Rubrics*
Computerized Assessment Bank
Web site: *http://www.mcgrawhill.ca*
Videotape series

The information and activities in this textbook have been carefully developed and reviewed by professionals to ensure safety and accuracy. However, the publisher shall not be liable for any damages resulting, in whole or in part, from the reader's use of the material. Although appropriate safety procedures are discussed in detail and highlighted throughout the textbook, the safety of students remains the responsibility of the classroom teacher, the principal, and the school board/district.

Our cover Bull elk in velvet, Jasper National Park, Alberta. Have you ever seen an elk such as this one? If so, where did you see it and what was it doing? What are its habits? What living and non-living things are a part of its life? In its natural environment, the elk's numbers are naturally controlled. How have people created an elk "problem" in some places? As you study Unit 1 in this textbook, do some research into the life of the elk, and expand your answers to the questions.

SCIENCE FOCUS 7

SCIENCE · TECHNOLOGY · SOCIETY

Author/Consultant Team

David Gue
Crescent Heights High School
Medicine Hat, Alberta

Dale Makar
Montgomery Junior High School
Calgary, Alberta

Jacqueline Martin
Simon Fraser Junior High School
Calgary, Alberta

Teresa Martin
F.E. Osborne Junior High School
Calgary, Alberta

Ian Strachan
Midsun Junior High School
Calgary, Alberta

Jean Bullard
Professional Writer
Parksville, British Columbia

Gene Krupa
University of Alberta
Edmonton, Alberta

Mary Krupa
Professional Writer
Kelowna, British Columbia

Betty Anne Kiddell
Acadia Junior High School
Winnipeg, Manitoba

Christina Clancy
Loyola Catholic Secondary School
Mississauga, Ontario

Don Galbraith
University of Toronto
Toronto, Ontario

Senior Program Consultant

Douglas A. Roberts
University of Calgary
Calgary, Alberta

Publishing Consultant

Trudy L. Rising

McGraw-Hill Ryerson

Toronto Montréal New York Burr Ridge Bangkok Beijing Bogotá Caracas Dubuque
Kuala Lumpur Lisbon London Madison Madrid Mexico City Milan New Delhi
San Francisco Santiago St. Louis Seoul Singapore Sydney Taipei

McGraw-Hill Ryerson Limited

A Subsidiary of The McGraw·Hill Companies

COPIES OF THIS BOOK MAY BE OBTAINED BY CONTACTING:

McGraw-Hill Ryerson Ltd.

WEB SITE:
http://www.mcgrawhill.ca

E-MAIL:
orders@mcgrawhill.ca

TOLL-FREE FAX:
1-800-463-5885

TOLL-FREE CALL:
1-800-565-5758

OR BY MAILING YOUR ORDER TO:
McGraw-Hill Ryerson
Order Department
300 Water Street
Whitby, ON L1N 9B6

Please quote the ISBN and title when placing your order.

Student Text ISBN:
0-07-086467-5

SCIENCEFOCUS 7
Science • Technology • Society

The information and activities in this textbook have been carefully developed and reviewed by professionals to ensure safety and accuracy. However, the publisher shall not be liable for any damages resulting, in whole or in part, from the reader's use of the material. Although appropriate safety procedures are discussed in detail and highlighted throughout the textbook, the safety of students remains the responsibility of the classroom teacher, the principal, and the school board/district.

ISBN-13: 978-0-07-086467-2
ISBN-10: 0-07-086467-5

Copies of this book may be obtained by contacting McGraw-Hill Ryerson Ltd.: e-mail: *orders@mcgrawhill.ca*; toll free fax: 1-800-463-5885: toll free call: 1-800-565-5758 or by mailing your order to: McGraw-Hill Ryerson Order Department, 300 Water Street, Whitby, Ontario, L1N 9B6. Please quote the ISBN and title when placing your order.

http://www.mcgrawhill.ca

9 TCP 1 9 8 7 6 5 4 3

Printed and bound in Canada

Care has been taken to trace ownership of copyright material contained in this textbook. The publisher will gladly take any information that will enable them to rectify any reference or credit in subsequent printings. Please note that products shown in photographs in this textbook do not reflect an endorsement by the publisher of those specific brand names.

Canadian Cataloguing in Publication Data

Main entry under title:

ScienceFocus 7: science, technology, society

Includes index.

ISBN 0-07-086467-5

1. Science – Juvenile literature. I. Bullard, Jean, date.

Q161.2.S353 2001   500   C00-932081-4

The SCIENCEFOCUS Development Team

SCIENCE PUBLISHERS: Trudy Rising, Jane McNulty
PROJECT MANAGER/SENIOR DEVELOPMENTAL EDITOR: Sheila Fletcher
DEVELOPMENTAL EDITORS: Tricia Armstrong, Jenna Dunlop, Nancy Landry, Adrienne Mason, Lauri Seidlitz
SENIOR SUPERVISING EDITOR: Linda Allison
PROJECT CO-ORDINATORS: Nancy Landry, Shannon Leahy
ASSISTANT PROJECT CO-ORDINATORS: Melissa Nippard, Janie Reeson
SPECIAL FEATURES: Trudee Romanek, Elma Schemenauer
COPY EDITORS: Valerie Ahwee, Janet Shorten
PERMISSIONS EDITOR: Ann Ludbrook
PRODUCTION SUPERVISOR: Yolanda Pigden
PRODUCTION CO-ORDINATOR: Jennifer Vassiliou
DESIGN AND ELECTRONIC PAGE MAKE-UP: Pronk&Associates
SET-UP PHOTOGRAPHY: Ian Crysler
SET-UP PHOTOGRAPHY CO-ORDINATORS: Jane Affleck, Julie Greener
TECHNICAL ART: Imagineering Scientific and Technical Artworks Inc./Pronk&Associates
ILLUSTRATIONS: Steve Attoe, Jun Park, Deborah Crowle, Dave Whamond, Theresa Sakno
COVER IMAGE: Bill Terry/Take Stock Inc.

Acknowledgements

Senior Program Consultant

Douglas A. Roberts
University of Calgary
Calgary, Alberta

Teacher Reviewers

Barry Byam
Hamilton Junior High School
Lethbridge, Alberta

Richard Gerlach
William D. Cuts School
St. Albert, Alberta

Dan Haley
St. Mary's School
Edmonton, Alberta

Kay Jauch
Edmonton Public Schools
Edmonton, Alberta

Joan Liland
Terry Fox Junior High School
Calgary, Alberta

Frank Lowe
Hamilton Junior High School
Lethbridge, Alberta

Robert Luck
Graminia School
Spruce Grove, Alberta

Roy McConnell
Woodhaven Junior High School
Spruce Grove, Alberta

Jacinthe Moquin
St. Mary's School
Edmonton, Alberta

Guy Pomahac
Wilson Middle School
Lethbridge, Alberta

Shawn Russell
Red Deer Public School District #104
Red Deer, Alberta

Gerry-Lynn Tober
St. Patrick's Community School
Red Deer, Alberta

Safety Reviewer

Professor Margaret-Ann Armour
Department of Chemistry
University of Alberta
Edmonton, Alberta

The publisher wishes to express thanks to the following teachers who field-tested *SCIENCEFOCUS* 7 for the publisher, and also those who field-tested for Alberta Learning. Their feedback, comments, and suggestions for practical classroom procedures were of immeasurable assistance during the final revision stage. We would also like to express our sincere appreciation to all of the Gr. 7 students who were part of this field test. Their responses to our material both pleased and challenged us to make the resources better.

Joy Bader
Mount Royal Junior High School
Calgary, Alberta

Elizabeth Bennett
Holy Spirit Catholic School
Cochrane, Alberta

Elaine Bolt
Sir John A. Macdonald School
Calgary, Alberta

Nola Bonner
St. Cecilia School
Edmonton, Alberta

Brian Calkins
I.V. Macklin School
Grande Prairie, Alberta

Sven Danzinger
Steele Heights School
Edmonton, Alberta

Henry Epp
Montgomery Junior High School
Calgary, Alberta

Deryk Hamilton
I.V. Macklin School
Grande Prairie, Alberta

Nancy Hopkins
St. Gregory School
Calgary, Alberta

Chad Kuzyk
Okotoks Junior High School
Okotoks, Alberta

Terry van Leeuwen
Allendale School
Edmonton, Alberta

Joan Liland
Mount Royal Junior High School
Calgary, Alberta

David Maguire
Landing Trail Intermediate School
Athabasca, Alberta

Dale Makar
Montgomery Junior High School
Calgary, Alberta

Mike Male
Wilma Hansen Junior High School
Calgary, Alberta

David Perkins
Steele Heights School
Edmonton, Alberta

Miriam Quapp
H.D. Cartwright School
Calgary, Alberta

Doug Simpson
Montgomery Junior High School
Calgary, Alberta

Kevin Sonico
I.V. Macklin School
Grande Prairie, Alberta

Laurie Stackhouse
Robert Warren School
Calgary, Alberta

Vin Stocking
Steele Heights School
Edmonton, Alberta

Beth Veale
Senator P. Burns School
Calgary, Alberta

Peter Walter
Robert Warren School
Calgary, Alberta

Teachers who field tested the program as part of Alberta Learning field tests:

Terry Van Leeuwen
Judy Knight
George Thomson
Eileen Stephens
Amy Christiansen
Rob Peet
Colin Desnoyers
Ernest Lockert
Tanya Faulkner
Jason Burke

Susan Oreski
Linda Hammond
Elaan Koshka
Robert Shkrobot
Mark Stranzinger
Theresa Lema
Ian Befus
Karen Mackay
Stuart Wilson
Ken Valgardson

Harry Vince
Gerald Paquette
Ken McKenzie
Nina Scrivens
Greg Borm
Julie Ann Pederson
Garry Bell
Mike Tyler

Contents

Unit 4 Structures and Forces 266

Unit 5 Planet Earth 350

To the Teacher

We are very pleased to have been part of the team of experienced science educators and editors working together to bring you and your students this new program — the *SCIENCEFOCUS 7–8* series of textbooks, and its French equivalent, *CONVERGENCES 7–8*. The *SCIENCEFOCUS* and *CONVERGENCES* student and teacher resources were specifically developed to provide 100 percent congruence with the new Alberta curriculum. As the titles *SCIENCEFOCUS* and *CONVERGENCES* suggest, these resources are designed to develop a focus for investigative activities and the application of ideas by students. This approach is intended to help students to understand our world, and to empower them to critically examine issues and questions from a societal and environmental perspective.

SCIENCEFOCUS/CONVERGENCES 7 provide:

- A science inquiry emphasis, in which students use the processes of science to address questions about the nature of science involving broad explorations as well as focussed investigations. Process skill areas emphasized include: careful observing; questioning; proposing ideas; predicting; hypothesizing; making inferences; designing experiments; gathering, processing, and interpreting data; and explaining and communicating.

- A technological problem-solving emphasis, in which students seek answers to practical problems. Problem solving may either precede knowledge acquisition or provide students with opportunities to apply their newly acquired science knowledge in novel ways. Skill areas emphasized include: understanding the problem; setting and/or understanding criteria; developing a design plan; carrying out the plan; evaluating; and communicating.

- A societal decision-making emphasis, in which students draw upon those science and technology concepts and skills that will inform the question or issue under consideration. Students are encouraged to focus attention on sustainability and stewardship. Wherever possible, these concepts are developed in relation to issues of local interest and concern. Skill areas that are emphasized include: identifying the issue; identifying alternatives; researching, reflecting, and deciding; taking action; evaluating; and communicating.

The particular emphases within a unit are, in part, suggested by the subject of the unit. The primary and secondary emphases for *SCIENCEFOCUS* 7 and *CONVERGENCES* 7 are listed in the table opposite.

Scientific literacy has become the goal in science education throughout the world, and this goal has been given expression in Canada in the *Common Framework of Science Learning Outcomes, K-12: Pan-Canadian Protocol for Collaboration on School Curriculum* (Council of Ministers of Education, Canada, 1997).

"Scientific literacy is an evolving combination of the science-related attitudes, skills, and knowledge students need to develop inquiry, problem-solving, and decision-making abilities, to become lifelong learners, and to maintain a sense of wonder about the world around them. To develop scientific literacy, students require diverse learning experiences which provide opportunity to explore, analyze, evaluate, synthesize, appreciate, and understand the interrelationships among science, technology, society, and the environment that will affect their personal lives, their careers, and their future."

	SCIENCEFOCUS 7/ CONVERGENCES 7 Unit	Primary Emphasis	Secondary Emphasis
Life Systems Interactions and Ecosystems	Unit 1 Interactions and Ecosystems	Social and Environmental Context (STS)	Nature of Science
Life Systems Plants for Food and Fibre	Unit 2 Plants for Food and Fibre	Science and Technology	Nature of Science
Energy and Control Heat and Temperature	Unit 3 Heat and Temperature	Social and Environmental Context (STS)	Science and Technology
Structures and Mechanisms Structures and Forces	Unit 4 Structures and Forces	Nature of Science	Science and Technology
Earth and Space Systems Planet Earth	Unit 5 Planet Earth	Science and Technology	Nature of Science

On the following two pages you will find charts that provide a ready reference for the Concept, Skill, and Attitude outcomes that are developed in each unit.

Through varied text features, **SCIENCEFOCUS** 7 enables students to understand and develop skills in the processes of scientific inquiry, and in relating science to technology, society, and the environment.

Like the other textbooks in our series, **SCIENCEFOCUS** 7 builds on the three basic goals of the curriculum and reflects the essential triad of knowledge, skills, and the ability to relate science to technology, society, and the environment (STS). Science is approached both as an intellectual pursuit, and also as an activity-based enterprise operating within a social context.

Our extensive *Teacher's Resource* provides essential planning and implementation strategies that you will find helpful and practical. Our *Blackline Masters* include materials that you can use for vocabulary building, skill building, and concept clarification, and as well as alternative activities for multiple learning styles. Our *Assessment Checklists* include forms for performance task assessment of student achievement that are specific to the unit of study, and forms for assessment that focus on larger encompassing skills of science, technology, and societal decision making. Our *Computerized Assessment Bank* will assist you in your full implementation of the **SCIENCEFOCUS** 7 program.

We feel confident that we have provided you with the best possible program to help ensure that your students achieve excellence and a high degree of scientific literacy through their course of study.

The Authors and Senior Program Consultants

Focus on

Key Concepts	Unit 1	Unit 2
	In this unit, you will investigate ■ the interactions between living things and their environment ■ how nutrients and energy cycle through the environment ■ the roles of organisms within the environment ■ how species in an environment can change over time ■ how species become endangered or extinct and how people are helping to save endangered species ■ how the impacts of human activities can be monitored, assessed, and managed to minimize their effects	In this unit, you will investigate ■ how we depend on plants for food and fibre ■ the role of plants in the environment ■ the structure and function of plant parts ■ how we grow and harvest plants for food and fibre ■ technologies and practices used to increase yield and to improve growing conditions for plants ■ soil characteristics and soil health ■ the role of fertilizers and control of pests

Key Skills

In this unit you will ■ ask questions about the relationships between and among living organisms (including people) and the environment ■ design an experiment to investigate a question ■ conduct investigations and gather and record data ■ analyze data and develop possible explanations ■ work in a team to solve problems	In this unit, you will ■ plan investigations that will show how various factors affect the growth of plants ■ construct and test prototype designs of a way to grow plants without soil ■ record and display data in a variety of ways ■ identify some of the problems and possible solutions in growing plants for food and fibre ■ evaluate the processes you used to plan, solve problems, make decisions, and complete a task

Key Attitudes

In this unit, you will be encouraged to ■ appreciate how science and technology contribute to an understanding of ecosystems ■ show awareness of and respect for people who contribute to an understanding of ecosystems ■ evaluate different approaches to investigations, problems, and issues ■ demonstrate responsibility in balancing the needs of humans with a sustainable environment	In this unit, you will be encouraged to ■ appreciate how science and technology contribute to the ability to produce plants ■ consider scientific knowledge and practical experience to improve how we grow plants for food and fibre ■ appreciate how people in various cultures have used and produced plants in different ways ■ consider how we must grow and harvest plants in a way that balances the needs of people with the need to maintain a healthy environment

Unit 3

In this unit, you will investigate
- the relationship between heat-related technologies and human needs
- how various devices and materials respond to temperature change
- ways in which technological devices control the transfer of energy
- how the particle model explains temperature and the effect of heat on solids, liquids, and gases
- advantages and disadvantages of using and controlling energy
- personal and societal choices in energy use and conservation

In this unit, you will
- carry out procedures that demonstrate how heat is transmitted by conduction, convection, and radiation in solids, liquids, and gases
- design, build, test, and evaluate structures that solve practical problems
- identify and evaluate different sources of heat and the environmental impacts of their use
- compare the energy consumption of alternative technologies for heat production and use, and identify related questions and issues

In this unit, you will be encouraged to
- appreciate the benefits of science and technology and to find ways to limit their negative effects
- find ways to conserve energy in order to sustain our fossil fuel resources
- be sensitive to human needs for technology and responsible in your use of energy

Unit 4

In this unit, you will investigate
- how form, function, joints, and materials affect structures
- the performance requirements of various types of structures and methods used to evaluate and improve structures
- how to identify and measure forces and loads that operate on and within structures
- how tension, compression, shearing, and bending forces cause structures to fail
- how a structure's foundation and distribution of mass affect its stability

In this unit, you will
- research traditional and classical structures and prepare a report
- carry out procedures to test and analyze the properties of materials
- design, build, test, and evaluate structures that solve practical problems
- organize and display data from investigations
- work co-operatively with team members to solve design problems
- apply findings from investigations to solve design problems

In this unit, you will be encouraged to
- appreciate the role of scientific knowledge in designing and building successful structures
- generate and evaluate ideas as the member of a team
- test and accurately report the limitations of your designs and prototypes
- appreciate that excellent structural forms come from various cultures and from nature

Unit 5

In this unit, you will investigate
- how rocks form and continue to change in a cycle
- how weathering and erosion affect your geographic area
- how technologies help scientists study Earth's crust and make models of Earth's interior
- how changes in Earth's crust can be sudden or gradual
- how earthquakes, volcanoes, and mountains are created
- how fossils, rocks, and climate provide clues to Earth's history

In this unit, you will
- identify characteristics of minerals
- construct a classification key for the three main classes of rocks
- explore theories about Earth's crust
- plot locations on a map, using latitude and longitude, to find out where plate boundaries and mountains occur
- analyze data to find patterns and trends in earthquake and volcano occurrence
- investigate fossil evidence of the ancient world

In this unit, you will be encouraged to
- express your interest in science-related questions, careers, and the contributions of individuals and groups
- work together to generate and evaluate ideas and carry out investigations
- plan and perform activities safely and responsibly
- appreciate the role, contributions, and limits of science and technology

A Tour of Your Textbook

Welcome to *SCIENCEFOCUS* 7. This textbook introduces you to some of the wonders of science and technology in the world around you. To understand the book's structure, begin by taking the brief tour on the following pages. Then do the *Feature Hunt* on page xxv to check your understanding of how to use this book.

Unit Opener

- *SCIENCEFOCUS* 7 has five major units.
- Each unit opener provides a clear overview of the unit's contents.
- The unit opener sparks interest in the subject. It might suggest a technological problem to think about, present science ideas to investigate, or highlight a societal issue to explore.
- The unit opener identifies the unit's Topics.

Unit Preview

Each unit preview draws you into the major emphasis of the unit: science inquiry, technology, or societal issues.

- **Focussing questions** invite you to reflect on what you already know (or will learn) about the upcoming Topics.
- Interesting photographs are combined with brief descriptions of what you will find in each cluster of Topics.

- **Looking Ahead** helps you to prepare for your end-of-unit challenge. It gives you an idea of what you will be doing and provides suggestions to get you started on this group task. This feature is always presented in a Palm Pilot™ frame to remind you to make the best use of the current technology that is available to you.

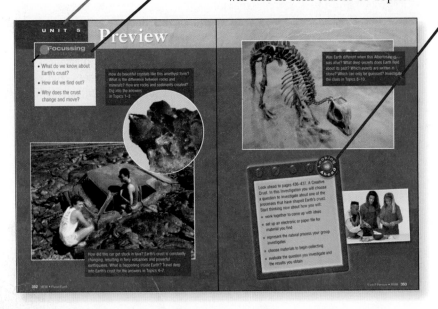

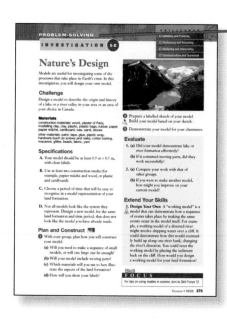

Problem-Solving Investigation

- These hands-on investigations set challenges to design and construct your own models, systems, or products. They teach design skills and blend science and technology in new and different ways.
- The co-operative group work icon signals that you will be doing these investigations in a team.
- The specifications provide a way to evaluate your results.
- You and your team members are then on your own to design and construct!

Decision-Making Investigation

- These investigations appear in units that invite you to look at societal issues related to science and/or technology. They present a problem related to the issues you are considering in the unit.
- In these investigations, you will usually work with your group to consider alternatives to the problem and present some alternatives that your group can analyze and discuss.
- The heading, "How Can Science Help?" reminds you to make use of the scientific skills and processes that you are learning about.

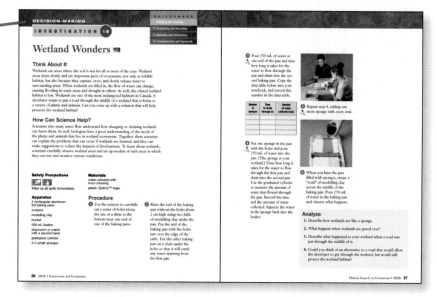

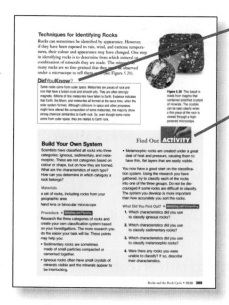

Did You Know?

- These features present interesting facts that are related to science, technology, nature, and the universe.

Find Out Activity

- These are usually short, informal inquiries that often involve hands-on exploration.
- They require simple materials and equipment.
- In these activities, as well as in the investigations, you will use important science process skills, such as predicting, estimating, and hypothesizing.

Inquiry Investigation

- One- to four-page "formal" labs provide an opportunity to develop science process skills using various equipment and materials.

- These investigations provide a chance to ask questions about science, to make observations, and to obtain results.

- You then analyze your results to determine what they tell you about the Topic you are investigating.

- Photographs showing each major step in the Procedure help you to carry out the investigation.

- Safety icons and Safety Precautions alert you to any special precautions you should take to help maintain a safe classroom environment.

- The pencil icon signals that you should make a written note of your predictions or observations.

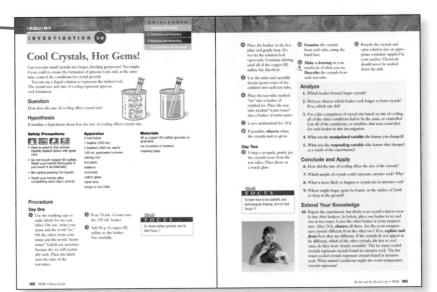

Think & Link Investigation

- One- to two-page "thought" or "paper-based" investigations let you explore ideas or connections that might be impractical or dangerous in the science classroom.

- These investigations emphasize a variety of skills. These skills include analyzing data, interpreting diagrams or photographs, and forming ideas, opinions, or recommendations based on analysis of a societal issue.

- They provide you with opportunities to "think and link" — to think about scientific results and issues that involve science and technology. You will increase your skills of analysis by doing these investigations.

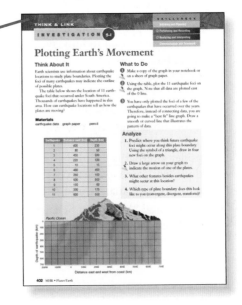

Mathconnect

- These features review mathematics skills that you need in order to do activities or investigations.

- They make connections between your science studies and your mathematics studies.

Cool Tools

- These features provide information about some of the equipment and instruments that have been invented to help humans explore the unknown.

- This information is often related to a variety of occupations and situations.

Topic Review

- A set of review questions appears at the end of each Topic.
- These questions provide opportunities for ongoing self-assessment.
- **Apply**, **Design Your Own**, and **Thinking Critically** questions give you additional challenges.

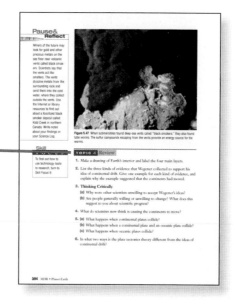

Pause&Reflect

Miners of the future may look for gold and other precious metals on the sea floor near volcanic vents called black smokers. Scientists say that the vents act like smelters. The vents dissolve metals from the surrounding rock and send them into the cold water, where they collect outside the vents. Use the Internet or library resources to find out about a fossilized black smoker deposit called Kidd Creek in northern Canada. Write notes about your findings in your Science Log.

Figure 5.47 When submersibles found deep-sea vents called "black smokers," they also found tube worms. The sulfur compounds escaping from the vents provide an energy source for the worms.

Skill

To find out how to use technology tools to research, turn to Skill Focus 9.

TOPIC 4 Review

1. Make a drawing of Earth's interior and label the four main layers.

2. List the three kinds of evidence that Wegener collected to support his idea of continental drift. Give one example for each kind of evidence, and explain why the example suggested that the continents had moved.

3. **Thinking Critically**
   (a) Why were other scientists unwilling to accept Wegener's ideas?
   (b) Are people generally willing or unwilling to change? What does this suggest to you about scientific progress?

4. What do scientists now think is causing the continents to move?

5. (a) What happens when continental plates collide?
   (b) What happens when a continental plate and an oceanic plate collide?
   (c) What happens when oceanic plates collide?

6. In what two ways is the plate tectonics theory different from the ideas of continental drift?

394 MHR • Planet Earth

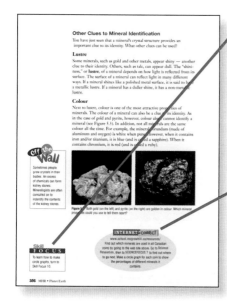

Other Clues to Mineral Identification

You have just seen that a mineral's crystal structure provides an important clue to its identity. What other clues can be used?

Lustre

Some minerals, such as gold and other metals, appear shiny — another clue to their identity. Others, such as talc, can appear dull. The "shininess," or **lustre**, of a mineral depends on how light is reflected from its surface. The surface of a mineral can reflect light in many different ways. If a mineral shines like a polished metal surface, it is said to have a metallic lustre. If a mineral has a duller shine, it has a non-metallic lustre.

Colour

Next to lustre, colour is one of the most attractive properties of minerals. The colour of a mineral can also be a clue to its identity. As in the case of gold and pyrite, however, colour alone cannot identify a mineral (see Figure 5.3). In addition, not all minerals are the same colour all the time. For example, the mineral corundum (made of aluminum and oxygen) is white when pure. However, when it contains iron and/or titanium, it is blue (and is called a sapphire). When it contains chromium, it is red (and is called a ruby).

Off the Wall

Sometimes people grow crystals in their bodies. An excess of chemicals can form kidney stones. Mineralogists are often consulted on to indentify the contents of the kidney stones.

Figure Both gold (on the left) and pyrite (on the right) are golden in colour. Which mineral properties could you use to tell them apart?

Skill FOCUS

To learn how to make circle graphs, turn to Skill Focus 10.

INTERNET CONNECT

www.school.mcgrawhill.ca/resources/
Find out which minerals are used in all Canadian coins by going to the web site above. Go to Science Resources, then to SCIENCEFOCUS 7 to find out where to go next. Make a circle graph for each coin to show the percentages of different minerals it contains.

356 MHR • Planet Earth

Skill Focus

- Skill development tips refer you to the **Science Skills Guide** at the back of this textbook.
- These tips provide specific skill development methods and activities as they are needed, for example in estimating and measuring and in scientific drawing. (The Contents page of the **Science Skills Guide** is shown on page xxv, "Wrapping Up the Tour.")

Internetconnect

- These features encourage productive use of the Internet by offering content-related sites.
- Web site suggestions will save you time as you do research.

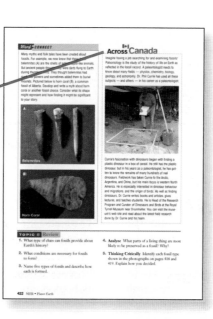

Word CONNECT

Many myths and folk tales have been created about fossils. For example, we now know that these tiny belemnites (A) are the shells of squid-like animals. But ancient people thought they were darts flung to Earth during thunderstorms. They thought belemnites had magical powers and sometimes added them to burial mounds. Pictured below is horn coral (B), a common fossil of Alberta. Develop and write a myth about horn coral or another fossil choice. Consider what its shape might represent and how finding it might be significant to your story.

A
Belemnites

B
Horn Coral

Across Canada

Imagine having a job searching for and examining fossils! Paleontology is the study of the history of life on Earth as reflected in the fossil record. A paleontologist needs to know about many fields — physics, chemistry, biology, geology, and astronomy. Dr. Phil Currie has used all these subjects — and others — in his career as a paleontologist.

Currie's fascination with dinosaurs began with finding a plastic dinosaur in a box of cereal. He still has the plastic dinosaur, but in his years as a paleontologist, he has gotten to know the remains of many hundreds of real dinosaurs. Fieldwork has taken Currie to the Arctic, Argentina, and China, but his main focus is western North America. He is especially interested in dinosaur behaviour and migrations, and the origin of birds. As well as finding dinosaurs, Dr. Currie writes books and articles, gives lectures, and teaches students. He is Head of the Research Program and Curator of Dinosaurs and Birds at the Royal Tyrrell Museum near Drumheller. You can visit the museum's web site and read about the latest field research done by Dr. Currie and his team.

TOPIC 8 Review

1. What type of clues can fossils provide about Earth's history?

2. What conditions are necessary for fossils to form?

3. Name five types of fossils and describe how each is formed.

4. **Analyze** What parts of a living thing are more likely to be preserved as a fossil? Why?

5. **Thinking Critically** Identify each fossil type shown in the photographs on pages 418 and 419. Explain how you decided.

422 MHR • Planet Earth

Across Canada

- These "mini-essays" feature information on Canadian scientists involved in important research and discoveries.
- The essays increase awareness and appreciation of the work of Canadian scientists. They also provide role models for those of you who are interested in careers or further study in science.

A Tour of Your Textbook • MHR **xxi**

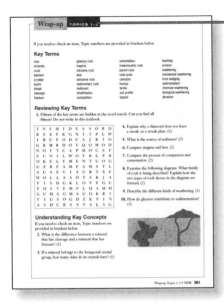

Wrap-up

- Located at the end of each cluster of Topics, this page provides self-assessment opportunities as you look back over two or three Topics.
- It gives parents or guardians an overview of what you have accomplished.

End-of-Unit Features

Ask an Expert

- Experts in every area of science and technology are working to understand better how the world "works" and to try to find solutions to difficult problems. The *Ask an Expert* feature at the end of each unit is an interview with one of these experts.
- After you read each interview, you will have a chance to do an activity that is related to the kind of work the expert does.

End-of-Unit Challenge:
Design Your Own Investigation
An Issue to Analyze
Project

- Each unit in *SCIENCEFOCUS* 7 presents a challenge that will provide an opportunity for you and your group to use what you have learned throughout the unit. These challenges will take three different forms, depending on the emphasis of the unit.
- Early in the unit, your teacher will ask you to begin to consider how you might research, organize, plan, and complete your end-of-unit challenge.

Design Your Own Investigation

- As you work through each unit, you will find answers to some science questions. You will also think of more questions of your own.
- The Design Your Own Investigation challenge enables you to develop an experimental procedure to answer your questions. You will work with your group to come up with a hypothesis or a prediction that you can test. Your question will be based on what you have learned in the unit.
- You will design and carry out your experimental procedure and then evaluate the results.

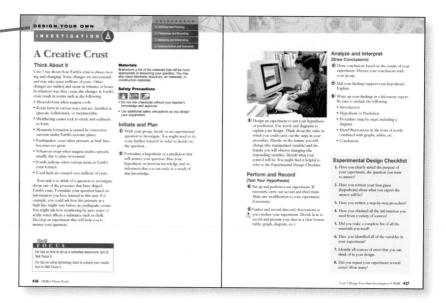

An Issue to Analyze

- You, your community, and society in general face complex issues in today's world. Understanding science and technology cannot provide a "correct" answer to the problems these issues present, but understanding will lead to more informed decisions. *An Issue to Analyze* gives you a chance to start thinking now about how you can use your understanding of Science Skills and concepts to help make the best decisions for yourself and your community, today and in the future.
- Each issue analysis is in the form of a simulation, a debate, or a case study.

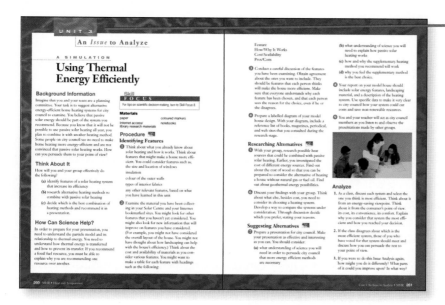

Project

- The Unit Project gives you a chance to use key concepts and skills from the unit to design and create a device, system, or model of your own.
- You will complete the project as part of a team.
- *More Project Ideas* offers additional suggestions for enjoyable ways to demonstrate your learning.

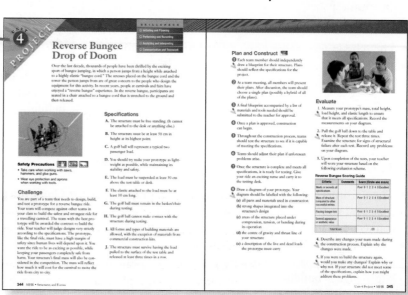

Unit Review

- This final wrap-up of each unit reviews basic concepts, skills of inquiry and communication, and skills relating science to technology, society, and the environment.
- These questions help you recall, think about, and apply what you have learned.

Other Important Features

- These items feature intriguing situations, odd events, or weird facts.
- Ideas for connecting science with other curriculum areas are often included.

STRETCH Your Mind

- These brain teasers are often related to mathematics.
- They draw upon your problem-solving skills and your imagination.

Pause & Reflect

- These features give you opportunities to reflect on what you know (or do not know) and to make connections among ideas throughout the textbook.
- They encourage you to construct your own learning on an ongoing basis and to keep track of how your knowledge is building.

Word CONNECT

- Word origins and a variety of language activities provide links to language arts.

Career CONNECT

- These features portray people with various levels of education, making practical use of science and technology in their jobs.

Computer CONNECT

- These features highlight opportunities where using spreadsheets or data base applications would be helpful.

Design Your Own

- Opportunities are given in investigations, activities, *Pause & Reflect* features, *Topic Reviews*, and *Topic Wrap-ups* for you to plan, design, and conduct your own experimental investigations.

Wrapping Up the Tour

At the back of **SCIENCEFOCUS** 7, you will find some additional features to help you review and develop skills and knowledge that you will need to be successful in this course. Are you having trouble with graphing? Would you like help setting up a data table? Have you forgotten how to make a concept map? Do you need a reminder about the metric system? The *Science Skills Guide* will help you review or improve your skills. A *Glossary* provides all the key vocabulary for the whole course, and an *Index* will help you find your way to a particular subject.

Special Icons

The co-operative group work icon alerts you to opportunities to work within a group, and the pencil icon signals you to record your predictions and observations on paper. The safety icons are extremely important because they alert you to any safety precautions you must take, such as wearing safety goggles or a lab apron. Other safety icons that are used in this book are shown on page 445. Make sure that you become familiar with what they mean, and remember to follow the precautions.

Instant Practice — Feature Hunt

To acquaint yourself further with your textbook before you start using it, see if you can find some of the features it contains. Work with a partner.

1. Find the following features. Briefly tell what each feature is about, and record the page number where you found it.
   (a) a *Stretch Your Mind* in Unit 5
   (b) an *Off the Wall* in Unit 1
   (c) a *Pause & Reflect* in Unit 4
   (d) a *Did You Know?* in Unit 1
   (e) an *Across Canada* in Unit 5
   (f) a *Find Out Activity* called "No Fishing Allowed" in Unit 1
   (g) a *Problem-Solving Investigation* entitled "The Windproof Wonder" in Unit 4

2. Find these words and their meanings.
   (a) force diagram (Unit 4)
   (b) symbiosis (Unit 1)
   (c) pollination (Unit 2)
   (d) calibrate (Unit 3)
   (e) erosion (Unit 5)
   (f) concept map (*Skill Focus 2*)
   (g) histogram (*Skill Focus 10*)

Extensions

3. How did you find the words in question 2? Give one other way to find each word and its meaning.

4. Prepare your own feature hunt for a classmate to do.

Safety in Your Science Classroom

Become familiar with the following safety rules and procedures. It is up to you to use them, and your teacher's instructions, to make your activities and investigations in *SCIENCEFOCUS* 7 safe and enjoyable. Your teacher will give you specific information about any other special safety rules and procedures that need to be used in your school.

1. Working with your teacher ...

- Listen carefully to any instructions your teacher gives you.
- Inform your teacher if you have any allergies, medical conditions, or other physical problems that could affect your work in the science classroom. Tell your teacher if you wear contact lenses or a hearing aid.
- Obtain your teacher's approval before beginning any activity you have designed yourself.
- Know the location and proper use of the nearest fire extinguisher, fire blanket, first-aid kit, and fire alarm.

2. Starting an activity or investigation ...

- Before starting an activity or investigation, read all of it. If you do not understand how to do any step, ask your teacher for help.
- Be sure you have checked the safety icons and have read and understood the safety precautions.
- Begin an activity or investigation only after your teacher tells you to begin.

3. Dressing for success in science ...

- When you are directed to do so, wear protective clothing, such as a lab apron and safety goggles. Always wear protective clothing when you are using materials that could pose a safety problem, such as unidentified substances, or when you are heating something.
- Tie back long hair, and avoid wearing scarves, ties, or long necklaces.

4. Acting responsibly ...

- Work carefully with a partner, and make sure that your work area is clear.
- Handle equipment and materials carefully.
- Make sure that stools and chairs are resting securely on the floor.
- If other students are doing something that you consider dangerous, report it to your teacher.

5. Handling edible substances ...

- Do not chew gum, eat, or drink in your science classroom.
- Do not taste any substances or use your mouth to draw any materials into a tube.

6. Working in a science classroom ...

- Make sure that you understand all the safety labels on school materials and materials you bring from home. Familiarize yourself with the WHMIS symbols and the special safety symbols used in this book (see page 445).
- When carrying equipment for an activity or investigation, hold it carefully. Carry only one object or container at a time.
- Be aware of others during activities and investigations. Make room for students who are carrying equipment to their work stations.

7. Working with sharp objects ...

- Always cut away from yourself and others when using a knife or razor blade.
- Always keep the pointed end of scissors or any other sharp object facing away from yourself and others if you have to walk with it.
- If you notice sharp or jagged edges on any equipment, take special care with it and report it to your teacher.
- Dispose of broken glass as your teacher directs.

8. Working with electrical equipment ...

- Make sure that your hands are dry when touching electrical cords, plugs, or sockets.
- Pull the plug, not the cord, when unplugging electrical equipment. Report damaged equipment or frayed cords to your teacher.
- Place electrical cords where people will not trip over them.

9. Working with heat ...

- When heating something, wear safety goggles and any other safety equipment that the textbook or your teacher advises.
- Always use heatproof containers.
- Do not use broken or cracked containers.
- Point the open end of a container that is being heated away from yourself and others.
- Do not allow a container to boil dry.
- Handle hot objects carefully. Be especially careful with a hot plate that might look as though it has cooled down.
- If you use a Bunsen burner, make sure that you understand how to light it and use it safely.
- If you do receive a burn, inform your teacher and apply cold water to the burned area immediately.

10. Working with various chemicals ...

- If any part of your body comes in contact with a substance, wash the area immediately and thoroughly with water. If you get anything in your eyes, do not touch them. Wash them immediately and continuously for 15 min, and inform your teacher.

- Always handle substances carefully. If you are asked to smell a substance, never smell it directly. Hold the container slightly in front of and beneath your nose, and waft the fumes toward your nostrils, as shown here.
- Hold containers away from your face when pouring a liquid, as shown below.

Use this method to smell a substance in the laboratory.

11. Working with living things ...

On a field trip:

- Try to disturb the area as little as possible.
- If you move something, do it carefully and always replace it carefully.
- If you are asked to remove plant material, remove it gently and take as little as possible.

In the classroom:

- Treat living creatures with respect.
- Make sure that living creatures receive humane treatment while they are in your care.
- If possible, return living creatures to their natural environment when your work is complete.

12. Cleaning up in the science classroom ...

- Clean up any spills, according to your teacher's instructions.
- Clean equipment before you put it away.
- Wash your hands thoroughly after doing an activity or an investigation.
- Dispose of materials as directed by your teacher. Never dispose of materials in a sink unless your teacher directs you to do this.

13. Designing, constructing, and experimenting with structures and mechanisms ...

- Use tools safely to cut, join, and shape objects.
- Handle modelling clay correctly. Wash your hands after using it.
- Follow proper procedures when studying mechanical systems and the way they operate.
- Use special care when observing and working with objects in motion (for example, gears and pulleys, elevated objects, and objects that spin, swing, bounce, or vibrate).
- Do not use power equipment, such as drills, sanders, saws, and lathes, unless you have specialized training in handling such tools.

Hold containers away from your face when pouring liquids.

Instant Practice

Get to know the safety logos in your textbook. Understanding what they mean and following what they tell you to do will help protect everyone in your science classroom.

What You Need

notebook
pens/pencils
Bristol board
markers
this textbook

What to Do

1. Divide the textbook into sections, so that each person in your group is responsible for one section. Have each person find and list all the safety logos that appear in a particular section.

2. Make a common group list, which includes one of each logo. Discuss each logo in your group, and write what it means beside it. Check with your teacher to make sure that you understand what all the logos mean.

3. Choose at least one logo, and brainstorm what your group might illustrate about it. You could come up with your own ideas, or you could use the safety rules in the textbook that relate to the logo(s) you have chosen.

4. Make a poster to illustrate your logo(s). Your poster should show the right way and the wrong way to do an activity or handle equipment. Place a large red X across the wrong way, so that everyone who sees your poster will understand that this is not safe. You might want to make a rough copy of your poster and get your teacher's approval before making the final copy.

5. Give your poster to your teacher for display.

Interactions and Ecosystems

It almost looks as though this whooping crane is jumping for joy. Although this "dance" is actually a courtship display, whooping cranes do have reason to jump for joy — they are lucky to be alive. In the 1940s just 22 whooping cranes could be found in the world. Today, their numbers are slowly increasing, but whooping cranes are still an endangered species. These majestic birds spend their summers in northern Alberta and the Northwest Territories. Like all living organisms, whooping cranes interact with their environment. They need food, water, and a clean environment in which to live. In this unit you will examine some questions about living things and their environment. Why do organisms live where they do? How do they interact with one another and with their environment? How and why do they become extinct?

Humans interact with the environment and with other living things, and we need a healthy environment too. Unfortunately, some human activities affect ecosystems in negative ways. It was largely due to people's actions that the populations of whooping cranes declined, but people have also helped their populations recover. In this unit you will learn how we can observe and monitor changes in ecosystems, and how we can measure the impacts of our actions. As well, you will learn how people are working to improve our environment and to help reverse some past mistakes.

Unit Contents

Preview

- How do human activities affect ecosystems?

- What methods can we use to observe and monitor changes in ecosystems?

- How can we assess the impacts of our actions?

How do organisms — including humans — interact with the environment? In Topics 1–3 you will look at how living things interact with one another and with the environment in which they live. You will see how we have learned from our past mistakes. You will also examine some of the choices we can make to improve our environment.

In Topics 4 and 5, you'll explore the roles that organisms play within an ecosystem. You will find answers to questions such as: What are the links in a food web? What happens if an ecosystem changes? How do nutrients, water, energy, and even pollution cycle through ecosystems?

Environments are always changing. Sometimes they change naturally and sometimes as a result of human activities. Environmental monitoring can help us reduce negative impacts on the environment. Scientific monitoring can also help us develop strategies for reducing our impact in the future. You will examine these concepts in Topics 6 and 7.

Looking Ahead

Read pages 82 – 83, "An Issue to Analyze: Beyond the Curb: Is Recycling Really Reducing Garbage?" As a class, organize a debate about whether to continue a Blue Box recycling program.

- Start a newspaper clipping file in which to keep news stories related to recycling and disposal of garbage in your area.

- Contact your city's or town's municipal office to gather information (such as amount of garbage collected locally, and what is done with recyclable items) to use in the debate.

- Invite key people in your area who are involved in recycling to present information to your class.

Interactions Within an Ecosystem

Imagine you are a swift fox living in the Alberta prairie. Your world consists of the open prairie where you nibble on grasses and berries and prey on grasshoppers, mice, or even the occasional rabbit. As you travel through the prairie you are alert for other creatures such as eagles, hawks, or wolves that might kill you for food. These are some ways that you and the other animals you share the prairie with interact with one another. You also interact with the prairie itself. The prairie is the place where you dig your dens, find your food, and raise your young. **Ecology** is the study of the relationship between living organisms and their environment. An **ecologist** is someone who studies these relationships. An ecologist studying swift foxes, for example, might study where they build their dens, what they eat, or how they raise their young.

Ecologists also explore the relationships between humans, animals, and the environment. Imagine … these tiny foxes almost entirely disappeared from Canada. In fact, until they were recently reintroduced, the last swift fox in Alberta was seen in 1928. What happened to these creatures? This is the sort of question that ecologists can help us answer. It turns out that hundreds of swift foxes were accidentally killed in the early 1900s when people were using poison to control the wolves and coyotes that preyed on them. As well, swift foxes lost most of their natural home — the native prairie grasslands — when this land was taken over for agriculture and other human developments such as cities. Now, humans are helping the swift fox. New programs are reintroducing swift foxes to the Prairies, and groups of concerned citizens are working with ecologists to ensure that swift foxes have the type of home that they need.

This Topic introduces you to ecology — the interactions between organisms, including people, and the places where they live.

Word CONNECT

Ecology comes from the Greek word meaning "home." In your Science Log write a sentence describing what you think the word "home" refers to.

Pause& Reflect

Look at the animals in the photographs. Did you know that these animals live in Alberta? Throughout this unit you will be asked to study the ecology of an Alberta animal. You will investigate how it interacts with other animals and with its environment. You will also learn how people interact with this animal. Take some time now to choose an animal. (It could be one of the animals shown here, but it does not have to be.) You can choose an animal with which you are familiar, or one you know nothing about, but it should live in Alberta. Note the name of your study animal in your Science Log. By the end of this unit, you will be an expert on this creature.

whooping crane

northern leopard frog

woodland caribou

badger

INTERNET CONNECT

www.mcgrawhill.ca/links/sciencefocus7

To learn more about the swift fox and the Swift Fox Reintroduction program in Alberta, visit the above web site. Click on **Web Links** to find out where to go next. In your notebook, draw a swift fox. Then draw the creatures that eat the swift fox and the food that the swift fox eats. Draw arrows from each creature to its food.

The Needs of Living Things

Imagine you are a cave dweller — long before the days of television, grocery stores, and the invention of the wheel! What are the things you would need to survive? (Remember that you are an animal and you have basic survival needs very similar to other animals.) If your list of basic needs includes food, a place to live (your **habitat**), air to breathe, and water to drink, you would be absolutely right. These are the basic needs that all living things require and you share these basic needs with everything from a sloth to a sunflower to a spider.

- Living things need food. Animals eat food, while plants make it. Food gives living things energy. Food also provides nutrients such as fat, protein, and carbohydrates, which help living things to grow, repair, and reproduce themselves.

- Living things need water. Water covers most of our planet and it also forms a large part of living things. You are almost two-thirds water! Living things cannot function properly and will eventually die without water.

- Living things need a suitable habitat. In almost every corner of our planet — from the frigid Antarctic ice to the dusty, dry desert — there are living things. Many creatures, such as the mountain goat, live in a particular sort of environment without any type of shelter. Others, including humans, beavers, and wasps, build protective shelters.

- Living things exchange gases. When this whale, and other animals, breathe in and out, its body is getting rid of the gas carbon dioxide and is breathing in oxygen. All living things exchange gases. Plants, for instance, use carbon dioxide to make food and "breathe" off oxygen. Other living things, including fungi and bacteria, need oxygen too.

When you take a breath, put on a warm coat, wave to friend, or move away from a buzzing bee, you are interacting with your environment and with other living things. Living things are always interacting with each other and with the non-living things in their environment. Take a closer look at how an animal meets its basic needs in the next activity.

Just the Basics

All organisms, including humans, share the same basic needs. Find out about an animal that lives near you to determine how these living things meet their basic needs for survival.

Materials

sheet of paper
pencil
shoe box or other small cardboard box
art materials

Procedure
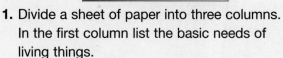
* Performing and Recording
* Communication and Teamwork

1. Divide a sheet of paper into three columns. In the first column list the basic needs of living things.

2. Brainstorm in a group and make a list of how you can meet the basic needs for survival. Record this list into the second column of your data sheet.

3. Choose either (a) or (b).

   (a) As a group, look for animals in your schoolyard or other nearby outdoor area. Carefully turn over rocks or logs, look for animals in ponds or ditches, or watch for birds flying nearby. Choose one animal and observe it closely without disturbing it.

   (b) Use resources in a library or on the Internet to determine the basic needs of the animal you chose as your study animal in the Pause & Reflect on page 7.

4. Record how your study animal meets its basic needs in the third column of your data sheet. For example, what type of environment does your study animal prefer and what type of food does it eat?

5. Use the cardboard box and the art materials to make a diorama showing the basic needs of your study animal. Display your dioramas in the classroom.

What Did You Find Out? * Analyzing and Interpreting

1. Compare the list of your needs with the list of your study animal's needs. How are they the same? How are they different?

2. List five changes that might affect the survival of your study animal. Think of small changes, such as someone riding a bike through its habitat, to large changes, such as a drought.

Computer CONNECT

Create a web tutorial about the needs of living things. Include information on how different organisms, such as a swift fox or a burrowing owl, meet their needs using the environment around them. Include a quiz with an answer key.

Adaptations

What do you think the bird in Figure 1.1 eats? Fish, small creatures, or flying insects? How does its bill compare to those of other birds? A robin's bill is different from a duck's, and an owl's is different from a hummingbird's. All of these bills are used to gather food, but they are **adapted**, or well-suited, to the food that the bird eats.

Living things are adapted so that they "fit" their surroundings. This ensures that they can survive in the environment in which they live. For example, many of the bones in a bird's body are hollow. This characteristic makes the bird lighter so it can more easily fly. The fit between an organism and its environment is called adaptation. An **adaptation** is an inherited characteristic that helps an organism survive and reproduce in its environment (see Figure 1.2). Sometimes characteristics that help animals survive in their environment are learned during the animal's lifetime. For example, humans learn to look both ways before crossing a street. This helps humans survive, but it is not an adaptation because it is not inherited; humans are not born knowing to look before crossing a street.

Figure 1.1 This curlew uses its long bill to probe for tiny organisms.

Figure 1.2 Robins' feet are an example of an adaptation. Like other perching birds, robins have feet with three front toes, one long hind toe, and a specialized tendon that automatically locks their hind toes around a branch when they land.

INTERNET CONNECT

www.mcgrawhill.ca/links/sciencefocus7

You have identified the needs of living things for survival, and one of those needs is food. Find out about some of the different ways in which animals obtain food by visiting the above web site. Click on **Web Links** to find out where to go next. Write about three of the ways you found, and make sketches to describe your findings. What would happen if the food these animals are best able to gather were suddenly in short supply? Would the animals be able to feed on something else?

Figure 1.3 These organisms are born with flippers that enable them to swim well.

Figure 1.4 These organisms have learned how to make flippers so that they can adapt their feet to a water environment.

Humans are able to survive — at least for short periods of time — in a wide variety of habitats. We have even ventured into space and the deep sea. Humans have used advances in science and technology to expand the different types of environments in which we can live. Can you think of other ways that we have used science and technology to enable us to live in habitats in which we would not normally be able to survive?

DidYouKnow?

Earthworms have developed special features over time that help them survive in their underground environment. They breathe directly through their thin skin, their bodies are long and thin and have no limbs, and they are able to eat soil. Earthworms cannot survive the drying heat of the Sun because their skin must stay moist in order for them to breathe properly. When rain falls, it floods their burrows, and earthworms must come to the surface to breathe. If they stay underground, they will drown. If they are away from soil when the rain stops, however, they cannot dig back into their burrows, and they dry out and die. This explains why there are so many dead earthworms on the pavement after a rain shower.

INQUIRY

INVESTIGATION 1-A

SKILLCHECK

Initiating and Planning

✿ Performing and Recording

✿ Analyzing and Interpreting

✿ Communication and Teamwork

Tools for the Task

You have seen that organisms are adapted, or well-suited, to their environments. Some animals eat a varied diet, while others eat very specific types of food. Would these animals be able to cope with change?

Question

Can animals switch to a different type of food if their usual food is in short supply?

Hypothesis

Form a hypothesis about whether an animal will be able to survive if its usual food supply is restricted.

Apparatus

toothpicks	small plastic
kitchen tongs	bags
clothespins	clock or watch
spoons	

Materials

rice	elastic bands
cereal in the shape of rings (such as Cheerios™)	raisins

Procedure

1. Your teacher will divide your class into four groups. Each group represents a different animal that uses a different type of utensil (toothpick, kitchen tongs, clothespin, or spoon) to feed.

2. Scatter piles of "food" (rice, cereal, elastic bands, or raisins, ten pieces in each pile) randomly throughout the room. There should be an equal number of each type of food pile and only one food pile per student.

3. Each of you will be given a plastic bag — your "stomach." Do not eat any of the food.

4. You will all start in the same location and you will have 30 s to gather one pile of food.

5. At the end of this round, **record** the type of food gathered by each animal. If an animal cannot gather a pile of food, it does not continue to the next round.

6. Repeat step 4 until no food remains.

7. Scatter the piles of food again as in step 2, but use only half the number of piles of raisins.

8. Repeat step 4 until no food remains.

Analyze

1. How do particular adaptations of animals affect what they eat?

2. Based on your observations, which type of "animal" was better able to cope with changes in food supply?

3. Is an animal's ability to eat a variety of food an adaptation? Explain your answer.

Conclude and Apply

4. Why do some animals die even when food seems to be abundant and varied?

Ecosystems

Did you know that there are more individual things living in the rotting log in Figure 1.5 than there are people on Earth? Bacteria, tiny worms and other animals, fungi and plants are all thriving in this small piece of decaying wood. Larger organisms use the log as well. A salamander might hide under the bark and woodpeckers visit for a meal of insects. The log is an example of an ecosystem. An **ecosystem** is the interactions between living and non-living things in a particular environment. The ecosystem of a rotting log is formed by the interactions between the organisms living in and on the log and the soil, temperature, and other non-living features around the log. A forest is also an ecosystem. All of the living things, such as trees and animals, and all of the non-living things, such as the sunlight and the air, are interacting.

Pause& Reflect

In what ecosystem does your study animal live? Find out as much as you can about its ecosystem and record your findings in your Science Log. Use a graphic organizer such as a spider map to organize your research.

Figure 1.5 A rotting log is like an apartment building for forest-dwelling organisms, and interactions constantly occur in their home.

Skill FOCUS

For tips on how to use graphic organizers, turn to Skill Focus 2.

Understanding how ecosystems function is all about understanding connections. In the last activity, you explored what might happen when food is in short supply in an ecosystem. All parts of an organism's world are connected. If one part is affected — climate, availability of water or food, or habitat — the organism will need to adjust somehow. Some organisms adjust well, and others do not.

When we know how an ecosystem functions, we can learn about the effects of changes on the ecosystem. Some ecosystems are easy to explore, but other ecosystems are more challenging. For example, if the ecosystem is too small or too big for us to observe easily, we cannot always know what living and non-living things are present. In order to study ecosystems, scientists often study one aspect of an ecosystem. They then work with other scientists to piece together the overall picture of how the ecosystem functions.

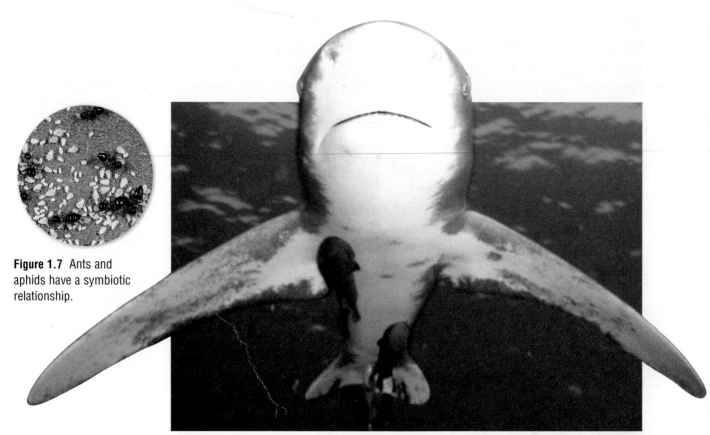

Figure 1.7 Ants and aphids have a symbiotic relationship.

Figure 1.6 A remora exists in a symbiotic relationship with a shark.

Interactions in Ecosystems

Imagine a great white shark cruising toward you through tropical waters. As a human, your only thought would be to get away. Yet one small fish, called a remora, cannot get close enough! It uses suckers on its head to attach itself firmly to the shark's skin and then dines on bacteria and micro-organisms that are unhealthy for the shark. **Symbiosis** occurs when two species live closely together in a relationship that lasts over time. The odd association between the fearsome shark and the little remora is an example of a symbiotic relationship called mutualism. **Mutualism** is a relationship between two different organisms, in which each partner benefits from the relationship.

Symbiotic relationships are common in the natural world. For example, aphids on a rosebush have a symbiotic relationship with the rosebush as they feed on it. Ants and aphids have a symbiotic relationship too (Figure 1.7). The ants protect the aphids from predators, and in return they drink the sweet liquid that aphids excrete.

There are three types of symbiotic relationships. Along with mutualism, there can be parasitism and commensalism. **Parasitism** is a symbiotic relationship in which one organism benefits and the other organism is harmed. Typically, one of the partners lives on or in the other organism and feeds on it. One of the organisms, the **parasite**, meets its needs at the expense of the other organism, the **host**.

The tapeworms in Figure 1.8, for example, can live in the small intestine of human beings and may grow as long as 10 m. They benefit by absorbing the nutrients from the humans' food. The hosts, the humans, are harmed because they do not get the nutrients from the food they eat. Tapeworm eggs live in meat or fish, so it is important to properly cook your food so that the heat will destroy the eggs.

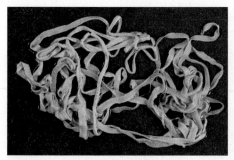

Figure 1.8 Tapeworms are common parasites that live inside other animals' intestines.

Figure 1.9 An orchid plant attached high up on a tree trunk.

Commensalism is a symbiotic relationship in which one partner benefits and the other partner appears neither to lose nor to gain from the relationship. For example, many species of flowering orchid, like the one in Figure 1.9, live high up, attached to the trunks of trees. The orchids benefit by having a safe place to live and a constant source of water from rain dripping down the tree trunks. The trees seem neither to benefit nor to lose from the presence of the orchid.

In 1986 scientist-filmmaker Greg Marshall watched a shark with a remora clinging to its side. He realized that if a camera could be attached to the side of the shark in a similar way, it would give an amazing close-up view of the shark's movements and behaviour. Thus was born a device called the "crittercam." It is a small battery-operated video camera that can be attached to the side of a shark by a small metal dart. The dart pierces the outer layer of the shark's hide without harming the shark. Shark food is thrown into the water to attract the shark close enough to a boat so that the crittercam can be attached. After a time, the crittercam is automatically released from the shark, tracked by radio signals, and retrieved.

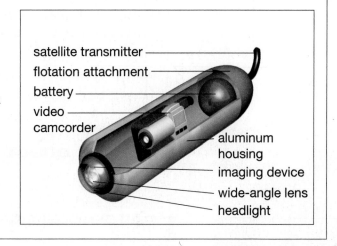

satellite transmitter
flotation attachment
battery
video camcorder
aluminum housing
imaging device
wide-angle lens
headlight

Impacts on Ecosystems

Symbiotic relationships are just a few of the ways in which organisms interact with one another in ecosystems. Recall that ecosystems are made up of organisms interacting with all of the parts, living and non-living, in an environment. As a result, all organisms have some kind of impact when they interact in their ecosystem.

Figure 1.10 A beaver dam drastically changes the ecosystem in which the beavers live.

Some animals have a large impact on their ecosystem. For example, a beaver cuts down trees to eat and to make dams. The dam drastically changes the ecosystem in which the beaver lives. The stream below the dam dries up, and the fish that lived in it can no longer survive. The animals that eat the fish can no longer live in the ecosystem either, so they must move to another ecosystem. Above the dam, a new pond has appeared. The presence of a pond has changed the types of animals that can live in that ecosystem. The impact of the beaver on its ecosystem has improved conditions for some organisms while making the environment unsuitable for others. The small act of a beaver cutting down some trees and creating a dam resulted in some surprising events.

Pause& Reflect

Consider how your study animal interacts with its ecosystem. Does it have a symbiotic relationship with another organism? With what other organisms does it interact? Does it have any behaviours that change the ecosystem? Record your thoughts in your Science Log.

Chain of Events

Have you ever thought about how one small event sets an entire chain of events in motion? Usually a small event will have only a small effect, but sometimes the results can be surprising.

Procedure

* Performing and Recording
* Communication and Teamwork

1. With a partner, read the following poem and discuss what it means. If you have any difficulty, invite other pairs of students to share their ideas.

   For want of a nail, the shoe was lost;
   For want of a shoe, the horse was lost;
   For want of a horse, the rider was lost;
   For want of the rider, the battle was lost;
   For want of the battle, the kingdom was lost.
   And all from the want of a horseshoe nail.

2. Relate the ideas in the poem to the world around you. Think of some different ways in which living and non-living things affect each other. Could a chain of events change those interactions?

3. Make up your own chains of events, starting with one small event. Include at least eight events in your chain. For example, you could start with the following event: There was no milk left when you went to have breakfast this morning, so …

4. What need was being met in your chain of events in question 3? What was the final impact of obtaining that initial need?

Extension

5. Write a poem about how different kinds of living things depend upon one another and on the environment around them.

TOPIC 1 Review

1. **(a)** List the basic needs that all organisms share.

   (b) Imagine that you are a white-footed mouse, living in a prairie grassland ecosystem. What are some different ways you can meet your needs?

2. Compare the falcon's feet to the duck's feet in the photographs on the right.

   (a) In what way are the duck's feet adapted for living in water?

   (b) In what way are the falcon's feet adapted for catching food?

   (c) Draw a sketch to illustrate how either the duck or the falcon uses its feet.

3. Describe two adaptations of a fish. Explain how these adaptations help the fish live in its environment.

4. Define symbiosis in your own words. Give one example of symbiosis from this Topic and one example from your own experience.

5. Think about a common organism that lives in your area. Think about some ways it might affect the environment in which it lives. List one positive and one negative effect the organism might have.

Human Impacts
on Ecosystems

Figure 1.11 How do you think the changes shown in these photographs might have affected the plants and animals that live in this ecosystem?

When you look out the window, are you looking at the same scene that you might have seen 100 years ago? Probably not. As Canada's population increased, land was cleared for homes and farms and eventually some of these settlements grew into the cities and towns we know today. Trees were cut for fuel and buildings, roads were built and eventually paved, and native prairie was ploughed under to create farmland. Humans affect the environment around them as they meet their needs. What types of changes to the environment can you see in the two pictures in Figure 1.11?

People are animals too, and we are part of nature. To meet our basic needs we rely on the ecosystem around us, just as all living things do. People use **natural resources** — the materials and products that are found in nature — to meet our basic needs. Trees, water, oil, and minerals are examples of natural resources that we use. Many human technologies depend on natural resources. For example, one way that electricity is generated is by tapping the energy of rivers. Large dams, such as the one in Figure 1.12, are built and water is trapped behind the dam. Instead of the river flowing freely as it once did, the water flow is controlled by the people who operate the dam.

Figure 1.12 Dams such as this one have a major effect on surrounding ecosystems.

Skill
F O C U S

For more information on Societal Decision Making, turn to Skill Focus 8.

Recall from Topic 1 how beaver dams affect river ecosystems. Human-built dams affect ecosystems as well since large areas behind the dam are flooded. Human impacts can be large or small. When one person cleared a plot of land to build a house 100 years ago, the impact to the ecosystem was minimal. However, as more people move to an area, more land is cleared and there is a greater demand for natural resources. If one person drives a car, the impact on the environment is not great. In reality, of course, millions of people drive cars and the number of people *and* cars in the world is rising every day. With cars come roads, parking lots, sprawling cities, and air pollution.

As the human population increases, more and more humans have needs that must be met. As their numbers grow, people have a greater impact on the ecosystems around them. Humans have the same habitat needs as other living things, but, unfortunately, our needs often conflict with the needs of other living things.

DidYou**Know**?

Human impacts on living things are not always easy to predict. Did you know that leaving the lights on in Toronto highrise buildings results in the deaths of thousands of songbirds? The birds are attracted to the lights of the buildings and crash into the glass. Concerned citizens and biologists educated building tenants about this problem and now some building owners voluntarily turn off the lights when there are high concentrations of birds in the area, such as when birds are migrating through to their breeding grounds.

People and Nature — A Changing Relationship

The ways that people interact with the environment have changed over time. Before the widespread use of engines and machines, people had a relatively low impact on the environment. They used available plants and animals for food and clothing and lived in simple shelters. If they travelled, they did so on foot, on horseback, or perhaps using canoes. Everything people needed, they found in the environment around them. The Aboriginal person in Figure 1.13 lived on the west coast of Canada. The clothing in the photograph was woven from the bark of the red cedar tree. The shelters in Figure 1.14 were made from long poles cut from trees, covered with the skin of buffalo.

Figure 1.13 The Nuu-cha-nulth (Nootka) were able to weave cedar bark to make clothing.

Figure 1.14 This shelter, called a tipi, consisted of long poles cut from trees and covered with buffalo skins.

Now, of course, our clothes and food come from different parts of the world, we live in fairly large homes or apartments that have electricity and heat, and we often travel in cars, trains, or airplanes. We drink more than just water, eat more than just the plants and animals in our ecosystem, and buy all sorts of items that we enjoy using but do not need. Such lifestyle changes have increased our impact on the ecosystems in which we live.

Gathering Food in Alberta: Then and Now

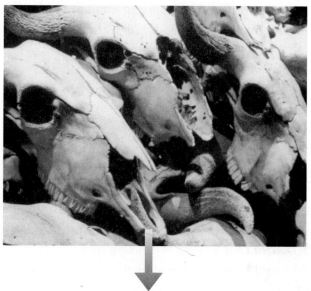

A These are the skulls of buffalo killed at Head-Smashed-In Buffalo Jump. Aboriginal people living on the plains of Alberta used this site at Porcupine Hills to hunt buffalo by driving them over a cliff. Buffalo that were not killed by the fall were killed with spears and arrows. The carcasses of the buffalo were then dragged to nearby camps to be processed into meat, hides, tools, and other necessary items. All parts of the buffalo were used, and there was very little waste. The technology needed for this type of hunting was minimal, and therefore had little environmental impact.

B Early settlers on the Prairies often kept small mixed farms where they raised crops and livestock. Instead of moving around to different locations from season to season following food sources, early settlers developed the technology to raise their own food on their own farms and they became self-supporting. This lifestyle had a larger impact on the environment than hunting buffalo because the farmland had to be modified to support the crops and the livestock.

C A feedlot contains a large number of cattle penned together and raised for meat. The cattle are fed a special diet to increase the amount of meat produced. Once the beef is processed, it is shipped out to consumers all over the country. This technology allows us to produce lots of food and transport it to many locations. The impact this has on the environment is very significant, however. For example, wastes from cattle go directly into the soil where they become concentrated. This changes the condition of the soil, and affects all of the organisms living in that environment.

When Is a Need a Want?

For the most part, Canadians do not have an ongoing challenge of finding food and shelter, so they have been able to turn their attention to their "wants" — things that make their lives more enjoyable.

For many of us, the line between "want" and "need" has become blurred. "I *need* new shoes, I *need* that new computer game, I *need* to call my friend." Meeting our needs and wants usually uses natural resources in some way. Each time we satisfy a need or a want that requires natural resources or energy, we are making a choice and having an impact on our environment. For example, take a look at the fruits and vegetables that you can find in your local grocery store year-round. Many of these foods are grown elsewhere and are shipped to local stores. Land was cleared, fuel was used, and air pollution was created to bring that food to you. Our impact would be quite different if we ate only locally grown food. Food is a basic need, but having food from distant locations available year-round is a luxury.

Find Out ACTIVITY

Alberta Grown

What would happen if you did not have access to grocery stores? What would you eat? What foods did the Aboriginal people who lived in Alberta eat?

Materials

plant guide books suitable for your region

Procedure ✳ **Performing and Recording**

1. Consult a plant book and find five edible plants (or plants that were used as medicine) that grow in Alberta. (Also see the Internet Connect below.) Sketch the plant and describe the parts that are edible (roots, berries, leaves, bark, etc.). If possible, note how you would prepare the food.

2. Create a meal plan using only plants and animals from Alberta.

INTERNET CONNECT

www.mcgrawhill.ca/links/sciencefocus7

To learn more about how Aboriginal people from Alberta used the plants in their ecosystem, visit the Internet site for the Native People's Garden at the Devonian Botanic Garden. Click on **Web Links** to find out where to go next. In your Science Log, note five plants Aboriginal people used, and how they used them.

Our demand for more consumer products often conflicts with the health of ecosystems and the plants or animals living there. Look at the photographs in Figure 1.15. How do these pictures show that we live beyond our basic needs? Of course most of us do not want to turn back the clock and give up all of the things we enjoy. We can however, make responsible choices. Today, many people are starting to question whether we need so much "stuff."

Figure 1.16 Sometimes, when we want to "go back to nature," our wants conflict with the needs of wildlife.

Figure 1.15 As North Americans we are lucky to have relatively comfortable lives. However, we consume far more than our share of the world's natural resources. We also create more than our share of pollution and impact on the land.

In our haste to satisfy our wants, we often forget the basic needs of plants and animals. For example, many people love to visit parks in the Rocky Mountains in order to camp and hike, but towns, campgrounds, and parking lots are at the bottom of the valley, which is the most important wildlife habitat for animals such as elk (Figure 1.16).

To satisfy people's desire for juicy, red tomatoes year-round, large greenhouses are being built on prime farmland just outside of Vancouver. This land is a very important habitat for thousands of shorebirds. Shorebirds rest here after flying hundreds, or even thousands, of kilometres enroute between their southern wintering grounds and their northern breeding grounds. Now, because so much of the land is being taken up by greenhouses, the shorebirds are left with very little habitat. These are just two examples of how the *wants* of people conflict with the *needs* of wildlife.

Figure 1.17 These "monster" greenhouses provide juicy, red tomatoes year round, but at what cost?

No Simple Answers

Figure 1.18 While letting wild fires rage through heavily used areas would not be practical, wardens now light and carefully control fires in certain areas to ensure there is adequate food for grazing animals.

You have heard about the terrible destruction caused by forest fires. Would it surprise you to learn that park wardens in Banff National Park deliberately set the fire shown in Figure 1.18? For years people have seen fire as having a devastating effect on the environment. Park wardens, along with the ecologists and biologists who work with them, however, found that naturally occurring fires can benefit the ecosystem. Periodic fires clear areas of small trees and leaves, needles, and other forest debris that gather on the ground. After a fire, new grasses and other plants sprout up and provide valuable food for elk, deer, and other animals that routinely graze in the valley bottoms.

Learning the benefits of fire is just one way to use scientific understanding in order to try to reduce human impact on the environment. Ecologists continue to study natural areas and natural systems to reduce our impact. For example, the peregrine chicks shown in Figure 1.19 have been helped by the actions of humans. Peregrine falcons were close to extinction in eastern Canada in the mid-1900s following the common use of the pesticide, DDT. Why? The use of this pesticide had some unfortunate side effects. One negative effect was that it caused the eggshells of many birds to become so thin and fragile that their chicks did not survive. DDT is no longer used in Canada. The ban on the use of DDT, and the programs such as the one shown here to help peregrine falcons achieve nesting success, are increasing the numbers of this majestic bird. Originally, peregrine falcons nested on cliffsides. Now they also use tall buildings for their nests — a human-made substitute.

Figure 1.19 Peregrine falcon chicks are being placed in a nest of a pair of peregrine falcons that have not been able to produce their own young.

Figure 1.20 The crates on the back of this horse-drawn carriage carry wolves that are being relocated to Yellowstone National Park in the United States, to replace wolves that had almost entirely disappeared from that environment.

Recall that part of the reason that swift foxes almost disappeared in Alberta was because they were accidentally poisoned. For years, natural predators such as wolves, coyotes, and cougars were seen as "bad" and unnecessary animals. They were thought to be dangerous and aggressive animals and were often shot on sight. As well, many of these animals were often poisoned. Unfortunately, when poisons were set out, they also resulted in the death of many other animals, including the swift fox. Now — again because people became concerned and learned more about the role of these animals in natural systems — these animals are regarded as an important part of ecosystems. Predators keep the numbers of deer, mice, rabbits, and other small animals in check. Without this sort of natural control, the population of these animals would increase to such an extent that vegetation would be threatened by overgrazing.

INTERNET CONNECT

www.mcgrawhill.ca/links/sciencefocus7

Take a peek at a peregrine nest by visiting the site of the Canadian Peregrine Foundation (CPN). The CPN has live cameras focused on peregrines nesting on buildings in Etobicoke, Hamilton, and Ottawa. To view peregrines, visit the above web site. Click on **Web Links** to find out where to go next. Monitor the site for a few days and note the activity on the nest during that time in your Science Log.

Wetland Wonders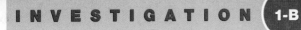

Think About It

Wetlands are areas where the soil is wet for all or most of the year. Wetland areas drain slowly and are important parts of ecosystems, not only as wildlife habitat, but also because they capture, store, and slowly release water to surrounding areas. When wetlands are filled in, the flow of water can change, causing flooding in some areas and drought in others. As well, the critical wetland habitat is lost. Wetlands are one of the most endangered habitats in Canada. A developer wants to put a road through the middle of a wetland that is home to a variety of plants and animals. Can you come up with a solution that will help preserve the wetland habitat?

How Can Science Help?

Scientists who study water flow understand how changing or draining wetlands can harm them. As well, biologists have a good understanding of the needs of the plants and animals that live in wetland ecosystems. Together, these scientists can explain the problems that can occur if wetlands are drained, and they can make suggestions to reduce the impacts of development. To learn about wetlands, scientists carefully observe wetland areas and set up models of such areas in which they can test and monitor various conditions.

Safety Precautions

Wipe up all spills immediately.

Materials

water coloured with food colouring

plastic Ziplock™ bags

Apparatus

2 rectangular aluminum foil baking pans

scissors

modelling clay

bucket

500 mL beaker

stopwatch or watch with a second hand

graduated cylinder

3–5 small sponges

Procedure

1 Use the scissors to carefully cut a series of holes about the size of a dime at the bottom near one end of one of the baking pans.

2 Raise the end of the baking pan without the holes about 2 cm high using two balls of modelling clay under the pan. Put the end of the baking pan with the holes just over the edge of the table. Put the other baking pan on a chair under the holes so that it will catch any water draining from the first pan.

3 Pour 250 mL of water at one end of the pan and time how long it takes for the water to flow through the pan and drain into the second baking pan. Copy the data table below into your notebook, and record this number in the data table.

Number of sponges	Time to drain through (s)	Amount of water collected (mL)

4 Put one sponge in the pan with the holes and pour 250 mL of water into the pan. (The sponge is your wetland.) Time how long it takes for the water to flow through the first pan and drain into the second pan. Use the graduated cylinder to measure the amount of water that flowed through the pan. Record the time and the amount of water collected. Squeeze the water in the sponge back into the beaker.

5 Repeat step 4, adding one more sponge with every trial.

6 When you have the pan filled with sponges, create a "road" of modelling clay across the middle of the baking pan. Pour 250 mL of water in the baking pan and observe what happens.

Analyze

1. Describe how wetlands are like a sponge.

2. What happens when wetlands are paved over?

3. Describe what happened to your wetland when a road was put through the middle of it.

4. Could you think of an alternative to a road that would allow the developer to get through the wetland, but would still protect the wetland habitat?

TOPIC 2 Review

1. What are natural resources? Give two examples of natural resources and explain how humans use them to meet their needs.

2. Complete the following chart.

Activity	Impact on the environment	Positive or negative impact	Alternative action to lessen negative impact
Using plastic bags in your lunch			
Mowing your lawn and putting the grass clippings in the garbage			
			Riding your bicycle

3. Think of two activities you perform in a typical day, and describe two impacts that each activity has on your environment. Are these activities wants or needs?

4. Describe two native plants that grow in Alberta.

5. Describe the habitat needs of one Alberta animal.

6. How has the relationship between humans and their environment changed in Alberta since the time the first settlers arrived here?

Figure 1.21 How big is your ecological footprint?

Your Ecological Footprint

We all depend on nature. Sometimes we seem to be so far removed from nature that we forget this. We buy food from the grocery store, seek shelter in houses or cars when the weather is bad, and flush our waste down the toilet or put it out at the curb for collection. Remember, though, our food and shelter come from natural resources that Earth provided, and all of our waste goes back to Earth. We not only *depend* on nature, we are *part* of nature.

As you have seen in earlier Topics, all living things need food, water, shelter, and space in which to live. People in North America and other wealthy countries, however, use far more than their share of Earth's natural resources. They do not live in a sustainable manner. **Sustainability** means that the resources of nature are being renewed at least as quickly as they are used, and that all wastes are able to be completely absorbed. Today there are concerns over dwindling resources on Earth. People are concerned at the rate in which our forests are being cut down or fish are being harvested, for example. Are we living sustainably, or are we living far beyond the ability of Earth to provide what we want?

Impact Here and There

Each human has an individual impact on the environment. The difference lies in *how much* of an impact we have on our environment. For example, the surface of our planet covers 51 billion ha. (A hectare is just under the size of a city block.) If you take away the ocean, desert, mountaintops, and land covered in concrete or pavement, only about 8.9 billion ha of usable land remain. Imagine that you could obtain all of your basic needs from the space and resources this land contains. If this land were equally divided among the close to 6 billion people in the world, each person would have about 1.5 ha. In reality, though, the average Canadian would need about 4.3 ha of land. That is about the size of three city blocks. If everyone in the world continued to live as we do in North America, we would need at least two more planets the size of Earth to provide the resources and absorb the wastes.

One way to determine how much of an impact you have is to determine your **ecological footprint**. An ecological footprint is a calculation of the total area of land and water needed to supply all of the materials and energy that you use, as well as absorb all of the waste that you produce. Materials include food, water, and the supplies to build shelters and to manufacture all of the products that you use. The energy you use includes electricity, natural gas, as well as all of the energy required to manufacture, run, and transport items that you buy.

Figure 1.22
WANTED: Two more good planets to support Earthlings.

Figure 1.23 Which scene has a bigger ecological footprint?

Figure 1.24 An individual can reduce his or her ecological footprint by making wise choices for daily activities.

Look at the people in Figure 1.24. If they travel 10 km to work and back each day, his or her ecological footprint will vary depending on the method of travel. If the person travels by bike, the ecological footprint for that activity is 122 m². By bus, it is 303 m², and if the individual travels alone in a car, the ecological footprint is 1530 m². The ecological footprint takes into consideration the resources used to build the bike, bus, or car, the energy used, and the pollution that the bike, bus, or car creates.

At present, the ecological footprint of the average Canadian is very large. Most Canadians are using many more resources and creating much more waste than is sustainable. Just think of the amount of garbage you produce in your home and how much water you use. Imagine how different life would be if you lived in a country with far more people and far fewer resources. However, each person can reduce the impact on the environment and the size of her or his ecological footprint. The first step in reducing your impact is to be aware of the natural resources you consume during a typical day. The next step is to reduce the amount of energy you use, the number of products you buy, and the amount of garbage you produce. Your ecological footprint will shrink, and the impact you have on the ecosystems around you will be reduced!

Pause& Reflect

In your Science Log, explain why using carpools, taking short showers, wearing second-hand clothes, and living in an apartment rather than a large home would reduce the size of your ecological footprint. Add your own thoughts about why you would or would not want to do any of these.

INTERNET CONNECT

www.mcgrawhill.ca/links/sciencefocus7

It is possible to calculate the actual size of your ecological footprint if you have the appropriate information. Find out what information you need by visiting the above web site. Click on **Web Links** to find out where to go next. Collect the information and calculate the size of your, or your family's, ecological footprint.

Putting Your Foot in Your Mouth

Find Out ACTIVITY

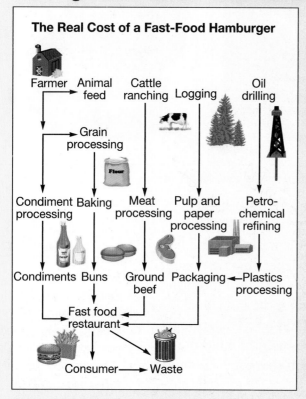

The Real Cost of a Fast-Food Hamburger

Farmer — Animal feed — Cattle ranching — Logging — Oil drilling

Grain processing

Condiment processing — Baking — Meat processing — Pulp and paper processing — Petro-chemical refining

Condiments — Buns — Ground beef — Packaging ← Plastics processing

Fast food restaurant

Consumer → Waste

Materials

coloured markers, large sheet of paper

buttons or other plastic chips

Procedure

1. Use the coloured markers to copy the chart *The Real Cost of a Fast-Food Hamburger* onto a large sheet of paper.

2. As a group, create a similar chart for a sandwich or hamburger made at home with store-bought ingredients. Consider all of the "costs" of each ingredient, including packaging, transportation to the store, transportation home from the store, electricity used, etc.

3. As a group, create a similar chart for a sandwich made at home with home-made ingredients (e.g., home-made bread, lettuce and tomatoes grown in a garden, etc.).

4. Use the poker chips to determine the real costs in energy and resources for each meal. For each "cost," place a poker chip on your chart. For example, in the above chart you would place two poker chips on farming, one for land used and one for energy used (fuel to run tractors, drive grain to market, etc.). This step would be the same for all of your charts to show the "cost" of producing the grain used in bread, or vegetables used in the sandwich or hamburger.

5. Compare the number of chips used in each of the three meals.

What Did You Find Out?

1. Which meal produces the largest ecological footprint? Explain your answer.

2. Why would a vegetarian meal have a smaller ecological footprint than a meal with meat?

3. List three practical ways in which people could reduce the ecological cost of their food. Explain how each of your suggestions reduces the environmental impact.

Reduce, Reuse, Recycle!

There are many ways in which you can help protect the environment from negative human impacts. These actions will also reduce the size of your ecological footprint. The 3 Rs — reduce, reuse, and recycle — will help you.

Figure 1.25 Recycling reduces stress on the environment.

Figure 1.26 Reduce, reuse, and recycle are three words to keep in mind and act upon if we wish to reduce our ecological footprint.

① **Reduce** the amount of garbage you produce. For example, try to avoid buying individually wrapped items, disposable items, and overpackaged items. Take your own reusable bags or a knapsack to carry your purchases when you go shopping.

② **Reuse** products rather than throwing them away. For example, buy products that you can use again and again rather than disposable ones. Use plastic containers to store leftovers. Give used clothing to other family members, sell it to a consignment store, or give it to charity. Take refillable containers back to the store and have them refilled instead of buying new products.

③ If you cannot reuse materials in their present form, look for ways to **recycle** them — turn them into something else. For example, compost kitchen scraps and yard wastes. Place newspapers, egg cartons, jars, cans, and other recyclable materials into recycling boxes, and set the boxes at the curb for pickup or take them to a recycling depot if you do not have curbside recycling. Whenever you have a choice, buy products made of recycled materials.

Waste-Reduction Diary

Think About It

Many companies conduct waste audits to keep track of what they throw away in order to decrease waste. With the help of family members, classmates, or others, try a similar investigation to determine how much garbage you produce.

Waste Reduction Diary Form

Type of waste	Day 1	Day 2
paper		
Organic (food waste, etc.)		
plastic		

Procedure

1. Create your own waste-reduction diary using the sample shown above. Keep your diary for one week.

2. Place your waste-reduction diary on a bulletin board, refrigerator, or other place where all the participants in your investigation can easily use it.

3. Discuss the contents of your diary with the other participants. Each of them should record each item discarded.

4. Each day for a week, have all the participants keep track of what they put into the garbage. For example, if you throw away a magazine on Day 1, put a check mark in the paper column under Day 1. If another participant also throws away a magazine on Day 1, he or she puts another check mark in the paper column under Day 1.

Analyze

1. At the end of the week, total the number of times the participants threw out the various items. Did some participants create more waste than others?

2. Compare how much waste was thrown away in the different categories. For example, how much paper was thrown out compared to organic waste?

3. As a group, choose one type of waste from your results, and create a flowchart similar to the one for the hamburger on page 32. Think of as many stages as possible, and add them to your flowchart.

4. What happens to waste once it leaves your home? Does it go to a landfill, a dump, or a recycling facility? Contact your municipal office to find out.

Conclude and Apply

5. List the needs and wants that resulted in the waste. For example, you needed food so you made a sandwich, and threw away the plastic bread bag and the packaging from the meat.

6. List five ways that you could have reduced the waste that you generated over the week.

Computer CONNECT

Use multimedia software to create a chart or other graphic organizer to show a product's journey from raw materials to disposal.

Reducing Waste

Waste-management consultants are people who study and give advice on garbage disposal matters, including Blue Box programs. Mayors, councillors, and other members of community governments are also involved with Blue Box programs and waste management. Executives of manufacturing companies and executives of companies who turn recyclables into goods that will be resold need to work closely with waste-management specialists.

Use your library or the Internet to find out what kind of education is needed to become a waste-management consultant. What kind of background would you need in order to work in waste management? What skills are most important to be effective at this job? Find out if there are any waste-management consultants in your area. What types of companies do they work for?

Looking Ahead

The 3 Rs can help us to protect our environment for the future. Imagine you are writing a letter to a friend who lives far away in another country. Explain the 3 Rs to your friend. Be sure to show how they are helping in your community. Write the letter in your Science Log. You can use the points from your letter in the end-of-unit debate.

Making the Connection

When humans affect the environment, it is often because they do not understand it. For example, when early settlers ploughed the Prairies for farmland, they were not purposely trying to destroy the swift fox's home. At the time, people did not realize the importance of this land to the swift fox and the other animals that lived there. In a country as vast as Canada, one so full of natural resources, it is hard to imagine that a human population that is relatively small can make such an impact, but, of course, we can.

If we know more about the places in which we live, perhaps we can begin to lessen our impact. How much do you know about the natural world where you live? Find out in this next activity.

Did You Know?

Technology has caused waste-management problems, but it can also help to solve them. For example, one creative company has recently found a way to turn plastics back into the material they were made from — refined oil. Researchers have also developed a process for making sweaters, like the one shown here, out of recycled soda bottles.

Figure 1.27 Although we depend on the natural world, we often ignore it.

Mapping Home

Materials

large sheets of paper   coloured markers

Procedure

1.

   On a large sheet of paper, use the coloured markers to make a map of your home by following the steps below. Use words and pictures on your map. Don't worry if you are not able to answer all of the questions. You will have a chance to find the answers later.

   (a) Draw your home in the centre of the page.

   (b) Draw the nearest body of fresh water.

   (c) Show the source of your drinking water.

   (d) Show where household wastes drain to.

   (e) Add any landforms, such as mountains or valleys.

   (f) Sketch three plants that are natural to the area.

   (g) Sketch three wild animals that are natural to the area. Choose one land animal, one bird, and one aquatic animal.

   (h) Show the direction in which the Sun rises.

   (i) Show one positive thing that is happening to the environment in your neighbourhood.

   (j) Show one negative thing that is happening to the environment in your neighbourhood.

2. **Communication and Teamwork** Share your map with your classmates. Discuss any questions that you had difficulty answering and add any new information to your map. If you still have questions that you are unable to answer, use the library or the Internet, or ask your teacher or another adult to help you find the answer.

What Did You Find Out?

1. How well do you think you understand the environment in which you live? Explain your answer.

2. What are some ways that you could increase your understanding of the environment in which you live?

TOPIC 3 Review

1. Make a list of your activities that influence the size of your ecological footprint. Choose two items on your list and explain in detail how they affect your ecological footprint.

2. What are the 3 Rs? Give one example of each R.

3. Create a survey to ask family, friends, and classmates about which environmentally friendly activities they participate in.

4. Imagine you have brought a chicken sandwich, an apple, and some orange juice to school for lunch. Where did you get the ingredients for your lunch? Imagine your great-great grandparent making the same lunch to take to school. Where would he or she have obtained the ingredients? How do these different ways of getting food differ in their impacts on the environment?

If you need to check an item, Topic numbers are provided in brackets below.

Key Terms

ecology	adaptation	parasitism	natural resources
ecologist	ecosystem	parasite	sustainability
habitat	symbiosis	host	ecological footprint
adapted	mutualism	commensalism	

Reviewing Key Terms

1. In your notebook, match the description in column A with the correct term in column B.

A

- a long-lasting relationship between two organisms
- all of the interacting living and non-living parts in an area
- a relationship between two organisms in which one organism benefits and the other organism is harmed
- a scientist who studies interactions occurring in the environment
- materials and products found in nature and used to meet humans' wants and needs
- using resources no more quickly than they can be renewed and discharging wastes no more quickly than they can absorbed
- the total area that would be needed to provide the natural resources used by an individual
- an inherited characteristic that helps an organism survive in its environment

B

- adaptation (1)
- ecological footprint (3)
- ecologist (1)
- symbiosis (1)
- natural resources (2)
- sustainability (3)
- parasitism (1)
- ecosystem (1)

Understanding Key Concepts

2. Examine the illustration. Choose two organisms and list their needs. How do they meet their needs? (For example, the butterflies eat the nectar from the flowers in the flowerbeds.) (1)

3. Adaptations allow organisms to "fit" in their environments. Describe two adaptations that you can see in the illustration. Explain how they help the organisms. (1)

4. In your own words, define the term "ecosystem." Name three ecosystems in the illustration. (1)

5. Humans use technologies to meet their needs and their wants. List three ways that you use technology every day to meet your needs. Describe how one of those technologies uses a natural resource. Does this have an impact on the environment? Explain. (2)

6. Explain how Aboriginal people who lived in Canada 200 years ago had different impacts on their environment than you do today. Give specific examples to support your answer. (2)

TOPIC 4 How Organisms Interact

As this lynx chases the hare, two living organisms are interacting in an environment. The lynx and the hare are two examples of the **biotic**, or living, parts of an ecosystem. All living organisms — including humans, bacteria, insects, and plants — are the biotic part of an ecosystem. The lynx and the hare are also interacting with the **abiotic**, or non-living, parts of their ecosystem. For example, if this photograph were taken in the summer, the hare's fur would be brown, not white. This is because the hare interacts, or responds, to the changing seasons (a non-living part of an environment) and it moults its fur as the seasons change. The abiotic parts of an ecosystem include the air, water, and soil.

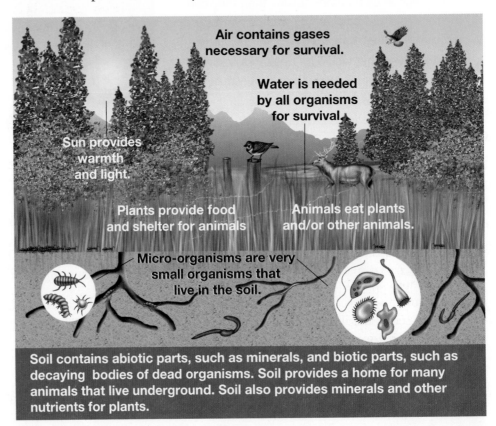

Air contains gases necessary for survival.

Water is needed by all organisms for survival.

Sun provides warmth and light.

Plants provide food and shelter for animals

Animals eat plants and/or other animals.

Micro-organisms are very small organisms that live in the soil.

Soil contains abiotic parts, such as minerals, and biotic parts, such as decaying bodies of dead organisms. Soil provides a home for many animals that live underground. Soil also provides minerals and other nutrients for plants.

INQUIRY

INVESTIGATION 1-D

SKILLCHECK
☼ Initiating and Planning
☼ Performing and Recording
☼ Analyzing and Interpreting
☼ Communication and Teamwork

A Mealworm's Ecosystem

Mealworms are a type of insect. Their home is usually their food — stored grains such as wheat. What type of habitat conditions do you think they would prefer — warm or cold, light or dark, wet or dry? Devise an experiment for finding their preferred habitat in this investigation.

Question

Which habitat conditions do mealworms prefer — warm or cold, light or dark, wet or dry?

Hypothesis

Form a hypothesis about the kind of habitat conditions that mealworms prefer.

Safety Precaution

Wash your hands when you have completed this investigation.

Materials

15 mealworms   3 petri dishes
materials of choice to complete investigation

Procedure

❶ Read through the procedure and write a hypothesis about the kind of habitat conditions that mealworms prefer. Predict what will happen in each experiment.

❷ Using mealworms, a petri dish, and other simple materials of your choice (such as black or white paper) **design** three experiments that test whether mealworms prefer a habitat that is warm or cold, light or dark, and wet or dry. Use five mealworms for each experiment.

❸ **Write** your experimental procedures, and review them with your teacher before beginning.

❹ Conduct your experiments and **record** your observations.

Analyze

1. What variable(s) did you manipulate in this investigation? What was the responding variable(s)? Which variable(s) did you control in this experiment?

2. Summarize your results in words or diagrams.

3. Compare your results with those of others in your classroom. Did everyone have the same results? If not, what could be causing the differences?

Conclude and Apply

4. Based on your observations, which habitat conditions do mealworms prefer?

5. How could you improve your experiment?

Extend Your Knowledge

6. Choose one of the experiments you designed and repeat it three times. Do you get the same results every time?

The Roles of Organisms in an Ecosystem

You, like all other members of human communities, play several different roles in your daily life. At school, you are a student. On the weekend, you might be a member of a sports team, or a volunteer at a food bank. Similarly, the organisms in a community of plants and animals play different roles, too. Each of these roles is known as a **niche**. One organism usually fills several niches.

Knowing an organism's niche can help explain why organisms act and interact as they do. To determine an organism's niche, you must look at what it eats, where it lives, and how it interacts with other organisms in its ecosystem.

Figure 1.28 What are the niches of the various organisms shown here?

Figure 1.29 Although there are over 600 kinds of eucalyptus, koalas eat only the leaves of 35 kinds that grow in eastern Australia. Today, koala bears are endangered because eucalyptus forests were cut down to make room for farms and other developments.

Plants and algae are able to grow using energy from the Sun and nutrients present in the soil. They fill the niche called **producers** because they produce food energy for themselves. Producers make life possible for all other organisms on Earth.

All other organisms are called **consumers**, because their niche is to consume (eat) the food made by the producers. Consumers occur in all sizes and shapes and may also eat other consumers. For example, the coyote in the ecosystem above is a consumer, so it must find food to eat by hunting and foraging. It also fills different niches when it finds or builds shelter, and stays safe from other organisms.

Consumers can be divided into three different groups: herbivores, carnivores, and omnivores. **Herbivores** are animals that eat producers and fill the plant-eating niche. Cows, prairie dogs, deer, herring, and tadpoles are examples of this group of consumers. **Carnivores** are animals that eat other consumers, filling the meat-eating niche. Lynx, cod, minnows, and dragonflies are examples of carnivores. **Predators** are consumers that kill and eat other animals called **prey**. Red foxes and golden eagles are examples of predators. **Omnivores** are animals such as raccoons, skunks, and humans (that are not vegetarians) that eat both producers and consumers.

What Goes Up Must Come Down

Think About It

The niches of the Canada lynx and the snowshoe hare are linked together. The Canada lynx feeds mainly on snowshoe hares. Snowshoe hares eat plants. When there are lots of plants for snowshoe hares to eat, more of them survive and reproduce. This means that the lynxes that feed on snowshoe hares have more food. Therefore, more lynxes survive and reproduce.

However, after several years there are so many lynxes killing snowshoe hares that the hare population starts to decline. Then the lynxes do not have enough food, and *their* numbers decline. Plants are able to grow because there are fewer snowshoe hares around to eat them. As new generations of snowshoe hares are born, there is plenty of food for them. Since there are fewer lynxes to hunt them, the hare population begins to increase. There is more food for the lynxes, so *their* numbers increase, too. So this whole cycle, which lasts about ten years, begins again. The graph below shows how the numbers of lynxes and hares harvested by trappers changed over a period of 90 years.

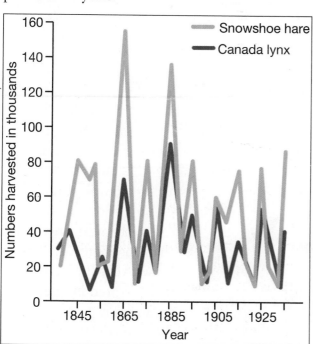

What to Do

Use the data in the graph to answer the following questions.

(a) In 1845, approximately how many lynxes were harvested by trappers?

(b) In 1845, how many hares were harvested by trappers?

(c) How many of each were harvested in 1855?

(d) In 1865, two years before Canada's Confederation, how did the two populations compare? What led to this change in the relative numbers of the two populations? What food that affects both hares and lynxes does not appear on this graph?

Analyze

1. Use the graph to explain how changes in the lynx population appear to follow changes in the hare population.

2. How can prey be said to control a predator's population? How can predators be said to control a prey's population?

3. The data in the graph are incomplete after the year 1935. Based on the data in the rest of the graph, estimate the populations of harvested lynxes and hares in 1940. Hypothesize about what might happen with these populations in 1945.

4. The last few years shown in the graph are the years of the Great Depression (1929–1939), a time of mass unemployment. How might this unemployment have affected populations such as these?

Food Chains

Grass and other plants grow by using energy from the Sun and nutrients in the soil as sources of food. The energy of the Sun is then stored in plants. When an animal, such as a cow, eats a plant, it obtains the Sun's energy indirectly in a useful form. When a meat-eating animal eats a steak, some of the stored energy in the cow is passed on to the consumer.

A **food chain** is a model that shows how energy stored in food passes from organism to organism (see Figure 1.30).

Word CONNECT

The word "herbivore" comes from the Latin words *herba* (herb or plant) and *vorare* (to devour). Using this knowledge, write what you think the Latin words *carnis* and *omnis* mean.

STRETCH Your Mind

Approximately 10 percent of available food energy is passed to the next level of a food chain. If tuna fish are four steps up a food chain, what mass of phytoplankton (the producers in the ocean) would be required to provide a human with 126 g of tuna for a sandwich?

Figure 1.30 In this prairie slough food chain, arrows show the flow of energy through the chain. At the top of the food chain is the top carnivore. This organism eats other carnivores. For example, a hawk preys on smaller insect-eating birds. In some cases top carnivores may also feed on herbivores, for example, the lynx eats snowshoe hares, and the wolf eats moose.

How does energy move through a food chain? At each step along the chain, energy is taken in by an organism and is used as fuel. As the organism uses the fuel, some energy is also released as heat. Some of the energy is stored in the organism's body tissues, while the energy that cannot be used passes out of the animal as waste. For example, when a grazing cow eats 2 kg of grass in one day, its mass does not increase 2 kg. Where does the mass of the grass go? Examine Figure 1.31.

Energy flow is the movement of energy, starting from the Sun, and passing from one organism to the next. In a food chain, as Figure 1.30 shows, very little energy that is stored in one organism is passed on to the next organism.

Figure 1.31 Most of the energy in grass eaten by a cow is not passed along the food chain. Only the 4 percent that goes to build and repair the cow's body tissues stays in the tissues. A little over 30 percent fuels the cow's normal activities such as breathing, mooing, and pumping blood through its body. Over 60 percent is passed out of its body as waste.

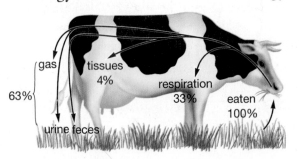

Food Webs

Food chains are rarely as simple as in Figure 1.30. Producers are usually eaten by many different consumers, and most consumers are eaten by more than one kind of predator. A mouse, for example, eats several kinds of plants and seeds. The mouse may be eaten by a hawk, a raccoon, or a snake. Figure 1.32 shows a typical **food web**. (network of interconnected food chains). Food webs can quickly become very large and complex.

Figure 1.33 A pyramid of numbers is a model of an ecosystem that represents the number of organisms consumed at each level. Producers always form the broad base.

Figure 1.32 Food webs are a combination of several food chains. They show the connections among the food chains.

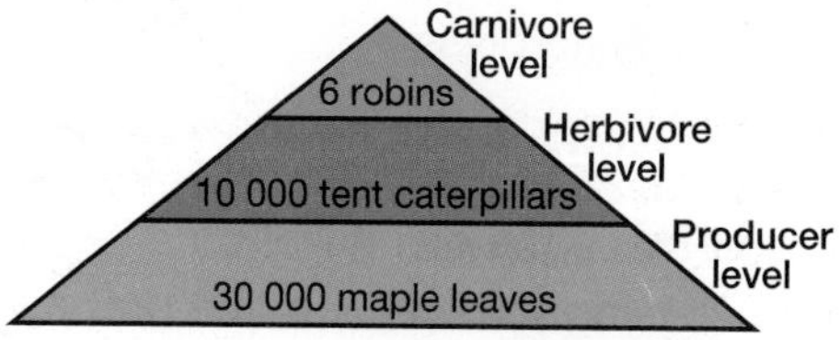

Carnivore level

6 robins

Herbivore level

10 000 tent caterpillars

Producer level

30 000 maple leaves

Figure 1.34 Each time a caterpillar eats a maple leaf, energy is lost and only a small amount is stored in its tissues. Thus, 10 000 caterpillars store only enough energy to feed six robins.

Pyramid of Numbers

Food chains and food webs show how food energy moves through an ecosystem, but not how many organisms are involved in the total energy transfer. In Figure 1.32, we do not know how many grasshoppers the snakes eat. We know only that snakes eat grasshoppers.

To solve this problem, ecologists build a **pyramid of numbers** (see Figure 1.33). It includes the same organisms as in a food chain, but the size of each level changes to show the number of organisms involved. There are always more animals being eaten than there are animals eating. There may be one hawk eating three woodpeckers, but not three hawks eating one woodpecker.

A pyramid of numbers does not indicate exactly *how much* energy is consumed. We can find this out by looking at how much each level of the pyramid weighs — how many kilograms of grasshoppers are needed to feed a kilogram of woodpeckers. **Biomass** is the total mass of all the organisms in an ecosystem. Just as each level in the pyramid of numbers has fewer organisms than the level below it, it also has less biomass. In any pyramid of numbers, the most biomass is in the base formed by the producers (see Figure 1.34).

What Was for Dinner?

Looking at an animal's scat (feces) or what an animal has in its stomach is one way to find out what niche it occupies! In this activity you will examine the contents of an owl pellet. Owl pellets are not scat, they are pellets of undigested food that are regurgitated by owls.

Safety Precautions

Wash your hands when you have completed this investigation.

Materials

owl pellet

paper towel

forceps or a fine probe

magnifying glass

Procedure ✴ Performing and Recording

1. Place the owl pellet on a paper towel. Using forceps or a fine probe, carefully break the pellet apart, separating out all of the smaller pieces.

2. Describe each item you were able to separate out from the pellet. Be as specific as possible.

3. Identify as many of the items from the pellet as you can. Study the illustration of contents of a pellet shown here.

4. Clean up as your teacher directs, and wash your hands after this activity.

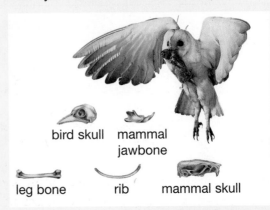

bird skull   mammal jawbone

leg bone   rib   mammal skull

What Did You Find Out? ✴ Analyzing and Interpreting

1. How many different organisms were represented by the remains in the pellet? Explain your answer.

2. What is the niche of an owl in its ecosystem? (Where does it live, and what and where does it eat?)

3. Is the owl a producer or a consumer? Explain your answer.

You may have seen a robin eat a worm, but have you ever seen a worm eat a robin? Try to explain how this might happen.

The Clean-Up Squads: Scavengers and Decomposers

Have you ever wondered why you seldom see a dead carcass in a natural environment? If dead organisms stayed whole, Earth would soon be covered in bodies! In every ecosystem, there must be "clean-up squads" that get rid of garbage and waste. These organisms break down dead material and waste. As the material breaks down, the nutrients that had been stored within it are released back into the ecosystem. They can then be taken in by other organisms and used for growth and other functions.

In a biological community, the clean-up squads are consumers called scavengers and decomposers. **Scavengers** are organisms that feed on dead or decaying plant or animal matter. Scavengers eat the dead material and break down the large carcasses into smaller pieces during digestion (see Figures 1.35A and B).

Decomposers are different from scavengers because they do not actually eat dead material. Instead, they grow on or in the dead or waste material, absorbing some of the nutrients into their own cells. The remaining nutrients recycle back into the ecosystem.

Figures 1.35A and B The magpie (above left) and the wolverine (above right) are common scavengers in Alberta. They eat dead and waste material, breaking it down into smaller parts and spreading the stored nutrients back into the ecosystem.

Have you ever found food covered in mould in the refrigerator? If so, you have witnessed decomposers at work. Many bacteria and fungi are decomposers. Although bacteria are micro-organisms (too small to see without a microscope), some fungi are quite large and visible (see Figure 1.36). In fact, you can see common fungi called mushrooms in any grocery store or vegetable market.

Decomposers play a key role in breaking down much of our kitchen waste. We can assist this process by composting lettuce leaves, apple cores, carrot peelings, and other kitchen wastes in a composter like the one shown in Figure 1.37. When we compost, we let nature's decomposers turn our kitchen wastes into rich soil we can use for fertilizing the garden. In the next investigation you will experiment with composters.

INTERNET CONNECT

www.mcgrawhill.ca/links/sciencefocus7

Find out more about decomposers by researching them on the Internet. Go to the above web site, click on **Web Links** to find out where to go next. Create a display of different decomposers and the ways in which they affect humans.

Did You Know?

The wreck of the *Titanic* could disappear completely from the ocean floor by 2030. Bacteria are removing the iron from its hull at a rate of one-tenth of a tonne a day.

Figure 1.36 Bracket fungus digests the dead cells of tree bark.

Figure 1.37 Kitchen wastes can be composted in a backyard composter.

INQUIRY

INVESTIGATION 1-F

SKILLCHECK

☼ Initiating and Planning

☼ Performing and Recording

☼ Analyzing and Interpreting

☼ Communication and Teamwork

Don't Waste It!

Under the right conditions, kitchen wastes, such as potato peelings, lettuce leaves, and eggshells, can be composted. Composting breaks them down so the nutrients that are trapped in them are released. The composted material can then be recycled, for instance, as garden fertilizer. What kinds of materials break down well? What kinds of materials do not break down at all? This investigation will enable you to explore the process of composting. (**Note**: While all food wastes will break down eventually, not all are appropriate to add to a home composter. Do not add meat, cooked food, and dairy products to home composters.)

Question

How can you find out which materials will decompose, and how long it takes for decomposition to occur?

Hypothesis

Form a hypothesis about the kinds of materials that can decompose.

Safety Precautions

Apparatus

large clay pots with drainage holes (1 per test material)

labels for the pots

saucers to go under the pots

pieces of window screen or a similar material

magnifying glass

Materials

garden soil (not sterilized)

small stones

water

some or all of the following test materials: banana peels, paper, cabbage leaves, grass clippings, aluminum foil, orange peels, plastic, glass, potato peels, carrot peels, eggshells

Procedure

❶ Before starting this investigation, **predict** what will happen to each of the materials you are going to test. Explain your prediction on the basis of your hypothesis.

❷ Set each clay pot on a saucer.

(a) Put a few small stones over the drainage hole in the bottom of each pot.

(b) Add garden soil to each pot until the pot is about half full.

❸ Put one test material in each pot. **Label** the pot to show what material is in it.

(a) Cover the materials in the pots with an equal amount of soil.

(b) Water the soil in each pot until a little water comes out the bottom into the saucer.

(c) Cover the open top of each pot with a piece of window screen.

(d) Put the pots in a permanent location for a few weeks. Moisten the soil every few days.

4 After a week, remove the upper layer of soil and check that it is moist. **Observe** the amount of decomposition. You could use the magnifying glass to examine the test materials. **Record** your observations. Replace the soil and continue the process until you can detect a difference in the condition of the materials.

5 Clean up your work area as your teacher directs, and wash your hands thoroughly after completing this investigation.

Skill
F O C U S

For tips on graphing, turn to Skill Focus 10.

Analyze

1. What variable(s) did you manipulate in this investigation? What was the responding variable(s)? Which variable(s) did you control in this investigation?

2. Which test materials decomposed rapidly?

3. Which test materials decomposed slowly?

4. Which materials did not decompose over the course of the investigation?

5. Was your hypothesis supported by your observations?

Conclude and Apply

6. Considering the health of the environment, what should be done to dispose of the materials you listed for questions 3 and 4?

7. What factors might speed up the decomposition of materials listed in question 3?

Extend Your Skills

8. Design an experiment to determine what effect, if any, temperature would have on the rate of decomposition. Make sure that your experiment is a fair test, and have your teacher approve your procedure before you carry out your experiment. (Hint: Your hypothesis should state whether you expect one variable, such as the rate of decomposition, to change when you alter another variable, such as temperature.)

9. Design an experiment that will test what effect, if any, using sterilized soil (such as potting soil) would have on the rate of decomposition. Your experiment should be a fair test, and your teacher must approve your procedure before you carry out your experiment. (Hint: Your hypothesis should state whether you expect one variable, such as the rate of decomposition, to change when you alter another variable, such as the type of soil.)

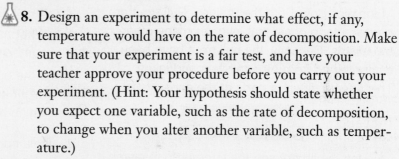

Math **CONNECT**

For each test material, estimate and record the percentage of decomposition every week. For example, strawberries may be half their original size, so they have decomposed about 50 percent. A plastic bag may have not have changed, so it has decomposed 0 percent. At the end of your investigation, graph your results. Finally, interpret your graphed data.

Across Canada

Dr. Kevin Vessey

"Curiosity is probably the most important characteristic that leads someone into a career in science," says Dr. Kevin Vessey, a scientist from the University of Manitoba. Kevin grew up in Prince Edward Island. As a teenager, he enjoyed watching marine biology shows, such as "The Undersea World of Jacques Cousteau," on television. Kevin's curiosity inspired him to study biology at Dalhousie University in Halifax, Nova Scotia, and then at Queen's University in Kingston, Ontario.

Dr. Vessey is interested in the many types of good bacteria in soil that help plants grow. The most common type of helpful bacteria are called rhizobia. They convert nitrogen from the air into ammonium, the mineral form of nitrogen. Plants cannot use nitrogen in the air, but they can use this mineral form of nitrogen to make protein. Rhizobia live in tumourlike growths on the roots of plants. When rhizobia attach themselves to a plant, they "infect" it. Dr. Vessey studies the development of infection by rhizobia in peas and soybeans (legumes). He says that this process of "nitrogen fixation" is similar to plants having their own fertilizer factory in their roots!

The research Dr. Vessey is doing will help farmers use helpful bacteria and fewer pesticides. You might have a chance to hear Dr. Vessey if you listen to "The Science Quiz" portion of "Quirks and Quarks" on CBC radio. He has taken part in this show in the past and plans to contribute more science questions for curious minds in the future.

No Fishing Allowed

Find Out ACTIVITY

Bull trout are large fish that live in the rivers flowing from the eastern slopes of the Rocky Mountains down into the Prairies. Bull trout are part of a food chain that involves many other organisms. Recently, the bull trout have been disappearing from Alberta rivers and lakes. This affects different parts of the ecosystem.

Procedure · **Performing and Recording** · **Analyzing and Interpreting**

1. Use the library and the Internet to research bull trout in Alberta. Look for answers to these questions.

- What other organisms are in the food chain? Where do the bull trout fit into the chain?
- What has caused the reduction in the numbers of bull trout?
- If the bull trout become extinct, what might happen to the food pyramid in which the bull trout are found?

2. Use a concept map to organize your findings. Write a brief report with the information that you found.

TOPIC 4 Review

1. Define the following terms in your own words, and give an example of each.

   (a) producer   (b) omnivore
   (c) predator   (d) decomposer

2. Use a Venn diagram to compare a pyramid of numbers and a food chain.

3. Explain why all of the energy in one level of a food pyramid is not available to other organisms in the pyramid.

4. Use arrows and words to draw three food chains you might find in the prairie ecosystem found on page 42. If you wish, you may add other prairie organisms not shown in the illustration.

5. **Thinking Critically** Choose and observe an ecosystem in your community (a local park, a ravine, or your own backyard). List the biotic and abiotic features. Indicate the niche occupied by each organism in your ecosystem.

Cycles in the Environment

When you or another animal breathe out, the gases are recycled in the air and are used by other living organisms. When an animal or tree dies, it eventually decomposes and the nutrients are recycled back into the environment. Even as the tree in Figure 1.38 dies and decays, many forest animals rely on it. Woodpeckers feed on insects that, in turn, feed on the bacteria in the decaying wood. Burrowing birds build nests in holes in the rotting tree. Bats find a home under the bark during the day. In this Topic you will learn about natural cycles in the environment.

The Carbon Cycle

Plankton are microscopic plants, animals, and other organisms that float in the ocean. All of these organisms contain carbon, which is what fossil fuels are made of. Phytoplankton are plankton, such as algae, that use sunlight to make their own food through photosynthesis. Over time and under great pressure, decomposing plankton changes into fossil fuels. (You will learns about fossil fuels in Units 3 and 5.) These fuels still contain the carbon that was present in the original organisms.

Carbon is necessary for all life to exist. Plants use carbon dioxide from the air in order to make their own food. Moose, mice, and other organisms eat the plants and release carbon dioxide when they exhale. Wolves, foxes, and other organisms eat the moose and mice, and obtain their stored carbon. They also exhale carbon dioxide into the air. Thus, carbon circulates around and around an ecosystem in the **carbon cycle** (see Figure 1. 39).

Figure 1.38
The environment is the ultimate recycler — it uses gases, water, and nutrients over and over again.

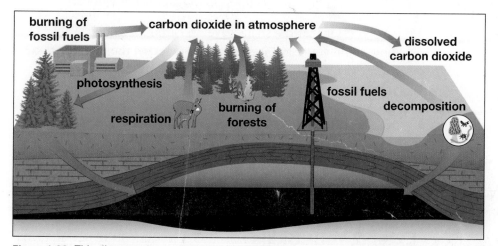

Figure 1.39 This diagram shows the carbon cycle. The oil derrick is pumping oil from deep under the ground

Looking Ahead

Fossil fuels are non-renewable resources. If the carbon cycle is really a cycle, why is there concern about using up all of the fossil fuels? You will want to consider the issue of renewable and non-renewable resources as you prepare for your end-of-unit debate.

Telltale Snails

Bromthymol blue is a liquid that changes colour from blue to green to yellow when carbon dioxide levels increase. How could you use it to demonstrate that snails give off carbon dioxide?

Question

How can you design an experiment to show that snails give off carbon dioxide when they breathe?

Hypothesis

Form a hypothesis about what will happen to the bromthymol blue when the snails breathe.

Safety Precautions

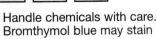

- Handle chemicals with care. Bromthymol blue may stain clothing.
- Follow your teacher's directions for disposing of materials safely.
- Always handle the creatures with care and respect, and return them to their habitat after you have studied them.

Apparatus
2 Erlenmeyer flasks
2 small, clear cups or similar containers
modelling clay
flexible drinking straws
small, live aquarium snails

Materials
bromthymol blue indicator
distilled water

Procedure

1. Before you begin, read carefully through all of the steps and design your hypothesis. **Predict** what will happen to the bromthymol blue. Explain your prediction, on the basis of your hypothesis.

2. With your group, decide how you might use the materials. Decide how you can demonstrate that any observed changes in the bromthymol blue are due to carbon dioxide given off by the snails.

3. **Draw** a labelled diagram of your set-up for the investigation. On your diagram, indicate how long you think your set-up should be in place. Show your diagram to your teacher for approval.

4. Set up your investigation.

5. **Observe** the experimental set-up. **Record** your observations.

6. Clean up as your teacher directs, and wash your hands after this investigation.

Analyze

1. What variable(s) did you manipulate in this investigation? What was the responding variable? What variable(s) did you control?

2. Was your hypothesis supported by your observations?

3. Was it clear that the snails gave off carbon dioxide? If not, how could you make it clear if you repeated the investigation?

Conclude and Apply

4. Predict what might happen if you put water plants in with the snails. With your teacher's permission, try it.

5. Did any group come up with a better way to carry out the investigation? How did the procedure or set-up differ from yours?

Extend Your Skills

6. Design a fair test to show that humans exhale carbon dioxide.

The Water Cycle

All living things require water. As Figure 1.40 shows, an apple is 84 percent water, a carrot is 88 percent water, and a tomato is 94 percent water. The human body is 60–70 percent water. Water is used for life processes such as supplying food throughout an organism's body in a form it can use in its cells, and carrying away wastes from those cells. Water moves constantly around the environment, changing form as it moves from the air to the ground to your body.

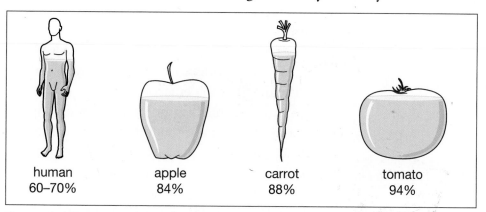

human 60–70%   apple 84%   carrot 88%   tomato 94%

Figure 1.40 All living things contain large amounts of water.

The **water cycle** is the continuous movement of water through an ecosystem (see Figure 1.41). This cycle involves four main processes. The first two processes — evaporation and transpiration — move water up from Earth into the atmosphere. The second two — condensation and precipitation — return water to Earth.

DidYouKnow?

Does it surprise you to know that the amount of water on Earth always stays more or less the same? The same water particles that were present hundreds of years ago in the days of your great-great-great-great-great-grandparents are still around today.

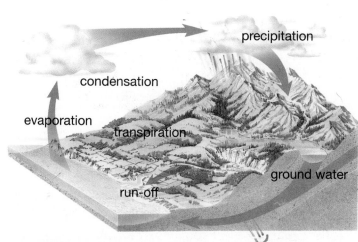

precipitation

condensation

evaporation

transpiration

run-off

ground water

Evaporation is the process in which a liquid changes into water vapour. Liquid water evaporates to form invisible water vapour.

Transpiration is the process in which water that is taken in through a plant's roots evaporates from the plant's leaves, stem, and flowers.

Condensation is the process in which water vapour changes into a liquid. Warm air contains water vapour. As air cools, however, it is able to hold less and less water. Condensation happens when air becomes so cool that it can no longer hold as much water vapour, and liquid water is released. This creates clouds, fog, or dew.

Precipitation is the process in which liquid water forms from condensation occurring inside clouds, and then falls as rain, sleet, snow, and hail.

Ground water is water in the soil. Plant roots can grow down to reach ground water. People can reach ground water by digging wells.

Run-off is water that runs off the ground into lakes, rivers, or streams.

Figure 1.41 The water cycle is the continuous movement of water through an ecosystem.

Pollution in the Environment

Figure 1.42 These trees were damaged by acid rain.

You have seen that matter, energy, carbon, and water all constantly cycle throughout ecosystems. Other substances can also enter and cycle throughout ecosystems. **Pollution** occurs when a substance is added to the environment at such a fast rate that it cannot be broken down, stored, or recycled in the air, land, or water in a non-damaging form. **Pollutants** are substances that cause pollution.

Many substances that occur naturally become pollutants when they are present in concentrations too high for the environment to absorb without a negative effect. For example, carbon dioxide is naturally present in the atmosphere. However, at this time, excess carbon dioxide, caused by burning fossil fuels, is damaging the environment.

Acid rain occurs when pollutants containing sulfur and nitrogen are found in high levels in the air. When fossil fuels are burned, sulphur and nitrogen are released as waste. These pollutants mix with water vapour, making it acidic. When it falls from the atmosphere as precipitation, it damages ecosystems. For example, entire lakes can "die," because the water is too acidic for fish and plants. Water with a pH value below 5.6 is considered acidic. Figure 1.43 shows the **pH** scale.

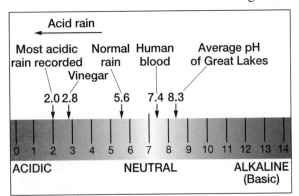

Figure 1.43 The pH scale measures the acidity of liquids, and ranges from 0 (very acidic) to 12 (not acidic).

Checking the pH

In this activity, you will determine how acidic the rain and water systems are in your area.

Materials

samples of rainwater collected from various areas

samples of water from water systems in your area

a sample of tap water

pH indicator paper

Safety Precautions

Procedure * Performing and Recording

1. Collect water samples from different sources in your area (puddles, streams or nearby sloughs, or melted snow).

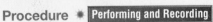

Find Out ACTIVITY

2. Dip a piece of pH indicator paper into the sample. Observe the colour of the paper and compare it to the pH chart on the paper's container. Record the pH of the sample.

3. Repeat the procedure for each sample of water that you have.

4. Clean your work area if necessary, and wash your hands after this activity.

What Did You Find Out? * Analyzing and Interpreting

1. Were your samples acidic, basic, or neutral?

2. How does the pH of the tap water compare with the pH of the samples you collected?

3. Based on your results, do you feel the water in your area has been affected by acid rain?

The Movement of Pollution

There are many different pollutants moving through the environment. For example, PCBs (polychlorinated biphenyl) are substances that were commonly used for a variety of purposes, including paints and packaging materials. PCBs were never meant to enter into the environment, but they accidentally leaked into the air, water, and ground through waste-disposal sites. PCBs break down very slowly, so they remain in the ground and in water for years and years. Once in the ground and in the water, they can cause harm to organisms.

Mercury is another substance that does not naturally move through the environment. Mercury was used by many different industries, including gold mining, and was disposed of as waste. Sometimes, mercury leaked out from the waste-disposal sites and dissolved in water. Then it would soak into the ground and end up in a body of water such as a river or lake. The bird in Figure 1.44 has been damaged by mercury poisoning.

DDT is a pesticide that was commonly used across Canada. In the 1940s, 1950s, and 1960s, it was sprayed onto crops and trees to kill harmful insects. DDT did control insect populations. However, it was very poisonous, and it started to damage other organisms as well. DDT is now banned in Canada, but it is not banned everywhere in the world. How do poisons such as DDT cycle through the environment?

Figure 1.44 This robin's beak has been deformed by poisons in its ecosystem.

Figure 1.45 Insecticides protect our trees, but do we always know the full extent of their impact on the environment?

Bioaccumulation

Pollutants move from level to level in a food web. They are stored in organisms in the same way that food energy is stored. This effect is called **bioaccumulation**. Bioaccumulation occurs when pollutants enter into the food web and accumulate in the higher level consumers (see Figure 1.46). For example, the large fish accumulates all of the pollutants contained in all of the small fish it ate. Most humans eat a variety of different foods from all levels of the food web. This means that we are at risk of accumulating many different types of poisons that have been stored in the organisms we consume. When we understand how pollutants enter the system, we can work toward reducing the levels of pollutants moving through the environment.

A Mercury enters the water after leaking out of a waste-disposal site and settles on the bottom of the lake.

B The mercury enters the systems of micro-organisms living in the sediment and algae in the water.

C Small fish eat the micro-organisms and the algae, and the mercury accumulates in their systems.

D Larger, carnivorous fish eat the smaller fish, and absorb the mercury contained from the small fish into their systems. The mercury stays dissolved in the fatty tissue in the fish.

E Finally, the large fish are caught and eaten by a human. The human needs several fish to make a meal, and accumulates the mercury that was in both of the fish eaten.

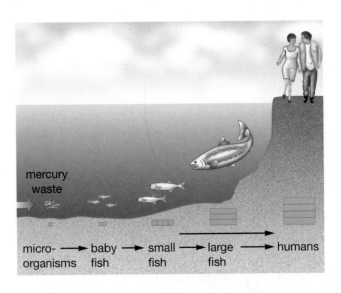

Figure 1.46 Pollutants are passed through a food chain along with energy

TOPIC 5 Review

1. The carbon cycle is balanced in stable ecosystems. What events might occur to upset this balance?

2. Pesticides are commonly used to control agricultural pests. In your own words, explain how this affects carnivores.

3. In your notebook draw a diagram of the water cycle, explaining the four main points.

4. Explain two ways in which cutting down forests and then burning the debris left behind can increase the level of carbon dioxide in the atmosphere.

5. **Thinking Critically** Explain the statement "Earth is an excellent recycler." Use examples to support your answer.

If you need to check an item, Topic numbers are provided in brackets below.

Key Terms

biotic	carnivores	food web	water cycle	run-off
abiotic	predators	pyramid of numbers	evaporation	pollution
niche	prey	biomass	transpiration	pollutants
producers	omnivores	scavengers	condensation	acid rain
consumers	food chain	decomposers	precipitation	pH
herbivores	energy flow	carbon cycle	ground water	bioaccumulation

Reviewing Key Terms

1. **(a)** In an ecosystem, _____ make their own food using the Sun's energy, and all other organisms are _____ because they cannot make their own food, they must acquire it. (4)

   (b) _____ are animals that kill and eat other animals called _____. (4)

   (c) Organisms that eat only producers are called _____ and organisms that can eat anything are called _____. (4)

   (d) Energy moves through the ecosystem, starting at the Sun and passing from organism to organism. This is called _____. (4)

   (e) The two types of organisms that break down dead and waste material are called _____ and _____. (4)

   (f) A _____ is a network of interconnected _____. (4)

   (g) To show how much energy is moving through a system, scientists use a _____. (4)

   (h) The two main naturally occurring cycles in the environment are the _____ and the _____. (5)

   (i) Pollutants enter a food chain and move from one organism to the next. The buildup of pollutants because of this movement is called _____. (5)

Understanding Key Concepts

2. If you found hawks, field mice, and corn in the same ecosystem, what role would each be playing in a food chain? (4)

3. List, with examples, five different niches in an ecosystem. (4)

4. Why are scavengers and decomposers important in an ecosystem? How do they differ? (4)

5. Explain the difference between a food web and a food chain. (4)

6. Draw a pyramid of numbers for the ecosystem described in question 2. Explain your answer. (4)

7. Humans usually eat food from all levels of a food chain, like those shown in the photograph. Construct two food chains based on food you typically eat. Make one food chain long (at least four levels), the other food chain short (two levels). Illustrate your food chains, or simply use words and numbers. (4)

Succession and Change in Ecosystems

Have you ever noticed grasses or plants growing in a vacant lot near your home? If you wait long enough, bushes and trees will grow, and animals will make their homes in the lot. How does this process happen?

Changes are constantly occurring in an ecosystem. Some changes are rapid. For example, a landslide might completely destroy an existing ecosystem. Other changes are slow. For instance, seeds carried by wind or water might take root in a vacant lot or in sidewalk cracks and result in a new population of plants. If conditions are good for growth, the new plants might become established and even replace plants that were already growing.

The gradual process by which some species replace other species in an ecosystem is called **succession**. In the process of succession, organisms that are present at one stage alter the environment in some way. This change makes it possible for some other species to move in.

A Lichens produce acids that help to break down the rock. The broken-down rock and the decomposing bodies of dead lichens contribute to soil formation.

B The resulting soil is poor and thin. However, mosses and ferns grow and slowly replace the lichens.

C The soil layer thickens, which means it can hold more water. Plants that need more soil and moisture, such as grasses and flowering weeds, take root and grow. They attract insects, such as bees and butterflies.

D Since the soil is now thicker and richer, bushes and trees take root. They provide shelter and food for birds, mammals, and other organisms, which now start moving in.

Figure 1.47 Succession is a long, slow process in which a stable natural ecosystem gradually develops over time.

Primary succession is the gradual growth of organisms in an area that was previously bare, such as rock. For example, lichens, mosses, and ferns will first appear on bare rock. As they become established and grow, they change the conditions of the area. (Lichens, for instance, may use chemicals in their tissue to slowly etch away the rock. This creates tiny depressions in the rock where soil and seeds from other plants can gather and eventually grow.) These new conditions allow other plants and animals to grow and survive. Succession can be a very slow process, taking hundreds, even thousands, of years.

Secondary Succession

The gradual growth of organisms in an area that previously had a number of organisms is known as **secondary succession**. The regeneration of a burned forest area is an example of secondary succession. Figure 1.48 shows the process of secondary succession in a burned forest. Wildflowers and other plants that grow best in strong sunlight are among the first to spring up. Blueberry bushes also thrive in these conditions, because they are adapted to grow in soil containing ash. Like blueberry bushes, a number of tree species actually grow better in soil that has been burned.

Figure 1.48A Forest fires often burn off the foliage but leave the tree trunks standing.

Figure 1.48B These wildflowers are thriving in soil that has been burned by fire.

DidYou**Know**?

The cones from jack pine and lodgepole pine trees lie closed for years on the forest floor until the heat of a fire pops them open and releases the seeds that will grow into new trees. These types of cones are called serotinous cones.

INQUIRY

INVESTIGATION **1-H**

SKILLCHECK
☼ Initiating and Planning
☼ Performing and Recording
☼ Analyzing and Interpreting
Communication and Teamwork

Nothing Succeeds Like Succession

Succession can take place in any kind of area, large or small, in a short period of time or over many years. For instance, weeds grow quickly in an untended patch of soil, but trees take many years to grow back in an area cleared by forest fire or logging.

Question

How does succession take place in an ecosystem?

Hypothesis

Make a hypothesis about how succession takes place in an ecosystem.

Safety Precautions

Materials

2 L clear plastic soda bottle with the top cut off or large-mouth jar

potting soil

water

a small aquatic plant (maybe from an aquarium supply store)

wild birdseed

Procedure

❶ Put soil in the bottom of the container, to a depth of 5 cm.

  (a) Fill the container with water, to a depth of 7.5 cm, thus covering the soil.

  (b) Place the container, uncovered, on a window sill, and allow the contents to settle overnight.

❷ The next day, plant an aquatic plant in the container. Although the water will evaporate over time, do *not* add more water to the container.

❸ Once a week, add 3 or 4 seeds from the wild bird seed mix to the container. **Predict** what will happen in the container. **Observe** and **record** your observations.

(a) Continue adding seeds weekly, even though the water evaporates. **Predict** what will happen in the container. **Observe** and **record** what happens to these seeds.

(b) After a few weeks, gradually start to add water again, as you would when watering a plant. Continue to **record** your observations.

Analyze

1. Keep a careful record of your observations. Describe what is occurring in your container.

2. Describe your observations during step 3. Were your predictions supported by your observations? Explain.

3. What was the significance of not adding water to your ecosystem? What happened to the aquatic plant?

Conclude and Apply

4. Compare your ecosystem at the beginning of this investigation with your ecosystem at the end. How did they differ?

5. To what extent does this investigation demonstrate succession?

6. Using your knowledge of succession, describe what you would expect to happen

if a fire burned through a forest, destroying most of the mature trees and vegetation.

Extend Your Skills

7. **Design Your Own** Design an experiment to determine what effects different environmental factors would have on your successional ecosystem. Remember to plan how you will measure the environmental variable that you will be measuring. Make sure that your experiment is a fair test, and have your teacher approve your procedure before you carry out your experiment. (Hint: Your hypothesis should state what effect changing one variable will have on another variable. For example, you might change an environmental condition of your choice in order to observe its effect on new plant growth.)

Changes Caused by Human Activity

Figure 1.49 Brown-headed cowbirds have spread across Canada.

Humans affect the environments around them in many different ways. Human technologies, such as those used in forestry and agriculture, can change the environment around us. The spread of urban areas, highways, and parking lots, can also change the environment.

Changing an ecosystem sometimes results in unexpected environmental changes. For example, in order to produce more food, vast tracts of previously forested land have been cleared. The land is used to grow oats, barley, potatoes, beans, and other crops. One unexpected result of clearing this land has been a reduction in the numbers of some bird species, such as small warblers and vireos. How did clearing land lead to the decline of these songbirds? You might be surprised that the culprit is the brown-headed cowbird, shown in Figure 1.49. The brown-headed cowbird adapts easily to change, so it spreads into areas that have been altered. The cowbird lays its eggs in the nests of other species of birds, such as warblers and vireos. When the cowbird chicks hatch, they loudly demand food. Cowbird chicks also grow quickly, often squeezing the smaller warbler and vireo chicks out of the nest. As a result, the warblers and vireos do not reproduce as successfully as they would without the cowbirds.

Some Species Adapt Better Than Others

The natural habitat of brown-headed cowbirds is the grassland biome of the Canadian Prairies. Since brown-headed cowbirds are adapted to living in open country, they quickly spread into newly cleared farmland. Brown-headed cowbirds have been quick to take advantage of the newly cleared habitat found east of the prairie grassland, across central Canada, and in the Atlantic provinces. The smaller birds that naturally occur in these areas are being forced into other habitats. They are not adapted to these new habitats, so they are not surviving as well as they did in their natural habitat.

You may have heard of coyotes being seen occasionally within cities (see Figure 1.50), but have you ever heard of a wolf being sighted inside city limits? Although both of these animals occupy similar environments, the coyote is better able to adapt to living in habitats altered by humans.

Figure 1.50 The coyote lives in the wild, but it will adapt to life in built-up areas if food is scarce.

Pest Control

Figure 1.51 Adult insects and late stage nymphs are responsible for most of the lygus bug damage to crops. The lygus bug is also known as the tarnished plant bug.

In Topic 5 you learned about the use of pesticides, such as DDT, to kill pests. Pests that affect human health and crops are a major problem. However, one possible consequence of using pesticides is that beneficial organisms living in the same environment as the pests could also be harmed. This can happen because many pesticides kill more than just the pest. For example, the lygus bug in Figure 1.51 is a pest that feeds on alfalfa and canola plants and causes severe damage to these crops. However, pesticides that are sprayed to kill lygus bugs also kill bees.

Another downside to using pesticides is that they can also harm the beneficial insects that normally prey on the pests. This can result in the populations of pests actually increasing because there are fewer organisms to prey on them!

Figure 1.52 Leafy spurge

Biological Control

Another way to control insect pests is to use their natural enemies. This method, called **biological control**, can be very effective and limits or eliminates the need for pesticides. For example, leafy spurge is a weed that was accidentally introduced into Canada in the late 1800s (see Figure 1.52). Leafy spurge grows faster than naturally occurring pasture grasses. Cattle will not eat leafy spurge, so land that is infested with this weed cannot carry livestock. The black dot spurge beetle is a small beetle that feeds on leafy spurge (see Figure 1.53). The beetle was introduced into Alberta in 1983, and has been very successful in controlling the spread of leafy spurge. Desirable plants, such as pasture and rangeland grasses, are returning to the areas where leafy spurge used to grow.

Although biological control can work very well, there can be risks. Whenever a new organism that is not native to the area is introduced to an ecosystem, there is always a risk that it will cause harm.

Figure 1.53 The black dot spurge beetle naturally controls the pest, leafy spurge. Natural control limits or eliminates the need for chemical controls such as pesticides.

The Good, the Bad, and the Buggy

Ladybird beetles are often sold at gardening and landscape stores to help control pests such as these aphids. There are many other insects that are used as biological controls to control pests in gardens and in agricultural fields in Alberta. In this activity you will investigate some of these insects.

Materials

reference materials

materials of your choice for a presentation

Procedure

* Performing and Recording
* Analyzing and Interpreting

1. Using the Internet or other reference sources, gather information on an insect or plant pest in Alberta that is being controlled using biological methods. You could also contact a local gardening store for assistance.

2. Organize the information you collected using a graphic organizer of your choice.

3. Present your research findings to your class using a presentation style of your choice. For example, you could prepare a web tutorial, or give a talk using visual aids such as pictures, sketches, or maps.

What Did You Find Out?

1. How are biological methods being used to control an insect or plant pest?

2. How would this pest be controlled if biological controls were not used?

Skill

FOCUS

For more information about using Technology in Science, turn to Skill Focus 9.

INTERNET CONNECT

www.mcgrawhill.ca/links/sciencefocus7

For information on the use of biological control in Alberta, go to the above web site. Click on **Web Links** to find out where to go next. Use this information to help you complete the Find Out Activity above.

Introduced Species

Today, purposely introducing a new species, such as the black dot spurge beetle, into an ecosystem is done only after extensive scientific tests show the new organism will do more good than harm. However, many species are accidentally introduced to an environment where they are not naturally found. These are called exotic or **introduced species**. Exotic species occur naturally in another part of the world, and are controlled by predators and other natural controls there. Exotic species have a large impact on the environment into which they are introduced. If they are able to survive and reproduce better than naturally occurring species, they become invasive and can take over a particular ecosystem.

Figure 1.54 With no natural predators in the Great Lakes, the zebra mussel thrives.

For example, zebra mussels (see Figure 1.54) were introduced by accident to the Great Lakes. The larvae of this mussel were discharged from ships. With no natural predators in the Great Lakes, the mussel was able to survive and thrive. Now it is a serious problem. It clogs water pipes and deprives animals that naturally occur there of space and food.

Historically, people purposely, but innocently, introduced many species, not realizing the problems that could result. In 1890 a group of people released 140 European starlings in Central Park in New York City. They wanted to introduce every species of bird mentioned in the plays of William Shakespeare into North America. Today, starlings have spread across North America and in many cases have taken the food or niche occupied by naturally occurring birds (see Figure 1.55). Today there are over 4 million starlings in the city of Vancouver alone!

The plant in Figure 1.58 is an introduced species that does not belong in North America. Imagine, only three seeds of scotch broom were planted on Vancouver Island in 1850, but today this plant is widespread. It has taken over the ecosystem of many native plants in British Columbia. Purple loosestrife, another plant that is not originally found in North America, is sometimes called the "beautiful killer" because it is deadly to other naturally occurring species. Purple loosestrife quickly takes over wetland areas and colonizes the habitat of native plant species (see Figures 1.56 and 1.57). As well, the animals that depend on these plants are forced to move to other areas if they are to survive.

Figure 1.55 Many species that we eat have been introduced (apples, corn, oysters, to name a few). Unlike invasive species such as starlings, they remain under control.

Figure 1.58 The introduced species, Scotch broom now growing over most of southern Vancouver Island, started with just three seeds.

Figure 1.56 Reported garden plantings of purple loosestrife in Alberta, 1999.

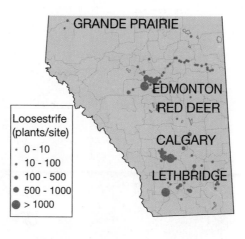

Loosestrife (plants/site)
- 0 - 10
- 10 - 100
- 100 - 500
- 500 - 1000
- > 1000

Figure 1.57 Reported infestations from escaped purple loosestrife in Alberta, 1999.

Is extinction forever? Perhaps not. Scientists are using DNA from the preserved bone of a woolly mammoth to see if an elephant — the woolly mammoth's closest living relative — could successfully give birth to a woolly mammoth.

Species in Danger

Many different species in Alberta and across Canada are in danger of extinction. If an organism becomes **extinct**, it no longer exists anywhere in the world. The loss of an organism's home, or habitat loss, is now the main reason why so many species are threatened with extinction. Humans have cleared land across Canada to build homes, cities, and roads, and to access natural resources and grow food. This has resulted in the loss of natural habitat for many different species. When an organism can no longer meet its needs in one habitat, it will move to a new habitat. Unfortunately, there is not enough habitat for all of the organisms that need a place to live.

Habitat loss is not the only cause of species extinction, however. Some biologists think that the problem of introduced species is so serious that it will one day replace habitat loss as the main cause of extinction. Plant and animal species can also be "overused." For example, passenger pigeons were hunted to extinction and, as you saw in Topic 4, bull trout are endangered as a result of overfishing. Pollution and changes in climate can also result in loss of species.

In Canada many species have become extinct. The great auk, sea mink, Dawson's caribou, and blue walleye all used to live in Canada and are now extinct. As well, there is a long list of species that are endangered. They include the eastern cougar, bowhead whale, right whale, burrowing owl, grizzly bear, and sea otter. The whooping crane and piping plover are two bird species that are endangered in Alberta (Figures 1.59A and B).

Figure 1.59A The whooping crane is an endangered species in Alberta.

Figure 1.59B The piping plover is an endangered species in Alberta.

Figure 1.59C The grizzly bear is an endangered species in Alberta.

Endangered Animal for a Day

What would it be like to be an animal threatened with extinction? Step into the "shoes" of an endangered animal in this activity.

Materials

10 blue plastic chips per student

10 red plastic chips per student

masking tape

a large bucket of water

small drinking cups

Procedure

* Performing and Recording
* Communication and Teamwork

1. Your teacher will divide all of the class except for three students into three equal-sized groups. Animals A can eat only red plastic chips. Animals B can eat only blue plastic chips. Animals C can eat either colour of plastic chip. The three remaining students are predators.

2. Mark off the boundary of the ecosystem (e.g., gymnasium, or an area half the size of a soccer field). Spread the plastic chips randomly throughout the playing area.

3. Use the masking tape to tape the thumbs of the Animals A and B to their second finger.

4. Give each animal a small drinking cup, which should be kept at the home base (starting place). Allow Animals A and B into the playing area for 3 min. They may pick up one plastic chip at a time and carry it back to the place where they started. During the 3 min that Animals A and B are in the playing area, they must have one cup of water and must rest at their home base for 30 s. Students can choose when they drink and when they rest. The predators can catch Animals A and B by tagging them. The predators also must drink one cup of water and rest for 30 s.

5. After 3 min, count how many plastic chips each animal has collected. How many animals did each predator catch? Replace all of the plastic chips in the playing area.

6. For the next 3 min, allow Animals C into the playing area as well. They may also pick up one plastic chip at a time, but can gather either colour of chip. They also must gather one cup of water and rest for 30 s. The predators *cannot* catch Animals C.

7. After 3 min count how many plastic chips each animal has collected. How many animals did each predator catch? Replace all of the plastic chips in the playing area.

8. Repeat the game in an area half the size.

What Did You Find Out? * Analyzing and Interpreting

1. Animal C was an exotic species. Explain how it affected the other animals in the ecosystem.

2. How did loss of habitat affect the animals in the ecosystem?

3. Which animal survived best in the smaller habitat, the native species (Animals A and B), or the introduced species (Animals C)? Explain why this happened.

INVESTIGATION 1-I

Keep Them Safe

The swift fox, burrowing owl, and the western blue flag (a plant) are all species at risk in Alberta. What can be done to help prevent them from becoming extinct?

Challenge

Devise a recovery plan to help keep a species at risk in Alberta from going extinct. Your plan should include a way to raise public awareness about the species and the risks it is facing.

Materials

research materials

materials for presentation, such as art materials, camera, video camera, computer

Design Specifications

A. Your plan must state the main threats to your species and suggest ways that these threats can be reduced or eliminated.

B. Develop a strategy to promote awareness of your species. You can use any method of communication you like, (posters, radio, or television programs, skits, interviews, or a presentation with visual aids).

C. If there is a recovery plan already in place for this species, describe the project and how people can support the project.

D. Explain how scientific knowledge is being used, or can be used, to help the recovery of this species.

Plan and Construct

A. With your group, develop a strategy for gathering information.

B. Develop a strategy for recording and organizing your information.

C. Develop a strategy for making the public aware of what they can do to help this species.

D. Complete your presentation.

Evaluate

1. Explain why this species is endangered.

2. How is science being used to help this species recover?

3. How can the general public help this species recover?

Extend Your Skills

1. Create a class computer database to compile all of the data for the species that your class researched.

2. Contrast and compare the different risk categories, threats, and recovery plans for the different species studied in your class. Why do some species have a better chance for recovery than others?

How Can You Help?

In the last investigation you learned about some of the ways that scientific research is helping endangered species and threatened species to recover. However, many recovery programs depend on the work and support from the general public, who are not necessarily scientists. Operation Burrowing Owl is one such program. Burrowing owls nest deep in abandoned burrows of ground squirrels (also called gophers) and badgers (see Figure 1.60). Since most burrowing owls nest on private land, land-owners are key players in the owls' conservation and recovery. In the Operation Burrowing Owl program, landowners voluntarily agree to help the burrowing owls by protecting their habitat and by not spraying chemicals near their burrows.

In the next Topic you will explore other methods that scientists use to observe and monitor changes in ecosystems. As well, you will learn how you can participate in assessing our impacts on these ecosystems.

Word CONNECT

What is the difference between a threatened species and an endangered species? Research this question, and write your answer in your Science Log. Include some examples.

Figure 1.60 Burrowing owls nest in abandoned burrows in the ground.

Figure 1.61 Landowners help burrowing owls by protecting their habitat.

TOPIC 6 Review

1. In nature, succession occurs naturally and slowly. Humans, however, sometimes make drastic changes that affect how succession works in an ecosystem. Explain, using either purple loosestrife or zebra mussels as an example.

2. Should humans simply leave all natural ecosystems exactly as they are, or is it acceptable to make changes? What kinds of changes are acceptable? Use these questions as the basis for a report, essay, article, or letter to a newspaper editor.

3. Imagine that you are a forester and have the option of using pesticides or biological control on an insect pest in the forest. Your employer does not want to use biological control because it costs more than using pesticides. What would you say to convince your boss that biological control is worth a try?

4. List four factors that can lead to the extinction of a species.

Off the Wall

A scientist on the island of Mauritius recently observed that the few Calvaria trees that remained on the island were all about 300 years old. He wondered why no new trees were growing. He knew that the dodo bird had become extinct about 300 years before, and he hypothesized that the two events were connected. Historical research showed that dodo birds ate Calvaria seeds, and that the seeds grew only after they had passed through a dodo's digestive system. Now scientists are experimenting with turkeys as a replacement for the dodo birds, hoping to ensure that the Calvaria tree does not become extinct.

TOPIC 7 Environmental Monitoring

When you are feeling sick, your temperature is periodically taken as a way of monitoring your health. Scientists also monitor ecosystems and the organisms that live there. **Ecosystem monitoring** (also called environmental monitoring) is a way to check the condition of an ecosystem by comparing the results of investigations done at different times. Monitoring helps scientists understand the impacts of disturbances and changes in the environment in order to try to reverse or reduce them. Both the biotic and abiotic parts of an ecosystem can be monitored. For instance, scientists might monitor temperature over a long period of time, or they might count the number of birds or butterflies in an area once a month. Figures 1.62 A, B, C, and D show some of the different types of ecosystem monitoring that can be done.

Figure 1.62A Physical monitoring uses satellites to track the changes in landscape over time. For example, satellite maps can show the changes to the land that occur due to construction of cities or deforestation.

Figure 1.62B Environmental monitoring tracks changes in climate, temperature, and weather patterns.

Figure 1.62C Chemical monitoring assesses the quality of air, soil, and water.

Figure 1.62D Biological monitoring tracks the changes in organisms or populations of organisms.

Volunteers are often an important part of monitoring programs. Across Canada hundreds of people, including many students like you, are helping scientists monitor organisms and ecosystems. For example, the Canadian Wildlife Federation sponsors a moth and butterfly survey program. This information is used to monitor habitat loss and ecosystem health. The Canadian Nature Federation monitors ladybird beetles to determine how introduced species of ladybird beetles are affecting native populations of beetles.

Figure 1.63 Students from Alberta schools participate in a River Watch program. The students monitor water quality and observe wildlife and human activities on the river.

When Do We Monitor?

Environmental monitoring can begin after a disturbance has occurred. For example, after an earthquake or other large disturbance, scientists may monitor succession of plants and animals on the disturbed landscape. In one such study, scientists studied the area around Mount St. Helens in Washington after a volcanic eruption in 1980 (see Figure 1.64). These scientists were interested to see how quickly spiders would inhabit the disturbed environment. They found that several species of spiders were blown by the wind for over 50 km to Mount St. Helens where they recolonized the site.

Environmental monitoring can also begin before a disturbance occurs, for example, before an area of land is cleared. Studies can tell us which organisms are living in the area, and other important information about the ecosystem. If we combine what we know about ecosystems with the results from other monitoring studies in similar areas, we may be able to predict what will happen to those organisms over time.

A key part of making environmental decisions is trying to balance human needs with the needs of other organisms in the ecosystem. Initial investigations give us scientific data about what lives in the environment. Continuous monitoring enables us to identify the changes in that environment over time.

Figure 1.64 The area around Mount St. Helen's has provided useful information to scientists about recovery in a disturbed environment.

Long-Term Monitoring Programs

Amphibians, including frogs, toads, and salamanders, are common in Alberta and throughout much of the world. Amphibians are very sensitive to environmental change, however. If there is too much change, amphibians will not be able to survive. This makes amphibians a good **indicator species** to help us monitor the overall health of our environment. Pesticides, acid rain, loss of habitat, and the introduction of non-native species can all affect amphibians.

Scientists from all over the world have started to notice a decline in the numbers of amphibians and an increase in the number of amphibians found with deformities, such as the frog in Figure 1.65. In general, we know very little about most species of amphibians, so it is hard to understand why amphibian numbers are declining. This is changing, however, as amphibian monitoring programs are being established throughout the world.

Figure 1.65 Frogs are considered to be indicator species, alerting us to environmental problems.

INTERNET CONNECT

www.mcgrawhill.ca/links/sciencefocus7

From counting butterflies, to identifying birds, to measuring water quality, there are several environmental monitoring programs in Canada in which you can participate. To find out how, go to the above web site. Click on **Web Links** to find out where to go next. Find a monitoring project that interests you and see how you can become involved.

Figure 1.66 These people are counting amphibians as part of the Amphibian Monitoring Program in Alberta.

Since the populations of amphibians naturally fluctuate from year to year, it is important to monitor populations over time. To study amphibian health and overall populations, a worldwide task force, made up of scientists and volunteers, has been created to monitor amphibian populations (see Figure 1.66). These people count the numbers of different amphibians in their region, which shows the status of amphibians in one local region. They also record any deformities they see in the animals. The results from the local studies are sent to one central location. This combined information helps answer larger questions, such as whether or not amphibian populations are really declining worldwide.

Studies such as these are done over time with the same sites monitored year after year. Populations of organisms fluctuate from year to year depending on many different factors. For example, think back to the lynx and the snowshoe hare populations shown on page 41. These populations varied in size over a cycle of approximately ten years. Monitoring an ecosystem over time gives a clearer picture of what is really happening.

INTERNET CONNECT

www.mcgrawhill.ca/links/sciencefocus7

To learn more about amphibian monitoring, go to the above web site. Click on **Web Links** to find out where to go next. Choose one amphibian and write a mini-report about its status. Report your findings to your classmates.

DidYou**Know**?

Natural climate changes can be major and long term. For example, about 18 000 years ago, large parts of Earth, including all of what is now Canada, were covered with a thick layer of ice. The climate was much colder than today's climate. By about 8000 years ago, the climate was warmer than our climate today, and major global warming had melted the ice all over Canada and high into the Arctic. Archaeologists have discovered the remains of tropical plants and animals in what is now the Arctic!

Across Canada

Briony Penn

Who says individuals can't make a difference? Briony Penn is proof that this just isn't so. Briony is a naturalist who lives in British Columbia and enjoys observing frogs and other amphibians. In the mid-1980s, she was living on the outskirts of Holyrood Park in Scotland. Holyrood Park is owned by the Royal Family. It is a semi-wild area inhabited by lots of wildlife, including a population of toads. Briony noticed that a massacre occurred each March. The male toads would migrate from the park to a pond area. There they would call to the females who would eventually join them to breed. In order to get to the pond, the toads had to cross a busy road. They crossed in large numbers at night, and many were killed by passing traffic. Realizing that there was a simple solution, Briony wrote to Queen Elizabeth II. She asked that the road be closed for the few days when the toads would be crossing to and from the pond. The Queen obliged, and the toad population of Holyrood Park has made its annual migration safely ever since. Briony is now back in her home on Salt Spring Island. Like other naturalists on the Gulf Islands, she has made maps of amphibian crossings so that motorists can take special care during breeding season. The photograph shows Briony with one of her frog and rough-skinned newt-crossing maps.

THINK & LINK

INVESTIGATION 1-J

SKILLCHECK

Initiating and Planning

Performing and Recording

☼ Analyzing and Interpreting

Communication and Teamwork

What's the Change?

Think About It

Monitoring the numbers and whereabouts of organisms provides information about the health of the ecosystem in which they live. What type of amphibians are found in Alberta and where are they found?

Materials

field guide to amphibians   paper

map of Alberta   pencil

What to Do

Table 1.1: Results from 1997 and 1998 Volunteer Amphibian Surveys

Species	Number of observations 1997	Number of individuals 1997	Number of observations 1998	Number of individuals 1998
Tiger salamander	37	299	26	45
Long-toed salamander	5	170	6	69
Plains spadefoot	4	33	17	440
Great Plains toad	6	57	6	63
Boreal toad	41	649	60	661
Canadian toad	33	183	10	64
Boreal chorus frog	354	15 213	292	6 105
Wood frog	351	8 978	310	3 210
Spotted frog	8	117	10	115
Northern leopard frog	11	405	20	4 120
Total records	850	26 104	757	14 892
Number of participants	107		144	

1. Use the field guide to look at pictures of each of the amphibian species.

2. Use the data in Table 1.1 to make a bar graph comparing the number of individuals observed in 1997 and 1998.

3. Locate the general area of the study sites from Table 1.2.

4. Use the data in Table 1.2 to make a bar graph comparing the numbers of individuals found at five different sites in Alberta.

Analyze

1. Use the tables and your graphs to answer the following questions:

   (a) What are the two most common amphibians in Alberta?

   (b) Which species has the largest/smallest distribution throughout Alberta?

   (c) How can the data collected in Table 1.1 and Table 1.2 add to the understanding of amphibians over the long term?

Table 1.2: Numbers of Amphibians Captured at Five Alberta Sites in 1998

Study site	LTSA	TISA	BCFR	WOFR	CSFR	NLFR	BOTO	CATO	TOTAL
Beaverhill Lake	0	1	17	182	0	0	0	0	200
Cypress Hills	0	31	2	0	0	5	0	0	38
Kananaskis	186	0	0	61	7	0	33	0	287
Lesser Slave Lake	0	0	5	33	0	0	23	1	62
Meanook	0	0	4	277	0	0	343	0	624
Total	186	32	28	553	7	5	399	1	1 211

LTSA – Long-toed salamander

TISA – Tiger salamander

BCFR – Boreal chorus frog

WOFR – Wood frog

CSFR – Columbia spotted frog

NLFR – Northern leopard frog

BOTO – Boreal toad

CATO – Canadian toad

Skill
FOCUS

For tips on making bar graphs, turn to Skill Focus 10.

Monitor Your Local Amphibians!

Think About It

There are 10 species of amphibians in Alberta. What do you need to know to effectively gather information on amphibians?

How Can Science Help?

Long-term monitoring distinguishes the difference between natural fluctuations in populations and changes that may be caused by pollution, habitat loss, or other factors.

Safety Precautions

- Conduct this investigation only under the supervision of your teacher.
- Never follow amphibians into the water.
- Do not handle amphibians if you have insect repellent or lotion on your hands.

Materials

paper

pencil

Apparatus

field guide to amphibians

small dip net

ice cream or plastic bucket with lid perforated with air holes

clipboard

thermometer

tape of frog calls (optional)

tape recorder and batteries (optional)

Rules For Observing Amphibians

- Handle each amphibian no longer than necessary, and limit the number of people who handle them.
- Make sure your hands are damp.
- Use only small nets to capture amphibians.
- Keep the amphibians cool and moist while you observe them.
- Return all amphibians to the place where they were caught.
- Wash your hands after handling amphibians.

Procedure

1. Using a field guide, the information from the Think & Link Investigation and the Internet Connect on the previous two pages, determine which species of amphibian would likely be found in your area and its breeding season.

2. Find a suitable area for studying amphibians near your school.

3. Review the amphibian key on the next page.

4. Create a data sheet to record: the date, the time of observation, the species observed, the number of individuals observed, whether the species was actually seen, or just heard, and any presence of eggs. Provide space for sketches on your data sheet.

5. Visit the study site and complete your data sheet.

6. At the study site, sketch a map of the habitat in which the amphibian was found. Draw in major geological features, rivers, lakes, roads, and how the land is used around the wetland.

Identification Key for Alberta Amphibians

To use the key, start at number one and choose option A or B, whichever best describes the amphibian you are trying to identify. Proceed to the next number as indicated until you reach a species name. Use photographs or illustrations in a field guide to confirm your identification.

	Go to
1. (a) Body covered with scales	This is a reptile
(b) Body does not have scales	2
2. (a) Hind legs same length as front legs and are not modified for hopping; long tail	3
(b) Hind legs much longer than front legs, and are muscular and modified for hopping; no tail	4
Salamanders	
3. (a) Irregular yellowish stripe (may be broken) down back; fourth toe on hind foot noticeably longer than other toes	Long-toed salamander
(b) Back and sides striped or spotted; fourth toe about the same length as others	Tiger salamander
Frogs and Toads	
4. (a) Ridges (dorsolateral folds) present on back	5
(b) No ridges (dorsolateral folds) present on back	7
5. (a) Green or brown, with light-coloured ridges on back and dark spots with light border	Northern leopard frog
(b) Ridges on back; small and not light coloured	6
6. (a) Dark eye mask; back smooth; no red on belly	Wood frog
(b) No eye mask; small warts on back; red colour on belly	Spotted frog
7. (a) Skin fairly smooth and poison (parotid) glands absent	8
(b) Skin very warty and poison (parotid) glands present	9
8. (a) Large, squat body; single black knob or "spade" on hind feet; vertical pupil	Plains spadefoot
(b) Small, slender body; no knob on hind feet; horizontal pupil	Boreal chorus frog
9. (a) No raised ridge between eyes	Western toad
(b) Raised ridge between eyes	10
10. (a) Raised ridge between eyes parallel or joined behind eyes to form one raised ridge; spotted belly	Canadian toad
(b) Raised ridge starts at snout and spreads out behind eyes; belly unspotted	Great plains toad

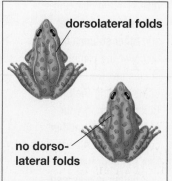

dorsolateral folds

no dorso-lateral folds

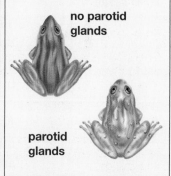

no parotid glands

parotid glands

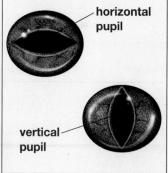

horizontal pupil

vertical pupil

Analyze

1. Use the procedures in this investigation to develop a long-term monitoring plan for your study area.

2. What other information should you gather besides the species and numbers of amphibians present in your study area to make your long-term study most useful?

3. What is the health of the amphibian habitat in your study area? Develop a plan for creating, maintaining, and/or protecting this habitat.

Baseline Data

Looking Ahead

Municipalities that have implemented Blue Box programs have done so only after a lot of research and planning. Research the Internet and other sources to discover the planning stages involved in implementing the Blue Box program in your community, or another community in Alberta. Use the information you gather in your end-of-unit debate.

In Topic 6 you learned about the effects of introduced species such as purple loosestrife. Many changes happen in an ecosystem after a natural event such as a flood, or a human-caused event such as the introduction of an exotic species. To determine the types of changes, it is important to know what the habitat was like before the disturbance occurred. To do this, scientists gather **baseline data**. Baseline data gives scientists a starting point to compare changes in the environment. Scientists often use **permanent plots**, or study areas, to monitor change. For example, one scientist is interested in seeing if global warming changes the plants growing in the forest. He has established several large permanent plots throughout North America. This researcher and his assistants visit the plots every few years or so to monitor changes in the forest. Ideally, several researchers will continue this study for many years to come. The researcher in Figure 1.67A is studying the plants in a permanent study plot. Other studies, such as bird surveys, are done at the same time and at the same place each year. The researcher in Figure 1.67B catches birds as they migrate between their wintering grounds and their summer breeding grounds. They place bands on the birds' legs with information on where and when the birds were captured.

Baseline data can also be used to predict changes in the environment. For example, if someone wants to drain a wetland to put in a shopping mall, scientists can refer to studies from that area, or from a similar area, to predict the effects. This also means that a plan could be developed to minimize the impacts or perhaps — if the changes are determined to be too serious — the development could be stopped. A report that outlines how an activity will affect the environment is called an **Environmental Impact Assessment**.

Figure 1.67A & B Studying plants in a permanent plot and examining migrating birds are two ways to obtain baseline data.

Common Alberta Organisms

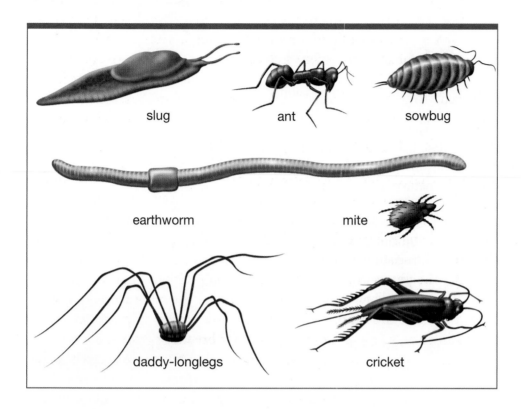

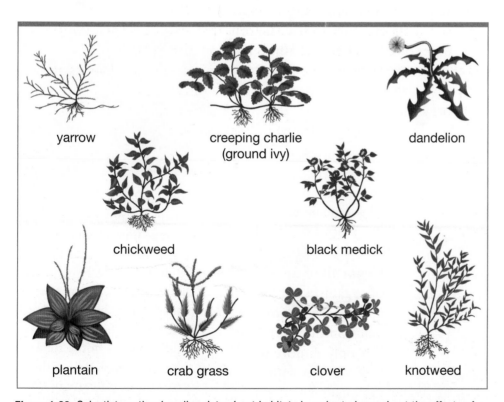

Figure 1.68 Scientists gather baseline data about habitats in order to learn about the effects of various environmental changes. The organisms shown here are common in Alberta. You can refer to them to help you identify the organisms you examine as you gather your own baseline data in the following investigation.

Comparing Ecosystems

Gather your own baseline data by comparing a disturbed habitat with an undisturbed habitat in your community. Different habitats have different characteristics, which affect the organisms that live within them. You will determine what organisms live in these habitats, describe them, and explain any differences you find. Choose a disturbed area, such as a section of lawn or school playing field, and a nearby natural area such as a forest.

Question

What kinds of organisms can be found living in two different habitats in your community?

Hypothesis

Form a hypothesis comparing the types of organisms found in a disturbed and a natural ecosystem.

Safety Precautions

Apparatus

4 metre sticks or 4 wooden pegs per group

several jars with caps that have holes in them

magnifying glass

clipboard

field guides

Materials

duct tape	string
paper for sketching	notebook

Procedure

1. Make an observation sheet by drawing a chart on a piece of paper. One column should list the names of plant and animal species you are likely to encounter. Leave several rows blank for species you cannot immediately identify. Add an additional column with a separate heading for every area (called a quadrat) you sample (quadrat 1, quadrat 2, etc.).

2. Based on the biotic and abiotic characteristics of your two habitats, **predict** the types of organisms you will find. For example, if one of your habitats has a lot of trees, you may find birds in the area that you will not see on an open field.

3. Make a 1m² quadrat using the metre sticks or pegs and string as shown here. Choose a suitable location for your study. Toss your pencil at random into the habitat. Place a corner of your quadrat where it lands.

   (a) **Count** all of each kind of organism within your quadrat. Count a plant on the boundary line only if more than half of it lies within the quadrat.

   (b) On your observation sheet, **record** the total of each kind of organism.

4. Repeat step 2 for two more quadrat samples.

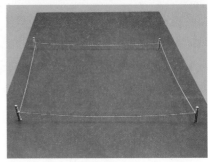

5. Average the totals for your quadrat samples to get the average number of each organism per square metre. Multiply the average number of each organism per square metre by your estimate of the number of square metres in the total ecosystem area. This will give you an estimate of the total population of each organism in the ecosystems. An example is given in the sample calculation.

6 If you find a plant you cannot name, make a sketch of it. Include an outline of the leaf. (This will help you to identify it later.) Use the illustration of common lawn plants on page 75. Use a letter code, such as B, to identify the unknown specimen.

7 If you find an insect or other animal you do not know, put one specimen in a jar, close the lid, and quickly make a simple sketch. (Be sure to check the number of legs and wings to help you identify it later.) Once you have completed your sketch, release the organism. Give your unknown specimen a number code, such as 2, for identification.

8 Repeat the experiment in the second ecosystem.

Name of species	Quadrat					Average # individuals per square metre	Total ecosystem area	Estimated total population
	1	2	3	4	5			

Sample calculation:

The number of blue beetles counted in five quadrat (1 m^2) samples is 13, 15, 16, 14, 13.

Total number of blue beetles in five quadrats = 71.

$$\text{Average} = \frac{\text{total number of blue beetles}}{\text{total area of quadrats}}$$

$$= \frac{71 \text{ blue beetles}}{5 \text{ quadrants} \times 1 \text{ m}^2}$$

$$= 14.2 \text{ blue beetles/m}^2$$

Total ecosystem area = length × width of ecosystem
$$= 50 \text{ m} \times 20 \text{ m}$$
$$= 1000 \text{ m}^2$$

Estimated total population of blue beetles in the ecosystem

$$= \frac{14.2 \text{ blue beetles}}{\text{m}^2} \times 1000 \text{ m}^2$$

$$= 14\ 200 \text{ blue beetles}$$

Skill FOCUS

For tips on scientific drawing, turn to Skill Focus 11.

Analyze

1. Try to identify your unknown organisms by matching them with pictures and descriptions in plant, insect, and animal books.

2. If possible, replace the number codes or letter codes on your observation sheets with the names of the specimens you have identified.

3. Complete your calculations to determine the numbers of different organisms in each habitat. As a class, create a chart comparing the different organisms present in the different habitats.

Conclude and Apply

4. What different biotic factors were present in your two habitats?

5. What different abiotic factors (non-living things) were present in your different habitats?

6. Your predictions were based only on the appearance of your habitats. Were your predictions supported by your observations? Explain.

Extend Your Knowledge

7. What other factors might affect the organisms living in your habitats?

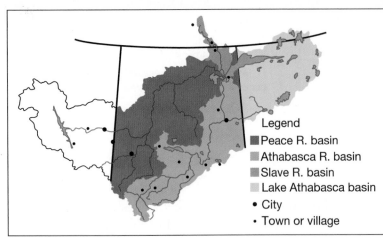

Figure 1.69 The Northern River Basins Study monitors and assesses the impact of development over a broad area.

Legend
- Peace R. basin
- Athabasca R. basin
- Slave R. basin
- Lake Athabasca basin
- • City
- • Town or village

Pause& Reflect

You have just sampled several different quadrats in areas that were chosen by randomly throwing your pencil. Explain why you sampled more than one area. What reasons can you think of for choosing the areas by chance? Write your answers in your Science Log.

Figure 1.70 Aboriginal cultures have extensive knowledge about the ecosystems in which they live, since many generations have lived on the same land.

Using Science in Real Ecosystems

The Northern River Basins region, made up of the Peace, Athabasca, and Slave River basins, covers a vast territory. Many Aboriginal people living in the Northern Basins region depend upon the land for food, clothing, medicines, and other natural resources. Their lifestyle is threatened by the economic development of the area's natural resources. To monitor and assess the impact of development in the area, a huge scientific project, called the Northern River Basins Study, began in 1991. Its goal was to learn how developments in the area were affecting the ecosystems.

Over 150 scientific studies looked at many aspects of the environment in this region. The results of the research were combined with traditional Aboriginal knowledge about the Northern Basins Region. This resulted in a large body of information about the relationships between the air, land, water, organisms, and the people living in this region. The impact of human developments was considered as well.

When the information was analyzed, results showed that industries being developed in the area were affecting the health of the ecosystems, often negatively. Fish living downstream from pulp mills were smaller and unhealthier than fish living away from pulp mills. Industrial waste also affected the amount of oxygen present in the water. Lower oxygen levels in the water killed many of the small organisms that normally lived there. As a result, fish, such as mountain white fish and bull trout which eat these small organisms, also began to die.

By understanding how ecosystems work and by learning to monitor ecosystem health, we can all work toward restoring and maintaining a healthy environment.

TOPIC 7 Review

1. Explain how long-term monitoring can be used to help protect natural ecosystems.

2. What are the four types of ecosystem monitoring? Give an example of something that would be measured or monitored for each type.

3. Describe a Canadian monitoring program that volunteers (including you!) could become involved in.

4. Explain what is meant by baseline data.

If you need to check an item, Topic numbers are provided in brackets throughout.

Key Terms

succession
primary succession
secondary succession
biological control

introduced species
extinct
ecosystem monitoring
indicator species

baseline data
permanent plots
environmental impact assessment

Reviewing Key Terms

1. Write a sentence to describe the relationship among the terms in each group.

   (a) introduced species and extinction (6)

   (b) primary succession and secondary succession (6)

   (c) biological control and introduced species (6)

   (d) baseline data and ecosystem monitoring (7)

2. Explain the process of succession. (6)

3. Why are amphibians good indicator species? (7)

Understanding Key Concepts

4. Explain why people should *not* release exotic pets, such as snakes, hedgehogs, or tarantulas, into the wild if they decide they do not want to keep them any longer. (6)

5. Label this diagram with explanations of what is happening in each stage of succession. (6)

6. Name two ways that you can become involved in environmental monitoring. (7)

7. Name two endangered species in Alberta. Describe the recovery plan for one of these species. (6)

8. Explain why it is important to carry out long-term, rather than short-term, monitoring. (7)

9. Imagine an alien has landed on Earth and has found a coloured pencil, a ballpoint pen, a felt pen, and a regular pencil. Write an identification key to help the alien identify these objects. (Refer back to page 73 for an example of an identification key.) (7)

10. Give two examples of natural disturbances and two examples of human-induced disturbances. (7)

11. Species have been going extinct for as long as there have been living things on Earth. If this is so, why are scientists so concerned about endangered species today? (6)

Ask an Expert

As more and more land in Canada is used for human activities, we can see the increasing impact of such development on the well-being of local wildlife and also on humans. Bernadette Tenning is a biologist who specializes in assessing the negative effects that new development can have on the environment, and helping people take steps to safeguard against them.

Q. **How long have you been assessing the effects of new development?**

A. I've been doing environmental assessments since 1998. That's when I graduated from university. Because of my First Nations descent, I've always been interested in biology and concerned about the environment, so after I had my children, I went back to university to study human geography and biology.

Q. **What sort of assessment do you do?**

A. I do a few different types. For example, I did an assessment for a timber company that was applying for a licence to operate in a northern community. They wanted me to assess the situation and show, in their application, that they had considered environmental factors and were taking steps to protect the ecosystem from damage.

Q. **What did your assessment show?**

A. I explained that the company proposed cutting the trees in winter when the ground was frozen. By doing this, the soil was less likely to erode away. (Soil erosion would decrease plant growth and negatively affect the animals that depend on those plants.) The company also

planned to avoid areas where there were plants and animals that were easily disturbed or harmed, and areas that are traditional First Nations hunting grounds.

Q. **Are all of your assessments done for companies that are proposing developments?**

A. No. One of the first assessments I ever did was for a First Nations lobby group concerned about a hog-processing plant proposed for their area. They wanted someone to assess the existing water quality and predict what sort of environmental impact the proposed plant would have.

Q. **So were you looking strictly at water?**

A. I was looking at the water as an indicator of environmental impact, but I had to consider the ecosystem of the whole area. Everything in an area is affected by the quality of the water. In this case, the quality of the water was already poor. The hog processor reported a high level of bacteria called E. coli in the water. Hog waste leads to high levels of bacteria. The processor believed, however, that additional waste from the hogs would not increase the amount of E. coli in the water beyond the level that was acceptable by government standards. I was concerned that the water had not been tested for parasites such as *Giardia*. Compared with E. coli, this parasite can infect other organisms at much lower levels. Disease could spread to local wildlife. Then deer or mice could potentially spread sickness to livestock and humans.

Q. If the hog plant had not yet been built, why was the quality of water already so poor?

A. There was a lot of existing development, such as construction and agriculture, in the area. When development takes place and waste materials are not disposed of properly, the natural balance of the ecosystem can be thrown out of whack. My biggest concern was that waste from the hogs could add to the imbalance if it were not disposed of properly. This might result in a positive feedback loop — something every biologist fears.

Q. What is a positive feedback loop?

A. It's a situation in which a chain of events changes an ecosystem in a way that cannot be reversed. For example, in the proposed hog plant situation, hog waste released into the water would add large amounts of substances with nitrogen. Nitrogen acts like a fertilizer in water and causes an increase in algae growth. As the algae grow, they take oxygen from the organisms that were in the water before they were. Fish populations begin to die from lack of oxygen, which affects birds, otters, bears — anything that depends on the fish for food.

Q. And you can't return the populations of fish and their predators to the way they once were, right?

A. Not easily. Once this situation happens, you usually lose the variety of organisms that used to grow in the environment. You end up with just a few organisms that adapt well to the new conditions. The algae begin to take over the water source. Gradually, the solid growth of algae can fill in the lake or river until it becomes a marsh and eventually dries up completely. Fortunately, the public is becoming more aware of these issues and more vocal in their demands for good-quality water. If enough people ask the right questions, more developers will become environmentally responsible.

EXPLORING Further

In the spring of 2000, the drinking water in Walkerton, Ontario, became contaminated with E. coli bacteria. Many people became ill and several died. These bacteria normally live in the intestines of people and other warm-blooded animals. They also occur in water systems in low numbers. However, the population of E. coli can increase if raw sewage from cities or farms enters the water. Conduct some research to find out what is done to monitor the levels of E. coli in drinking water. What measures must be taken to ensure that this type of tragedy never occurs again? Work with a partner and present your findings along with a series of recommendations.

An *Issue* to Analyze

Beyond the Curb: Is Recycling Really Reducing Garbage?

In this Unit you have learned about how humans affect the environment, often without even realizing it. For instance, our garbage goes to landfills. Landfills can contribute waste gases (called greenhouse gases) to the atmosphere and can add toxins to ground water and run-off. Presently, landfills and garbage dumps are being filled faster than ever. The main way that you can help to reduce waste in landfills by following the 3 Rs: reduce, reuse, and recycle.

Assume that you are following the 3 Rs to the best of your ability — you are confident that you separate and sort all the recyclable items in your garbage. How can you be sure that other people are as committed as you are, so that, together, you can make a difference in the garbage crisis?

Rising municipal taxes have caused some people to complain about the cost of the Blue Box program. These people argue that recycling is not helping the environment, but instead it is using up a lot of time, energy, and money. They would prefer to see the Blue Box program eliminated.

Resolution

Be it resolved that recycling programs, such as the Blue Box program, have not been effective in reducing the impact of garbage on the environment.

What to Do

1 Read the In Favour and Against points listed on the next page, and think about other points that could be made in favour of and against the resolution.

2 Four students will debate the resolution. Two students will speak in support of the resolution and two will speak against it. **Note:** No matter what view you actually hold, you must try your best to convince the jury, or debate listeners, of the point your side is defending.

③ To aid the two teams, two other students will work with them to help gather background information. This is needed to put forward a strong case for the point that each side is defending.

④ The rest of the class will act as the jury in hearing the debate. In preparation for the debate, they should do their own research in order to understand the science and technology behind the issues raised.

⑤ Your teacher will provide you with the proper debating procedures to follow.

In Favour

- Garbage is only one of many environmental concerns we face today. The rising level of energy consumption is perhaps of greater concern. The full recycling process uses a great amount of energy — much more than is required simply to dump garbage at a landfill.

- The quality of products made from recycled materials is generally lower than the quality of products made from new materials. In addition, most plastics and paper can be recycled only once, or maybe twice, before the product quality is so low that the products are unusable.

- Many people are still unwilling to make the effort required to recycle properly. The end result is that landfills are still overflowing with both recyclable and non-recyclable garbage.

- Recycling costs money and unless companies can make a profit by manufacturing products from recycled materials, they cannot afford to do it. Consumers pay for the cost of recycling by paying more for products made with recycled materials. Some consumers are unwilling to do this.

Against

- Recycling programs have made people much more aware of the garbage they produce.

- Much less energy is needed to recycle some materials than to process them from raw materials because of refined processing technologies.

- Although early technologies for cleaning, purifying, and reusing recycled materials were very limited, present technologies have allowed a wide range of plastics and papers to be added to the list of recyclable materials.

- Many resources are non-renewable and limited in quantity. If they are not recycled, they end up in dumps and landfills where they are inaccessible. It is important to continue recycling before our resources become depleted.

Analyze

1. Which team won the debate, based on a class vote?

2. Did the winning team produce better research or make a better presentation? Explain.

3. Did you find any studies or any other reliable information that contradicts the arguments that were presented? If so, explain.

4. Did your initial viewpoint change as a result of the points presented in the debate? Explain why or why not.

Extension

5. One proposal to motivate people to recycle more, and to do so more efficiently, is to charge individuals and businesses for each bag of garbage that is picked up. What do you think? Prepare arguments in favour of and against this idea to help you determine whether this proposal might, in fact, work.

Unit at a Glance

- Ecology is the study of the relationship between living organisms and their environment.
- The basic needs of living things include food, a suitable habitat, water, and appropriate gases (oxygen, carbon dioxide).
- Organisms adapt to "fit" their environment.
- An adaptation is an inherited characteristic that helps an organism survive and reproduce in its environment.
- Ecosystems include biotic and abiotic components.
- Organisms interact with one another and some are interdependent on one another.
- Humans' needs and wants result in impacts on natural environments.
- The impacts of human activities are not always easy to predict.
- People's interactions with the environment have changed over time.
- We have used our understanding of science and technology to assess how we affect the environment, and how the impacts can be reduced.
- Organisms fill several niches within an ecosystem.
- Impacts in the environment can be a result of natural disturbance or they can be caused by human actions.
- Energy, carbon, and water cycle through ecosystems.
- The effect of pollutants can be magnified as they move through food chains.
- Succession is the gradual process by which some species replace other species in an ecosystem.
- Human impacts on the environment are often unexpected (e.g., the effects of exotic species).
- Species can become endangered because of habitat loss, introduced species, pollution and/or overharvesting.
- Environmental monitoring is a way to check the condition of an ecosystem by comparing the results of investigations done over time.
- Environmental impact assessments are used to predict impacts on the environment based on an understanding of scientific concepts and technology.

Understanding Key Concepts

1. Think of five different ecosystems that might be found in an area such as a national park. List the biotic and abiotic factors each ecosystem might contain. (Hint: Remember that ecosystems can be large, like a forest, or small, like a rotting log, as long as they include all of the biotic and abiotic factors present.)

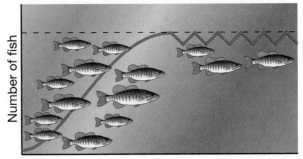

Time

2. Look at this illustration. The dashed line at the top of the graph indicates that above that line there will not be enough food to support any more fish. What do you think will happen to the number of fish if the present level of food remains available?

3. (a) Why are quadrats used to carry out ecosystem studies?

   (b) How would you use a quadrat to estimate population sizes? Why is the result only an estimate and not an exact figure?

4. Choose an organism and describe at least one adaptation it possesses that helps it survive in its environment.

5. Choose an organism and explain how it interacts with sunlight, air, water, and soil. Give two examples of living things that interact.

6. Describe three human activities that can endanger a species.

7. In your notebook use words, arrows, and sketches to show the food web in this diagram. Name two herbivores, two producers, and two carnivores.

8. A family cultivated part of their lawn and turned it into a vegetable garden. The family then moved away. The house remained empty, and nobody looked after the garden. Ten years later, the family came back for a visit. Their lawn looked similar, though much weedier. They were surprised, however, to see wildflowers, shrubs, and small trees growing in their deserted garden. Explain why this is an example of succession.

9. What is the carbon cycle? What role do each of the following play in it?
  (a) fossil fuels burning
  (b) forests burning
  (c) animals respiring
  (d) plants carrying out the process of photosynthesis

10. Explain how the extinction of various species results in a less diverse ecosystem. How can this lead to the extinction of even more species?

11. (a) Give two examples of how organisms interact with one another.
  (b) Give two examples of organisms that are dependent on one another.

12. Make a chart, poster, or other representation to summarize how human activities can affect ecosystems.

13. Explain the methods that can be used to observe and monitor changes in ecosystems.

14. Based on your knowledge of cycles, explain the slogan "Have you thanked a plant today?"

Developing Skills

15. Think of (and observe if possible) an ecosystem near your home. Make a chart or diagram to show abiotic-biotic interactions in an ecosystem.

16. (a) Give two or more examples of how plants are adapted for interactions with abiotic factors in their environment.
  (b) Choose one plant in the ecosystem you studied in question 15, and explain how it is adapted to its environment.

17. Imagine that you are teaching the topic of adaptation to a class of younger students. Devise two questions you could ask to assess the students' understanding of an adaptation.

18. As a class, think about how you might create a model of an ecosystem. What would you include in your ecosystem? Why?

19. Design a poster that describes and defines an ecological footprint. Use an example that compares the ecological footprint of two activities (e.g., eating food grown in your garden and eating food imported from Europe).

20. Look at the graph in question 2. Design an experiment to investigate what will happen to the number of fish if more food were available. (Alternatively, select a different variable to investigate what you think would affect the number of fish.)

21. How have farming and forestry affected brown-headed cowbird populations in Canada? Give your answer in the form of a numbered list of steps, a labelled diagram, or a flowchart.

22. Design an activity that would increase the diversity of species where you live. What role might be played by a bird feeder or herbs growing in pots? What are some advantages of species diversity?

23. Design a poster, game, or model to explain bioaccumulation.

Problem Solving/Applying

24. Do you have a fish, hamster, or other living creature in your classroom or school? Observe it and write some notes about its original (wild) habitat based on visible adaptations. (For example, what kind of teeth does it have? What kind of feet does it have? Can it run quickly?)

25. Why do humans use running shoes, winter boots, snowshoes, skis, or flippers? Explain why these are not biological adaptations.

26. Imagine that you are an ecologist. A group of people in your community wants to introduce an organism into the local ecosystem that will get rid of the mosquito population. Identify the mosquito's place in the food chain and explain to the group why introducing a new organism would not be a good idea.

27. A sailor survived a shipwreck. She managed to save several hens and a bag of grain from the cargo. She is now on an island far from land, in an area where there are no other people. It may be months before she is rescued. To survive as long as possible, what should she do?

(a) Feed the grain to the hens, and eat the eggs they lay.

(b) Eat the grain, and then eat the hens.

(c) Eat the hens, and then eat the grain.

Explain why you think the option you chose is best. If you do not agree with any of the options listed above, what other solution would you propose?

28. Imagine that you are a water particle. Trace a possible path that you might take as you move through one complete water cycle. Begin the cycle as a snowflake falling in winter.

29. You are a researcher working on methods of controlling insect pests. Identify some concerns you might have relating to preserving ecosystems. As well, what are some concerns relating to economic activities, such as forestry and farming?

Critical Thinking

30. Imagine you are a biologist, and the company you work for assesses the impact of development projects. There is a plan to build a new luxury resort on the shore of a large bay. Builders need to know what environmental impact the project will have on particular ecosystems. Your job is to estimate the number of organisms in these different ecosystems. How could you sample:

(a) the number of insects in a large tree

(b) the number of whales in a large bay off the coast

(c) the number of fish in a small lake

(d) the number of groundhogs living in a local golf course

31. Think about each of the following pairs of organisms, and name the type of symbiotic relationship the partners might have. Indicate what the gains and/or losses might be for each partner:

(a) a flowering plant and an insect

(b) a whale and a barnacle living on the whale's back

(c) a dog and a flea

(d) a nectar-eating bat and a flowering cactus

(e) a bird and a water buffalo

32. Think about a food chain that includes grass ➡ field mice ➡ snakes ➡ owls. Describe what would happen if many mice died as a result of disease. What would happen to the owls? What would happen to the snakes? What would be the probable results in the ecosystem?

33. Why do most humans have more food choices than many animals do? On your own or in a group, brainstorm answers to this question.

34. Consider the ecosystem you observed in question 15. Predict what would happen if each of the following major changes occurred:

(a) People began to use chemical fertilizers.

(b) The rain becomes acidic.

(c) A hydro line is built through the area.

(d) The area is hit by a severe hailstorm.

(e) The butterflies do not appear one spring.

(f) The earthworms are attacked by a parasite, and their numbers are severely reduced.

(g) An oil spill occurs.

35. Think again about the changes you considered in question 34. What roles might people play to reduce or reverse the impact on the ecosystem?

36. What are the benefits and problems relating to the 3 Rs: reduce, reuse, and recycle?

37. Use the balance scale below to explain the concept of balance as it relates to ideas and issues in this unit.

38. Identify three examples of human impacts on the ecosystem. Is there a link between these impacts and people's needs and wants?

Pause& Reflect

1. In a number of cases, humans have introduced different organisms, or deliberately changed an ecosystem in other ways. To what extent can we or should we change natural ecosystems? What are some advantages and disadvantages of changing ecosystems?

2. Identify a specific issue raised by this unit. Explain why it is important to you. Plan and carry out positive actions by which you personally improve a situation related to the issue.

3. Now that you have completed this unit, go back to the Focussing Questions on page 4. Write answers to these questions in your Science Log.

Plants for Food and Fibre

Imagine for a moment that you are flying over Alberta. What would your first impressions be? Many people are astonished by the vast forests and fields that cover the province. We have used these tremendous natural resources, our knowledge of plants, and various technologies to become important producers of food and fibre. Thousands of people work to produce and process these products, which contribute billions of dollars to our economy each year.

Not long ago some types of farming practices and farm equipment damaged the soil. Scientists and producers of food and fibre are now developing better practices, enabling us to produce and harvest plants while keeping forests and fields healthy. New plant-breeding research, new machinery, and new techniques in farming and forestry are making this possible. In this unit you will explore the many ways that we use plants for food and fibre. Do you know, for example, that all of the items in the small photograph on this page come from plants? You will also grow your own plants under varying conditions to identify the best growing conditions for plants. As well, you will learn how we grow and harvest plants for food and fibre and some of the challenges this presents.

Unit Contents

Preview

Focussing Questions

- How do we produce products from plants?

- What techniques do we use to grow plants for food and fibre?

- How can we grow plants without harming the environment?

What do Aspirin™, spacesuits, aircraft tires, and movie filmstrips have in common? They all include products that come from plants. Food, fibre, and many other things are made from plants. Each of the plants that we use to make products are adapted to living in different environments and under different conditions.

In Topics 1 and 2 you will learn how we use plants for food and fibre. You will also learn what the parts of the plant contribute to the growth and health of plants. In Topic 3 you will learn how plants reproduce and how people can use special techniques to breed plants with particular characteristics.

We plant and harvest crops and trees to supply our need for plant fibre. What are some of the challenges in trying to grow plants for food and fibre while still maintaining healthy soil and water? How do we control pests? You will learn about these issues in Topics 4–6.

Looking Ahead

Get Growing! Read pages 178–179 to find out about the Unit 2 Project. It gives you a chance to use what you learn in this unit to grow some great plants. Begin this project after you have completed Topic 5. See your plants grow before you finish this unit!

- Carefully read the Challenge posed on page 178. Start thinking about the crop you might grow.

- As you work through Topics 1–5, think about how your knowledge of plants and their needs will help you grow your plant.

- Save your ideas for growing plants in a Project Planning file.

People and Plants

Science Log

In your Science Log, list five ways that plants help you and five ways that they help the environment. Could we survive in the world as we know it without plants?

Skill FOCUS

For tips on using a Science Log or Science Journal, turn to Skill Focus 3.

DidYou**Know**?

It takes four large trees to absorb the excess carbon dioxide put into the atmosphere when a car is driven for 1 h.

How do humans use plants? Your first reaction might very well be "to eat!" Of course, people have always used plants for food. Plants are used for much more than food, however. Plants provide fibre, which humans use for clothing, paper, and building materials. **Fibre** is the tissue of plants from the stem, leaves, seeds, or roots. Plants are used in a wide range of products. Did you know, for instance, that many medicines are made from plants? Imagine a world without plants! In this Topic you will learn about the many ways we use plants. You will also investigate what a plant needs to grow and stay healthy.

Plants in the Environment

Plants are a critical part of ecosystems. They produce the oxygen that most organisms require for life. Industrial activities and automobiles add excess carbon dioxide and pollutants to the atmosphere. Plants help reduce this problem by using carbon dioxide. A hectare of trees, for example, can remove over 10 tonnes of carbon dioxide each year.

Plants are also the basis of most food webs. Whether an animal is a herbivore or a carnivore, it relies on plants for its existence. Plants also provide shelter for countless animals. Plants help clean and filter water and absorb it, thus regulating the flow and storage of water. As well, the roots of plants help keep soil in place and prevent it from being washed or blown away.

Plants for Food

Vegetables and fruits are probably among the first edible plants you think of, but they are not the only plants we eat. Today, nearly 75 percent of the world's food supply is based on seven major crops: wheat, rice, maize (corn), potatoes, barley, cassava, and sorghum. Many of the world's peoples have a diet based on one of these main crops.

Figure 2.1 This meal was made from the leaves, roots, seeds, and stems of many different plants. Which plants were used to make this meal, including the packaging?

From Plant to Final Product

While a peach, a cob of corn, or a walnut are recognizable as parts of plants, many plants look considerably different by the time we eat them. Try to match the plants below, with the products in which they are used.

A Chocolate is made from the fruit of a cocoa tree. Tropical countries in West Africa and South America produce most of the world's cocoa. To harvest cocoa, the beans of a cocoa pod are spread out in the Sun to dry. They are roasted, shelled, and crushed in a factory. A giant press then separates the cocoa butter from the powder in the crushed beans. The powder is mixed with milk to make chocolate.

B Did you know that we get oil from plants? In Canada, over 78 percent of vegetable oil production is from the canola plant. Oil is pressed from canola seeds. Canola oil is sold as a salad and frying oil and is also used in margarine, shortening, baked goods, potato chips, and french fries. Canola was developed from rapeseed by Canadian plant breeders during the 1970s.

C Seaweeds contain traces of important nutrients such as iodine. Seaweed is a valuable food resource in some parts of the world. Hundreds of thousands of tonnes are collected each year in Japan for use in soup broths or dishes such as sushi. Products from seaweeds are also used in ice cream, chocolate milk, yogurt, whipped cream, pies, jellies, and candies. Seaweed products are often used to thicken food. The terms "alginate," "agar," or "carrageenan" on a food label indicate the product contains seaweed.

D Almost half the world's sugar comes from sugar beets. They are grown in northern countries, including Russia, France, Germany, Poland, the United States, and Canada. The sugar is found in the thick plant roots. The roots are first shredded and then heated in running water to remove impurities. The clear liquid that remains is concentrated and crystallized to produce a sugar similar to that made from sugar cane.

Word **CONNECT**

Are you familiar with the plants cassava and sorghum? Use a dictionary or encyclopedia to find out about these plants and how they are used.

Plants for Fibre

Plants provide fibres for a variety of needs, including clothing, paper, and shelter. How many uses of plants can you see in the photographs below?

People discovered early in history that the fibres of plants, separated out and processed in some way, were very useful for making clothes. Recall in Unit 1 how Aboriginal people from Canada's west coast wove clothing from the bark of the western red cedar. Today, much of our clothing comes from synthetic (manufactured) material such as polyester or nylon. Plants, however, still provide important fibre to make cloth. Cotton, hemp, and flax are all natural fibres that we use.

Figure 2.2 The flowers of cotton plants bloom in the morning and by the afternoon begin to wither. The next day they are rose coloured and fall from the plant. Once the petals fall off, a "boll" develops. After four months the boll splits open and at last you can see the cotton inside.

Cotton

Cotton is a natural fibre that has been grown and used by humans for centuries. In fact, you are probably wearing at least one garment made from cotton right now. Cotton is even used for spacesuits. Cotton fibres are different from synthetic fibres in that cotton absorbs moisture and then allows it to evaporate easily. Cotton is currently the world's most important non-edible plant.

Cotton fibres come from the plant's seeds. The plant uses silky fibres to spread its seeds in the wind. The fibres are strong, flexible, and have a gradual spiral that causes the strands to interlock when twisted. This makes them ideal for spinning into thread. Beneath these long fibrous hairs lies a second layer of shorter fibres known as "fuzzy" fibres. These fibres are used to make cotton batting, rayon, and various types of plastics and paper.

Hemp

If you had one of the first pairs of blue jeans ever made in the late nineteenth century, you would have been wearing jeans made from hemp. Today jeans are made of cotton.

Hemp is the oldest cultivated fibre plant in the world. The first Bible made on a printing press was printed on hemp paper, and early sails and ropes were made of hemp as well.

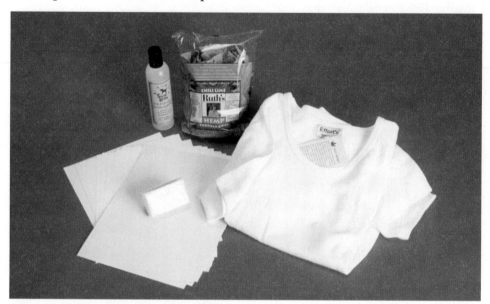

Figure 2.3 Today you can buy paper, clothing, and even shoes, made from hemp fibre.

Hemp has a less negative effect on the environment than other sources of fibre do. For example, 1 ha of hemp can produce four times more fibre than the same area planted in trees. A hemp crop is ready to harvest in one year, whereas it takes decades until a tree is ready to harvest. As well, hemp paper lasts longer than paper made from wood pulp and it can be recycled up to seven times. (Paper made from wood pulp can be recycled about four times.) Hemp plants also grow quickly and therefore choke out weeds naturally. Hemp is not eaten by most insect pests, so chemicals to control weeds and insects are not needed.

Flax

Flax is a food and fibre crop that is grown in the northern, cooler regions of the world. Flax fibres are taken from the stem of the plant and are two to three times as strong as those of cotton. As well, flax fibres are naturally smooth and straight. Europe and North America depended on flax for cloth until the nineteenth century, when cotton overtook flax as the most common plant used for making clothes. Flax fibre is also used for making linen paper.

Flax is grown on the Canadian Prairies for linseed oil, which is used as a drying oil in paints and varnish and in products such as linoleum and printing inks.

Did You Know?

Levi Strauss invented blue jeans as tough, protective work clothes. The cloth he used for his jeans was imported from Nîmes in France. The French name for this material, serge de Nîmes, soon turned into the word "denim" in North America.

Did You Know?

Wood pulp is the basic raw material for almost all disposable diapers. Aboriginal people in Canada used certain types of moss for baby diapers. Mothers packed absorbent moss between their baby's legs and held it there with a soft strip of animal skin.

Fibre Face-off

Paper is made from the fibre of trees, flax, hemp, or other plants. The fibre is processed into a pulp before it is pressed into sheets of paper.

Question

Which type of plant fibre is the strongest?

Safety Precautions

- Take care not to touch the hot base plate of the iron.
- Wipe up any spills, as wet floors are slippery.

Apparatus

large jar or plastic container

blender or food processor

large rubber tub or sink filled with warm water

1 screen

2 dishcloths

newspapers

sponge

clothes iron

magnifying glass or microscope

Materials

several sheets of linen writing paper or envelopes, newspaper, construction paper, manila envelopes, or photocopy paper

warm water

white glue

Procedure

Part 1

1. **Predict** which paper will be the strongest.

2. Choose one paper to work with from the Materials list.

3. Rip your paper into small pieces and place it in the jar or plastic container. Cover with warm water and leave overnight.

4. Place the fluid from step 2 into a blender and slowly blend until you have a smooth pulp. **Note:** Add more water if necessary.

5. Add five drops of white glue to the pulp and blend well.

6. Add the pulp to the rubber tub or sink filled with 10 cm of warm water.

7. Place the screen into the water and swish it around until your pulp forms a thin, even layer on the screen.

8. Lift the screen out of the water and let the water drain off.

9. Lay a damp dishcloth on a stack of newspapers.

10. Flip the screen, with the pulp, onto the dishcloth. Use the sponge to soak up any excess moisture off the back of the screen.

11. Gently remove the screen so that the pulp stays on the dishcloth.

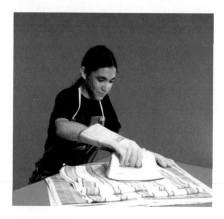

Take care using the iron.

12 Cover the pulp with the second dishcloth and iron at medium temperature for 1–2 min.

13 Gently pull the dishcloth away from the paper and let the paper air dry on a flat surface.

14 When the paper is completely dry, proceed to Part 2.

Part 2

1 **Design** a way to test the strength of the paper you have made.

2 **Discuss** your testing methods with students who have made paper from other materials and agree upon a strategy for testing paper strength.

3 **Review** your testing strategy with your teacher and then conduct your tests.

4 **Examine** the paper fibres in your recycled paper sheets using a magnifying glass or microscope.

Skill
FOCUS

For tips on using graphic organizers turn to Skill Focus 2.

For tips on making predictions, turn to Skill Focus 6.

Analyze

1. Which paper was the strongest? Explain your results based on your knowledge of plant fibre.

2. What other variables could you have tested to evaluate your paper? (For example, is strength the only quality to look for when choosing paper?)

3. Does the length of fibre affect paper strength? Explain.

Conclude and Apply

4. Photocopy paper is made from wood pulp and linen paper is made from flax. What do we use these types of paper for?

Extend Your Knowledge

5. Research how paper is actually recycled. Draw a flowchart or other graphic organizer to illustrate this process.

Plants for Medicine

The saying "An apple a day keeps the doctor away" may be closer to the truth than you realize. Many medicines contain ingredients made from plants. In fact, more than 7000 medicines are made from plants, including heart drugs, cancer medicines, antibiotics, and pain medication. Plants were the original medicines. Aboriginal people have known about the medicinal use of plants for centuries. They used the plants around them before the medicines we now have were available. You may even have a plant-based home remedy that you use in your family. For example, some people make tea from ginger root to soothe an upset stomach.

Pain Medication

Plants often give us the "blueprints" for medicines that scientists can then copy in laboratories. For example, for centuries it was well known that the bark of the white willow eased pain. The exact ingredient was isolated through testing, and now these pain medications are manufactured synthetically in laboratories. Aspirin is one example.

Figure 2.4 Tropical rain forests are home to more than 50 percent of plant species on the planet.

Figure 2.5 Morphine, a powerful pain medication, is found only in the thick fluid of the opium poppy's seed pod. It cannot be manufactured.

Opium poppies (Figure 2.5) are the source of morphine, the most powerful natural pain medication of all. Morphine is found in the milky fluid of the poppy's seed pod and also in the stems and leaves. Codeine is also found in the poppy. It is used in cough medicines and for the relief of other cold symptoms.

Quinine comes from cinchona trees (see Figure 2.6). It is used as a prevention for malaria, a deadly disease carried by certain tropical mosquitoes. Until quinine became widely available, malaria killed approximately 2 million people each year.

Since quinine was discovered in 1820, there has been a steady demand for the drug. In 1944 American scientists devised a way to produce synthetic quinine. However, the malarial parasite has since developed resistance to manufactured quinine and it is no longer effective in some areas of the world. Natural quinine is effective everywhere.

Figure 2.6 The cinchona tree grows in the humid forests of the South American Andes. It is the source of quinine.

Herbal Remedies

Does anyone in your family or someone you know use herbal remedies?

CAUTION Do not use herbal remedies without first checking with your doctor.

Procedure ✴ Performing and Recording

1. Link the common herbs below, with their descriptions. Do research in the library and on the Internet if necessary.

   A. echinacea   **D.** ginkgo biloba

   B. feverfew   **E.** ginseng

   C. garlic   **F.** aloe vera

   (a) This bulb, a natural antibiotic, has been used to prevent infections. In World War I the juice from this bulb was squeezed onto moss and used to dress wounds.

   (b) The leaves of this plant are used to heal skin problems, such as minor burns.

   (c) This plant is considered an effective treatment for migraine headaches.

Find Out ACTIVITY

   (d) This plant is one of the world's oldest living trees. It is often called the smart herb because it increases the supply of oxygen to the brain.

   (e) This root has long been important for health in Chinese culture. It enhances mental activity and is said to stimulate the central nervous system.

   (f) This plant is used to combat cold, cough, flu viruses, and sore throats.

2. Choose one of the herbs above or another herbal remedy or medicine to research further. Use the library or Internet resources to prepare a one-page summary of your research, listing important points about the herb's history and claims for its effectiveness.

What Did You Find Out?
✴ Analyzing and Interpreting
✴ Communication and Teamwork

1. How are herbal remedies and many modern medicines similar?

2. How is the use of herbal remedies controlled?

Extension

3. As a class, discuss herbal remedies and why the Western medical profession is sometimes concerned about their use.

Plants for Transportation and Construction

Did a plant help transport you to school today? Unless you walked barefoot, one probably did. Rubber is one of the most important plant products that people use. When humans figured out how to turn liquid rubber (called latex) into a hard, yet flexible, material, our world changed dramatically. Without rubber, it is unlikely we would have cars, airplanes, or spacecraft!

Natural rubber comes from the Brazilian rubber tree (see Figure 2.7). This tree is currently the only source of natural rubber. Since the demand for natural rubber is increasing faster than we can grow rubber trees, scientists are researching alternative plants to supply this useful product. Today most vehicle tires contain some synthetic rubber made from coal and oil by-products, but natural rubber is still an important part of them.

Plants have also influenced transportation on water. For instance, Aboriginal people in Canada made canoes from trees (see Figures 2.8 and 2.9).

Figure 2.7 Latex being tapped from a rubber tree

Figure 2.8 On the west coast of Canada, Aboriginal people hollowed out the huge trunk of the western red cedar with a combination of carving and controlled burning.

Figure 2.9 Aboriginal people of the interior regions of North America used the bark of the white birch to make canoes.

Certain plants are the source of lubricants. Lubricants are used to oil machinery parts to ensure that they work properly. The racing car in Figure 2.10, as well as airplane engines, uses lubricants made partially from coconut and castor bean oils.

Plants are also used for construction all around the world. In North America, 90 percent of all houses are made of wood. Most timber used today for construction comes from softwood trees. Forests of the Pacific Northwest, especially those of British Columbia, provide a large proportion of the softwood timber used around the world.

Did You Know?

Softwood trees are conifers, such as hemlock or fir. Conifers have needles and cones.

Plants for Fuel

If you use wood or coal to heat your home you have plants to thank for keeping you dry and warm. In many places in the world, wood is still burned for fuel. In other countries, plants that were growing on Earth millions of years ago provide the energy. These ancient plants died and were covered with sediment. Over many years the layers of sediment built up and the weight compressed the plant tissues. Under intense pressure and heat, they underwent chemical and physical changes to become coal.

The sugar in some plants can be turned into a type of liquid fuel called ethanol. Methanol is another type of liquid fuel that is made from wood. Methanol is also called wood alcohol.

Producing fuel from plants is economical but not very energy efficient. A large amount of energy is required to grow and harvest the crop and a lot of energy is lost when plants are converted to fuel. Still, liquid fuels provide an alternative fuel source in our world where oil and gasoline from traditional sources are limited.

Figure 2.10 Many racing cars use lubricants made from coconut and castor bean oils.

Figure 2.11 Will there always be enough plants to support the need of the human population for food and fibre?

Human Needs and Plant Needs

If Canadians and other producers of plants are to meet the growing need for plants, we need to make sure that plants survive and thrive. We need to maintain healthy conditions to support the plants that help support us. What do plants need to survive and stay healthy? You will find out in the next investigation.

Growing Conditions for Healthy Plants

Plants growing in natural conditions are well suited to their environment and the amount of light, heat, and water they naturally receive. Plants grown by people, however, are often helped a bit so that the health and yield of the plants (how much is harvested) is maximized.

Challenge

Grow the healthiest plants that you can by varying the light, temperature, and water.

Apparatus

thumbtack	ruler
graduated cylinder	thermometer
plant grow lights (optional)	space heater (optional)

Materials

seeds sprouted between layers of moist paper towel

paper cups, or small peat pots

potting soil or garden soil

water

Design Specifications

A. You will be given nine sprouted seeds from one type of plant. Divide your seeds into three groups and plant them at the same depth in the same type of soil and in the same type of container. Use a peat pot or a paper cup with holes poked in the bottom (use a thumbtack).

B. Design an experiment that shows how the amount of light, temperature, and water affects plant growth.

C. You may change only one variable for each group of plants. (For example, if you are varying the amount of light, the temperature and water should stay the same.)

D. Design appropriate graphs and tables for recording your data.

Plan and Construct

1. Design appropriate ways to vary light, temperature, and water.

2. Review the design of your experiment with your teacher. Then proceed with your experiment.

3. Measure and graph the growth of your plants daily for a week or more.

4. Record the temperature, amount of water, and approximate amount of light daily.

Evaluate

1. Why was it important that all of your seeds were planted at the same depth, in the same soil, and in the same type of container?

2. Why was it was important to begin your experiment with sprouted seeds?

3. Which combination of light, temperature, and water would result in the healthiest plant?

4. Is a healthy plant always the tallest plant?

5. Describe and draw the condition of a healthy plant.

Extension

6. What other factors might have affected the growth of your plant other than those tested?

1. List ten plant-based products that you have used today. Classify your use of plants into "plants for food" and "plants for fibre." Which type of use is most common for you? Discuss the results as a class.

2. Describe the process that is used to create (a) chocolate from cocoa pods, and (b) sugar from sugar beets.

3. Look at these circle graphs. Why do you think the usage of wood in developing countries (such as India or Thailand) differs from the ways it is used in developed countries (such as North America)?

A. Wood use in developing countries   **B.** Wood use in developed countries

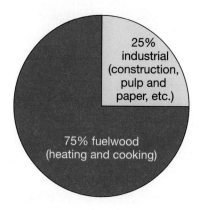

25% industrial (construction, pulp and paper, etc.)

75% fuelwood (heating and cooking)

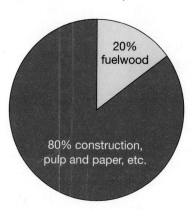

20% fuelwood

80% construction, pulp and paper, etc.

4. Describe the role of plants in the environment.

5. What advantages does hemp have over other fibre plants such as wood and cotton?

6. Name two ways in which plants are used in transportation.

7. **Thinking Critically** Imagine a population of people that depends on only one crop for food, clothing, transportation, and construction needs. What might this plant look like? What would be the effects of depending on only one crop for all human needs?

8. **Thinking Critically** If all the plants on Earth died, what are some of the effects we would face? Which effects would be most immediate and serious?

Perennials and annuals have very different survival strategies. Use your dictionary to determine the difference between these two types of plants.

Plants are found in almost all habitats on Earth. Each habitat has a unique set of environmental characteristics, such as temperature, light, water, and soil conditions. A plant's structure helps it adapt to these conditions. For example, a desert plant's roots are adapted to gather moisture from deep in the soil.

We need to understand the structure of plants and how they adapt so that we can match the plants with conditions where they can grow well. We can sometimes use this knowledge to alter growing conditions and improve yield.

Find Out ACTIVITY

Digging into Dandelions

In this activity, examine a dandelion to see what you already know about plant structure.

Materials
trowel
dandelion with roots, leaves, stem, and flower (if possible)
ruler
magnifying glass
scissors

Procedure ✻ Performing and Recording

1. Dig up a dandelion from your backyard or schoolyard. Remove the remaining soil on the plant. Be careful not to break the big root. If you do break it, dig out the pieces remaining in the soil.

2. Draw a sketch of the plant and label the roots, stem, flower, and leaves.

3. Use a magnifying glass to examine the dandelion flower or the parachute-like seeds if it has gone to seed. Record your observations.

4. Measure and compare the length of the root with the part of the plant above ground.

5. Use the scissors to cut across the stem and describe what you see. Examine the stem and any fluids under a magnifying glass.

6. Tear the stem lengthwise and describe the kinds of fibres that make up the stem.

7. Examine both sides of the leaves. Are they the same? Describe any differences and indicate them on your drawing.

8. Wash your hands thoroughly.

What Did You Find Out? ✻ Analyzing and Interpreting

1. Describe what you know about the functions of the roots, stems, leaves, and flower of a plant. Base your answer on what you observed about the dandelion's structure.

2. How do you think the length of the root helps the plant survive?

3. How are other plants the same or different from the dandelion? Predict how an alpine plant and a rain forest plant might be different from a dandelion.

Roots

When you look at a plant, you see only part of it. As you saw with the dandelion, plants can be a bit like icebergs — there is often much more beneath the surface than what you might think. In many cases, up to one-third of a plant, its root, lies hidden below the ground.

Roots perform several important functions:

- they absorb water and minerals from soil;

- they support and anchor the plant so that it is not blown over by wind or washed away by water; and

- they store food to help the plant survive during times of scarcity.

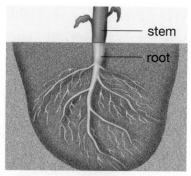

Figure 2.12 A taproot system. It can reach deep into the ground to obtain moisture.

Figure 2.13 A fibrous root system

Many plants have a single, prominent **taproot** with numerous small roots coming out of it (see Figure 2.12). These smaller roots are covered in tiny **root hairs**. The smaller roots and root hairs increase the ability of the plant to absorb water and nutrients from the soil. Most trees and large desert plants grow taproots that reach deep into the ground, as do dandelions. Other plants have **fibrous roots**. This is a shallow system of similar-sized roots that can quickly soak up moisture (see Figure 2.13).

Roots are often specially adapted to a plant's habitat. For example, moss campion, shown in Figure 2.14, is an Alberta plant that grows on mountains where it is high, cold, and dry. The plant grows very low to the ground, thus trapping heat, preventing wind damage, and reducing water loss. When a moss campion seedling begins to grow, its first few years are spent making roots. After five years the taproot can reach 2 m into the mountain, whereas the leaves and stems remain smaller than a bottle cap. Moss campion may take up to 25 years to bloom. In contrast, the duckweed, a common plant found on ponds in spring and summer, has tiny roots that grow off the underside of the leaf and are surrounded entirely by water (see Figure 2.15).

In 1930 at the University of Iowa, scientists planted a single winter rye plant. They let it grow for four months and then carefully removed the root system from the soil and measured it. They found the total length (including the root hairs) was more than 11 000 km.

Figure 2.14 Moss campion is a common cushion plant found on rocky mountain slopes. Its roots can reach 2 m deep.

Figure 2.15 The underside of duckweed leaves are covered in tiny roots.

Root Crops

When you eat the vegetables in Figure 2.16 you are eating a root. Carrots, beets, turnips, radishes, and parsnips are all roots.

Figure 2.16 Root crops generally grow in a short period of time and, since they have deeper roots, can survive where there is less rainfall. These qualities, combined with the length of time they can be stored, make root crops an important part of the diet of many people in the world.

Getting to the Root of Roots

A primary function of roots is to absorb water and minerals and transfer them to the stem. To find out more about how root absorption works, complete this activity using a large root, a carrot.

Materials

water

blue food colouring

carrot with the leaves intact

250 mL beaker

table knife

scale

Procedure * `Performing and Recording`

1. Pour water into the jar and add enough food colouring to turn the water deep blue.

2. Cut off the tip of the carrot. Use care when cutting the carrot. Cut in a direction away from your body. Place the carrot into the dye solution. Set it in bright light for several hours.

3. Remove the carrot from the jar and estimate, then measure the mass of the carrot.

4. Cut the leaves and stem from the root.

Find Out ACTIVITY

5. Estimate, then measure the mass of the carrot root.

6. Estimate, then measure the mass of the carrot leaves and stem.

7. Cut the carrot lengthwise down the middle and observe the location of the dye.

What Did You Find Out? * `Analyzing and Interpreting`

1. Which part of the plant did the food colouring enter? Explain what this tells you about roots.

2. Describe the major functions of the carrot root.

3. Compare the root mass to the total mass of your carrot. What percent of the total mass are the leaf and stem of the carrot? How might this percent differ in a garden crop such as lettuce?

Skill
F O C U S

For tips on estimating, turn to Skill Focus 5.

Diffusion and Osmosis

Diffusion and osmosis are two key processes that allow roots to absorb water and dissolved substances such as minerals. **Diffusion** is the tendency of particles in a gas or a liquid to become evenly distributed by moving from areas of greater concentration to areas of lesser concentration. The particles continue to spread until they are evenly spaced in an area. Diffusion occurs, for example, when a perfume bottle is opened in the corner of a room. The scent quickly becomes uniformly distributed throughout the air in the room.

Osmosis is a type of diffusion in which only some types of particles are allowed to pass through a barrier. Imagine a mesh bag filled with marbles and sand. Sand will get through the mesh, but the marbles will remain. The mesh bag is like the cells in the root. The cells are **differentially permeable**. This means that they allow some materials to pass through, such as water and specific nutrients, and keep out other materials. **Osmosis** is the diffusion of water through a differentially permeable membrane. Figures 2.17A, B, and C explain osmosis further.

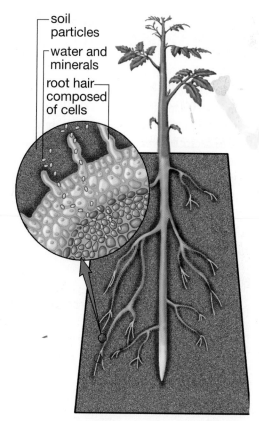

soil particles

water and minerals

root hair composed of cells

Figure 2.17A Water and dissolved minerals enter the plant by osmosis through cells in the root hairs.

Figure 2.17B Wilting occurs when more water leaves the cells than enters them.

Figure 2.17C When a plant has enough water, no more water will enter the roots until the cells have lost some of their water.

Stems

Where do the water and dissolved nutrients go after they are absorbed by the roots? One function of stems is to transport water and nutrients between the leaves and roots. Figure 2.18 shows an example of one common type of stem — the trunk of a tree — and the tissues that make it work.

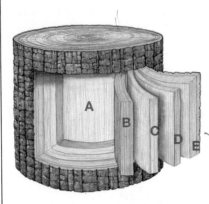

A. Heartwood is dead wood in the centre of the tree. It gives the tree its strength.

B. Xylem carries water and nutrients from the roots up to the leaves. As new layers develop, the inner layers die and become heartwood.

C. Cambium is the growing part of the trunk. Each year the cambium produces new phloem and xylem.

D. Phloem is the layer of cells that carries sugars from the leaves to the rest of the tree. As these cells die, they become part of the outer bark.

E. Bark is the woody skin that stops a tree from drying out. It protects and insulates the tree.

Figure 2.18 The layers of a tree

Find Out ACTIVITY

Celery Superhighway

Complete this activity to find out how water and nutrients travel through stems.

Materials

blue or red food colouring

500 mL beaker

celery stalk with leaves (with 1 cm cut from base)

water

magnifying glass or microscope

Procedure ✳ Performing and Recording

1. Add food colouring to water.

2. Place the celery in coloured water.

3. Set the celery in bright light overnight.

4. The next day observe the cut end of the celery. Record your observations.

What Did You Find Out? ✳ Analyzing and Interpreting

1. What are the coloured tubes in your celery?

2. Why did step 4 instruct you to place a stalk cut from the base of the celery into the water?

3. How might your results change if you bent the celery stalk in half before placing it in the food colouring? Write a prediction for the results of such a trial.

Extension

4. How can you increase the flow of water to the leaves? Rewrite at least one of your ideas as a problem that you could test.

5. **Design Your Own** The celery you used in this activity does not have its roots. Why did water move up the stem? How could you find out if your idea is correct? Design an investigation to answer this question.

Support

A second function of a stem is to support the leaves and to ensure that they receive adequate light, which the plant needs to produce food. To perform this task, most stems grow above the soil. Stems range in size from a few millimetres to over 100 m (see Figure 2.19).

Food Storage

Some stems also store food for the plant. They store the food produced in the leaves of the plant. Potatoes, for example, are swollen underground stems known as tubers. They store food in the form of starch, which the potato plant uses for growth.

Although plants generally store food in the form of starch, as potatoes do, some plants store food as sugar. The plant best known for storing sugar in its stem is sugar cane. Sugar cane is a grass plant that grows naturally in tropical areas.

Different Types of Stems

Examine Figure 2.20 to see some other types of stems.

Figure 2.19 Sequoia trees have the tallest stems in the world. They can grow as high as 110 m. The bark of a sequoia tree is more than 50 cm thick.

Figure 2.20A The stem of the common strawberry plant grows horizontally on the ground and is called a runner. At various spots along the stem, roots begin to grow.

Figure 2.20B Corms are also underground stems. Crocus and gladioli also grow from corms.

Figure 2.20C Cattails have fleshy horizontal stems called rhizomes, which allow the plant to spread underground.

Figure 2.20D Several cacti, like the prickly pear, have flattened stems. This adaptation ensures that part of the plant always faces away from the Sun, helping the cactus to preserve water.

Pause&
Reflect

In the fall, when many plants stop producing chlorophyll, leaves turn other colours, such as brown, yellow, orange, and red. What happens to the leaves and the plant after this colour change occurs? How is this related to food production in the plant? Write your responses in your Science Log.

Leaves

During spring and summer — the major growing seasons for plants — a pigment called **chlorophyll** makes leaves green. Most of the chlorophyll is in the tops of leaves. Leaves are the part of the plant that use the energy of sunlight and change it to a kind of chemical energy. They do this by combining two simple materials, carbon dioxide (from the air) and water. These combine to make the material that we know as sugar. Sugar is a kind of energy-storing chemical made by plants. This process is called **photosynthesis** (see Figure 2.21).

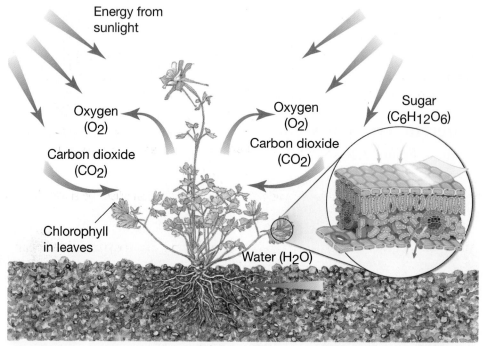

Figure 2.21 During photosynthesis, carbon dioxide from the air, water in the soil, and energy from the Sun react to form sugar and oxygen.

Carbon dioxide enters plants through tiny holes in leaves called stomata (singular: stoma) (see Figure 2.22). Because leaves usually have more stomata on the lower surface, more carbon dioxide reaches the spaces in the spongy layer, as shown in Figure 2.23. The spongy layer is also where much of the leaf's water is stored.

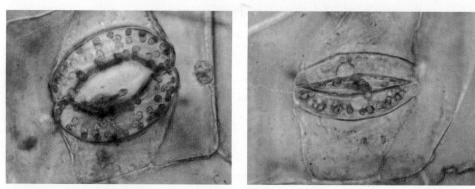

Figure 2.22 These stomata have been magnified many times. Stomata open during the daytime and close at night. Why do you think this is advantageous for the plant?

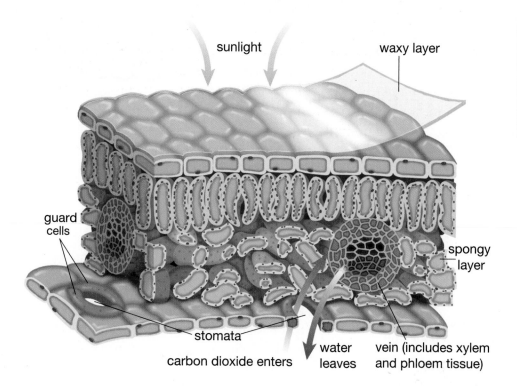

sunlight

waxy layer

guard cells

spongy layer

stomata

carbon dioxide enters

water leaves

vein (includes xylem and phloem tissue)

Figure 2.23 Photosynthesis takes place near the top surface of the leaf where the sunlight is strongest. Gas exchange occurs through the stomata.

Along with sugar, plants produce oxygen during photosynthesis. Sugar is carried throughout the plant for the food it needs to live and grow. Oxygen gas escapes through the stomata. Photosynthesis is the source of all food on Earth. Plants convert the Sun's energy into plant tissues, which animals use for food. The oxygen produced by photosynthesis in plants is the source of all oxygen in our atmosphere.

Plants need oxygen as well. At night, when photosynthesis does not occur, respiration does. **Respiration** is a process by which plants release carbon dioxide and let oxygen into their cells.

Guard cells are cells on the leaf surface that surround each stoma, controlling the size of the opening. Water moves in and out of the guard cells by osmosis. When guard cells absorb water, they swell and the stoma opens, letting in carbon dioxide and letting out water vapour. This loss of water from a plant through evaporation is called **transpiration**. When guard cells lose water, they relax and the stoma closes.

Moving Water in Plants

Water loss through transpiration is part of an important system that ensures water moves throughout the plant. Think of the water network in a plant as a series of thin, hollow tubes. Water drawn into the root hairs by osmosis pushes thin columns of water up the plant. At the same time, water lost from the leaves by transpiration pulls water up the xylem tissues from the roots. Both these actions, pushing and pulling, move water to the top of plants, even the world's tallest trees!

Off the Wall

For St. Patrick's Day, some florists dye white carnations green. They put white flowers in green dye and let the principle of water movement in plants do the work for them. Water is pushed and pulled up the stem by transpiration. You just did something similar when you put a stalk of celery in a glass of water dyed with food colouring.

INVESTIGATION 2-C

Design a Plant for Its Habitat

Use your problem-solving skills to design a useful plant with adaptations to survive in an extreme environment.

Challenge

Use your knowledge of plant structure and adaptation and your understanding of human needs for plants to design a plant. Your plant must be able to help a human population living in either a dry alpine environment, a desert, a temperate forest where winters are long and cold, or a tropical rain forest.

Materials

poster paper   pencils   art materials

Design Specifications

A. Your design must include details about how your plant's roots, stems, and leaves will be able to perform their jobs.

B. Your plant must be useful for the human population living near your extreme environment. Use what you learned in Topic 1 to provide details about the ways that your plant is useful.

C. Your group must produce a drawing of the plant with labels.

D. Your group must present its design to the class. As part of your report, you must include at least three problems your plant faces.

E. Your plant must be able to grow naturally in its environment without help from humans.

Plan and Construct

1 With your group and teacher, select the environment you wish your plant to grow in. Brainstorm with your group about the challenges this environment will pose to your plant.

2 Each member of your design team should sketch a possible design for your plant.

3 Evaluate the designs and as a group choose the best design or come up with a new design that will best achieve the specifications of this activity. Be as creative as you like! Your presentation should include other adaptations such as how long your plant lives, any special relationships it may have with insects or other animals, or any other characteristics of your plant.

4 Assign one person to draw, one to label, and two or more to prepare and give the oral presentation.

5 After groups are finished preparing, give your presentation to the class.

Evaluate

1. What would happen to your plant if you put it in a different environment?

2. Suggest ways you might help the plant survive in its new home. Would your suggestions be practical? Explain.

Extend Your Skills

3. Make a model of your plant out of materials such as papier-mâché, wire, cardboard, or modelling clay.

Skill
FOCUS

For tips on scientific drawing, turn to Skill Focus 11.

For tips on using models in science, turn to Skill Focus 12.

Food and Fibre Plants in Alberta

Think About It

Although Alberta is often known for its field crops of flax or canola, this province grows a variety of crops for food and fibre. Some of these plants are shown here. Different plants are harvested for their stems, leaves, root, or fruit. Crops are chosen by farmers because of their suitability to the local environment and the needs of consumers.

What are the special conditions for growing crops in Alberta? Are some parts of Alberta better than others for growing certain plants for food and fibre? What do these plants need to stay healthy and produce a maximum yield? Finally, what are these plants used for? In this investigation you will answer some of these questions.

What to Do

① Choose one Alberta plant that is grown for its roots, one that is grown for its stem, and one that is grown for its leaves, fruit, or flower. Using resources in the library or on the Internet, find the following information:

- The region in Alberta where the plant is grown.

- How the plant is suited to grow in Alberta.

- What special environmental conditions, if any, make that area of Alberta better for growing this plant.

- Whether the environment is changed or enhanced to make it possible to have a more successful crop. (For example, are greenhouses used?)

- What the plant is used for and who uses this plant.

Analyze

1. Based on your research and the information presented by your classmates, are certain regions of Alberta better suited for growing certain plants?

2. Explain why it is important for a farmer or other person who grows plants to understand a plant's needs as well as the environmental conditions of the area in which the plant will grow.

3. Name two ways that the environment can be altered to enhance the growth of plants.

INTERNET CONNECT

www.mcgrawhill.ca/links/sciencefocus7

Learn more about the crops grown in Alberta by going to the above web site. Click on **Web Links** to find out where to go next. Use the information you find on this site to help you prepare your presentation.

Skill
FOCUS

For tips on researching on the Internet, turn to Skill Focus 9.

TOPIC 2 Review

1. Explain the primary function of roots, stems, and leaves using a diagram of a plant.

2. Describe how osmosis works, using the example of a model if you like. Why is osmosis an important process for plants?

3. What is the advantage of having most of the chlorophyll in cells near the top of the leaf?

4. Explain the relationship between the following pairs of words:
   (a) xylem and phloem
   (b) diffusion and osmosis
   (c) chlorophyll and photosynthesis
   (d) root crop and tuber

5. Explain the role of stomata in photosynthesis.

6. Name two Alberta plants that are harvested for their roots, stems, leaves, seeds, or fruit.

7. **Apply** The shape and structure of the leaves of many desert plants reduce their rate of water loss. In cacti, for example, the leaves have been drastically reduced and modified into spines. Many of the adaptations that are found in plants in the desert are also found in plants growing in northern countries. Explain how an evergreen tree has adapted to life in a cold climate.

8. **Apply** In cities with few green spaces, people sometimes have rooftop gardens or patio gardens. How can this improve the air quality?

TOPIC 3 Plant Reproduction and Breeding

Early humans met their nutritional needs by collecting wild plants and hunting wild animals. Eventually people began to grow and tend plants near their home. They even began to adapt plants to meet their needs through selective breeding. **Selective breeding** means that people choose specific plants with particular characteristics and encourage these plants to reproduce. For example, the modern corn plant does not resemble the plant from which it was bred. People encouraged the growth of corn with large "ears" and removed weaker, smaller plants until only the corn that grew large ears remained. They were able to do this because they learned how plants reproduce. In this Topic you will study plant reproduction.

Look at the varieties of apples in Figure 2.25A. Plants are also bred for their ability to withstand certain environmental conditions (hardiness), how much food or fibre they produce (yield), and their resistance to disease. Today, how well a food stores and ships are other factors that may be considered when breeding new plants. Look at the cherries in Figure 2.25. This variety has recently been developed by the Summerland Research Centre in British Columbia. Sweetheart cherries have firm flesh, split-resistant skin, and strong, green stems. Why do you think these are desirable characteristics?

Figure 2.24 Wild roses (top); cultivated roses (bottom)

Figure 2.25A Each variety of apple above has a different taste and use. For example, some are great baking apples, while others are best (and tastiest) eaten raw.

Figure 2.25B Sweetheart, a new variety of cherry.

Apple Varieties

For what characteristics are apples bred?

CAUTION Use thermal gloves or oven mitts to remove pans from the oven.

Materials

knife

baking pan

several varieties of apples

small paper lunch bags (1 per apple)

oven (optional)

thermal gloves or oven mitts

Procedure

1. Make a data table like the one below. Give your table a suitable title. You will be testing your apples for flavour, juiciness, appearance, storage, and other characteristics of your choice.

Apple Variety	Properties Tested				
	Appearance	Flavour		Juiciness	Storage
		Fresh	Baked		

2. Cut the apples into slices. Taste the apples and rate their flavour and juiciness on a scale from 1 to 5 (with a score of 5 being the tastiest or juiciest).

3. If you have access to a stove, test the texture and appearance of apple slices after they have been baked at 200°C for 1 h.

4. Place one of each variety of apple in a small paper bag. Place in a cool place and monitor how well the apples store over one week.

What Did You Find Out?

1. For which characteristics was each apple variety bred?

2. How did apples grown in home gardens or market gardens, differ from apples you bought in the grocery store?

3. Where were most of the apples grown? Are any of the varieties you tested grown in Alberta? in Canada?

4. Does the time of year in which you are doing your study affect the varieties of apples that might be available for testing?

Did You Know?

There are over 7500 varieties of apples grown in the world. Approximately over 2500 varieties are grown in North America. How many varieties are there in a supermarket? Why do you think there are so few?

Across Canada

Dr. Thomas Li

In 1992, Agriculture and Agri-Food Canada asked Dr. Thomas Li, horticulturist and plant breeder, to begin developing alternative crops — things besides the traditional crops such as wheat and apples — for the country's farmers to grow. Dr. Li was up to the challenge. Since then he has researched, selected, and introduced to Canada many alternative crops including vegetable soybean, Asian pears, echinacea, ginseng, and winter kiwi.

Dr. Li begins by researching plants that will grow in Canada's environment. He chooses the most appropriate species of a plant, and uses selective breeding to propagate varieties that have desirable characteristics — maximum yield, for example. This new, high-quality plant can then be produced and grown by farmers across the country.

One of Dr. Li's most recent successes is the shrub Indian-Summer, a variety of sea buckthorn originally imported from Russia. It has very high amounts of vitamins A, C, and E in its fruit, protein in its leaves, and medicinal oils in its seed and pulp. Because of its many marketable traits, Dr. Li says it is Canada's "most promising crop right now." So superior is this variety, it is known around the world and grown in every province in Canada.

New Genes?

Canadian research and development teams are responsible for developing canola, a name that comes from the words "Canadian" and "oil." (See Figure 2.26.) Canola was developed using selective breeding and originated from a plant called rapeseed. The new variety yielded seeds that created a good-tasting oil. Work on canola has continued, and breeders have developed canola crops that are resistant to disease, drought, and even certain chemicals.

Figure 2.26 Canola was developed from rapeseed. Rapeseed oil was in demand during World War II as an engine lubricant. Edible oil from rapeseed was not very successful, however, so breeders created canola. Modern varieties of canola are genetically modified to make them immune to many herbicides.

Plant scientists now have the ability to make changes to plants by going inside an individual plant cell and changing some of its material. They do this by first removing the parts of the cell that control its characteristics. This material is called the genetic material or **genes** of the plant. It is then combined with genetic material from another plant. When this new combination of genetic material is put back into the cell, the cell can be used to start a new plant. This new plant will have characteristics that come partly from one kind of plant and partly from another. This process is usually called genetic modification but is sometimes called genetic engineering.

Other examples of genetically modified plants include grains and fruit that resist viruses; tomatoes that ripen more slowly (resulting in better flavour and colour); rice with high levels of Vitamin A; and peanuts that do not cause allergic reactions in humans.

INTERNET CONNECT

www.mcgrawhill.ca/links/sciencefocus7

Go to the above web site to find out about genetically modified organisms. Click on **Web Links** to find out where to go next. Genetic modification is controversial. Try to find out why and discuss this issue with a partner.

Types of Plant Reproduction

Plants can reproduce in two quite different ways. **Sexual reproduction** involves the production of seeds and fruits from specialized cells of two plants. **Asexual**, or **vegetative reproduction**, occurs when a "parent" plant grows new plants from its roots, stems, or leaves. People use both methods to grow and selectively breed plants.

Vegetative Reproduction

Vegetative reproduction is a useful technique for farmers or gardeners. When a plant reproduces vegetatively, the young plants are identical to the parent. If farmers have a plant with characteristics they like, they can reproduce it knowing that each young plant it produces will have the same characteristics. Many trees spread by producing new plants from their roots.

Growers also use layering, in which plants reproduce from stems. Blackberry, raspberry, and rosebushes can be grown from a parent plant using this technique. A branch of the parent plant is bent down to the ground and part of it is covered with soil (see Figure 2.27). Roots will grow from the buried stem and eventually a new plant will grow. This new plant can then be cut away and replanted.

Figure 2.28 A grafted stem

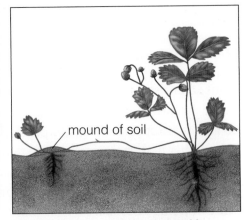

mound of soil

Figure 2.27 A new plant is produced by layering. What advantage does the offspring have by remaining attached to its parent while it develops?

Grafting means to take a branch from one tree and attach it to another tree. This technique is often used with fruit trees and roses (see Figure 2.28). Soon the branch begins to grow on the tree and in several years will produce fruit or flowers.

Plant growers who produce plants commercially will often use cuttings — small sections of leaf and stem cut from a parent plant — to grow new plants. This guarantees that the plants they want to produce will always be the same as the parent plant.

Grow a Plant from a Cutting

What are the best types of cuttings to take? Find out in this investigation.

Problem

How well will plant cuttings with one leaf, two leaves, three leaves, and no leaves grow?

Hypothesis

Make and test a hypothesis about how well different types of cuttings taken from a parent plant will grow.

Coleus plant

Your cutting should include two to three leaves.

Apparatus

scissors (or utility knife)

ruler

small flowerpot or plastic cup

Materials

4 plastic cups

labels (or grease pencil)

aluminum foil

several large *Coleus* plants

water

Procedure

1. Prepare a table to record your results.

Cutting	Day 1	Day 2	Day 3	Day 4	Day 5	Day 6
No leaf						
1 leaf						
2 leaves						
3 leaves						

2. Label each cup with your name, the cutting type and fill the cup with water. Cover the top of the cup with foil, and use a pencil to punch a small hole in the centre of the foil.

3. Use the scissors to take four small cuttings about 5 cm long. Take one cutting with no leaves, one with one leaf, one with two leaves, and one with three leaves. Ensure that your group's cuttings all come from the same plant.

4. Insert the cut end of the cuttings through the hole in the foil, ensuring the bottom 3 cm of the cutting dips into the water.

5. In the table, **record** the date, and **draw** the cut end of each cutting.

6. **Observe** any changes in the cuttings each day for the next week.

7. **Record** the date in your table when you first see roots, and draw what you see. Repeat this in two or three more days. Use your ruler to **measure** root growth. With your group, decide when the cuttings are ready to plant in potting soil.

Analyze

1. Compare cuttings taken from the same plant with other groups. In what ways are they similar? In what ways are they different?

Conclude and Apply

2. Explain how leaves affect root growth.

3. What advantage might there be to planting the cuttings in soil rather than leaving them in water?

Seed Plant Reproduction

In vegetative reproduction, plants produce new plants identical to themselves. In sexual reproduction — when plants reproduce using seeds — however, the resulting plants are all slightly different from their parents. These differences help plants to adapt to changes in their environment.

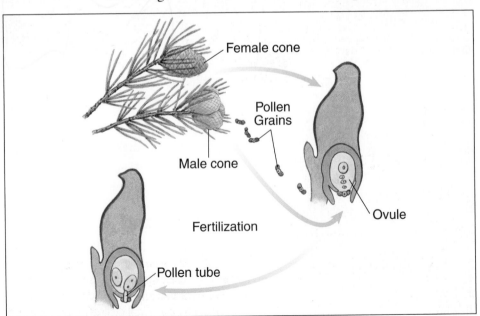

Figure 2.29 Cones come from a variety of conifers, not just pine trees.

Cones

Have you ever collected tree cones in the fall? The **cone** is the part of the tree that has a series of woody scales. Cones come in different shapes and sizes and many cone-bearing trees can be identified by their cones (see Figure 2.29).

Pine trees and other cone-bearing trees produce male and female cones. Female cones contain **ovules** (eggs); they are in the small bumps you see at the end of the scale in a cone. Pollen grains containing sperm develop on the smaller male cone. Wind carries pollen grain to the female cones. At certain times of year you can even see wafts of yellowish pollen floating through the air.

Most of this pollen never reaches the female cones because the wind blows it onto other plants, water, and the ground. When a pollen grain does get blown between the scales of a female cone of the same species, it gets caught in a sticky fluid near the ovule (see Figure 2.30). A pollen tube then grows down from the pollen grain to the ovule and sperm swims down the pollen tube and fertilizes the egg. As a result, the tiny fertilized seed begins to grow. The process of pollen travelling to the female cone is called **pollination**.

Figure 2.30 Fertilization in pine trees

Female cones of pine trees mature, open, and release their seeds during the fall or winter months. It may take a long time for seeds to be released from a pine cone. From the moment a pollen grain falls on the female cone until the time the seeds are released takes at least two years, depending on the species. Once seeds are released from a pine cone, they can be carried away, eaten, or buried by animals. The buried seeds will eventually sprout and grow into new pine trees.

Flowers

Flowers also play an important role in sexual reproduction. Large flowers with bright-coloured petals often attract insects and other animals. These animals pollinate the flowers while feeding on the flower's nectar and pollen. Flowers aren't all large and showy as you can see in Figure 2.31. Flowers that aren't brightly coloured often depend on wind to spread their pollen. Their petals may be small, or they may have no petals at all. Flowers that open at night often have strong scents to guide insects and other pollinators to them (see Figure 2.32).

Figure 2.31 Why do you think there is such variety among flowers?

Figure 2.32 Some flowers bloom at night. Those that do are usually light coloured or white, and they also have a strong scent. Aside from bats, what other animals might pollinate plants at night?

Parts of a Flower

As you read this paragraph, look at each numbered part in the diagram. Most flowers have male and female parts that are needed for reproduction. The male part is called the **stamen** (1) and the female part is known as the **pistil** (2). The stamen and pistil are surrounded by petals and sepals. **Petals** (3) are usually the brightly coloured parts of the flower. They are the flower's banner to advertise its tasty nectar or pollen. **Sepals** (4) are usually green and are underneath the flower. They protect the flower before it opens. When you look at a flower bud, you usually can see the sepals enclosing the tightly bound petals.

When you look in the middle of a flower, you can see most parts of the pistil and the stamen. The pistil has three main parts. The sticky tip is called the **stigma** (5). The tube connecting the stigma and ovary is called the **style** (6). At the bottom of the style is a tiny chamber called an **ovary** (7). Inside the ovary is the plant's ovule (eggs)(8). Each stamen has two parts, a stalk called the **filament** (9) and a tip called the **anther** (10). The anther produces pollen (11). The number of stamens on a plant can vary.

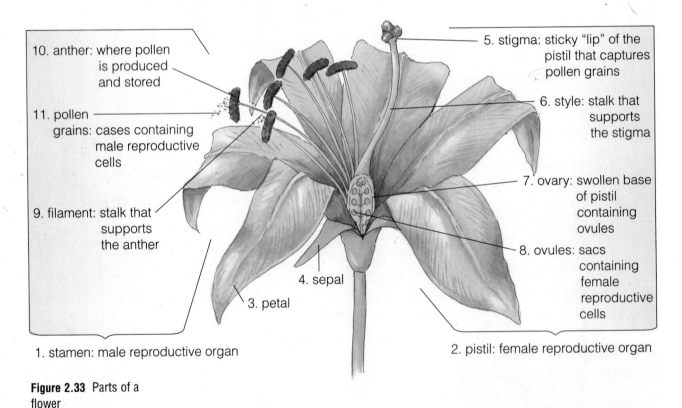

10. anther: where pollen is produced and stored

11. pollen grains: cases containing male reproductive cells

9. filament: stalk that supports the anther

3. petal

4. sepal

5. stigma: sticky "lip" of the pistil that captures pollen grains

6. style: stalk that supports the stigma

7. ovary: swollen base of pistil containing ovules

8. ovules: sacs containing female reproductive cells

1. stamen: male reproductive organ

2. pistil: female reproductive organ

Figure 2.33 Parts of a flower

Pause& Reflect

Flowers function to attract specific insects or other animals (such as hummingbirds). Think of some flowers you know and predict what type of insects or other animal pollinates them. For example, flowers with long tubelike flowers are pollinated by insects with long "tongues," such as butterflies.

The Role of the Flower

Most flowers contain both male and female reproductive parts. In this activity, you will identify the parts of the flower that have a role in reproduction: stamen, anther, filament, pollen grains, pistil, stigma, style, ovary, petals, and eggs.

Materials

a flower   magnifying glass

dark-coloured paper   paper

pencil

Procedure ✷ **Performing and Recording**

1. Make a sketch of your flower showing the different parts.

2. Make a table with the following headings.

Name of part	Location of part	Function of part

3. Refer to Figure 2.33 as you examine your flower and complete your table.

4. Examine the stamens. Remove one anther and brush it against a piece of dark-

coloured paper. Use the magnifying glass to observe the pollen grains.

5. Locate the pistil. Look for its three parts. Break open the ovary and look for the ovules (eggs).

6. Without referring to your table or textbook, label as many reproductive parts as you can on your diagram. Include a short definition of each part.

What Did You Find Out? ✷ **Analyzing and Interpreting**

1. How similar was your flower to Figure 2.33? How did it differ?

2. **(a)** What features of the stigma make it suited for capturing pollen grains?

   (b) What features of the pollen grain make it suited for being brushed off on insects or blown away by air currents?

3. Where do you think the seeds are formed?

Skill
FOCUS

For tips on making a scientific drawing, turn to Skill Focus 11.

Corn on the cob is actually the giant female flower of the corn plant. On the corn plant, the male pollen-making flowers are at the top of the plant. The large "tassel" on the corn are the stamens. (One corn plant can produce 50 million pollen grains!) The female flowers are lower down on the stalk and appear to be dense clusters of succulent strands of corn silk. These are the stigma of a long pistil. Each long strand ends at an ovule, an immature seed. If a pollen grain lands on the tip of a strand of silk, the pollen will grow down and fertilize the ovule at its base, creating a seed. The seeds that have been fertilized are the plump kernels that you eat. The ovules that are not fertilized remain small and undeveloped.

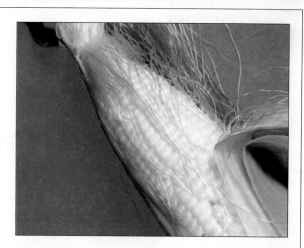

Pollination

Pollination can happen in several ways. Some plants, such as wheat and barley, self-pollinate. This means the sperm fertilizes the eggs in the same plant. In cross-pollination the eggs of one plant are fertilized by sperm from another plant of the same species. In the wild, cross-pollination can occur when the wind or animals carry pollen from one flower to another. Figure 2.34 shows what happens once the pollen grain lands on a stigma.

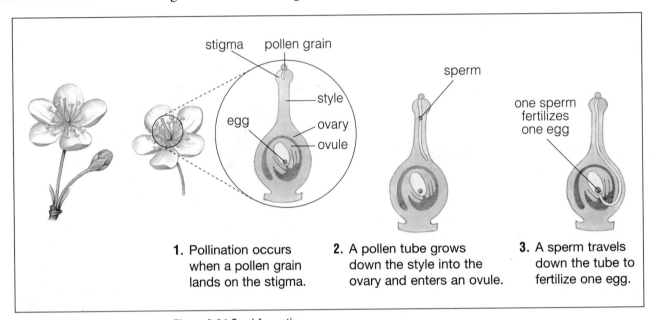

1. Pollination occurs when a pollen grain lands on the stigma.

2. A pollen tube grows down the style into the ovary and enters an ovule.

3. A sperm travels down the tube to fertilize one egg.

Figure 2.34 Seed formation

Figure 2.35 A bee's work of spreading pollen is so important that some farmers put hives in orchards, fields, and gardens so the bees and flowers can be close together.

For farmers who depend on pollination to produce fruits and vegetables, one pollinator stands out above the rest — the bee. Bees pollinate more crops than any other insect. Each time a bee visits a flower in search of nectar and pollen, some pollen gets caught in the hair on its body. The bee spreads this pollen from flower to flower. Without bees, farmers would produce one-third less fruits and vegetables than they do today.

Artificial pollination can also be used to breed varieties of plants for specific purposes. In many cases, the plant breeders are trying to produce a crop that has a better yield or that is resistant to environmental conditions such as cold winters. For example, people believed that cold temperatures killed seeds. Recent scientific research indicates that it is long exposure to these cold temperatures that kills seeds, not the temperatures alone.

From Seed to Fruit

Once a plant has been pollinated, a seed is formed (see Figure 2.36). Inside the seed is a tiny living plant called an **embryo** and a food reserve to keep it alive. The plant and its food are protected inside a seed coat. Some seeds stay alive only a few days after they mature. Other seeds need a rest or dormant period before they sprout. In what environment would you expect seeds to be adapted to surviving long periods of time without sprouting?

Fruit

When you bite into a pear, or peach, or slice of watermelon, have you ever thought about the function of fruit for a plant? A **fruit** is the growing ovary of the plant that swells and protects the developing seeds of a plant until they are ripe. You know that apples, raspberries, and cherries are fruits, but so are cucumbers, green beans, tomatoes, and pumpkins. They all have seeds inside them, so they are all fruits. Not all fruits can be eaten — at least by humans. A cotton boll is a fruit, for example. Can you think of others?

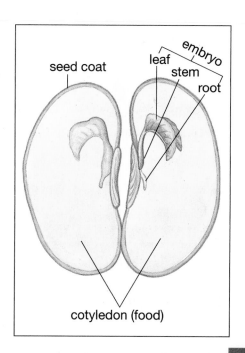

seed coat

embryo
leaf
stem
root

cotyledon (food)

Figure 2.36 The seed is a plant in storage. What conditions do you think it needs to be able to grow?

Find Out ACTIVITY

Inside Seeds

What's inside a seed? To see for yourself, complete this activity.

Materials

dried lima beans   jar or a glass
water   magnifying glass

Procedure

1. Observe a dried lima bean. Try to remove its outer coating or break it open with your finger.

2. Soak two lima beans in a jar of water overnight.

3. Remove the beans from the water. Sketch and label the part of the bean you can identify.

4. Peel off the outer coat of the seed and carefully break the seed into two halves. Sketch and label the parts of the bean you can identify.

What Did You Find Out?

1. Which takes up more space — the seed, the embryo, or the plant's food?

2. How did water affect the seed? What role do you think water might play in growing a plant from a seed?

Classifying Fruits

There are many different kinds of fruits. Some, like peaches and apricots, contain just one big seed. Others, like watermelon, pumpkins, and peas have many seeds inside them. Some fruits are soft, such as apples and oranges, and others like acorns or walnuts are hard. In this activity you will take a look at different kinds of fruits and the seeds inside them to develop a useful classification system.

Materials

6–10 different fruits such as apples, squash, beans, tomatoes, blackberries, grapes, or cucumbers.

paper   pencil

knife   magnifying glass

Safety Precaution

Use care when handling sharp knives. Always be sure to cut away from you and use a cutting board or other surface to protect the counter or desk.

Procedure ✳ Performing and Recording

1. Read over the instructions and prepare a data table to record your observations. Be sure you leave space for labelled diagrams.

2. Take a close look at your collection of fruits. Can you tell which end of the fruit was attached to the plant? Record your observations using labelled diagrams.

3. Cut open the fruits. Observe how the seeds are arranged. How many seeds does each fruit have? Some fruits have so many seeds that you can't count all of them. Count the seeds in one section and estimate the number of seeds in the whole fruit.

4. Use the magnifying glass to observe the seeds closely. Sketch the different type of seeds.

5. Measure the size of each type of seed.

6. With your group, review your observations and classify the fruits into groups. You might use shape, size, number of seeds, colour, or any other categories that might work for your collection of fruits.

What Did You Find Out? ✳ Analyzing and Interpreting

1. Why do you think some fruits have so few seeds and some have so many?

2. When you cut open your fruit, did you see any ovules that were not fertilized? How could you tell?

3. Does a large seed always mean the plant has a large fruit? Explain your answer using the data you collected in this activity.

4. Do you think your classification system for fruits would be useful? If so, explain how it could be used. If not, explain what further information or questions you would need to answer to make it useful.

DidYou**Know**?

The size of a seed is no clue to how big the plant will be. The tallest plant in the world, the giant redwood, starts out as a seed smaller than your thumbnail.

Seed Dispersal

How do seeds get from the flower to the ground so they can begin to grow? In many plants, the fruit helps in the seed's dispersal. Dispersal is the transport of seeds away from the parent plant. Figure 2.37 shows some ways that seeds are dispersed.

Figure 2.37A After flowering, tumbleweeds snap off at their roots in strong winds and bounce along at speeds of up to 80 km/h, spreading their seeds as they go!

Figure 2.37B Coconuts grow on palm trees that drop their fruits into rivers or the sea. This enables the young palms to sprout thousands of kilometres away from where they started.

Figure 2.37C Some seeds pass almost unchanged through fruit-eating birds and bats. In this way they can be sown many kilometres from the parent plant. Feces, which is full of nutrients, will help the seed grow.

Figure 2.37D Seeds such as burdock may "hitch a ride" on the furry coats of mammals, where they stick until they are rubbed off or removed.

Figure 2.37E The seeds of the lodgepole pine are sealed inside the cone by sticky pitch. Fire or intense heat is required to release the seeds. This is why lodgepole pine is usually the first tree to grow after a forest fire.

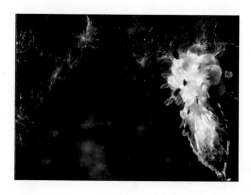

Figure 2.37F Seeds, such as these milkweed seeds, are blown about by the wind.

Figure 2.38 Combines gathering grain

Spreading and Harvesting Seeds in the Field

Farmers use machines to spread seeds. Seeds from field crops such as wheat, canola, and barley are usually harvested in two steps. First, a swather cuts the plants about 10–20 cm from the ground and lays them in rows in the field. The stubble (the part of the plant still in the ground) keeps the plants off the soil so that seeds can ripen further. Once the seeds are dry enough, a combine separates the grain from the rest of the plant. If the seeds are ripe and dry enough, both of these operations can be done at the same time.

The combine in Figure 2.38 carries out several steps. The machine first picks the grain off the ground. Next, the seeds are separated from the straw. The straw is then baled or spread evenly over the field.

Germination

Once the seed is dispersed and reaches the ground, it stays inactive until conditions are right for its growth. **Germination** is the development of a seed into a new plant. Study Figure 2.39 to see how a bean seed germinates and grows into a young plant. When the young bean plant grows and develops its own flowers, it is mature and ready to produce the next plant generation.

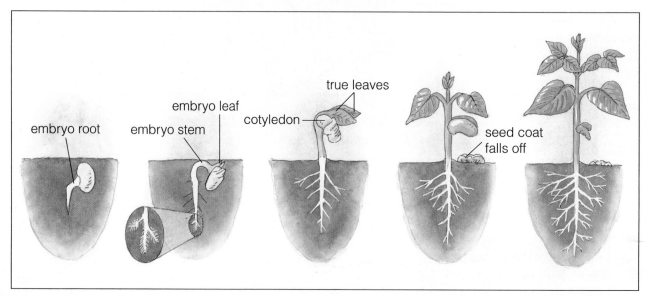

Figure 2.39 Germination of a bean seed.

Speeding Up Germination

Many factors in the environment can affect the germination of seeds. Among these are soil temperature, air temperature, moisture content of the soil, and salt content of the soil. What happens to the germination rate when one of these variables is changed?

Question

How does seed germination vary with environmental changes?

Hypothesis

Make and test a hypothesis about how seeds germinate when one environmental factor changes.

Safety Precautions

Wash your hands after working with soil.

Apparatus

plant trays or plastic cups
thermometer
seedling warming cables (optional)
graduated cylinder
250 mL beakers
ruler

Materials

bean seeds	paper towels
distilled water	other materials of students' choice
salt	
potting soil	

Procedure

1 List the steps that you need to take to test your hypothesis.
Describe:
– the variable you will test
– the measurements you will take
– the data you will collect
– the frequency of data collection

2 List your materials. If you need a data table, design one.

3 Have your teacher approve your procedures and materials.

4 Set up the experiment. You will need to **observe** your experiment over several days.

Skill
F O C U S

For tips on designing your own experiment, turn to Skill Focus 6.

For tips on making graphs and data tables, turn to Skill Focus 10.

Analyze

1. What are the controlling variables in your experiment? What is the responding variable?

2. Graph your results using a bar graph, placing the growth on the *y*-axis and the environmental variable on the *x*-axis.

Conclude and Apply

3. What happened to the germination of your seeds when you changed a variable?

4. Discuss experimental results and compare graphs with other students in your class who changed a variable that was different from the one you changed. What are the best conditions for germinating bean seeds?

Helping Plants Grow

As you have seen, there are many steps involved in producing seeds and fruit, and ultimately growing a crop. There are many stages at which a new plant might have a problem that might prevent its reproduction. For example, birds might eat seeds before they can germinate, or there might be a drought, preventing the seed from sprouting. Perhaps there is a cool spring and very few bees are around to pollinate flowers. How might growers help to prevent these problems during the plant's life cycle?

Materials

large sheets of paper   felt pens

Procedure   ✳ **Performing and Recording**
                 ✳ **Communication and Teamwork**

1. As a group, draw the life cycle of a plant on the large sheet of paper.

2. Brainstorm some problems that a growing plant might have that will prevent it from completing its life cycle.

3. Do some research in the library or on the Internet to determine how farmers and fruit growers try to ensure that their crop survives. You could also get information directly from farmers or growers, or from garden shops.

What Did You Find Out ✳ **Analyzing and Interpreting**

1. Describe three situations in a plant's life cycle that may prevent it from completing its life cycle.

2. Explain how people can help ensure that plants will grow.

Looking Ahead

Keep careful notes on what you have learned in the previous two activities. Think about how you could use your knowledge to complete your Unit 2 Project, Get Growing!

TOPIC 3 Review

1. Give two examples of how growers can use vegetative reproduction to cultivate plants.

2. Explain how keeping bees might help a farmer.

3. Describe two problems a plant might encounter during reproduction. Explain how growers might intervene in the plant's life cycle to solve these problems.

4. **Apply** When you go to a grocery store to buy apples, how do you choose your fruit? List characteristics of apples that you want to buy. What are characteristics of apples that are less appealing? Imagine that you are an apple grower participating in a research project to breed new varieties of apples. How would your list of desirable and less desirable characteristics of apples affect your research goals? Write a question your research will investigate based on consumer demands.

5. **Thinking Critically** A corn plant produces thousands of pollen grains on top of the plant in flowers that have no odour or colour. The pistils grow from the cob lower down on the plant. Write a hypothesis for how a corn plant is probably pollinated.

If you need to check an item, Topic numbers are provided in brackets below.

Key Terms

fibre	photosynthesis	ovules	ovary
taproot	transpiration	pollination	filament
root hairs	respiration	stamen	anther
fibrous roots	selective breeding	pistil	embryo
diffusion	genes	petals	fruit
differentially permeable	sexual reproduction	sepals	germination
osmosis	asexual reproduction	stigma	
chlorophyll	vegetative reproduction	style	

Reviewing Key Terms

1. In your notebook, fill in the blanks in the sentences below.

    (a) ▨▨▨▨▨ is the loss of water from a plant by evaporation. (2)

    (b) The large, single root in a plant is called the ▨▨▨▨. (2)

    (c) ▨▨▨▨▨ is a type of diffusion that occurs when two solutions are separated by a barrier through which only some materials can pass. (2)

    (d) ▨▨▨▨▨ is the tissue of plants from the stem, leaves, seeds, or roots. (1)

    (e) In ▨▨▨▨ ▨▨▨▨▨ a grower chooses and breeds plants with particular characteristics. (3)

    (f) Layering is a form of ▨▨▨▨▨ reproduction. (3)

2. Copy these terms into your notebook: pistil, stigma, style, ovary, ovule, stamen, filament, and anther. Briefly describe the role of each part of the flower. (3)

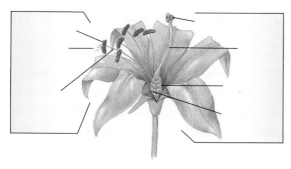

3. Describe how water moves through a plant using the terms diffusion, osmosis, root hairs, and transpiration. (2)

Understanding Key Concepts

4. Describe two functions of each of the following plant parts: roots, leaves, stem, and flowers. (2)

5. List four plants grown in Alberta that are used for food and/or fibre. Which part(s) of each plant is (are) used? (1, 2, 3)

6. Describe three ways that plants can reproduce asexually. (3)

7. List three ways, other than as food, that Aboriginal people used plants. (1)

8. What adaptations of dandelions make them such difficult plants to get rid of? (2)

9. Describe the process of photosynthesis. Use sketches or equations if you wish. (2)

Meeting the Need for Food and Fibre

Figure 2.40 Canadian food and fibre products are exported to countries around the world.

Canadians have used our tremendous natural resources and expertise in agriculture to become major world producers of food and fibre. Millions of people are employed producing, transporting, and processing agriculture and forestry products. We grow far more than we consume, so we export, or sell, our surpluses to other countries around the world. Canada is also a leader in agricultural and forestry science.

While Canada has earned a lot of its wealth from forestry and agriculture, this success has led to challenges and problems. For example, as you learned in Unit 1, much of the native prairie grassland has been changed into agricultural fields. How has this changed the native plants and animals that grew here before land was cleared for farms and cities? Harvesting timber from forests changes the nature of that ecosystem as well.

Figure 2.41 The organisms within a natural system live in a balance. When the timber was harvested from the area shown here, all of the organisms that lived there were affected.

Canadian scientists are working to understand more about how the complex natural systems work. Scientists, farmers, and foresters are developing practices that will reduce negative effects that sometimes occur when we harvest plants for food and fibre. We are concerned about **sustainability** — being able to grow food and fibre while keeping our natural systems healthy for the long term.

In this Topic you will learn about food and fibre plants that grow in Alberta, some of the practices used to produce them, and some of the problems we created in our attempts to produce more.

Agriculture in Alberta

Agriculture is an important but very new industry in Alberta today.

The first settlers from Europe found communities of Aboriginal people who had lived with nature for thousands of years. In general, the European pioneers cut the trees on large areas of forest and cultivated the grasslands so that they could grow crops. In the forests, the supply of wood seemed limitless, and it was used for construction, manufacturing, and fuel.

Figure 2.42 In less than 30 years after settlers arrived in Alberta, most of the native grassland was converted to cropland.

Pause& Reflect

When natural areas are cultivated to grow crops, native plants there are destroyed. What changes do you think might occur in soil underneath grassland when it is cultivated year after year? If you wanted to restore the cropland to the original grassland, what would you have to do? Record your answers in your Science Log.

In the late 1800s and early 1900s, thousands of settlers came to western Canada on the new railway. Early crops and prices were good, export markets were discovered, and farmers were encouraged to grow more and more grain. Within a period of 30 years, settlers occupied nearly all of the grassland in the prairie provinces and had ploughed up much of the native plants that had grown there for thousands of years.

As you can see in Figure 2.43, a large area of aspen parkland, grassland, and boreal forest in Alberta has been cultivated to grow crops. Of the 60 million hectare land area of Alberta, over 20 million is now managed as farmland.

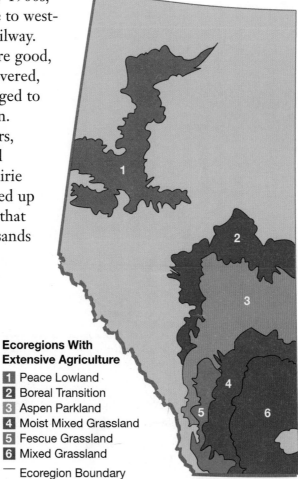

Ecoregions With Extensive Agriculture

1 Peace Lowland
2 Boreal Transition
3 Aspen Parkland
4 Moist Mixed Grassland
5 Fescue Grassland
6 Mixed Grassland
— Ecoregion Boundary

Figure 2.43 Native grassland and forest that has been cultivated and converted to cropland.

Who's Who in Crop Country?

If you were to travel from Athabasca to Lethbridge, you would drive all day and never leave fields producing food. Every year, Alberta farmers produce food crops worth almost $3 billion. The food industry is second only to oil and natural gas in terms of earnings. Wheat, canola, barley, and oats are all grown for their seeds and are the most common field crops in Alberta. These crops are also sold in large quantities to other countries.

Wheat

One-third of the world's people use wheat to make food. The seeds of this billion-dollar Alberta crop are ground to produce flour for making bread, pasta, and hundreds of processed products. Wheat seeds can tolerate cool soil and are planted early in the spring. The crop needs a long growing season, though, so it is most successful in the southern part of the province.

Oats

Most of the oats grown are fed to livestock. Horse trainers from Kentucky even request oats from Alberta. This grain is eaten by people, too. The oat plant is best adapted to the cooler and moister regions of Alberta. It also grows well in acidic or poorly drained soils. It is planted along the forests in the northern and western regions.

Canola

Canola is the second most valuable Alberta crop. Oil is pressed out of the seed and is used to make margarine, cooking oil, and salad dressing. Livestock and poultry eat the leftover "meal," which is high in protein.

Barley

The third most valuable crop in Alberta is barley. Barley can tolerate saltier soils and drier conditions than other crops. Most barley is fed to livestock and about one-quarter is used by humans for making malt flavouring for use in many foods.

Field corn is a grain crop that is used to make silage to feed dairy cattle. (Silage is a finely chopped crop that is allowed to ferment.) Field corn has a higher yield per hectare than any other crop, and provides more energy per kilogram than any other type of silage. Older varieties of corn, however, needed quite a bit of heat to germinate and grow. For this reason, field corn could only be grown in southern Alberta. Recently, plant breeders created a variety that needs much less heat to grow. Now farmers in central and southern Alberta can grow field corn for silage, too.

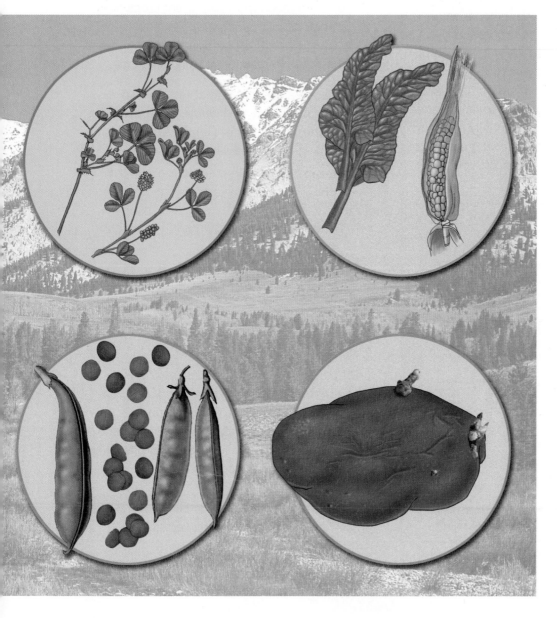

Specialty Crops

The extra heat and irrigation available in parts of southern Alberta enable farmers to grow sunflowers and other crops that cannot be grown elsewhere. These specialty crops include beans, field corn, sugar beets, lentils, safflower, and spices.

Alfalfa

Some crops are not grown for their seeds, but for their leaves and stems. These crops are fed to livestock and are known as hay crops or forages. Alfalfa is the most common forage crop. It has a strong taproot that penetrates deep into soil in search of water and nutrients.

Legumes

The Parkland and Peace River regions of Alberta have cool, wet growing seasons and are ideally suited to growing high-protein legume crops such as field peas, faba (or fava) beans, and lentils.

Potatoes

Much of Alberta has a cool climate that is ideal for growing potatoes. About half of Alberta potatoes are processed into frozen french fries and potato chips. Each year, about $20 million worth of potatoes are sold as seed to other farmers.

Fruit and Vegetable Crops

Vegetables and fruit crops are a multimillion-dollar industry in Alberta. Potatoes are the most valuable vegetable crop and are worth over $55 million each year. Alberta also grows a variety of vegetables that are sold fresh (including carrots, cabbage, onions, cauliflower) and others that are processed by canning or freezing (peas, beans, and corn). Market gardens grow specialty vegetables that are not generally grown in large crops, and also grow fruits such as raspberries, blueberries, and Saskatoon berries. Finally, tree and shrub nurseries, and commercial greenhouses are a small but important part of Alberta's agriculture industry.

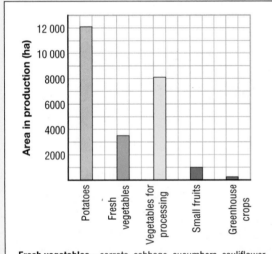

Fresh vegetables = carrots, cabbage, cucumbers, cauliflower

Processed vegetables = peas, beans, corn, carrots

Greenhouse crops = bedding plants, potted plants, cucumbers, tomatoes, flowers, lettuce, peppers

Find Out ACTIVITY

Procedure
* **Performing and Recording**
* **Analyzing and Interpreting**

1. In southern Ontario and in the Vancouver area of British Columbia, fruits and vegetables are much more important crops than wheat, canola, and barley. The reverse is true in Alberta. In a small group, brainstorm the possible reasons for this difference.

2. Choose a fruit or vegetable crop and investigate how and where it is grown in Alberta. The Internet Connect on this page will also help you with your research.

3. Present your findings to your class.

What Did You Find Out

1. Where is the crop grown and why is it grown there?

2. What are some of the methods used to improve growing conditions for the crop?

3. Have new varieties of this crop been developed through selective breeding?

Extension

4. Look at the bar graph. One year the Alberta potato industry made $56 million and the greenhouse industry made $48 million. Compare the amount of land used for these two industries. Explain why they had similar incomes.

Skill
FOCUS

For tips on doing Internet research, turn to Skill Focus 9.

INTERNET CONNECT

www.mcgrawhill.ca/links/sciencefocus7

You can find out more information on crops grown in Alberta by going to the above web site. Click on **Web Links** to find out where to go next. Use this information to help you prepare a one-page report on an Alberta crop. Include information such as where the crop is grown and the overall economic importance of this crop.

Did You Know?

A hectare (ha) is an SI unit used for measuring land. It is equivalent to 10 000 m^2.

Growing Under Glass

All of the crops on pages 134–135 are grown outside in fields. The yield from these crops is very dependent on the particular growing conditions for that region. For example, the weather conditions, climate, and soil types will all affect yield. What specific growing conditions do you think could be controlled in a greenhouse environment? A wide range of warm-season crops, including seedless cucumbers, tomatoes, lettuce, peppers, house plants, and cut flowers, are grown in greenhouses.

Figure 2.44 Greenhouses allow warm-weather crops to be grown in Alberta.

Across Canada

Lois Hole

What do you do if you want to garden in a climate such as Alberta's where many varieties of plants are unable to grow? If you're Lois Hole, you don't give up; you meet the challenge by developing your own seed varieties. In 1952, Lois Hole and her husband bought a small farm property in St. Albert, Alberta, and gradually developed it into one of the largest garden centres in Canada. In the greenhouses at that garden centre, Lois helped to develop special hardy seed varieties that could thrive in the Alberta climate. In the process, Lois became a highly respected author, lecturer, and broadcaster all across the country.

Lois got her start in her mother's garden in Saskatchewan, the province of her birth. Her interest in gardening remained with her when she moved to Alberta and after she married (another gardening enthusiast) and had her family. Over the years, Lois amassed a tremendous amount of knowledge about plants and began to be sought out by people who wanted to learn to be successful gardeners. She also passed on her love of gardening to her children, involving them in the family business.

Lois has written a number of books, including a series of popular books that give advice on how to grow certain varieties of a particular type of plant such as roses or tomatoes. She has also been a regular newspaper columnist and popular guest on television gardening shows such as "The Canadian Gardener." Her contribution to Canadian gardening and to other aspects of Canadian life have won her many honours. For example, in 1998 she was elected to a four-year term as the sixteenth chancellor of the University of Alberta. In 1999 she was made a Member of the Order of Canada, the highest honour this country can confer. In February, 2000 she was installed as the Lieutenant Governor of Alberta. Not bad for a gardener from a place where things aren't easy to grow!

INVESTIGATION 2-G

Greenhouse Growing Conditions

Greenhouses help control the temperature for plants, but are designed to allow control of other growing conditions as well. Light can be increased or decreased. Water and nutrients can be added as required and adjusted to particular plants. The soil can be cooled or heated, or made more acidic or basic. What effect does a greenhouse environment have on the growth of various crops? Is this a sustainable way of growing plants for food and fibre?

Question

What effect does a greenhouse environment have on growth of various crops?

Hypothesis

Based on your understanding and observation of what plants need to grow, state a hypothesis about the effect of the greenhouse on crops growing indoors and outdoors.

Apparatus

thumbtack or pushpin
potting soil
4 trays or saucers for holding cups
scissors

clear adhesive tape
thermometer
plant grow lights (optional)
graduated cylinder
ruler
4 coloured pencils

Materials

8 paper or foam drinking cups
sprouted seeds
4 clear plastic drinking cups or plastic pop bottles
water

Procedure

1. Read through the investigation and **write your hypothesis**.

2. **Make a data table**.

3. Use the thumbtack or pushpin to put drainage holes in the bottom of eight paper or foam drinking cups.

4. Fill the cups with potting soil and plant one seed in each cup. Place two cups on each tray or saucer.

5. Your teacher will prepare the pop bottle by cutting the bottom off it. This will be your "greenhouse."

6. Your teacher will cut a small hole, or slit, in the drinking cup or clear pop bottle. Cover this hole with adhesive tape.

7 Place a clear plastic cup or clear pop bottle over each of the cups in two of the trays.

8 Place one tray with greenhouses and one tray without greenhouses outside (weather permitting).

9 Place one tray with greenhouses and one tray without greenhouses inside near a window. If a window is not available, place these greenhouses under grow lights.

10 Give your plants the same amount of water every two days.

11 At the same time each day, measure:
- the air temperature in the greenhouse (put the thermometer through the opening you made) or around the plant if the plant is growing without a greenhouse
- the soil temperature
- the height of the plant
- other observations such as colour

  Note: Handle the thermometer carefully. It is easily broken.

12 Plot the data on a line graph with the day on the *x*-axis and plant measurement on the *y*-axis. Use a different coloured pencil for each plant.

Skill
F O C U S

For tips on writing a hypothesis, turn to Skill Focus 6.

For tips on making data tables and drawing line graphs, turn to Skill Focus 10.

Analyze

1. Compare the growth of each of the crops in the four environments.

2. Which growing conditions does a greenhouse improve?

3. Why did you use two seeds in each of the four environments?

4. Which was the manipulated variable? Which was the responding variable?

Conclude and Apply

5. Was your hypothesis supported by your investigation? Explain.

6. Are there any problems with growing plants in greenhouses? Explain. Could greenhouses be used to produce all our plants for food and fibre? Why or why not?

Extend Your Knowledge

7. How do actual greenhouses deal with low levels of heat, overheating, pests, and irrigation?

Farming Practices

In order to stay in business, farmers need to earn more money than they spend on growing crops. They have to produce each crop as efficiently as possible. Using large farm machinery enables farmers to grow crops over a larger area.

Figure 2.45 Farmers must ensure that their farming practices are sustainable, so that they can continue to grow crops for generations to come.

Adding nutrients to the soil helps the plants grow and produce more. Farmers also **irrigate**, or water, their crops using a system of large pipes and sprinklers. Most farmers grow their crops as a **monoculture**, only one type of plant in a field. Why might growing a crop as a monoculture be the most efficient use of a farmer's energy and equipment?

Farming Then and Now

In Alberta, farming practices changed from using human and animal power in the early 1900s to almost total mechanization by the 1950s. In the last 50 years, farm equipment has increased in size. Many farms now use computer controls on their machinery. The goal of farmers has stayed the same, but the way that they farm has changed dramatically. Look at Figure 2.46 to see how farmers grew crops in central Alberta in the early 1900s compared to today.

Activity	Technology of the Early 1900s	Technology of Today
1. Some farmers cultivate in the spring to loosen the soil for seeds. It also kills weeds. Other farmers use chemicals to kill weeds instead.	Oxen or horse-drawn cultivator	Machines called cultivators are used to prepare and fertilize soil.
2. Fertilizer is added to provide more nutrients for plants.	Manure was a common source of fertilizer.	
3. Fungi is controlled to protect plants when they are seedlings.	There were few controls for fungi in early years.	Special chemicals are used to control fungi.
4. Seeds are spread evenly to reduce competition for light and nutrients between crop plants.	Seeds were spread by hand.	Air seeders and seed drills are used to plant seeds.
5. Weeds and insects are controlled.	People, including children, pulled weeds by hand.	Crops are sprayed with chemicals to control weeds and insects. Other farmers use methods that do not use chemicals.
6. Grain is cut to allow it to dry and ripen.	Farmers used a scythe to cut crops.	Swathers are used to cut hay.
7. Grain is threshed. Threshing means separating the grain from the other plant material. Wind can help by removing the lighter stem and seed head (straw and chaff).	Grain was picked by hand. To separate grain from the rest of the plant, the grain was tossed in the air and caught in a basket. The wind carried straw away.	Combines are used to harvest grain and separate seeds.
8. Grain is hauled for storage or to market.	Horse-drawn carts were used.	Large trailer trucks are used.
9. Soil is turned and mixed to help kill weeds and disease organisms, to mix soil and plant matter, and to aid decomposition.	A horse-drawn plough was used (see Figure 2.46).	A modern plough is used (see Figure 2.46).

Did You Know?

The plough, invented in the Middle East, has been important to farmers for over 5000 years. It enabled early farmers to turn over the soil and bury weeds. This reduced the competition for the crop they wanted to seed, such as barley or wheat. Overploughing by farmers in the early 1900s, however, was partly responsible for the incredible loss of soil by wind erosion in "The Dirty Thirties."

Figure 2.46 Both of these ploughs were modern advances at one time. What do you think were the advantages and disadvantages of these two technologies?

Figure 2.47A Large "sprinklers" are used for irrigation.

Figure 2.47B Irrigation canals bring water to areas where it is in short supply.

Saving Soil Moisture

Farmers must try to make sure that the soil is moist enough for crop growth, even in dry weather. Moisture is lost through evaporation from the soil and also through transpiration in the leaves. Eventually, lack of moisture causes plants to stop growing. Field crops in the grasslands often run out of moisture and, as a result, do not produce as high a yield as they would in wetter conditions.

Farmers who live close to rivers and large lakes are able to add moisture using irrigation systems (see Figure 2.47A). Water from lakes, reservoirs, and rivers is channelled into large irrigation canals, such as those in Figure 2.47B. These canals have been built throughout southern and eastern Alberta to provide water to farms.

Maintaining Moisture

What are some ways to maintain soil moisture?

Materials

foam meat trays, baking pans or other similar pans

garden soil or potting soil

organic material such as wood shavings, grass clippings, or leaves

water

fan (optional)

grow light or heat lamp (optional)

paper towel

soil moisture metre (optional)

Procedure ✷ `Performing and Recording`

1. Add equal amounts of soil to each tray.

2. Cover the soil in one tray with organic matter. Mix the organic matter in with the soil in the second tray. Do not add organic matter to the third tray.

3. Dampen the soil in the trays using equal amounts of water. Do not saturate the soil.

4. Leave the trays in a warm area, under grow lights, or place them in front of a fan.

5. After several hours press a sheet of paper towel on the soil in each tray. Compare the amount of moisture on each paper towel. You can also use a soil moisture metre for this step.

What Did You Find Out? ✷ `Performing and Recording`

1. Which tray had the highest soil moisture?

2. How was the amount of soil moisture affected by placing the organic on top of the soil or mixing it?

3. What is another way you could measure soil moisture?

Fibre Plants and the Forestry Industry

Did you know that trees cover over 4.5 million square kilometres of land in Canada — an area larger than eastern and western Europe combined? Canada has about 10 percent of the world's forests, and produces many kinds of lumber and pulp and paper products. The wood fibre industry employs over 800 000 Canadians. British Columbia, Alberta, Ontario, and Quebec have vibrant forest industries. Alberta's forestry industry has grown considerably in the last ten years, and is now a very important industry in the northern part of the province.

In the next few pages, you will learn about the trees most desired for fibre, and how they are harvested. You will also learn about some of the practices that foresters use to improve growing conditions for trees.

A forest is much more than just the trees that live there. Forests have many types of trees, shrubs, and smaller plants. There are also many animals living in, around, and under these plants. The **diversity** or variety of plants and animals found in an ecosystem varies from one ecosystem to another. The presence of a large variety of organisms is often used as an indicator of a healthy ecosystem.

Like all natural systems, the species in a forest community are interdependent. When natural or human events disturb the balance, all the species are affected. Fire was a natural part of the process by which Alberta forests developed. This resulted in the emergence of species that required large amounts of light. As the forests grew, they became ideal for populations of species that require more shade. You can see how a cycle develops as a result of burning and/or cutting followed by regrowth. Forestry practices can increase the diversity of forest species by careful cutting that lets more light and air into the forest.

Pause & Reflect

In what ways do you think a mature forest would be different from a recently cut area? Examine these two photographs and think about the appearance of the forest, as well as the animals and the soil within it. Describe the differences in drawings and words.

Pause & Reflect

Do you play any role in how food and fibre is produced and harvested? Think of the food and fibre products that you need or want. Write your thoughts in your Science Log.

Figure 2.48A A mature forest.

Figure 2.48B This forest has been logged and replanted.

Who's Who in FibreSpace?

Some common Alberta tree species that are used for forest products are shown below. Which ones do you recognize? Which ones likely grow in your area?

Lodgepole Pine

Lodgepole pine is Alberta's provincial tree. Its seeds are released by fire. The lodgepole pine's straightness and strength was highly valued. Aboriginal people used it to build their lodges, early settlers built fences and cabins with this pine, and builders of the first railway across Canada used it for railway ties. Today, carpenters use pine for building walls and roofs.

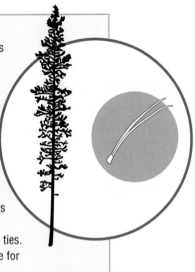

White Spruce

White spruce are widespread throughout the forested parts of Alberta. This tree takes over from aspen and pine as forests develop and mature. Spruce wood is light and soft, but strong and straight. It is valued for lumber, plywood, and pulp, which is used to make paper and paper products.

Black Spruce

Black spruce is well adapted to muskeg and poorly drained soils in western and northern Alberta. The wood is light and strong and is used for lumber and pulp. The black spruce's long fibres help make strong paper.

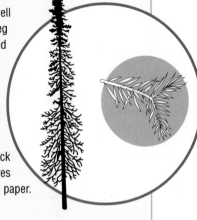

Aspen

This tree is also known as "trembling aspen" because of the way its leaves seem to shake or tremble in a breeze. It is the most widespread tree in Alberta and its range extends well into the grassland regions. Aspen is especially good for wood panel products and furniture, and is often used for pulp and paper.

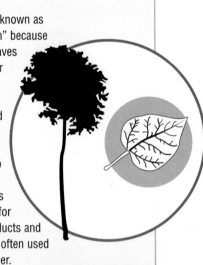

Key It Out

Classification keys are used to help identify trees and other organisms. (You used a classification key to identify amphibians in Unit 1.) In this activity you will create an identification key for the six most common Alberta trees.

Materials

paper

pencil

plant identification books (optional)

Find Out ACTIVITY

Procedure

Look at the leaves and needles of the trees on this page. Create an identification key to help someone identify the tree species. Look at examples of identification keys in plant books or review the amphibian key on page 73. You may use small illustrations in your key if you wish.

White Birch

White birch grows in moist areas and along rivers and lakes. Its heavy, strong wood is used to make furniture and cabinets, and is also considered to be one of the best woods for firewood.

Tamarack (Larch)

Tamarack, or Larch, is another water-loving species. Like black spruce, it is adapted to cooler wet conditions such as muskeg. Tamarack grows slowly and has heavy wood. It resists fungi and the decay they can cause, so it is useful for fence posts and railway ties.

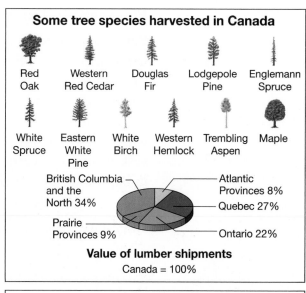

Some tree species harvested in Canada

Red Oak   Western Red Cedar   Douglas Fir   Lodgepole Pine   Englemann Spruce

White Spruce   Eastern White Pine   White Birch   Western Hemlock   Trembling Aspen   Maple

British Columbia and the North 34%
Atlantic Provinces 8%
Quebec 27%
Prairie Provinces 9%
Ontario 22%

Value of lumber shipments
Canada = 100%

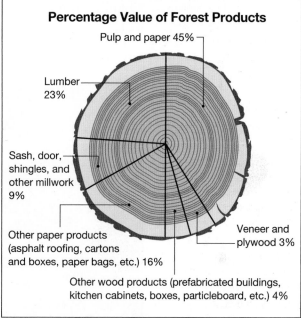

Percentage Value of Forest Products

Pulp and paper 45%
Lumber 23%
Sash, door, shingles, and other millwork 9%
Other paper products (asphalt roofing, cartons and boxes, paper bags, etc.) 16%
Other wood products (prefabricated buildings, kitchen cabinets, boxes, particleboard, etc.) 4%
Veneer and plywood 3%

Forest Products in Canada

The forest industry is the largest industry in Canada and is a vital part of Alberta's economy. What processes does lumber from Alberta and other parts of Canada undergo in order to turn into finished products?

Procedure ✳ **Performing and Recording** ✳ **Communication and Teamwork**

1. Examine the illustrations above. In which three provinces is forestry especially important to the economy?

Find Out ACTIVITY

2. How are the harvested trees used? If you do not understand any of the terms in the graphs, use a dictionary or encyclopedia to help you find a definition.

3. Choose one product made from wood and find out how raw lumber becomes a finished product.

Harvesting Trees

Before any trees are cut, foresters explore an area thoroughly. They make maps that outline the location of trees that will be cut and any special features they should consider. Then they create a plan for making a road and harvesting the trees. They also decide how they will cut the trees. For example, they may choose to clear-cut an area, where all of the trees are removed, or they may choose selective harvest, where only certain trees are removed. Some of the steps involved in harvesting trees include the following:

- planning the cut (based on a careful review of the site)
- building a road into the area
- felling (cutting down) and delimbing the trees
- dragging (or "skidding") the logs to a central loading point
- hauling the logs by truck to a saw mill or pulp mill
- preparing the site for reforestation (this step is called "scarification")
- reforestation (reseeding and replanting, if needed)

Figure 2.49 Feller-bunchers like this one are replacing the axe and chainsaw methods of the past. This machine quickly cuts the trees, removes the branches, and cuts the trunk to log length. A powerful rotary (or circular) saw uses hydraulic technology to cut the trunk.

Reforestation

Like farmers, foresters are concerned about maintaining and improving growing conditions. They analyze conditions such as light, water, and nutrients when they plan forest management.

When trees are cut, some branches and fallen trees are left behind. In the past, burning this debris changed it to ash. The remaining bare soil provided poor habitat for wildlife. It also removed many starting materials needed for regrowth, so the area had to be reseeded by hand, as shown in Figure 2.50. Today, the leftover plant material stays, providing nutrients and starting materials for regrowth.

Figure 2.50 Tree planter

Figure 2.51 Fire tower lookout, and firefighter lowered into action.

On most sites, no manual replanting of trees occurs. Seeds left behind in the forest debris sprout naturally and become new trees. In the years after a forest is cut, the opening up of the area to light favours growth of plants that have strong needs for bright sunlight. These species grow rapidly. Tree species such as poplar and pine are especially favoured. They provide the shade in which other, more shade-tolerant species, will grow.

In Alberta forests, the nutrients for tree growth come from the recycling of materials in the forest soil, rather than use of chemical fertilizers. Pesticides are sometimes used to control insect infestations, but are used not nearly as much as in agriculture.

Global Problems

One of the most serious problems worldwide is soil **erosion** (soil that is blown away by wind and water). North Africa once had very fertile land. Frequent and long-lasting droughts have resulted in desertification — a process in which the desert has taken over much of the agricultural land.

DidYouKnow?

Fire control is a major part of forest management. Most fires are caused by lightning strikes, but some are caused by human carelessness. People watch for fires from fire towers throughout Alberta. Firefighting measures are often taken as soon as possible after a fire is spotted. Sometimes a fire is allowed to burn in a controlled way, to open up and renew an area of forest.

INTERNET CONNECT

www.mcgrawhill.ca/links/sciencefocus7

How old do you think trees in Alberta are? What do you think might be the major factors that limit how old they become? Write your estimate of age and reasons in your Science Log. Then go the above web site to find out more. Click on **Web Links** to find out where to go next.

Figure 2.52 Drought-stricken area.

Where vegetation has been removed in Brazil and West Africa, soils became hard and useless for growing crops. In some areas of Europe and United States, high levels of agricultural chemicals in the water systems have caused serious pollution.

Irrigation in Pakistan helped to boost production at first. Excessive irrigation, however, brought salts to some areas, making it impossible for plants to grow.

It is possible to create sustainable systems, but scientists and community leaders must work closely together. Do ordinary citizens have a role, too? How do our demands for certain products help determine what kinds of crops are harvested and how they are produced? Producers and consumers both need to understand the complex web of life in which we live and respect the delicate balance that exists.

Media Monitor

What are some of the current issues related to agriculture and forestry where you live or in other parts of Canada?

Procedure ❋ **Performing and Recording**

1. Working alone or with a group, search various sources for current information on agriculture and forestry. Be sure to look at newspapers, news magazines, television guides, and the Internet.

2. Try to find articles related to the issues introduced in the last four Topics.

3. Post the information on a bulletin board.

Find Out **ACTIVITY**

What Did You Find Out?

❋ **Analyzing and Interpreting**
❋ **Communication and Teamwork**

From the information collected by the class, answer the following questions:

(a) Which issues seem to be receiving the most attention in the media?

(b) Why do you think that they are receiving so much attention?

(c) Do any of these issues relate to advances in food or fibre production? In sustainability?

Figure 2.53 In Nepal, wood needed for fuel and forests has been removed from hillsides, resulting in massive erosion.

TOPIC 4 Review

1. Describe three plants grown for food and three plants grown for fibre species in Alberta.

2. Explain what sustainability means.

3. Describe an example of modern technology that is used to help grow or harvest plants for food or fibre.

4. Explain how greenhouses modify the environment to improve growing conditions for plants.

5. Describe the advantages and disadvantages of growing crops as a monoculture.

TOPIC 5 Sustaining the Soil

Imagine what would happen if the soil suddenly disappeared. While animals run and leap, and plants dazzle with their bright colours, the soil often goes unnoticed. But healthy soil is critical in natural ecosystems and sustains our need to grow plants for food and fibre.

Figure 2.54 What might happen if we lost most of our soil?

Soil gives plants a place to sink their roots and anchor themselves. Without soil, strong winds and violent storms would tear plants out of the soil or tip them over. As well as being an anchor for plants, soil is an amazing natural community, with billions of residents per cubic metre. It is like a huge buffet table that stores nutrients, air, and water, and supplies them to plants as required. To lose the soil, or its ability to produce, would be a disaster. In some areas this has already happened (see Figure 2.55).

In this Topic, you will have an opportunity to examine soil closely and find out how it works. You will learn how soil is formed, how it matures, how it helps plants grow, and what it needs to stay healthy.

Figure 2.55 Severe erosion by water has removed topsoil. It dramatically reduced the productivity of this land, and will continue to do so for generations to come. What could be done to prevent such disasters?

How Do Soils Develop?

Five major factors determine how soils develop: parent material, climate, vegetation, landscape (which affects the amount of water), and time.

- **Parent material** is the mineral (non-organic) matter (rock, soil, clay) from which the soil developed.

- Climate determines what kinds of plants will grow, and how fast they decompose. Warmth and moisture are required for soil organisms to break down plant and animal matter and change it to a rich, dark soil called **humus**. Humus holds nutrients and water for plants.

- The vegetation growing in the area determines the amount and type of organic matter in and on the soil. It also protects the soil from erosion.

- Water brings new soil and nutrients. In healthy soil, spaces between the particles hold water and air for roots. If soil is saturated with water, less oxygen is available.

- All of these processes happen over long periods of time.

Figure 2.56 shows how different soils might develop under different vegetation and water conditions. Time, climate, and parent material were the same for all three. Note how soil **horizons** (the layers in a cross section of soil) vary.

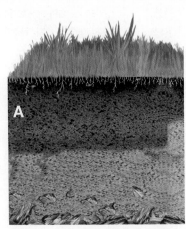

A In well-drained soils, roots are active throughout the upper layers of the soil. As roots die, bacteria decompose them. The resulting organic matter gives the upper horizon — **topsoil** — a brown or black colour. In general, the more moisture such grassland receives, the more organic matter there is, and the darker the topsoil.

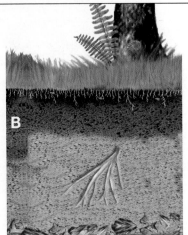

B In well-drained soils under forests, most of the organic matter is added at the top as leaves, instead of below as roots, since tree roots live a long time. The soil remains grey-brown (the colour of the parent material or lighter). Fungi cause most of the decomposition of the leaves at the surface. The top horizon in this type of soil is quite acidic.

C Soils that are saturated with water have little oxygen available for any kind of decomposer to live and work. Organic matter does not decay, but collects on the soil surface. The parent material often changes little, except for the colour. Saturated soils often have a bluish tinge.

Figure 2.56 A. Soil under grassland **B.** Soil under forest **C.** Soil under water

Soil: A Lively Community

Figure 2.57 There's more to the soil than first meets the eye.

DidYouKnow?

The earthworms in 1 ha (100 m x 100 m) of healthy soil grind, digest, and mix up to 30 t of matter per year. Charles Darwin honoured them by giving them the title "Intestines of the soil." Today, some people have special home worm composters to help digest fruit and vegetable waste in their homes.

Healthy soil contains an amazing collection of creatures — gophers, earthworms, insects, and billions of microscopic bacteria and fungi. All are part of an ever-changing community. The decomposers break down plant and animal tissue, forming humus. This helps roots to move into the soil, and enables water and air to move more freely. The four key types of decomposers each work a little differently.

- Bacteria are the most diverse and numerous of all soil organisms. In healthy grasslands, billions of bacteria live in every kilogram of soil. A hectare could have up to 4 t of live bacteria, all actively breaking down dead plant and animal tissues.

- Fungi include moulds and mushrooms. These organisms are especially important in forest soils and where soils are cooler and more acidic. The fungi make nutrients available to the plants and receive carbohydrates in return.

- Microscopic actinomycetes are a special type of bacteria that also play a vital role in decomposing organic matter and forming humus.

- Soil that contains lots of earthworms is usually healthy. As earthworms eat the soil, they grind, digest, and mix it. They produce casts that are richer in nutrients and bacteria than the soil they took in! Earthworm tunnels help air and water move through the soil. The mucus that worms add helps stick soil particles together. Earthworms also bring up nutrients from lower levels of the soil as they tunnel through it.

DidYouKnow?

Soil organisms are often mixed in with seeds and seedlings to help improve growing conditions. For example, a special bacterium is mixed with alfalfa seed, and the two together produce nitrogen — a nutrient that alfalfa and other plants need. Many tree seedlings grown for reforestation are given a type of fungus called mycorrhizae to help them get nutrients from the soils in which they will be planted.

INQUIRY

INVESTIGATION 2-H

SKILLCHECK
Initiating and Planning
☼ Performing and Recording
☼ Analyzing and Interpreting
Communication and Teamwork

Soil Sleuth

Use the following tests to learn about soil health by comparing potting soil with garden or yard soil.

Question

How do sand, potting soil, and garden (or yard) soil differ?

Hypothesis

Write a hypothesis about how sand, potting soil, and garden soil differ. Think about how each might differ in terms of organic matter, texture, and water-holding ability.

Safety Precautions

Apparatus

thumbtack

scissors

spoon

magnifying glass

ruler

microscope (optional)

balance

measuring cup or graduated cylinder

3 glasses or beakers (250 mL)

3 small jars with screw lids (250–500 mL)

Materials

6 disposable cups (250 mL)

labels

3 plastic lids (such as from a yogurt container)

water

sand

potting soil

garden or yard soil

3 cone-shaped coffee filters

Part 1

Texture Test
Procedure

❶ 1. Label each sample A, B, and C.

❷ In your notebook, prepare an observation page, as shown here. Complete the "Sample source" section by indicating the brand of potting soil you are testing or the site of the soil sample.

Sample letter
Sample source
Particle size and texture tests
• crumble or clump
• formed ribbon (yes/no)
• length of ribbon
• rubbing test
• method used to estimate particle size
• estimate of average particle size
Organics
• evidence of organic material
• float test
• soup test
Drainage test
• start time for pouring
• time when water first drained
• stop time (no drips for 30 s)
• quantity of water drained

3 Squeeze test:

(a) Take a handful of moist soil (add a little water if it's dry), and squeeze it in your fist. Open your hand. Decide whether the soil formed a clump that holds together or crumbles when you press it.

(b) If you have a ball of soil, try to rub the soil between your index finger and thumb to form a ribbon. Soils with more clay will form longer ribbons.

(c) **Record** your observations.

4 Wet rubbing test:

(a) Add water to make a soupy mud. Rub the mud with the end of your finger.

(b) **Record** whether the mud feels mostly gritty, equally gritty and smooth, or mostly smooth.

5 Particle size:

(a) Use your observations to try to **predict** which soil sample has the largest particle size.

(b) **Examine** the soil and **describe** any evidence of particle size.

(c) **Record** any difficulty in estimating particle size. Don't worry if you have trouble; this task is not as easy as it may seem!

Part 2
Organic Matter Test
Procedure

1 Visual test:

(a) Pick apart the sample. Use your magnifying glass to search for any materials that you think might be organic.

(b) **Record** your observations.

2 Float test:

(a) Place about 10 mL of soil into a clear container full of water.

(b) **Observe** what floats on top. In natural soil, the material that floats is likely to be organic. In a potting soil mix, it may also include perlite or vermiculite.

(c) **Record** your observations.

3 Soup test:

(a) Place about 125 mL of soil in the small jar and half fill with water. Screw on the lid and shake well.

(b) Let the "soil soup" settle for 5 min. Then **draw** the layers you see.

4 Repeat these tests with the other two samples.

Part 3
Drainage Test
Procedure

1 Prepare the disposable cups as follows

(a) Label the cups as sand, potting soil, and (name of site of other sample).

(b) Using the thumbtack, punch 15 holes in the bottom of three of the cups.

CONTINUED ▶

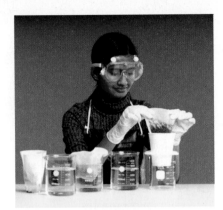

2 To hold each cup over the glass or beaker, cut a hole in a coffee-can or yogurt container lid so that the cup will just fit into the hole. Place a cup and lid over a glass or beaker.

3 Place the soil sample in the cup. Press it down firmly with your finger. Your soil should half fill the cup.

4 It is important to do this step *slowly*. Pour 100 mL of water into the cup.

5 **Record** the time when the water is first poured into the cup. **Record** the time when the water first drips from the cup.

6 Allow the water to drip for 20 min. Use the graduated cylinder to **measure** and

record the amount of water that has collected in the glass or beaker.

7 **Repeat** the above steps with the other two samples.

8 Wash your hands thoroughly after completing this investigation.

Analyze

1. Read through the soil descriptions below. Which description best matches your soil sample?

Sandy soil	Clay soil
• has few or no lumps	• often has hard lumps that may be so hard you cannot break them with your fingers
• has lumps that crumble when you touch them lightly	• forms a sticky ball when water is added and ball is squeezed
• when wet, may clump together briefly, but will fall apart as soon as you try to pick it up	• may be difficult to wash off hands
• has particles of grains of sand that are easily seen with the magnifying glass	• has particles that are so tiny they cannot be seen under the microscope
• feels loose and grainy when dry, gritty when wet	• has small spaces between particles, so water cannot easily move through
• has a thick sand layer in the soup test	• expands when wet and shrinks when dry, causing large cracks to form in soil
• has large spaces between the particles that allow water to move through quickly	• can form a hard crust on top and prevent seedlings from emerging
• does not hold as much food or water for plants	• can be rich in nutrients

2. Use the chart below to locate the texture name of each sample.

Ribbon length	Mostly gritty	Both gritty and smooth	Mostly smooth
shorter than 2.5 cm	sandy and sandy loam	loam	silty loam
2.5–5 cm	sandy clay loam	clay loam	silty clay loam
over 5 cm	sandy clay	silty clay	clay

3. Which sample do you think has the greatest amount of organic matter? Which had the least?

4. How did the samples compare in their ability to hold water?

5. Which variable was controlled in this experiment?

Conclude and Apply

6. Which types of soil would be the best to grow vegetables in your garden? Why?

All You Can Eat!

Healthy, growing plants require large amounts of six nutrients: nitrogen (N), phosphorus (P), potassium (K), sulphur (S), calcium (Ca), and magnesium (Mg). Different parts of plants use different amounts of each of these. For example, nitrogen helps make leaves green. Newly planted seeds and stems need extra phosphorus for the best growing conditions, and flowers and seeds require phosphorus and potassium.

Sulphur, calcium, and nitrogen are usually present in the parent material of soil. Nitrogen, phosphorus, and potassium often need to be added in fertilizer.

Figure 2.58 The soil is like a buffet table that holds the water and nutrients that plants need.

What's in the Bag?

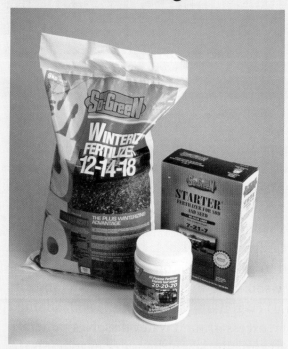

Plants often need more of the major nutrients, nitrogen, phosphorus, and potassium. A bag of fertilizer usually has three numbers that indicate the percentage of each of three nutrients. For example, a bag of fertilizer marked 12–14–18 contains 12 percent nitrogen, 14 percent phosphorus, and 18 percent potassium.

Find Out **ACTIVITY**

Procedure ✳ **Performing and Recording**

Arrange to visit a garden store or nursery or speak with a knowledgeable resource person. Find answers to the following questions:

1. What formulations of fertilizer are available locally?

2. How is each formulation used? (For example, is it used for a specific crop, or applied at a certain stage of growth?)

3. Which fertilizer is used most commonly? (Which sells the best?)

4. What forms of fertilizer are popular, and how are they used? (For example, fish fertilizers might be used for plants, and slow-release nitrogen for lawns.)

What Did You Find Out?
✳ **Analyzing and Interpreting**
✳ **Communication and Teamwork**

1. Organize your findings in a table to present to your class.

2. What amount of fertilizer is best for a plant? (Can plants have too much fertilizer?) Rewrite this question so that you could test it.

Challenges and Solutions

Production practices have sometimes damaged large areas of soil in the prairie provinces. Here is a summary of the problems or challenges, and some of the solutions that are being used and developed. Over time, the practices will help soils become healthier and better able to resist damage.

Salinization: Salty Soil

Have you ever noticed a white crust on the soil surface like the one in Figure 2.59? Sometimes this white crust is in a ring pattern around a slough. The crust is salt that has collected on the surface of the soil. This condition is called **salinization**.

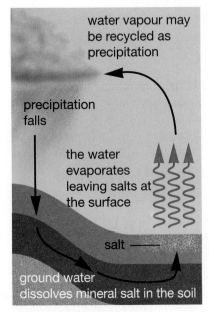

Figure 2.59 A white crust on the soil is evidence of salinization.

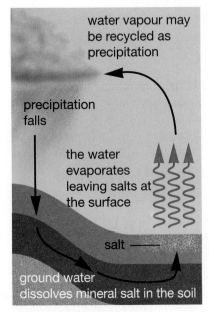

water vapour may be recycled as precipitation

precipitation falls

the water evaporates leaving salts at the surface

salt

ground water dissolves mineral salt in the soil

Figure 2.60 Ground water flows from higher elevations to lower elevations, carrying salts along with it.

High levels of salt in the soil have the same effect as dry conditions. Every year that salt collects in soil, the soil becomes less and less able to grow crops. In some areas, growing crops is now impossible.

Two factors lead to salinization: too little vegetation and too much water (excess irrigation). Look at Figure 2.60. When farmers cultivate land to grow field crops, they remove vegetation. Water enters the soil since there are no plants to absorb water. Irrigation brings even more water into the soil, adding to the ground water. The excess ground water dissolves minerals (salts) from the soil. Eventually, when the water evaporates the salts are left behind.

The problem of soil salinization can be solved by replanting the areas so that plants use up the water that falls before it has a chance to seep away. Farmers also monitor irrigation much more closely now, and have also lined water canals to stop the canal water from draining into the ground water.

Looking Ahead

Keeping soil healthy and understanding what type of fertilizer to use and how much to apply are important. Using the previous two activities as your basis, do some research to extend your knowledge of these aspects of plant growing. Discuss with your group how you can use what you learn in your Unit 2 Project, Get Growing!

Organic Matter and Erosion

Figure 2.61 Soil erosion is a serious problem in agriculture.

The most serious problem in soils is the loss of organic matter. This in turn leads to soil erosion (see Figure 2.61). It is estimated that, on average, 15–30 percent of organic matter — the work of earthworms and other soil organisms for over 10 000 years — has been lost in just a few decades of cultivation. Soil then is less able to hold nutrients, water, and air. This makes the soil poor for growing plants.

Figure 2.62 shows how soil damage often begins. Natural vegetation was removed from prairie farms, exposing soil to Sun and wind. In an effort to control weeds and prepare perfect seedbeds, producers ploughed and cultivated the soil too much. Regular summer fallow was a common practice. (Summer fallow is the practice of cultivating land to control weeds but planting no crops.) This exposed the soil to sunlight and higher temperatures and encouraged bacteria to decompose the organic matter at a rapid rate. All of these practices depleted the soil.

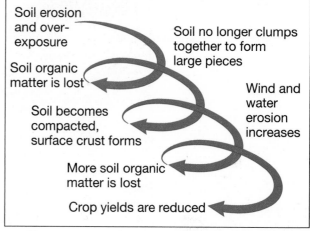

Soil erosion and over-exposure

Soil no longer clumps together to form large pieces

Soil organic matter is lost

Wind and water erosion increases

Soil becomes compacted, surface crust forms

More soil organic matter is lost

Crop yields are reduced

Figure 2.62 The common path to reduced soil quality.

me everyday

some somewhere operate

Saving the Soil

What are some ways that farmers can help preserve the soil? Soil erosion can be solved by planting a cover of vegetation on the surface of the ground to slow the flow of water. This gives the soil more time to absorb the water. When more water soaks in, less will flow along the surface and cause erosion. Vegetation covers also protect soil from the wind.

Farmers, particularly those in drier areas, have realized how important it is to "keep the covers on" their fields. They need ways to keep protective vegetation on the field, while still being able to remove weeds. One solution is shown in Figure 2.63A.

Figure 2.63A In zero tillage, the stubble from last year's crop remains on the field. A zero-tillage seed drill, like the one shown here, plants the seeds through the stubble.

Figure 2.63B Some farmers cultivate less, and use a special wide-shovel cultivator which cuts weeds below the surface but does not disturb the surface soil too much. This cultivator keeps over 90 percent of the vegetation on top of the soil.

Instead of cultivating land some farmers use special seeding equipment, called seed drills (see Figure 2.63B). These drills push seed right through the stubble of the previous crop into the undisturbed soil. This technique, called zero-tillage, protects the soil from wind and water erosion. Other benefits are: lower tillage costs, improved soil structure, and more soil moisture for the next crop. Its disadvantages are that weeds and disease-causing organisms previously killed by cultivation can now be controlled only with pesticide sprays.

Other methods of saving soil are shown in Figure 2.64A, B, and C. Farmers plant **shelterbelts** (rows of trees) along the edges of fields. They also modify waterways, and they use crop rotation.

Figure 2.64A Shelterbelts reduce wind damage to crops, trap snow to increase soil moisture, and provide wildlife with habitat.

Figure 2.64B Many farmers have reshaped and seeded waterways to reduce erosion. Strong rains and spring meltwater can form small streams that wash away soils. These grassed waterways provide food, shelter, and travel corridors for many wildlife species.

Figure 2.64C Many farmers use forages (legumes and grasses) in a crop rotation to add organic matter and provide protection from wind and water erosion. Manure from livestock is often used to add organic matter, improve soil structure, and increase nutrients. Manure must be added carefully, however, in order to avoid adding weed seeds and disease organisms.

Pause&
Reflect

The Soil Conservation Council of Canada's mission is "to promote the preservation and enrichment of Canada's soils and related water resources for the benefit of present and future generations." In your Science Log, list some ways that you could be part of this mission.

Hydroponic Technology

Hydroponics is a technique for growing plants without soil (see Figure 2.65). Plants are usually grown in a non-organic growing medium. Gravel or "rock wool" (rock that has been heated and spun) and nutrients are added to the water. In warmer parts of the world, farmers use hydroponic technology in their fields. In Canada, hydroponics is used in greenhouses. In the next investigation you will set up your own hydroponic system. There are many ways to do this. Below is the procedure that one student used.

Figure 2.65 The yield and quality of vegetable crops under greenhouse hydroponic conditions can be far better than field production. It is expensive to grow plants this way, though, and the nutrients and other growing conditions must be closely monitored.

1. Use a pencil to poke a large hole in the bottom of a foam cup.

2. Roll a 20 x 20 cm square of cotton cloth into a tight roll.

3. Push one end of the cloth through the hole in the cup until it is about three-quarters of the way into the cup.

4. Fill the cup around the cloth with peat moss, pressing it firmly.

5. Add fertilizer and water solution (mixed according to directions) to a large container.

6. Suspend the cup on a ring stand so that it is just above the level of the nutrient solution, with the rolled cotton cloth lowered deeply into the solution.

7. Plant seeds in the cup and set it under a grow light.

Ask an Expert

On page 176 you will meet Muhammad Younus, who will tell you more about hydroponics.

Word CONNECT

Hydroponics means growing plants without soil in a water solution. With a partner, write down as many "hydro" words as you can, then check a dictionary to find out how many there are.

Off the Wall

Aquaponics takes the idea of a "nutrient solution" one step further. This technology combines raising fish and growing plants in an aquaculture system. Water used by the fish provides nutrients for plants. The plants remove nutrients and clean up this water, which goes back to the fish. Aquaponics is becoming more common in northern greenhouses and could eventually become a significant source of fish and plants for food.

Construct a Hydroponic Garden

Challenge

Design a model to show how you might grow plants using hydroponic technology.

Safety Precautions

Apparatus

container for the plants (Styrofoam™ cup, peat pot, plastic seedling container)

container for solution (large jar, aquarium, plastic tank, plastic pail)

a means of suspending the plant above the solution

source of light for the plants

a means of bringing the solution to the plant (cotton cloth, about 20 cm x 20 cm, to use as a wick; or a water pump)

Materials

selection of materials to choose from: non-organic medium (gravel, sand, peat, vermiculite, perlite, pumice)

sprouted seeds (radish, lettuce, peas, or beans) or seedlings (tomatoes)

hydroponic fertilizer

Design Specifications

A. Your model must demonstrate how nutrients and water can be supplied without soil.

B. Your model must enable plants to grow for two to three weeks.

C. Your model must be easy to monitor and maintain.

D. Your model must permit you to make best use of other growing conditions, such as temperature and light.

Skill
FOCUS

For tips on scientific problem solving turn to Skill Focus 7.

Plan and Construct

1 With your group, discuss how you might create your hydroponic system.

2 Draw a labelled sketch of your model, indicating what materials you will use.

3 Obtain your teacher's approval. Then construct the model.

4 Improve the model until you are satisfied with the way it works, and feel confident that it can be used to grow plants for the required period.

5 Demonstrate your model to your class.

6 Wash your hands thoroughly after you have completed this investigation.

Evaluate

1. Did your model work as expected?

2. What adjustments did you make so that it would work better?

3. What scientific knowledge did you use to develop your model?

4. What knowledge did you gain from creating this model?

5. What ideas did other groups use that you would like to use?

6. How would you change your model if you wanted to actually produce food (for example, grow large tomato plants that would produce large fruit you could harvest)?

Saving Soil in Forests

Looking Ahead

You are now ready to start your Unit 2 Project, Get Growing! Examine your Project Planning file and discuss ideas with your group. What else do you need to know before starting your project? Divide any tasks among your group members, and — Get Growing!

Forestry can also have an impact on soils. When trees are cut and removed from an area, wind and water can erode the soil. To minimize damage, some trees and debris such as logs and stumps are left on cut areas. As the debris decays, it adds organic matter to the soil. Forests are also replanted with new trees shortly after they are harvested. As well, trees and shrubs are usually left around streams and gullies to minimize soil loss.

Figure 2.66 These erosion control methods slow the flow of water and enable trees and shrubs to take root in the gully again.

TOPIC 5 Review

1. What are the major factors that determine how soils develop?

2. What kinds of organisms live in the soil? What roles do they play?

3. Explain how soils that develop under grassland might be different from those that develop under forest vegetation. What causes them to develop differently?

4. Why is the loss of organic matter in soil so serious?

5. Name five farming or forestry practices that help prevent soil erosion or improve soil health.

6. What are the three major components of fertilizer?

TOPIC 6 Pests and Pest Control

Every year, tonnes of chemicals are used to control pest organisms that reduce plants' ability to produce food and fibre. What are the effects on our natural systems? Are there alternatives?

What Is a Pest?

What do you think a pest would say if you were to interview one?

Pause&
Reflect

Planting fields with single crops (monocultures) makes them attractive to pests. Do you think monocultures might also make it easier for farmers to control pests?

From the point of view of a farmer or forester, a pest is any organism that is causing plants to die or produce less than they otherwise would. From a pest's point of view, though, things look different. Are bees pests? Are ants pests? When they are part of a natural system or are beneficial to people, no. When they annoy us or affect our ability to produce food and fibre, yes, they are pests. Insects are not the only types of pests, however. Fungi, weeds, and other animals such as slugs or birds can also be pests in certain situations.

Friend or Foe?

How would you define a pest? Is a bee a pest or an important pollinator? Perhaps it is both. What about the insects and other animals shown here? Are they pests? In small groups, brainstorm about pests.

Materials

large sheets of paper   felt markers

Procedure ✳ Performing and Recording
           ✳ Communication and Teamwork

1. With your group, brainstorm a list of pests that affect you directly (for example,

mosquitoes) or indirectly (for example, cabbage moth larvae that eat cabbage). Use the Internet, library, or other resources (such as employees of a garden centre or farm) to help you make your lists. Remember that pests are not only insects. They can also be weeds, fungi, or other animals.

2. Choose one pest and investigate the damage it does, and how it is controlled.

3. Are these control measures successful? Are other methods being tried?

4. Report your findings to your class in a 5 min presentation.

What Did You Find Out?

1. What kinds of technologies are used to control pests?

2. What concerns are there with the technologies that are used to control pests?

People encouraged us to move here by growing lots of food for us. Your monoculture is a perfect place for my family and me to live, so we reproduce and raise millions of others like us. Just when things are going well and our population is soaring, you try to kill us with machines and chemicals! It's just awful!

Could you tell us why you chose to come to this neighbourhood in the first place?

The Pest Problem

In natural systems, organisms have parasites, predators, or competing plants that help keep their numbers in check.

The pests that cause most damage are insects, fungi, and weedy plants. Weeds are "thieves"; they steal moisture, nutrients, space, or light from the crop. Insects usually eat some part of the plant, and fungi and bacteria can cause infections, destroying parts or all of the plant.

Insects and diseases consume over 50 percent of Canada's annual harvest. Farmers spend millions of dollars each year to control them and avoid food crop losses.

Dandelion: Profile of a Champion Competitor

What makes dandelions such successful weed pests?

3. Super Seeds

2. Broad Leaves

4. Adaptable

1. Powerful Roots

1. **Powerful Roots** Dandelions have a long taproot that is anchored deep below the soil surface. If you try to pull up a dandelion, it usually breaks off near the surface, leaving most of the root in the soil. The root can grow new leaves and flowers. Dandelions store nutrients in their roots throughout the summer so that in early spring they can get a strong start and grow more quickly than the competition.

2. **Broad Leaves** Dandelions have long, wide leaves that shade out many nearby plants, making them strong competitors for light.

3. **Super Seeds** Dandelions are able to produce flowers and seeds all summer long. Each flower produces hundreds of seeds, which are carried a long distance on the wind.

4. **Adaptable** Dandelions grow well in all kinds of soil, including soil that is poor in nutrients. They also adapt quickly as a species to different situations because there is such a variety of these plants. For example, in a frequently mowed lawn, dandelions with very short flower stalks will survive because their flowers are missed by the lawn mower. Consequently, the homeowner will still have dandelions!

Chemical Weapons Dandelions release chemical agents to slow down the growth of grass and other plants nearby. This leaves more nutrients, water, and sunlight available for the dandelion plants.

Canola and Its Pests

Canola is popular with fungi, insects, and weeds. Here are some of the worst pests, and some of the strategies that make them successful.

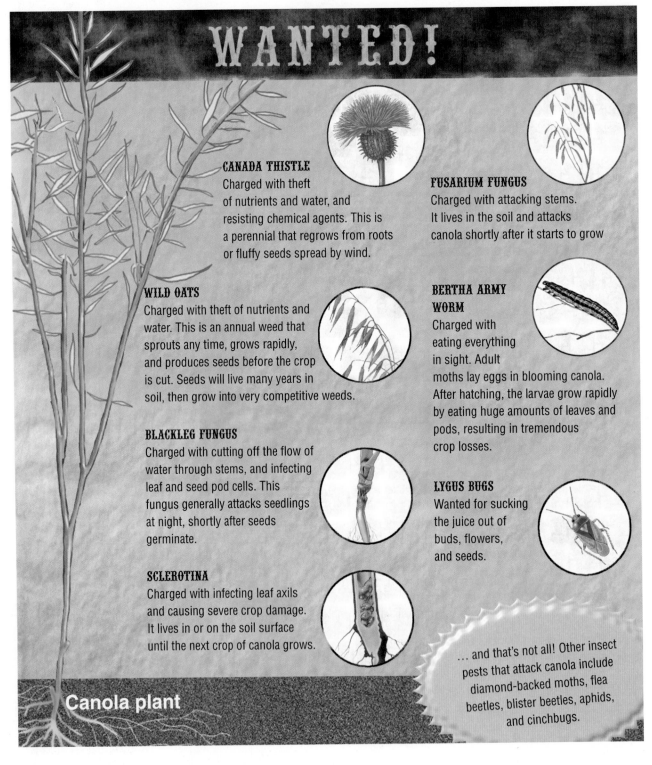

WANTED!

CANADA THISTLE
Charged with theft of nutrients and water, and resisting chemical agents. This is a perennial that regrows from roots or fluffy seeds spread by wind.

WILD OATS
Charged with theft of nutrients and water. This is an annual weed that sprouts any time, grows rapidly, and produces seeds before the crop is cut. Seeds will live many years in soil, then grow into very competitive weeds.

BLACKLEG FUNGUS
Charged with cutting off the flow of water through stems, and infecting leaf and seed pod cells. This fungus generally attacks seedlings at night, shortly after seeds germinate.

SCLEROTINA
Charged with infecting leaf axils and causing severe crop damage. It lives in or on the soil surface until the next crop of canola grows.

FUSARIUM FUNGUS
Charged with attacking stems. It lives in the soil and attacks canola shortly after it starts to grow

BERTHA ARMY WORM
Charged with eating everything in sight. Adult moths lay eggs in blooming canola. After hatching, the larvae grow rapidly by eating huge amounts of leaves and pods, resulting in tremendous crop losses.

LYGUS BUGS
Wanted for sucking the juice out of buds, flowers, and seeds.

... and that's not all! Other insect pests that attack canola include diamond-backed moths, flea beetles, blister beetles, aphids, and cinchbugs.

Canola plant

DidYouKnow?

Technologists have developed new strains of canola that are resistant to herbicides. This means that a farmer can spray a field for weeds without killing the canola plants.

Introduced Species

Each food and fibre crop species has a set of pest weeds, insects, and fungi (see Figure 2.67). Many of the worst weed and insect pests are organisms introduced from other countries. They are called introduced, or exotic species. Introduced species become serious pests because they have few, if any, natural controls. Most of the weeds that cause crop losses (and increased expense) were accidentally introduced from Europe. Quack grass, thistles, and chickweed are examples (see Figure 2.68).

Some of the foreign weed species came by accident, but others were introduced intentionally. Dandelions, for example, were brought from Europe to be used as a salad vegetable. Unfortunately, the set of insects and diseases that naturally control dandelion plants did not come with them.

Non-native insects also cause problems in fields and forests. The tiny European bark-boring beetle arrived in North America in 1940 with a shipment of elm logs from the Netherlands (see Figure 2.69). The beetle's damage to elm trees was relatively light. Unfortunately, it brought a fungus called Dutch elm disease that has since wiped out nearly all the native elm trees of North America.

Figure 2.67 This picture was taken in July, when tree branches are normally covered in leaves. Tent caterpillars, however, have consumed almost every leaf. Aspen forests in Northern Alberta were severely affected by tent caterpillars in the 1980s.

Did You Know?

The cane toad was released in many areas of Australia to control pests in sugar cane fields on farms. Unfortunately, the huge toads liked to live in cities too, and they became a major nuisance in both urban and rural areas.

Figure 2.68 Chickweed is a common weed pest that was introduced to Canada from Europe.

Figure 2.69 European bark-boring beetle

Did You Know?

Plant diseases have been responsible for immigration. For example, the potato blight fungus in Ireland resulted in failure of potato crops and widespread hunger. Large numbers of Irish people came to North America and many settled in Alberta.

Controlling Pests

Since people have been growing crops, they have tried different ways to control pests. Large pests could be chased or scared away, and smaller pests could be picked off plants by hand. Over the past 200 years, machines such as ploughs and cultivators have been developed to uproot or cut weeds at the soil surface (see Figure 2.71).

In the past farmers grew different crops each year as a way of controlling some weeds and diseases. In this practice of crop rotation, a field might grow wheat in the first year, barley in the second, potatoes in the third, and hay crops in the fourth, fifth, and sixth years. This system gave pests no opportunity to establish themselves since a new crop was grown each year. Regular summer fallow helped control a variety of weeds and crop diseases, but it led to soil damage.

As introduced species and other pests began to further threaten crops, chemical controls were developed. Chemical control seemed to be effective and relatively inexpensive. Herbicides, insecticides, and fungicides controlled weeds, insects, and fungi. These chemicals were simple to use, gave impressive results, and were considered safe. It took several decades of chemical use, however, before the major problems with the use of these controls became apparent.

Figure 2.70 Pests come in all shapes and sizes.

Figure 2.71 Zero-tillage cultivators cut weeds near the soil surface, disturbing it as little as possible.

Concerns with Chemical Controls

Producers in Canada are becoming increasingly aware of long-term problems created by pesticides. Try the following activity to find one problem.

Passing on the Poison

How can chemicals that are meant to kill weeds or insects affect birds, fish, and mammals?

Materials

small squares of red and green paper

three different colours of ribbon

plastic bags

stopwatch

Procedure
* Performing and Recording
* Communication and Teamwork

1. Divide the class into producers, herbivores, and carnivores. Choose one top predator. Tie a different-coloured ribbon around the arm of each student to signify whether the student is a producer, a herbivore, or a carnivore. The top predator needs no ribbon.

2. In a large area, scatter the pieces of red and green paper. These are the plants in your food web.

3. Give the producers 1 min to collect as much "food" as they can. They can store the food in their "stomach" (the plastic bag).

4. After 1 min, stop the game and have each producer count and record the number of green and the number of red pieces of paper in each bag.

5. Now have the herbivores "eat" for 1 min. They eat by tagging the producers. If they tag a producer, the producer must hand over his or her stomach. Producers who are tagged are out of the game.

6. After 1 min, stop the game and have the herbivores count and record the number of green and the number of red pieces of paper in their bag(s).

7. Now have the carnivores "eat" for 1 min. Carnivores can tag only herbivores, and herbivores can tag only producers. If a herbivore is tagged, the herbivore passes *all* the bags to the carnivore and is out of the game.

8. After 1 min, stop the game and have each herbivore and each carnivore count and record the number of green squares and the number of red squares in the bag(s).

9. Now have the top predator "eat" for 1 min.

10. Stop the game. All remaining players count their red and green squares.

What Did You Find Out?

If the red squares represented chemically sprayed plants, explain how these squares got into the stomachs of predators that did not eat that food directly.

Two technologies — global positioning systems (GPS) and precision farming techniques — enable farmers to apply the right amount of chemicals to all areas of each field. GPS tells the farmer the exact position of the farm equipment. Precise measurements of soil and other factors are taken as the farm equipment moves across the field. A computer combines this information with other data about yield of the previous crop in that spot and adjusts the amount of fertilizer and pesticide for each part of the field.

Bioaccumulation of Chemicals

As you saw in the previous activity, pollutants such as chemicals in pesticides can accumulate through the food chain. The pollutants move from level to level and get stored in organisms in the same way that food energy is stored. This effect is called **bioaccumulation**. Bioaccumulation is one of the primary concerns with the use of chemical pesticides. Animals at the top of the food chain, such as the bald eagle in Figure 2.72, are particularly affected by bioaccumulation.

Figure 2.72 Animals at the top of the food chain, such as bald eagles, are affected when chemical pollutants enter the food chain.

Soil Residue

Some of the chemicals wash off the plants and leave **residues** in the soil and water. If the pesticides are not easily decomposed, they can stay in the environment and remain poisonous. Toxic residues have been found in polar ice that is thousands of kilometres from the nearest source of the chemical.

Harming Non-Target Organisms

Pesticides are often toxic to more than one organism. In most cases, beneficial organisms, which are not the target of the chemical control, also die when pest organisms are killed. For example, earthworms are often non-target organisms that are affected by chemical controls. Killing non-target species often worsens the pest problem. For example, ladybird beetles eat aphids, but ladybirds are killed by an insecticide used to control aphids. The aphids soon return and, without the ladybirds present, their numbers and the damage they cause increase quickly.

Math CONNECT

The chemical DDT has been used to control insects carrying the fungal infection that causes Dutch elm disease. The elm leaves accumulated about 20 parts per million (ppm) of the DDT. Earthworms ate the leaves and accumulated over 80 ppm. After eating earthworms for the season, the bodies of robins had over 340 ppm.

A. Estimate the rate of increase of DDT in the first three species in the food chain above.

B. Suppose the concentration increased at a similar rate for the next species in the chain — the robins' predators. Estimate the concentration (in ppm) that you would expect in the tissues of the larger animals that prey on the robins.

Resistant Species

Scientists have discovered that, as pesticide use increases, the number of insect species that can withstand their effects (are **resistant**) is increasing as well. Target insects that survive have become naturally resistant to the chemical. Each generation of insects then becomes more and more resistant to the chemicals. The graph in Figure 2.73 shows how this can occur.

The only way to control these tough insects with chemicals is to use higher dosages and to develop new pesticides. These higher dosages could have even more harmful effects on the environment.

Pause& Reflect

If chemical controls have so many potential problems, why do you think they are so widely used? Discuss this question with a partner.

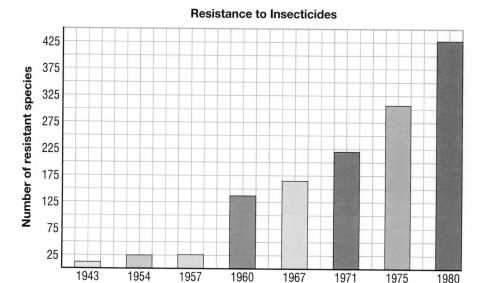

Figure 2.73 This graph shows how resistance to insecticides has steadily increased.

Pesticide Safety Labels

Universal symbols such as the ones below are used to indicate the dangers involved in handling pesticides and other hazardous chemicals.

instruction sheets photocopied from pesticides

Procedure ✳ **Performing and Recording**

1. Choose a pesticide and prepare a brief report on the following questions:

   (a) What is this pesticide used for?

Find Out ACTIVITY

(b) What safety precautions are necessary in order to apply the pesticide safely?

(c) What special equipment do you need?

(d) What conditions are required for safe storage and disposal?

(e) What action should you take if someone accidentally ingests or inhales this pesticide?

What Did You Find Out? ✳ **Analyzing and Interpreting**

Are the instructions on the labels enough to keep all users and the environment safe? If not, what additional training or education should be required before people use pesticides?

Organic Food Production

Have you noticed foods labelled ORGANIC in grocery stores? **Organic** food is food that has been grown without the use of chemical fertilizers and chemical pesticides. Organic food growers use manure and compost to add nutrients to the soil. They fight weeds and other pests using a combination of methods such as tilling, crop rotations, mulching, planting their crop alongside plants that discourage insects (called companion planting), and removing insects by hand. Soaps can also be used to control many insect pests.

Figure 2.74A Organic food is grown without chemical fertilizers or pesticides.

Figure 2.74B An organic farm

Other practices that both organic and non-organic producers use to reduce the need for chemicals include:

• sowing good quality seeds
• removing weeds before their seeds mature by tillage or mowing
• cutting weeds along property edges
• cleaning equipment so that it doesn't transfer weeds from one field to another.

Many organic farmers also grow a variety of crops instead of monocultures. Increasing diversity helps reduce weeds, insects, fungal diseases, and the drain on some soil nutrients.

Producing without chemicals requires careful monitoring and extra work, so it can be expensive. Benefits include higher prices for produce, increased safety for the farmer, and less chance of residue buildup in the land. Consumers enjoy reduced chemical exposure, but must pay a little more for their food.

Pause& Reflect

Food produced organically presently costs more but it is safer for people and the environment. Would you be willing to pay more for food grown organically?

INTERNET CONNECT

www.mcgrawhill.ca/links/sciencefocus7s

Meet some organic farmers by visiting the above web site. You can also find information about organizations that promote and support organic farming. Click on **Web Links** to find out where to go next. Prepare a mini-report about one organic farmer. How is food produced without chemical fertilizers or pesticides?

Controlling Slugs the Organic Way

Find Out ACTIVITY

Have you ever encountered a slug in a garden or on a vegetable or fruit? These members of the snail family feed on plants and can cause a lot of damage. How would you control slugs without using chemicals?

Procedure ✳ Initiating and Planning
✳ Performing and Recording

1. Read the information about a slug's lifestyle below.

A Slug's Life

Slugs lay eggs on the surface of the soil in the fall. They like soil rich in organic matter. The eggs hatch in late spring and the growing slugs feed on almost any plant material within their reach. Slugs need to stay moist, so they do most of their eating during the evening and early in the morning. During the heat of the day, they hide under plants, rocks, boards, etc. These slippery visitors are attracted to liquids containing yeast and sugar.

2. Design a plan for reducing garden damage caused by slugs. What type of measures would you take to reduce damage by slugs?

What Did You Find Out? ✳ Analyzing and Interpreting

1. How do the strategies that you designed differ in terms of time and cost from simply using chemical pesticides to kill the slugs?

2. What are the advantages and disadvantages of using organic controls instead of chemical controls?

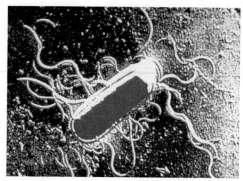

Biological Control

Biological control means using a pest's natural enemies to control it. It's like using one pest (insects, fungi, or bacteria) to control another. For example, the soil bacterium *Bacillus thuringiensis* (Bt) produces a toxin that is deadly to certain insects but is apparently harmless to humans and other animals (see Figure 2.75).

Some growers use ladybugs or predatory wasps to control insect pests such as aphids or white flies. In Unit 1 you learned how the black dot spurge beetle was successfully used to control the weed leafy spurge.

Figure 2.75 The bacterium *Bacillus thuringiensis* is commonly used as an insecticide.

Producers and Consumers — Partners in Sustainability

In Unit 1 you learned about producers and consumers in ecological systems. A similar relationship exists when we talk about growing plants for food and fibre. As you can see in Figure 2.76A, producing food and fibre has become increasingly complex. Farmers and foresters have to consider many factors in addition to conservation and sustainability. In the end, though, producers need to make a reasonable income. Are consumers willing to pay more for food and fibre products that are produced with less impact on the environment? We all have a part to play in the partnership between the plants we produce for food and fibre and the products we consume.

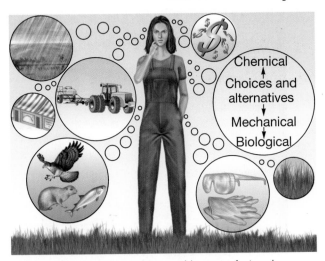

Figure 2.76A Farmers need to consider many factors in decisions about how and what to produce.

Figure 2.76B Consumers need to think about more than just the cost of their food. They are also partners in ensuring that the production of food and fibre is sustainable.

Pause& Reflect

What is your role in how plants for food and fibre are produced? Have you ever wasted products such as paper? Do you eat only food that is cheaper or that looks "perfect?" What is the cost, in terms of the sustainability of soil, water, and forests, of consumers' demands? Record your answers in your Science Log.

TOPIC 6 Review

1. What three kinds of organisms cause the greatest loss of food and fibre production? Give two examples of each, describing the crop species they prefer and how they cause crop loss.

2. Why are non-native pests sometimes so difficult to control?

3. If you were to design the ultimate weed, what features would you be sure to include?

4. **Apply** In a large garden, how might you apply simple, organic farming practices to control dandelions?

5. **Thinking Critically** Do you think the simple techniques described for controlling slugs could be applied in a large market garden? Why or why not? What further development of technology might make it cost effective?

If you need to check an item, Topic numbers are provided in brackets below.

Key Terms

sustainability
irrigate
monoculture
diversity
erosion

parent material
humus
horizons
topsoil
salinization

shelterbelt
bioaccumulation
resistant
organic

Reviewing Key Terms

1. In your notebook, match the description in column A with the correct term in column B.

A	B
• trees planted to reduce erosion from wind	• parent material (5)
• what a pest is when it becomes able to withstand chemicals and pesticides	• resistant (6)
• plants grown without soil	• monoculture (4, 5)
• dark, organic matter in soil that holds nutrients	• shelter belt (5)
• when only one type of plant is grown in an area	• hydroponic (6)
• non-organic material from which soil develops	• humus (5)

2. Explain the relationship between the following terms:

   (a) diversity and monoculture (4, 6)

   (b) irrigate and salinization (4, 5)

   (c) erosion and topsoil (5)

Understanding Key Concepts

3. How are natural forests or grasslands different from agricultural fields or areas of forest that have been cut and replanted? (4)

4. Explain what is meant by sustainability. (4)

5. Explain why farmers should understand the climate and soil type for the area in which they farm. (4)

6. What are three economically important crops grown in Alberta? (4)

7. Describe one way in which farming technology has changed from 100 years ago? Is farming technology still changing? Explain your answer. (4)

8. Describe the practice of summer fallow. How did this practice damage the soil? (4, 5)

9. Describe some ways to save soil moisture. (4, 5)

10. How does the amount of organic matter and the amount of water in soil affect the ability of plants to grow? (5)

11. Why are earthworms sometimes referred to as the "intestines of the soil?" (5)

12. What do the numbers on this bag of fertilizer refer to? (6)

13. What characteristics of dandelions make them such successful plants? (6)

14. Describe three farming practices that reduce the need for chemical pesticides. (6)

UNIT 2
Ask an Expert

If you were a farmer trying to grow tomatoes in Canada in November, Muhammad Younus would be a very important person to know. Muhammad works for Alberta Agriculture, Food and Rural Development in the Greenhouse Crops division of Edmonton's Crop Diversification Centre North.

Q What sort of work do you do?

A I spend part of my day answering questions and giving advice to people who grow greenhouse crops such as tomatoes, cucumbers, and bedding plants. Sometimes they have a crop-related problem that they need solved, or they may need advice on setting up a new crop in a greenhouse. I get e-mails, letters, and telephone calls from growers all over Canada and sometimes as far away as Hawaii.

Q What are the advantages of growing crops in greenhouses rather than outside?

A Here in Canada the greatest advantage is that inside a greenhouse you can control the temperature, which means you can grow plants for a much longer period than you can in the natural environment. Most commercial greenhouses — those that grow food and plants to be sold in grocery stores and plant nurseries — are fully automated. A computer is programmed to control the temperature, light, and humidity in the building automatically. It also controls the amount of water and fertilizer that each individual plant will receive.

The black tubes visible in the photograph bring food and water to these young eggplant plants.

Q So, growing in a greenhouse means your crop can't be damaged if there is too much rain, for example?

A That's right. It also makes it easier to control disease and pest problems that can affect outdoor crops. Everything in the greenhouse environment is predictable. So, vegetable growers have a better idea of what their yield will be, and growers of container plants such as poinsettias and Easter Lilies can make sure that their plants are ready to bloom at the right time of year. Once they know what growing conditions work best, they can get a good product from every plant.

Q But how do growers find out what growing conditions work best?

A That's the other part of my job. I do research here in our greenhouses to develop techniques for successfully growing certain greenhouse crops. Once I've tested them, these techniques get passed along to the growers.

Q So, you experiment with the ideal temperature and amount of water and so on?

A Correct. I also try growing different crops in different artificial media to see how well they will grow.

Q What do you mean by artificial media?

A The medium is the material that the plant grows in. A plant outdoors usually grows in soil, but many greenhouse plants are grown in something different. It may be sawdust or peat, or it could be crushed Styrofoam™ or even glass beads. There is one medium called perlite, which is made from rock that has been blown like popcorn. Another, called rock wool, is rock that has been melted down and then spun into a mat of fibres, like fibreglass.

Q But plants surely wouldn't get many nutrients from things like rock and Styrofoam™?

A No, that's exactly the point. The media doesn't provide any nutrients to the plant. That way, the grower has complete control over what and how much the plant gets. This type of growing is called hydroponics. All of the food that the plant will get is delivered in the water-based feeding solution.

Q How did you learn so much about growing plants?

A I started out just by paying attention. When I was young, my paternal grandmother used many different plants to treat our illnesses. I found it fascinating. At about 16, I began making notes on the plants' names and what she used each of them for. Soon, people in the area were coming to me for information. In grade 12, my botany teacher made the study of plants sound so attractive, I decided it was for me. I got my masters degree in plant science from the Punjab University of Lahore, Pakistan, and after coming to Canada, began to work here at the Crop Diversification Centre North in 1988. And I continue to learn every day.

EXPLORING Further

So Much to Learn

Find out more about growing crops in a greenhouse. Visit some greenhouse web sites and maybe even grow a virtual greenhouse tomato! Go to **www.school.mcgrawhill.ca/resources/**.

Go to **Science Resources**, then to **SCIENCEFOCUS**™ 7 to find out where to go next.

You can also find out more, at the same site, about the Crop Diversification Centre North where Muhammad Younus works.

Get Growing!

Millions of people in Canada grow plants indoors or outdoors for a hobby or as a job. Do you have a "green thumb"? After completing this unit you should have a better understanding about the conditions in which plants grow best. Here is your chance to put all of that knowledge together to grow some great crops.

Challenge

You are part of a team that has been asked to design a way to grow the healthiest crop possible. How will you adjust the soil type, and the amount of water, light, and fertilizer to grow the best crop?

Apparatus

graduated cylinder
ruler
labels
felt marker
artificial growing lights (optional)
500 mL beaker

Materials

seeds (pea, radish, lentil, alfalfa, nasturtium, bean or other seeds of your choice)

3 clear plastic cups

paper towels

water

potting soil

growing mediums such as vermiculite, sand, perlite, peat moss, etc.

6 small paper cups or plant pots

500 mL of liquid fertilizer (mixed and provided by your teacher)

Safety Precautions

- Follow the instructions for safe disposal on the fertilizer package.

- Teachers should mix fertilizer for students.

Design Criteria

A. Choose two crops to grow. (You will receive 12 seeds of each crop and four seeds will be planted in each plant pot or "field".)

B. Sprout your crops in a germination chamber. (A plastic cup lined with a paper towel. Use one germination chamber for each crop.) Place the seeds between the paper towel and the outside of the cup so that you can see them. Once seeds have sprouted plant four seeds in each of three "fields" (small plant pots). Label each pot.

C. You can vary the type of soil, and amount of light, water, and/or fertilizer in each field. All growing conditions must be recorded.

D. You will be given only 500 mL of fertilizer.

E. Plants will be grown and monitored for three weeks.

F. You must submit a summary outlining the growing conditions that resulted in the healthiest crop of plants. Include your criteria for determining plant health.

Plan and Construct

1. As a class, decide on the criteria you will use to rate plant growth. For example, is the tallest plant the healthiest? Is it the plant with the most leaves or the best root growth? Or will this definition vary from species to species? Devise a system of scoring plant health.

2. In your group, review what you learned about plants and growing conditions in general in this unit. As well, review what you know about your two crops. (For example, did you use either of these varieties in an experiment earlier in this unit?)

3. Identify ways in which you could improve conditions for the roots, stems, and leaves of your crops.

4. As a group, decide on how you will vary the temperature, water, and/or light to encourage germination. (You do not have to vary all three.) Devise a way to measure and record seed growth.

5. As a group, decide on the type of soil or soil-less growing medium you will grow your crops in. You may use a different soil or growing medium (or a mixture) for each pot you will plant. The type of soil or growing medium used must be measured and recorded.

6. As a team, create the plan for growing your crops and recording your data. Make a list of materials you will need for your project.

7. Submit your group's final plan to your teacher. When you have received your teacher's approval, carry out your plan.

8. Monitor the growth of your plant for three weeks or more. (This includes germination time.)

Remember to wash your hands after handling potting soil, growing medium, or fertilizer.

Evaluate

1. At the end of three weeks, which plant was the healthiest? How did you determine plant health?

2. What condition(s) resulted in the best growing conditions in your experiment? Explain why you think these conditions improved the growing conditions for your plants.

3. What condition(s) resulted in poor plant growth? Explain why you think these conditions resulted in poor growth.

4. If you were to grow your crops again, what changes (if any) would you make? Why?

5. While increasing the amount of light, heat, or fertilizer may result in larger plants, there could be a cost to the environment. Explain this statement.

> **MORE PROJECT IDEAS**
>
> Would using a greenhouse change the results of your experiment? Devise a simple greenhouse and use it on one or more of your fields. Does a greenhouse improve the rate of growth? Does it improve the overall health of the crops?

Unit at a Glance

- Plants are critical to the environment and affect soil, water, and air. They cycle nutrients, create oxygen, and provide food and habitats.

- There are many kinds of plants, each adapted to particular growing conditions. Roots, stems, and leaves vary depending on these conditions.

- People use plants to meet their needs for food, medicines, and shelter. People also use plants as raw materials to manufacture many products.

- People have used our vast forests and grasslands, our knowledge of plants, and various technologies to become important producers of food and fibre.

- Plants reproduce sexually and asexually.

- Selective breeding can be used to create varieties of plants with desirable characteristics.

- Some farming practices have dramatically changed native forests and grasslands.

- It is important to grow plants for food and fibre in a sustainable manner so that natural systems remain healthy for future generations.

- Maintaining healthy soil is critical to sustainable harvesting of plants for food and fibre.

- Some agricultural crops can be grown in soil-less media.

- Some farming practices, for example, growing crops in monocultures, have resulted in problems such as the increased need for pest control.

- Alternative practices, such as organic farming and biological pest control, are being used to address the challenges of growing plants for food and fibre while still maintaining a healthy environment.

- Consumers also have a role to play in ensuring the sustainability of growing and harvesting plants for food and fibre.

Understanding Key Concepts

1. Describe two technologies that can be used to modify the growing conditions for a plant.

2. Describe a monoculture. How does this kind agricultural practice make production more efficient? What problems may result?

3. Describe five problems that have resulted from the widespread use of chemical controls.

4. Write a sentence using the words osmosis and diffusion to describe what happens when a tea bag and a spoonful of sugar are placed in a cup of hot water.

5. Name two common medicines that are produced from plants. Explain what each medicine is used to treat.

6. Describe the difference between annuals and perennials.

7. How is photosynthesis significant to the food chain?

8. How is seed dispersal important to the survival of plant species?

9. Describe the essential roles of plants in the environment.

10. Describe three ways that Aboriginal people use plants.

11. Compare the terms selective breeding and genetic modification.

12. Give three examples of characteristics that plants might be bred for. Provide a real example.

13. For each pair of terms below, explain what they have in common and how they differ.

(a) pistil and stamen

(b) flower and cone

(c) anther and stigma

14. Explain why seeds can be referred to as "plants in storage."

15. How are seeds adapted for dispersal by wind? By water? By animals?

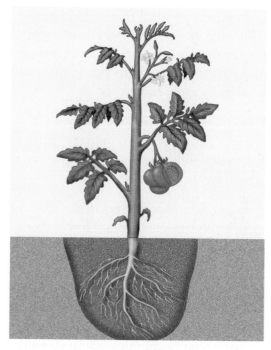

16. Sketch this plant in your notebook. Label the plant parts and their function.

17. Explain what causes soil erosion and three ways in which it can be prevented.

18. Answer the following questions based on the photograph above.

(a) Explain what has happened in this photograph.

(b) Explain how this situation could be a problem for plants.

(c) How can farming practices be altered so that this does not happen?

Developing Skills

19. Make a diagram or a flowchart that demonstrates how photosynthesis works.

20. Use a graphic organizer of your choice to show the steps involved in changing a plant into a product. (For example, show the steps involved in processing trees into lumber.)

21. Use a labelled diagram to show how water enters and moves through a plant.

22. Design an experiment that would determine how different types of fertilizers affect plant growth.

23. Describe two ways to monitor plant growth.

24. Describe how you could monitor and describe plant health.

Problem Solving/Applying

25. During germination, the young plant parts inside the seed begin to grow. Explain why water is one of the most important requirements for germination to begin.

26. Many plants have adaptations that prevent them from self-pollinating. How does this benefit the species?

27. Imagine that you have been awarded the contract to introduce a biological control for dandelions. What factors would you need to consider as you search for the control? As you test it?

28. There are different challenges that arise when improving growing conditions in different settings. Choose one food plant. Compare the challenges one would face in optimizing the growing conditions for this plant in:
    (a) a field
    (b) a greenhouse
    (c) your classroom

29. Over millions of years plants have adapted their structure to survive in their environment. Consider the following structures and describe what problems they solve for the plant.
    (a) Lodgepole pine cones open only when there is intense heat.
    (b) Dandelions have long taproots.
    (c) Strawberry plants have horizontal runners.
    (d) The leaves of the barrel cactus are modified into spines.
    (e) Arctic lupine have seeds that can wait for centuries before sprouting.
    (f) Milkweed seeds are light and feathery.

Critical Thinking

30. Why are many people concerned about the rapid loss of rain forests around the world?

31. In 1883 the tropical island of Krakatoa exploded leaving the entire island devoid of vegetation. It did not take long, however, for plants to begin growing again on this island. Describe three ways in which seeds might have reached the island.

32. There are many stages at which a new plant might have a problem that would prevent pollination or germination. For example, cool weather or lack of pollinators. What steps can growers take to try to ensure that plants successfully grow and reproduce?

33. A beech tree has small, green-coloured flowers. Explain why it is unlikely that beech flowers are pollinated by insects. Suggest the most likely method of pollination.

34. In many of the experiments in this unit you started with sprouted seeds. How is this important to achieving accurate results?

35. Explain why it is important to produce plants for food and fibre in a sustainable manner.

36. What are some factors that farmers or foresters need to consider before choosing a plant to grow in a certain area?

37. Name two plants grown in Alberta for food and/or fibre. Where do these plants grow? What make these plants well suited for growing in this province?

38. Imagine that you are an experienced field crop farmer. You are thinking about buying a particular parcel of land and want to check the soil. Answer the following questions.

(a) How could you test the soil for organic matter?

(b) Why would you be concerned about organic matter?

(c) If the soil is low in organic matter, how could you improve it?

39. Many people who are concerned about the environment would like to see hemp become an important source of fibre in Canada. They say that hemp fibre is more environmentally friendly than wood fibre. Explain the characteristics of hemp that support this position.

40. Why might a farmer decide to use chemical controls rather than other kinds of controls for an insect pest?

Pause&
Reflect

1. People have always used knowledge and technology to help us produce useful products from plants. Give some examples of how our technology and knowledge have changed in the last 100 years.

2. Explain how it is sometimes a challenge to achieve a balance between the needs of people and a sustainable, healthy environment. Use examples that you learned about in this unit.

3. Now that you have completed this unit, go back to the Focussing Questions on page 90. Write answers to these questions in your Science Log.

Heat and Temperature

Imagine a world where people had not learned how to warm or cool anything. Without furnaces or air conditioners, homes and schools would get uncomfortably hot or dangerously cold. No one would ever enjoy a hot meal (no stoves) or an ice-cream treat (no freezers). Almost nothing would be made of metal or glass because these materials require intense heat for shaping. Automobiles, trucks, buses, and even bicycles would not exist. Most of the comforts and conveniences we now enjoy would not exist.

There is no question that devices that use heat and control temperature make our homes more comfortable and our lives more convenient. However, what happens to heat when you open the refrigerator door and stand gazing inside, wondering what to eat? How many hours in a month or a year is your refrigerator door open? How does that affect the amount of energy it uses? If you decide what you want to eat before opening the refrigerator door, will that make a difference? What if your whole class or your whole school decides to limit the amount of time their refrigerator doors stay open? What would be the impact of such an action? In this unit you will investigate some scientific principles that will help you make knowledgeable decisions about energy use.

Unit Contents

- How do you use energy every day?

- What happens to materials when they are heated?

- How can we reduce the amount of energy we use?

How does the energy that keeps us warm and cooks our food get out of control? What do we do then? Topics 1–3 will introduce you to the basics of heat and temperature. You will then move on to find out how to control this energy and how to use it efficiently.

Up and away! Heat technology enables hot air balloons like this one to take off, float through the air, and come back to land. Heat affects other substances, besides air. In Topics 4–6, you can find out what they are and how controlling them benefits us.

How does this experimental aircraft harness energy from the Sun? How will the kind of technology it uses help us to conserve energy resources? In Topics 7–8, you will learn about some exciting possibilities that will meet human needs and benefit our planet.

Looking Ahead

Read the Unit Issue Analysis on pages 260–261. Will there be enough energy resources to last throughout your lifetime? your children's lifetime? your grandchildren's lifetime? How can you get ready for your issue analysis? Here are some ways:

- Start a Solar Centre for material you find about solar energy.

- Become Super Savers by making an energy-saver poster.

- Become Internet Experts. Research and bookmark solar energy sites on the Internet.

- Become Energy Sleuths. Find out about energy and how it "works" by doing the activities and investigations in this unit.

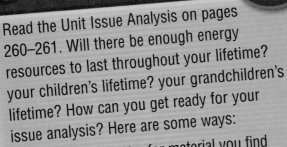

Since ancient times, people have needed thermal energy (heat) to cook their food and to keep them warm. And since the beginning of time, uncontrolled heat has scorched and spoiled the taste of food and has destroyed buildings and homes. In what ways have humans made thermal energy work for them?

Look at the following photographs to see some of the ways in which this form of energy has been used throughout history.

Figure 3.1A Open fires cook food, but they are hard to control, dangerous, and messy.

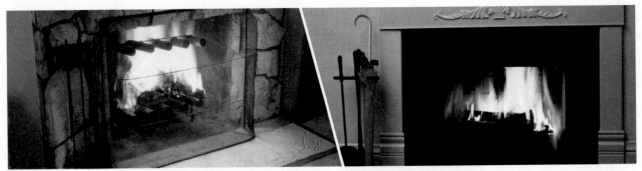

Figure 3.1B Open wood-burning fireplaces (at right) draw the warmth from a room. Modern gas fireplaces (above) use energy efficiently, directing warm air back into the room.

Figure 3.1C Pioneer stoves did double duty heating the home and cooking the food.

Figure 3.1D Modern stoves are attractive, easy to control, and relatively safe to use.

Figure 3.1E This Inuit hunter has built an igloo shelter. When he perspires inside the igloo, the moisture will condense when it hits the ice, sealing the igloo.

Figure 3.1F Sod houses provided protection from the weather, and the soil helped to prevent heat from escaping.

INVESTIGATION 3-A

Using Energy

Think About It

How are your home and school heated? What cooking devices do people in your community use most often—stoves, microwave ovens, toaster ovens, or other appliances? What sources of energy heat buildings and cook food, and power other daily activities where you live? Do people you know rely on solar energy, electricity, natural gas, propane, or fuel oil? Use your skills of communication, organization, and interpreting data to find out.

Procedure

1. With your group, prepare a survey similar to the one shown here. Use it to find out from family and community members the different ways of cooking food and heating homes and workplaces that are used in your community. Find out how often each method is used and why it is chosen.

2. From your group, select one member to be part of a class delegation. The delegation will interview people at your school who look after the heating and ventilation system and any cooking facilities. The delegation can arrange one meeting with the appropriate person(s) and then report back to the other groups.

3. Use library or Internet research to try to find out which energy source is most commonly used in Alberta for:

   (a) heating   (b) cooking

4. Chart the class results of your survey and research.

Respondent	Source of energy to heat building	Source of energy to cook	Method	Why chosen?
Person 1				
Person 2				
Person 3				

Analyze

1. According to your results, which source(s) of energy are used most commonly for heating buildings and cooking food in your community?

2. How well do the results of your survey agree with your findings about the most common energy choices across Alberta? Suggest reasons for any differences.

Extend Your Knowledge

Find out what sources of energy are commonly used in other provinces. Why might the use of these particular sources of energy sometimes result in problems for the users? (You might find out, for example, about the source of energy that is used in the province of Québec. Why did it pose a problem during the Ice Storm of January 1998?)

More Uses of Energy

Over the years we have learned a great deal about efficient ways of heating our homes and cooking our food. The pan of water that boiled dry over the cookfire has been replaced by a whistling kettle on a gas or electric stove. Even more advanced technology has given us "cordless" electric kettles that shut themselves off when the water they contain reaches boiling point. Many other technologies also use thermal energy to make our lives easier or more comfortable.

New technology in electric blankets can help warm up your cold feet without scorching the rest of your body. These blankets have micro-sensors that work like invisible thermostats. They measure the temperature of different parts of your body and generate heat accordingly.

Figure 3.2 Laundry can dry naturally in the open air. Why did humans develop machines to dry their laundry?

As people's ways of life, needs, and wants change, we learn new ways to change and improve technology. As a result, we often can choose among several ways of doing a task. For example, you might sometimes wash your hair and let it dry naturally. If you wash it before you come to school, you might need to dry it more quickly, especially in winter. To do so, you can choose to use a hair dryer.

Looking Ahead

Ask adults you know whether they feel energy conservation is important. If any can suggest ways to conserve energy for cooking and home heating, add their ideas to your Super Saver poster.

As you work through this unit, you will understand how some of these methods work (or why they do not work!).

Figure 3.3 Hair dryers are made to meet various kinds of needs. Why are the buttons necessary?

INTERNET CONNECT

www.mcgrawhill.ca/links/
sciencefocus7

Find out about "soddies." Click on **Web Links** to find out where to go next. Write a story about a day in the life of a "soddie" dweller.

How Was It Made?

Heat technology has been used extensively in industry, as you will see in this activity.

Materials

access to the Internet (if available)

library resources

audiovisual materials

writing materials

Procedure **Performing and Recording**
Communication and Teamwork

1. With your group decide which of the following areas involving the use of heat-related technologies you would like to investigate:

   • ceramics

   • metallurgy (working with metals)

   • use of engines

   You will be finding out about the history of each industry and presenting an audio-visual report on your findings.

2. Decide how to divide the tasks among your group members.

3. Use as many research resources as you can to find out information such as the following:

   • When did this industry begin?

   • Why did it begin? (What needs led to its start and development?)

• What does it produce? If the product is used in a further process or to produce another product, what is the process?

• Were there times when the industry grew especially slowly or quickly?

• What other events in history might have affected its growth or lack of growth?

• How has the technology changed over time?

• What has brought about those changes?

Add your own questions to investigate.

4. When you have completed your research, prepare an audiovisual presentation about what you have learned. Use charts and graphs wherever possible. Be sure to indicate the sources of the information you found.

5. Complete your report by suggesting (with reasons) what your group thinks the future holds for this industry.

What Did You Find Out? ✳ **Analyzing and Interpreting**

1. What kinds of events slowed or speeded up growth in the industry you investigated? Why do you think that was the case?

2. Will future changes in the industry be based on changing needs or on the availability of newer technology — or are the two really the same thing?

TOPIC 1 Review

1. What problems have people experienced in using energy from heat? Give some examples from the text and from your own experience of ways people have tried to resolve these problems.

2. **Apply** What need can you identify in your own life that current technology does not meet? Share your ideas with a partner or with your group and try to think of a new device that will benefit you and your group. Prepare a computer graphic to describe and advertise it.

Measuring Temperature

"Ooh, that wind is as cold as ice. Better stir up the campfire to get those red-hot coals burning again. There, that feels a lot warmer. I hope my hot chocolate hasn't cooled down too much."

You probably think of temperature as a number that tells you how hot or cold something is. That is a practical, everyday definition. As you work through this Topic and the next, you will learn more about the scientific picture of temperature.

Everyday life is full of descriptions of temperature; that is, how warm or cool things are. One way to estimate temperature is just to touch something. Some nerve endings in human skin are quite sensitive to different temperatures, so people can learn to recognize the feeling of particular temperatures by experience. Health-care workers can recognize dangerous body temperatures by touching a patient's forehead with the back of a hand. People who work with very hot, glowing materials can estimate the temperature of the materials by the colour of the light they give off. Welders and glass blowers can estimate when a flame is hot enough to soften metal or glass. Astronomers judge the temperature of stars by the colour of the light they emit.

Estimating temperatures with your eyes or skin is not always safe or reliable, however. Even if glass and metal are not glowing, they can be hot enough to burn you badly. In the winter, when the air temperature rises above freezing after a cold snap, people feel warm and take off their heavy clothing. In the summer, cool winds before a thunderstorm can make people shiver and reach for sweaters, even though the temperature is still far above freezing.

Did You Know?

The record Canadian low temperature of –62.8°C was recorded at Snag, in the Yukon Territory. The Canadian record high temperature of 45°C was recorded in Sweetgrass, Saskatchewan. Try to locate Snag and Sweetgrass on a map of Canada. Then try to find the record high and low temperatures in your area and the dates they were recorded.

Baffle Your Skin

How hot something seems to be when you touch it depends on how warm your skin already is. You can experience this for yourself.

Materials

3 bowls of water, large enough to dip a hand in

hot (not burning) tap water

room-temperature water

cold tap water

Procedure ✴ Performing and Recording

1. Put one hand in the bowl of cold water and the other hand in the bowl of hot water. Hold them there for 1 min.

2. Quickly put both hands in the bowl of room-temperature water. Notice how each hand feels.

3. Repeat steps 1 and 2, but switch hands in step 1.

4. In clear sentences, record how warm the room-temperature water felt to each hand in step 2 and in step 3.

What Did You Find Out? ✴ Analyzing and Interpreting

1. Was there any difference in your observations in steps 2 and 3? If there was, suggest a reason why.

2. Use your observations in this activity to explain how the same air temperature can seem warm in the winter and cool in the summer.

Thermometers

Your senses are easily fooled, but **thermometers** are more reliable. Thermometers are mechanical or electrical devices for measuring temperature. A thermometer similar to the one in Figure 3.4A was constructed by the Italian scientist Galileo in the early seventeenth century. One hundred years later, the design was improved, as Figure 3.4B shows. However, an important part of modern thermometers was still missing. Examine the photographs carefully to find out what it was.

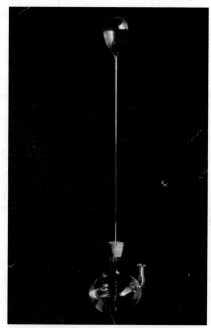

Figure 3.4A Galileo invented his air thermometer around 1600. As the air in the upper bulb cooled or warmed, a bubble of liquid moved up or down in the tube.

Figure 3.4B More portable thermometers, like this liquid thermometer invented around 1700, were made by putting the liquid in the bulb and part way up the stem.

Temperature Scales

When you examined Figures 3.4A and 3.4B, you probably noticed that these early thermometers do not have **scales**. That is, they have no markings with numbers to indicate a precise temperature. As scientists discovered more and more about the effects of temperature, they needed to measure temperatures precisely. Modern thermometers, such as the one in Figure 3.4C, have gradations or evenly spaced lines that allow you to read exact temperatures.

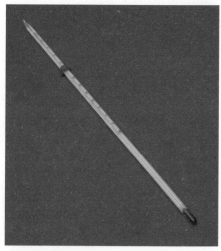

Figure 3.4C A modern laboratory thermometer has a smaller bulb and a much narrower opening in the glass stem.

Figure 3.5 Anders Celsius suggested his temperature scale in 1742.

For any form of measurement, someone has to decide on a unit and a standard for comparison. Today, the temperature scale commonly used in Canada and many other countries is called the **Celsius scale** in honour of Anders Celsius (1701–1744). He used the "degree" as the unit of temperature. He based his standards for comparison on the properties of water, the most abundant liquid on Earth. Celsius assigned zero degrees to the temperature at which ice melts at sea level. He assigned a value of one hundred degrees to the temperature at which liquid water boils at sea level. Then he separated the region between these temperatures into 100 evenly spaced units or degrees. (The degrees below zero and above 100 are also evenly spaced.)

loose and packed snow

"firn" (snow/ice grains)

solid glacial ice

moving (plastic) ice

Figure 3.6 The bottom layer of a glacier does not behave like solid ice. It acts more like a very stiff liquid! The tremendous weight pressing down on the base of the glacier slowly squeezes the ice crystals out of shape, causing the glacier to flow forward. High pressure also changes the nature of ice crystals in other ways. Light shining through the lower part of the glacier appears bluish-green even though ice itself is colourless.

Step 1

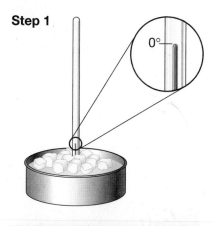

Step 2

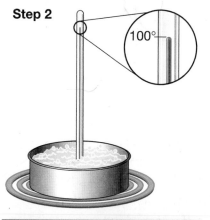

Step 3

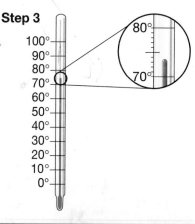

The liquid level in an ice-water bath is marked as 0°.

The liquid level in boiling water is marked as 100°.

The scale is divided into 100 equal degrees and numbered.

Figure 3.7 Steps in calibrating a Celsius thermometer at sea level.

The two fixed temperatures that Celsius chose — freezing water (0°C) and boiling water (100°C) — can be used for calibrating thermometers. Study Figure 3.7 to find one way this can be done. To be accurate, this type of calibration must be done at sea level using very pure water. Impurities in water change its boiling and freezing points. Salt water, for example does not freeze until it is colder than 0°C.

Pressure also affects the boiling point and freezing point of water. Extremely high pressures, such as those under a glacier or a skate blade, cause ice to flow or even melt at temperatures below 0°C (Figure 3.6). Ice skaters actually glide on a thin layer of water! Under low pressure, water boils before it reaches 100°C. In Alberta, for example, the high altitude means that the weight of the air above you is smaller than it would be at sea level. As a result, water in Alberta boils at several degrees less than 100°C. At the top of Mount Everest, water would boil at only 69°C.

As scientists developed theories to explain the behaviour of gases at different temperatures, they realized that they needed a temperature scale that started at the coldest possible temperature, or "absolute zero." This new temperature scale was named the **Kelvin scale**, in honour of William Thomson (1824–1907), who was given the title Lord Kelvin. Although no one has ever been able to cool anything down to absolute zero, scientists predict that the temperature is –273.15°C.

The units of temperature on the Kelvin scale are not degrees but are simply called kelvins. For example, the freezing temperature of water at sea level is 273.15 K (read, two hundred seventy three point one five kelvins). When it is not necessary to be extremely precise, this temperature is usually rounded to 273 K.

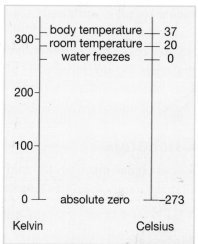

Figure 3.8 The Kelvin temperature scale is used by scientists. Try to use the diagram to express room temperature, body temperature, and other common temperatures in Kelvins.

Make Your Own Thermometer

A

- cold damp dishcloth
- air
- straw
- airtight plug
- coloured water

B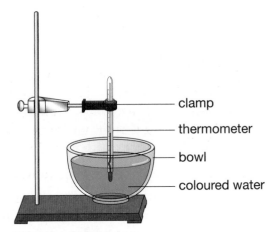

- clamp
- thermometer
- bowl
- coloured water

Today thermometers and other scientific instruments are mass-produced in factories. Early scientists, however, had to build their own measuring devices. Their clever designs used everyday materials, yet produced accurate measurements. Can you use modern materials to build a working model of one of the earliest thermometer designs?

Challenge

Use everyday materials to build a thermometer that accurately measures temperatures in your classroom.

Materials

small glass bottle with a narrow neck (for example, a small pop bottle)

drinking straw or length of tubing

one-hole stopper

laboratory stand and ring clamp

dishcloth

paper

pen

ruler

calculator

bowl of water with food colouring added

modelling clay or silicone glue

ice-cold water

The class also needs two calibration devices, assembled as in diagram B.

Safety Precautions

Silicone glue does not wash off hands or clothing. It irritates skin and emits fumes as it hardens. If you use it, follow your teacher's directions carefully and work in a well-ventilated area. Wear gloves, eye protection, and an apron, and work on newspaper. Use craft sticks or wide toothpicks to apply and shape the smallest possible quantity of the glue. Roll up the craft sticks in the newspaper when you are finished, and discard them in the garbage.

Specifications

A. Thermometers built in Part 1 should detect increases in temperature when your teacher warms them gently with a hair dryer and decreases in temperature when they are cooled with a cold washcloth.

B. At the end of Part 2, the thermometer will have a properly constructed scale with evenly spaced degree markings and suitable numbering.

C. The thermometer must measure the temperature of the classroom accurately. The reading should be within 2°C of the temperature measured by a standard laboratory thermometer.

Skill
FOCUS

For tips on scientific problem solving, turn to Skill Focus 7.

Part 1

Assembling the Thermometer

Plan and Construct

1 Using the materials your teacher provides, your group will design and assemble a thermometer like the one illustrated in diagram A. The straw or tubing needs to have an airtight seal against the bottle neck. Tape does not work very well. If necessary, put it in a one-hole stopper that fits the bottle. You could use modelling clay to make a good seal.

2 Warm the bottle with your hands. Record what happens in the dish at the end of the straw. Troubleshooting: If nothing happens, your hands are probably about the same temperature as the bottle. Try wetting a dishcloth with warm water, wringing it out, and draping it over the top of the bottle.

3 Wet a dishcloth with cold water, wring it out, and drape it over the bottle. What happens to the level of water inside the straw?

4 When you are sure that your thermometer is working correctly, have your teacher certify that it meets Specification A.

Evaluate

1. Which part of your thermometer responds to changes in temperature? Describe how it responds when the air in the bottle

   (a) warms up   **(b)** cools down

2. Why might you add marks and numbers to your thermometer? Where would you put them?

Part 2

Calibrating the Thermometer

Plan and Construct

1 Plan how to create a scale for your thermometer so that it can measure temperatures accurately. Here are some hints:

(a) Your scale needs to be fastened to the thermometer, then taken off for measuring and marking, and then replaced on the thermometer in its original position.

(b) Start by marking the scale at two known temperatures at least 10 degrees apart. You could use two wet washcloths or sponges. Soak one in water with a known cool temperature. Wrap it around the top of your thermometer and watch the liquid level fall. Mark the lowest level.

(c) Repeat (b) using a washcloth soaked in water with a known warm temperature. Mark the highest level the liquid in your thermometer reaches.

(d) You now have two markings on your scale, for two different temperatures. Take the scale off the thermometer and mark the proper temperatures beside each mark.

(e) Measure the number of millimetres between the two marks.

(f) Subtract to find the number of degrees between the two marks.

(g) Divide to find how many millimetres on your scale stand for each degree celsius. Ask your teacher for help if necessary.

2 Use your calculations to finish marking your thermometer scale. Be sure to number the scale every 5 or 10 degrees.

3 Show your teacher or another lab group that your calibrated thermometer meets Specifications B and C.

Evaluate

1. Did your thermometer meet the design specifications? How could you improve it?

2. Describe the main problems that you had building your thermometer. How did you overcome each problem?

3. Why are thermometers designed like yours not very useful in everyday life?

Boiling Hot, Freezing Cold

Think About It

You can probably guess many familiar temperatures quite accurately. Other temperatures may surprise you! As you follow the directions, make sure that you learn the temperatures described in italics.

Procedure

1. In your notebook, make a table with three columns labelled "Very cold," "Everyday," and "Very hot." Give your table a title.

2. Copy each description from the table on the right into the proper column in your table.

3. For each description, choose the correct temperature from the right-hand column of the table. Write the temperature beside the description. Discuss your answers with your partner until you agree on each one.

4. Check your answers against the list your teacher has. Correct any mistakes you made.

5. Have your partner quiz you to make sure that you know the common temperatures, which are printed in italics.

This "Morning Glory Pool" is heated by energy from deep within Earth. The water remains about 95°C even with snow on the ground nearby.

	Description	Temperature (°C)
1	temperature of lava from Hawaiian volcanoes	4 to 10
2	temperature of ocean currents off Canada's east coast	−5
3	temperature of ocean currents off Canada's west coast	−87
4	world record coldest air temperature	−121 to −156
5	*comfortable room temperature*	92
6	body temperature of a budgie bird	15 000 000
7	temperature where the Space Shuttle flies in orbit	−10 to −15
8	temperature of a candle flame	200
9	comfortable temperature for heat-loving bacteria	20 to 25
10	*normal human body temperature*	37
11	temperature of ice cream	40
12	oven temperature for baking bread	1
13	temperature of food in a freezer	100
14	temperature of the interior of the Sun	6000
15	temperature of hot tea or coffee	1150
16	*temperature of boiling water at sea level*	55
17	*temperature of a slush of pure water and ice*	800
18	temperature of the surface of the Sun	0

The descriptions in this table do not match the temperature in the column beside them. Your job is to work with a partner to unscramble them.

The Right Device for the Job

Could you use the same device to measure the temperature of the surface of the Sun and the body temperature of a parrot? Probably not. Thermometers have been developed to suit almost every purpose, from measuring the extreme cold of outer space to estimating the temperatures of stars. Each of the thermometers described below contains a **sensor** — a material which is affected by changes in some feature of the environment, such as temperature. The sensor produces a **signal** — information about temperature, such as an electrical current. The signal affects a **responder** — a pointer, light, or other mechanism that uses the signal in some way.

The Thermocouple

In a thermocouple, wires made of two different metals are twisted together. When the twisted wire tips are heated, a small electrical current is generated. The amount of current depends on the temperature of the wires. The electrical current from the thermocouple can be used to turn a switch or a valve on or off if the temperature changes.

Thermocouples can measure temperatures so high that ordinary laboratory thermometers fail because the liquid in them would start to boil. They cannot be used to measure low temperatures accurately.

The Bimetallic Strip

A bimetallic strip is made of two different metals joined firmly together. As the strip is heated, one metal expands more than the other. The strip is forced to coil more tightly. When the strip cools, the process is reversed. The same metal that expanded rapidly now contracts rapidly and the strip uncoils again. Movements of the strip can operate a type of electrical switch, which can be used to control furnaces, air conditioners, refrigerators, or other devices. Examine Figure 3.10 to find out how a bimetallic strip turns a furnace on and off.

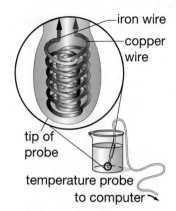

Figure 3.9 A thermocouple being used to measure the temperature of a liquid

Pause&Reflect

Try to identify the parts of each thermometer described here. What is the function of each responder? Does it display information, make a permanent record, control some other device, or do some other useful task?

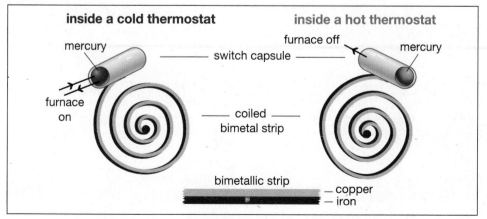

Figure 3.10 In a thermostat, the bimetallic strip is fastened to a glass capsule containing a drop of liquid mercury metal. When the bimetallic strip cools, the capsule tilts. The mercury rolls to one end, fills the gap between two wires, and completes an electrical circuit. The furnace or air conditioner is switched on. When the bimetallic strip bends the other way, the mercury rolls away from the wires, breaking the circuit. The furnace or air conditioner is switched off.

DidYouKnow?

Your body has its own temperature sensor inside your brain. It monitors your internal temperature. If the temperature outside your body changes, the sensor signals the brain to release chemicals that will enable your body to adjust to its normal 37°C.

The Recording Thermometer

In one type of recording thermometer, a bimetallic strip coils and uncoils as the temperature changes. One end of the strip is attached to a long, light metal lever that holds a special pen. Tiny movements of the bimetallic strip cause much larger movements of the free end of the lever and the pen. The pen traces a rising and falling line on a strip of paper attached to a slowly turning drum. The drum usually makes one turn every seven days, so each strip of paper contains a record of temperature changes for an entire week. (You will find out about another instrument that works in a similar way in Unit 5.)

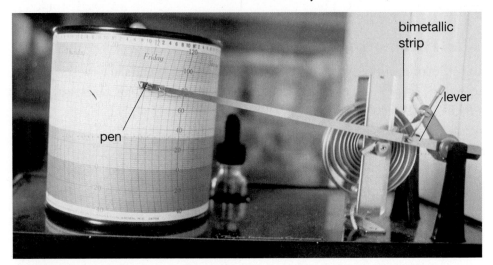

Figure 3.11 This recording thermometer uses a bimetallic strip to detect changes in temperature. The end of the coil is attached to the short end of a lever. The long end of the lever is attached to a pen that makes a permanent recording of the temperature on graph paper attached to a rotating drum.

The Infrared Thermogram

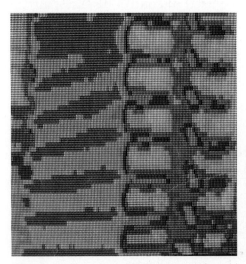

The photograph on the left shows an infrared image; the one on the right is a normal photograph of the same image. What colours in the thermogram indicate the highest and lowest temperatures? In the winter, how could you identify air leaks around doors and windows from an infrared image? How could a building owner use this information to reduce heating costs and conserve fuel?

Objects do not have to be glowing red hot to give off radiation. Anything that is warmer than absolute zero gives off infrared radiation (IR), a type of radiation similar to light, that your eyes cannot detect. Your skin can detect infrared radiation when you are near hot objects. Even if you are not actually touching the object, you can feel the warmth. Infrared radiation can be photographed with special films or detected by electronic sensors that display images on television screens. The colour or brightness of the infrared image shows the temperature of the object (see Figure 3.12). In Topic 8, you will learn more about a Cool Tool that uses IR.

INTERNET CONNECT

www.mcgrawhill.ca/links/sciencefocus7

Warm objects, such as your body, give off more infrared radiation than cool objects. Thermograms of certain body parts can help physicians diagnose some medical problems. To explore more about this topic go to the web site above. Click on **Web Links** to find out where to go next.

TOPIC 2 Review

1. Suppose that you were present on the hottest day ever reported in Canada.

   (a) What would your body temperature have been?

   (b) If the air temperature had dropped by 5°C, would you have felt warm or cold?

2. Describe how a thermostat controls the temperature in a building.

3. **Apply** What might be the advantages and disadvantages of using a thermocouple instead of a regular lab thermometer?

4. **Apply** Many household appliances, such as irons, are heated electrically. They usually contain a thermostat that switches electricity on and off to keep the appliance at a constant temperature. Think of at least three examples of other appliances that might use thermostats to switch electricity on and off.

5. **Thinking Critically** Choose the most appropriate temperature-measuring instrument to use in each situation below. In each case, explain your choice.

   (a) controlling an electric frying pan

   (b) making long-term temperature records at a weather office

   (c) detecting small forest fires before they spread

   (d) monitoring temperatures inside a furnace

   (e) checking trains for overheating wheel bearings as they pass by a station

   (f) studying temperature changes inside a building over a 24 h period

DidYouKnow?

Some kinds of crystals turn certain colours at different temperatures. You may have seen these crystals in strips used to take your temperature. When you place the strip on your forehead, the crystals that change colour will show the temperature of your skin.

TOPIC 3 The Particle Model, Temperature, and Thermal Energy

Try waving your hand in the air. Now think about moving your hand through water. Is that easier or more difficult? What if you tried to move your hand through wood or steel? How difficult is that? Why? Moving your hand through air is easy because the particles that make up air are spaced far enough apart. Your hand can easily move them aside. Why might such movement be more difficult where the other substances are concerned?

First, you should know that the particles in all matter are extremely small. What do the words "extremely small" mean in relation to the particle model? Imagine a drop of water balanced on your fingertip. How many individual water particles are clinging together to create the drop? The answer is about 1 700 000 000 000 000 000 000 — one thousand seven hundred million million million! No wonder you cannot see the particles with your unaided eye.

Pouring? Shaping? Filling?

Scientists use the idea of particles to explain the properties that are common to all solids, all liquids, and all gases. This diagram shows how the particle model explains a solid, liquid, and gas.

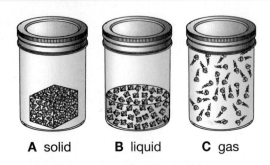

A solid   **B** liquid   **C** gas

Procedure ✳ Analyzing and Interpreting

Examine the diagram to find the answers to the following questions.

Find Out ACTIVITY

1. Name the state(s) in which a material
   (a) has a fixed shape
   (b) takes the shape of its container
   (c) always fills whatever container it is in

2. Name the state(s) in which the particles are
   (a) far apart from each other
   (b) relatively close together
   (c) free to move around
   (d) held in fixed positions

What Did You Find Out? ✳ Analyzing and Interpreting

Use the particle model to explain your answers to questions 1 and 2.

The **particle model of matter** is a scientific description of many different features of these tiny particles. Three of the most important ideas of the model are:

- All substances are made of tiny particles too small to be seen.
- The particles are always in motion—vibrating, rotating, and (in liquids and gases) moving from place to place.
- The particles have spaces between them.

Detect a Connection

Find Out **ACTIVITY**

How does a material change when it is warmed or cooled? How does warming or cooling affect the tiny particles of which everything is made?

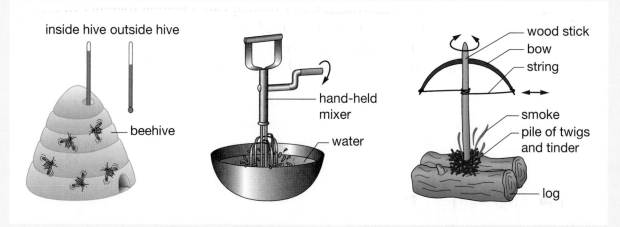

inside hive outside hive

beehive

hand-held mixer

water

wood stick
bow
string

smoke
pile of twigs and tinder

log

Procedure ✳ Analyzing and Interpreting

Carefully examine each picture. Then answer the following questions.

1. One way that bees control the temperature in their hive is by beating their wings vigorously. Explain what happens to
   (a) the motion of the air particles in the hive
   (b) the air temperature in the hive

2. Water warms up slightly if it is stirred vigorously.
   (a) What happens to the motion of the water particles as they are stirred?
   (b) How is the behaviour of the water particles similar to the behaviour of the air particles in the beehive in question 1?

3. To start a fire, early people used a fire drill to twirl a stick pressed against a piece of wood.
   (a) What happened to the temperature at the pointed end of the drill?
   (b) What do you think caused the particles of wood to change temperature?

What Did You Find Out? ✳ Analyzing and Interpreting

1. What common feature caused the changes in temperature in each example you examined?

2. Identify at least two other situations that are similar to the three examples in this activity.

Temperature and the Particle Model

As you probably noticed in the last activity, if the motion of the particles in a substance changes, the temperature of the substance changes, too. When a substance warms — when its temperature increases — its particles are moving faster. When a substance cools — when its temperature decreases — its particles are moving more slowly.

This idea forms the basis for a fourth point in the particle model:

• The motion of the particles increases when the temperature increases. The motion of the particles decreases when the temperature decreases.

It is not easy to test this idea directly. As you now know, the smallest particles of matter are too tiny to observe clearly. They can be observed only in large groups. In any substance, some particles always seem to be moving faster than average. Other particles seem to be moving unusually slowly. The *average* speed of many particles, however, is always indicated by their temperature.

Temperature indicates the average speed of particle motion in a substance.

What Is Energy?

Energy is a measure of something's ability to do work — in other words, to cause changes. Whenever something happens, scientists are sure that energy is being transferred from one thing to another. Figure 3.13 shows some everyday examples. As you study the illustrations, try to describe three features of each situation:

• What has high energy? What has low energy?

• What change is being caused as energy is transferred?

• What source provides energy for the change? To what is the energy transferred?

Figure 3.13A Fully charged batteries can power a stereo; dead batteries cannot. A charged battery stores more energy than a dead battery.

Figure 3.13B A hot drink warms you more than a cold drink. Hot substances have higher thermal energy than cold materials.

Figure 3.13C Catching a heavy, fast-moving baseball stings more than catching a light, slow-moving Ping-Pong™ ball. The baseball has much more energy of motion than the Ping-Pong™ ball.

Hot-air balloons, ovens, a hot tub — these and many other devices are designed to release and transfer **thermal energy** (energy associated with hot objects). The fuel in a hot-air balloon burns, transferring thermal energy to air, which warms, expands, and lifts the balloon. Hot metal elements in an oven transfer thermal energy to food, warming and cooking it. Hot water in a hot tub transfers thermal energy to people in the tub.

Have you noticed the same two features of each energy example in this section? You can identify them in any situation where change is occurring.

(a) Changes happen when there is a *difference* of energy. Every useful energy system has a high-energy source that powers the changes.

(b) Energy is always transferred in the same direction: *from* a high-energy source *to* something with lower energy.

Word CONNECT

The term "thermal energy" has a precise scientific meaning, but it is not used very much in everyday language. Scientists sometimes use the word "heat," but they give it a specific meaning: thermal energy being transferred because of temperature differences. To avoid confusion, this textbook uses the scientific terms "thermal energy" and "energy transfer" whenever possible. Can you think of other words that have slightly different meanings in science and everyday life?

Cool Tools

Energy is measured in joules (J), in honour of James Joule (1818–1889), an amateur scientist who devoted his life to studying energy. To investigate the connection between energy and temperature changes, Joule built many ingenious devices. One was a set of paddle wheels that stirred water as they were turned by falling weights. The temperature of the water increased a small, but measurable, amount. If you have a sensitive computerized temperature probe, you could repeat Joule's experiment using an electric mixer or a blender to stir the water.

Thermal Energy and Temperature Changes

Does your bedroom get chilly on cold winter nights? In just a few minutes, a small electric heater can warm the room up. The heater transfers thermal energy to the air. The air particles move faster as their average energy increases. You notice the temperature rising.

Now imagine trying to warm a very large building — maybe your school gymnasium — using the same heater running for the same amount of time. What a hopeless task! The same amount of thermal energy would be transferred to the air. But in the larger room there are many more air particles. Each particle gets only a tiny share of the extra energy. The average energy of the particles increases, but only a tiny bit. The air temperature rises, but not very much.

You can see that there is a connection between thermal energy and temperature. Heating anything increases the *total* energy of all its particles. The *average* energy of the particles — the temperature of the substance — may increase a little or a lot. The temperature change depends on the number of particles; that is, the amount of material you are heating.

What about cooling? Imagine putting an ice cube in a glass of warm lemonade. The ice *absorbs* thermal energy as it melts. With less energy, the average motion of the particles in the lemonade slows down. The temperature of the lemonade drops.

Potters need to check the very high temperatures inside the kilns that bake and harden their pottery. To do this, they use small ceramic pyramids called "pyrometric cones" like the ones shown in the photograph. Sets of four cones are placed in the kiln along with the pottery being fired. Two of the cones soften and bend over as the kiln heats up. The third cone bends at the desired temperature. If the fourth cone bends, the kiln has overheated and the pottery may be damaged. Potters refer to cones by code numbers. For example, a number 022 cone bends at 585°C, a number 1 cone bends at 1125°C, and a number 26 cone bends at 1595°C.

Could the same ice cube cool off a bath or hot tub filled with steaming water? Hardly! The ice would absorb the same total amount of thermal energy as it melted. The average energy of the particles would drop only a tiny bit, because there are so many of them. Again, the temperature change depends on the amount of material, as well as on the change in thermal energy.

What Energy Is ... and Is Not

"I just don't have enough energy to do my homework."
"I'm so hungry! I need a big meal to get enough energy for the soccer game."
"You look exhausted! Did cleaning your room use up all your energy?"

Energy is *not* a substance. It cannot be weighed. It does not take up space. Energy describes a quality or condition. Think about words that describe other qualities or conditions. You might describe the drums in a band as "loud," but that does not mean they are filled with extra "loudness." If the guitar is played softly, that does not mean its "loudness" is almost used up.

What is energy? Energy is a property or quality of an object or substance that gives it the ability to move, do work, or cause changes. Energy is the topic of one of the most important laws of nature. The Law of Conservation of Energy states that: *Energy cannot be created or destroyed. It can only be transformed from one type to another or passed from one object to another.*

Is it still okay to say, "Wow, I'm feeling full of energy today"? Of course! Everyday language is fine for everyday life. Just remember to be more precise when you are giving a scientific description.

Across Canada

Imagine trying to keep a toboggan hill covered in ice in the blazing sun, with the temperature well above freezing. That is the challenge that Bruce Welsh often faces between September and March each year. Bruce is supervisor of the refrigeration plant at Canada Olympic Park in Calgary, Alberta. As part of his job, he looks after the 2 km winding track that is used for bobsled and luge races. No matter what the weather, the ice on the track must be kept at 0 or −1°C. That's the ideal temperature for the high-level competitions and training that take place there.

The track is made of concrete. Inside it, just below the surface, is a system of pipes. Equipment in the refrigeration plant cools a liquid called a refrigerant and pumps it through these pipes to chill the track. This helps build up the layer of ice each September and keeps it from melting throughout the season. Bruce and his staff monitor the weather, and adjust the equipment to chill the refrigerant

Bruce Welsh

to a temperature that will keep the ice at the freezing point. Some days that's not easy.

"One year," Bruce recalls, "the air temperature reached 18°C in December. We had to run virtually every piece of equipment in our plant to successfully hold the ice." Very cold days can be a problem too. Frost forms on the ice making it "sticky" and slowing down the sleds. Bruce can raise the ice temperature only by having crew members carefully spray it with water between races.

Dealing with whatever nature throws his way doesn't faze Bruce. "It's challenging, but the variety is what makes my job really interesting."

TOPIC 3 Review

1. List the main points of the particle model of matter that were presented in this section. (Hint: Look back to pages 203 and 204.)

2. Why is it so hard to test the particle model to see if it is correct? (Hint: see page 204.)

3. Describe two situations in your life in which caused changes in something.

4. Name an important discovery or idea contributed by each of these scientists.
   (a) James Joule
   (b) Anders Celsius
   (c) Lord Kelvin

5. How is thermal energy different from temperature? (Hint: You have studied three answers to this question so far).

6. **Thinking Critically** Modern scientists do not use Lavoisier's "caloric fluid" theory (see the Did You Know? on page 204). If this theory is wrong, why do you suppose it is discussed in many science textbooks?

7. **Thinking Critically** Think of a form of energy that you knew by name before you studied Topic 3.

Pause & Reflect

The ideas in this Topic are tricky! Use them to write a short explanation in your Science Log that demonstrates your understanding of temperature, particle motion, and energy (especially thermal energy). Use your own words, and include examples or diagrams. With a partner, take turns reading your explanations. How are your ideas similar? How are they different?

If you need to check an item, Topic numbers are provided in brackets below.

Key Terms

thermometers	energy	responder
scales	Celsius scale	thermal energy
particle model	sensor	temperature
of matter	signal	Kelvin scale

Reviewing Key Terms

1. In your notebook, copy and complete the word game to find the name of a form of energy that you have studied in this unit.

   (a) _ _ _ ▮ _ _ _ _

   (b) _ ▮ _ _ _ _ _ _ _ ▮ ▮

   (c) _ _ ▮ _ _ _

   (d) _ _ _ _ ▮ _ _ _

   (e) _ _ ▮ _ _ _ _ _ _ _

   (f) _ _ ▮ _ _ _

   (g) _ _ ▮ _ _ _ _

   (a) The ▮▮▮▮▮ model of matter (3)

   (b) temperature-measuring device (2)

   (c) a measurement of something's ability to do work (3)

   (d) correctly position the number lines on a thermometer (2)

   (e) measure of the average speed of a substance's particles (2)

   (f) number markings that indicate a precise temperature (2)

   (g) temperature scale commonly used in Canada (2)

Understanding Key Concepts

2. Give a reasonable temperature (in degrees Celsius) for each of the following situations: freezing water, room temperature, normal human body temperature, boiling water. (2)

3. Describe three steps in calibrating a thermometer. (2)

4. (a) What do thermometers measure? (2)

   (b) What do thermometers actually detect about the moving particles that make up a sample of matter? (3)

5. What points in the particle model did you use in Topics 1–3? List them in point form. (2–3)

6. In your notebook, copy and complete the following table to explain the meaning of thermal energy. Give your table a title. (3)

	Substance with a large amount of thermal energy	Substance with a small amount of thermal energy
Average speed of particle motion		
Temperature		

7. In your notebook, copy and complete the following table to compare thermal energy and temperature. Give your table a title. (2)

	Thermal energy	Temperature
SI units of measurement		
What it tells about particles of matter		
Measuring device or method		

8. Explain how to make a rechargeable battery have each of these forms of energy: electrical energy, thermal energy. (3)

9. Copy and complete each of the following sentence starters.

   (a) As particle motion increases, the temperature … (3)

   (b) As thermal energy increases, particles in a substance move … (3)

   (c) As thermal energy increases, particles' average speed … (3)

10. With a partner, create a short skit to show the behaviour of particles of matter in each of these situations: low temperature, warming up, small amount of thermal energy, a large amount of thermal energy. (2, 3)

Expansion and Contraction

As materials warm up, the particle model of matter says that their particles move faster and spread apart. We expect substances to **expand** (increase in volume) as their temperature rises. Falling temperature means that average particle motion is slowing down. It seems logical to expect substances to **contract** (decrease in volume) as they cool.

You can check those predictions by observing the behaviour of common pure substances. A pure substance is a type of matter that is made of only one kind of particle. On Earth, a pure substance may exist as a solid, liquid, or gas. These are the three states or phases of matter. Gold, oxygen, and water are examples of pure substances. Examine the illustrations to review the key characteristics of each state.

Figure 3.14 The three states of matter

In the solid state, materials keep their shape and size. Solids like ice have a definite shape and volume and cannot be compressed into a smaller space. In the liquid state, materials have a definite size (volume), but no fixed shape. Liquids like water settle to the bottom of their container and take its shape. Liquids cannot be compressed. Gases have no definite shape or volume. They expand to fill all parts of their container and can easily be compressed into a smaller space. Many gases cannot be seen. For example, the space just above a kettle's spout is filled with invisible water vapour (steam). As the water vapour (water in the gaseous state) rises and cools, it forms a cloud of tiny drops of liquid water.

Pause& Reflect

Write some ideas to answer the questions below. Do not worry about being "correct." You can change your ideas as you work through this Topic.

(a) Are the ice, liquid water, and water vapour in the illustrations made of the same kind of particle, or are they different types of matter?

(b) How does the motion of particles in solids, liquids, and gases differ?

Room to Grow

Civil engineers have to think about thermal expansion and contraction when planning roadways, sidewalks, and bridges.

Imagine that a builder or a civil engineer has been invited to speak to your class. Write five questions that you would like to ask this person about engineering as a profession. Make sure that your questions are clearly worded, and that they will help you find out what you want to know.

Expansion and Contraction of Solids

The lengths of solid bars of different materials can be measured at different temperatures using very precise equipment. Table 1 shows some of these measurements. You can see that the changes in a 100 cm long bar are very small. If the bar were twice as long, however, the changes would be twice as large. In a very long structure, such as a bridge or a train track, the small changes can add up and become very important.

Table 1 Expansion and Contraction of Solids

Material	Length at –100°C (cm)	Length at 0°C (cm)	Length at 100°C (cm)
lead	99.71	100.00	100.29
steel	99.89	100.00	100.11
aluminum	99.77	100.00	100.23
brass	99.81	100.00	100.19
copper	99.83	100.00	100.17
glass	99.91	100.00	100.09
Pyrex™	99.97	100.00	100.03

Stretch and Shrink

Are there similarities in how substances expand when heated? Are there similarities in how they behave when cooled? This activity will help you to identify any patterns.

Find Out ACTIVITY

Procedure ❋ Performing and Recording

1. Examine Table 1 above, and use it to answer these questions.

   (a) What similarity do you see in how all the materials react as they warm?

   (b) In what way do the materials react differently as they warm?

   (c) Which material expands the most as it warms?

   (d) Which material expands the least as it warms?

2. Copy the list of materials in Table 1, but arrange them in order, starting with the material that expands the most and ending with the one that expands the least.

What Did You Find Out? ❋ Analyzing and Interpreting

1. What do you notice about your list when you examine how the materials cool and contract? Does the material that expands the most at a high temperature also contract the most at a low temperature?

2. **Apply** A baker places a paper cone into the centre of a fruit pie before putting the pie in the oven. Explain why this would keep juice from running out of the pie during baking.

Expanding Solids

When substances are heated and cooled, changes in size can be small and easy to overlook. Make a prediction and then check it in this activity.

Question

What evidence can you observe of solid materials expanding as they are warmed, and contracting as they are cooled?

Hypothesis

1 Complete the following hypothesis statements. Particle theory suggests that

(a) when a material is heated it will …

(b) when a material is cooled it will …

Safety Precautions

You will be working with an open flame and hot objects. Be careful!

Apparatus

long copper or iron wire

small hooked mass (200 g or 500 g)

metre stick

ball-and-ring apparatus

laboratory burner

2 lab stands

2 C clamps

Materials

candles, matches, cold water

Skill
FOCUS

For tips on making predictions, turn to Skill Focus 6.

Part 1
The Sagging Wire

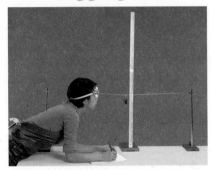 

Procedure

1 Study the procedure steps below. Then use your hypothesis to **write a specific prediction**. What will happen to the weight as the wire warms and cools?

2 Clamp two supports firmly to the table and stretch the wire tightly between them. Place the small mass in the middle of the wire. Put the metre stick behind the mass, and **record** its height.

3 Use lighted candles to warm the entire length of the wire for several minutes. **Observe** and carefully **record** the height of the mass after each 30 s of heating.

4 Stop warming the wire. **Observe** and **record** what happens to the height of the mass during the next 2 or 3 min.

Analyze

1. (a) If the wire sags, the mass moves down. Does this mean that the wire is getting longer or shorter?

(b) What is happening to the length of the wire if the mass moves up?

2. Did you **observe** what you predicted would happen?

3. Did your observations **support your hypothesis**?

Part 2

Your teacher will do the heating in Part 2 as a demonstration.

The Ball and Ring

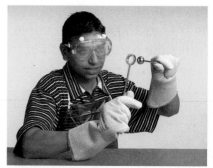

Procedure

1 **Observe** whether the brass ball fits through the brass ring when both the ball and the ring are at room temperature.

2 Study the procedure steps that follow. Then use your hypothesis to **write a specific prediction**. How will heating change whether the ball fits through the ring?

3 **Observe** whether the ball fits through the ring when your teacher warms only the ring in a hot flame for 30 s.

4 **Observe** what happens when your teacher warms both the ring and the ball.

5 As a class, brainstorm possible ways to make the ball fit through the ring. You or your teacher will test the ideas until one method works. With the ball through the ring, cool both the ball and ring. Try to pull the ball back through the ring. If you cannot, find a way to separate them by warming or cooling.

Analyze

1. How did the demonstration give evidence that solids can expand? Describe what your teacher did to cause the expansion and which part of the apparatus (the ball, the ring, or both) expanded.

2. How did the demonstration give evidence that solids can contract? Describe what you did to cause the contraction and which part of the apparatus (the ball, the ring, or both) contracted.

3. How well did your hypothesis help you predict the behaviour of the ball and ring? Was it a useful hypothesis, or would you like to modify it?

4. Use the particle model to **explain** why objects expand and contract when heated. Review page 210 for clues.

Conclude and Apply

5. **Predict** how the position of the electric transmission lines in the photograph below, taken in summer, would change as the temperature dropped in winter. Why would it be a bad idea to stretch the transmission lines more tightly between the towers so they would sag less in the summer?

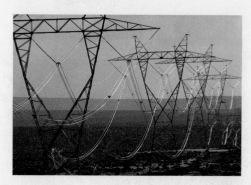

Pause&
Reflect

You have observed gases expanding, in your work in this unit and in every-day life. Think about the situations below, and answer the questions in your Science Log.

(a) A spray can, even when it is almost empty, contains compressed gases. Why does the safety warning on the label tell you not to dispose of the can by putting it in a fire?

(b) The tires on a car are filled with compressed air. In the winter, when the air temperature drops very low, the tires become slightly flat, even when they are not leaking. Why?

Expansion and Contraction in Gases

Because most common gases are colourless, they are difficult to observe. As well, gases have no fixed shape or size. (Remember that they always take the shape and size of their container.) If you put gases in a flexible container such as a balloon, however, you can see that they expand and contract much more than solids when the temperature changes. Warming a sample of helium from 0°C to 100°C, for example, increases its volume by about one third. Unlike the particles in solids, the particles in gases are far apart and moving fast and freely.

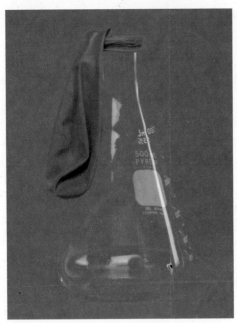

Figure 3.15 The particle model predicts that warming air will cause its particles to move faster and spread farther apart. When the air in the flask is warmed, the air expands and fills the balloon.

You are familiar with three states of matter. There is a fourth state of matter, called *plasma*. To change a material into a plasma, extremely high temperatures are required, like those inside the Sun—millions of degrees Celsius! In a plasma, individual particles that make up the material start to break apart into tinier pieces called electrons and ions. Plasmas can be produced on Earth, but only under extreme conditions. Matter on Earth exists as a solid, liquid, or gas almost all of the time.

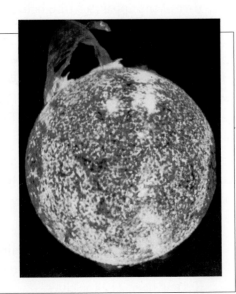

Bulging Balloons

In science, even ideas that seem like common sense are checked to see if they agree with observations and the rules for logical thinking. Can you find evidence to support the following statement, which you read earlier in this Topic?

If you put gases in a flexible container, such as a balloon, you can see that they expand and contract.

Materials ✳

2 identical balloons

refrigerator or freezer

hair dryer, electric heater, or toaster

Procedure

1. Blow up the balloons several times to stretch them. Then blow up both of them to the same size, and tie them so that no air can get in or out.

2. Put one balloon in the refrigerator or freezer to cool it. Leave the other balloon at room temperature. After an hour, compare the size of the two balloons.

3. Warm the cold balloon by blowing warm air from a hair dryer over it, or by holding it in warm air from a heater or above a toaster. Observe what happens as the air in the balloon warms. Continue until the balloon feels much warmer than room temperature.

What Did You Find Out? ✳ Analyzing and Interpreting

1. Describe what you observed using the words "expand" and "contract."

2. How well do your observations support the statement you were testing: completely, partially, or not at all?

3. Describe any differences between what you expected to happen and what did happen.

4. In this activity, one balloon is called the *control* and the other is called the *test*. Which is which? Why?

5. At which point in this activity were air particles in one balloon farthest apart? When were they closest together?

Expansion and Contraction in Liquids

Imagine watching a laboratory thermometer as its temperature changes. As the thermometer liquid moves up the glass tubing (the bore), it takes up more space. In other words, the liquid expands as it warms. As the thermometer cools, the liquid contracts, so it moves back down the tubing. The liquid must be contracting as it cools. Do all liquids expand and contract in this way? Do some liquids change volume more than others as they warm and cool? Follow the next activity carefully to find out.

Race for the Top

You have already observed a liquid in a thermometer expanding and contracting. Do all liquids behave the same way? Write a hypothesis, and explain why you think as you do. Check your hypothesis by observing the behaviour of liquids in this activity. (Your teacher may choose to demonstrate some or all of the steps for you.)

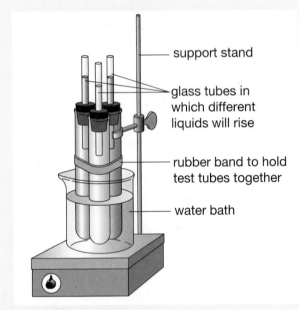

support stand

glass tubes in which different liquids will rise

rubber band to hold test tubes together

water bath

Materials

3 liquids (coloured water, ethyl alcohol, and cooking oil)

3 large test tubes

3 one-hole rubber stoppers, with 50 cm pieces of glass tubing inserted

laboratory stand and clamps

rubber bands

markers

2 large tin cans or 500 mL beakers

very hot water

ice-cold water

Procedure ✴ Performing and Recording

1. Completely fill one test tube with coloured water, the second with ethyl alcohol, and the third test tube with cooking oil. Insert a

stopper in each test tube so there are no air bubbles and the liquid rises a few centimetres up the glass tubing. Hold the test tubes together with the rubber band so the liquids are at the same level in the glass tubing, and arrange the apparatus as shown in the diagram.

2. Use the markers to mark the starting height of each liquid on the glass tubing.

3. Pour the hot water into the beaker around the test tubes. Watch the height of the liquids closely as the liquids warm.

4. Before the liquids overflow the glass tubes, lift the apparatus out of the hot water and put it into the ice-cold water. Keep watching the height of the liquids as they cool.

What Did You Find Out? ✴ Analyzing and Interpreting

1. Did all the liquids expand by the same amount as they warmed? If not, answer the following questions.

    (a) Which liquid expanded more?

    (b) Did the liquid that expanded more as it warmed also contract more as it cooled?

2. At the end of the activity, did the liquids return to their original heights in the tubes? Did you expect them to? Explain.

3. Was your hypothesis supported by your observations? If not, how might you modify it?

4. Explain which of the liquids you tested would be most suitable for making a thermometer that could be used to

    (a) show small changes in temperature very clearly;

    (b) measure large changes in temperature, without the thermometer being too large.

TOPIC 4 Review

1. Name the three states of matter. Give examples of three substances that are each in a different state at room temperature.

2. From your observations in this Topic, write a general description of what happens to solids, liquids, and gases as they are

   (a) warmed

   (b) cooled

3. Which state of matter shows the largest change in volume when warmed or cooled? Which state shows the smallest change?

4. The graphs below show the volume of mercury in a thermometer.

   (a) Which graph could be called a warming curve? Explain why.

   (b) Which graph could be called a cooling curve? Explain why.

   (c) Which graph shows what happens as soon as a thermometer is placed in hot soup?

   (d) Which graph shows what happens as soon as a thermometer is placed in ice cream?

5. **Apply** Bridges are made from materials that contract and expand as the temperature changes. The photographs below show an expansion joint between components of a bridge in winter and in summer.

   (a) Which season is shown in each picture? Explain how you know.

   (b) Why do you suppose concrete roadways and sidewalks are laid in sections with grooves between them?

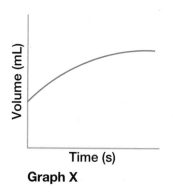

Graph X

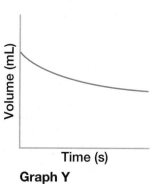

Graph Y

The Particle Model and Changes of State

Figure 3.16 The same hot Sun beats down on both sand and water at the beach. The sand warms up quickly. The temperature of the water changes much more slowly.

You have seen that different materials expand by different amounts as they warm up. Another difference in the way that materials respond when they are heated is the amount that their temperature rises when a certain amount of thermal energy is added. Some materials, such as sand, warm and cool quickly. Under identical conditions, other materials, such as water, warm and cool slowly.

Suppose you are studying the beach pictured above. Sunlight shines down equally on the sand and water. After some time, the thermal energy of both sand and water will increase by about the same amount. The temperature of the two materials will also change, but quite differently. Can you predict which one will warm up more? How do you know?

Exactly how fast does an object warm up? Scientists use two properties of an object to help answer this question. Examine the table to learn about these properties.

Table 2 Heat Capacity and Specific Heat Capacity

	Heat capacity	**Specific heat capacity**
Definition	amount of thermal energy that warms or cools the object by one degree Celsius	amount of thermal energy that warms or cools one gram of a material by one degree Celsius
Describes	a particular object	a particular material
Depends on	mass of the object and material the object is made of	material the object is made of

Hot Stuff!

Think About It

Scientists have measured the specific heat capacities of many common materials. In this investigation, you will study illustrations to learn one idea from each about specific heat capacity. This will help you to explore how the specific heat capacity of a material affects its behaviour.

Part 1
Rate of Temperature Change

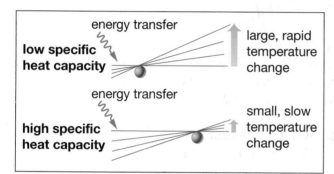

1 Examine the illustration above. Copy the table below into your notebook. It shows speed of warming and cooling. Fill in the blanks in the Rate of temp. change column using complete sentences containing the words *more quickly* and *more slowly*.

Material	Rate of temp. change	Specific heat
sand on beach	warms ??	??
water in lake	warms ??	??

2 Fill in the blanks in the Specific heat capacity column using sentences containing the words *higher* and *lower*.

3 Decide if each object in the list that follows should be made from material that warms quickly or slowly. In your notebook make a three-column chart. Put the name of each object listed below in the first column, and your answer in the second column. Use the third column for your answers to question 4.

(a) the bottom of a cooking pot

(b) a cold pack for treating athletic injuries

(c) solid glue in a glue gun

4 Decide if each object listed above should be made from a material with high specific heat capacity or low specific heat capacity.

Part 2
Size of Temperature Change

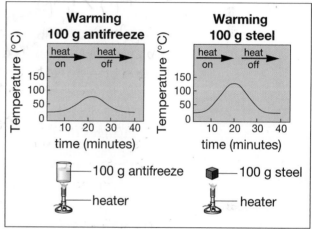

5 The graphs above show size of temperature change. According to the graphs, which material warmed faster? Which material cooled faster?

6 Which material had the higher specific heat capacity? *Hint: Use the ideas from Part 1.*

7 What is the best description of a material with a high specific heat capacity?

(a) warms slowly

(b) cools slowly

(c) both warms and cools slowly

8 Write a sentence to describe *both* the warming and cooling of a material with low specific heat capacity. *Hint: make sure your answer agrees with your answer to question 7.*

Changes of State

Figure 3.17A At the top of the candle, solid wax melts into a liquid, which flows up the wick. There the liquid wax vaporizes and burns.

Figure 3.17B Imagine how much thermal energy would be required to cause fusion to occur throughout this icy landscape.

In a candle, the same substance — wax — changes between all three states of matter: solid, liquid, and gaseous states. You can observe the same phase changes or changes of state with another common substance — water. Everyday changes in temperature cause water to **melt** (turn from solid ice into liquid water)

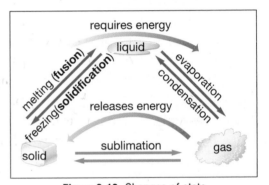

Figure 3.18 Changes of state

or **freeze** (turn from liquid water into ice). Temperature changes can also cause water to **evaporate** (turn into invisible water vapour, the gaseous form of water) and **condense** (turn back from a gas into liquid water). **Sublimation** occurs when a gas changes directly to a solid or a solid changes directly to a gas (see Figure 3.18).

Most other substances are not so easy to study. Hydrogen, for example, is a gas, even at the coldest winter temperatures. If you want to make liquid hydrogen, you need to cool hydrogen gas to –253°C! To make solid hydrogen, you need even lower temperatures, as well as extremely high pressures.

Any pure substance can exist in all three states of matter. You can cause any substance to change state if you warm or cool and, possibly, change the pressure of the substance enough. Changes in temperature, however, are just a sign of changes in particle motion, which means changes in thermal energy. In this Topic, you will explore links among these three ideas: state of matter, temperature, and thermal energy. You will experiment with water, but your conclusions will apply to other substances as well.

Melting and Boiling Points

The melting and boiling points of a substance are vital pieces of information, and not only for scientists. You have already seen that water has an unusually high heat capacity. Another unusual feature of water as a substance, and one that is even more important for Earth's climate, is the temperature range at which water is a liquid. A glance at Table 3 will show you that most common substances are either gases or solids at everyday temperatures on Earth.

Table 3 Melting and Boiling Points of Pure Substances

Substance	Melting point (°C)	Boiling point (°C)
oxygen	−218	−183
mercury	−39	357
water	0	100
tin	232	2602
lead	328	1740
aluminum	660	2519
table salt (sodium chloride)	801	1413
silver	962	2162
gold	1064	2856
iron	1535	2861

What Happens When a Liquid Evaporates?

When you take part in an energetic activity, you sometimes become hot and start to perspire. That seems to cool you down. The particle model can explain this!

In a liquid, particles are moving at many different speeds. At the surface of the liquid, some of the faster-moving particles are able to escape into the air. Slower-moving particles stay in the liquid state. Slower motion means lower average energy, however, and this means lower temperature. As high-energy particles leave the surface of a liquid, the remaining liquid is cooler than the original liquid. The cool liquid then cools the surface on which it is resting. Scientists call this phenomenon **evaporative cooling**.

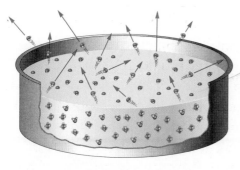

Figure 3.19 Evaporation cools a liquid, because the most energetic particles escape from its surface.

Evaporative cooling is common and can be very useful. Can you think of other examples besides the ones below?

- Joggers feel cold as their clothes dry out after getting soaked in a rainstorm.

- A home-owner sprays the roof of a house with water to cool the house on a hot summer day.

- A first-aid worker puts a wet cloth on the forehead of a person with a high fever.

Figure 3.20

INQUIRY

INVESTIGATION 3-F

SKILLCHECK
Initiating and Planning
☼ Performing and Recording
☼ Analyzing and Interpreting
☼ Communication and Teamwork

The Plateau Problem

When water freezes or vaporizes, it takes time. What happens while the water is changing state?

Question

What happens to the temperature of water while it changes state?

Hypothesis

Form two hypotheses about familiar situations in which ice is melting or liquid water is boiling. In your notebook, complete the following two statements, with reasons.

(a) While solid ice changes to liquid water, the temperature will (drop/stay the same/increase), because …

(b) While liquid water boils into gas, the temperature will (drop/stay the same/increase), because …

Safety Precautions

- Use oven mitts, hot pads, or tongs to handle the beaker of boiling water.
- Unplug the hot plate at the end of the investigation, and let it cool before putting it away.

Apparatus

2 laboratory thermometers
stirring rod
hot plate
kettle
2 beakers (250 mL)
clock or watch

Materials

crushed ice
ice-cold water
hot water (almost boiling)

Procedure

1 **Make a data table** like the one shown here. You will need space for at least five observations.

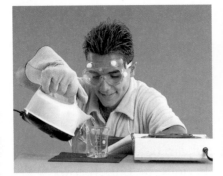

2 Fill one beaker with hot water from the kettle, and put it on the hot plate to boil.

3 In the other beaker, make a slush of crushed ice and a little cold water.

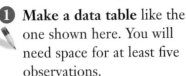

Time (min)	Temperature of melting ice (°C)	Temperature of boiling water (°C)

Skill
FOCUS

For some tips on the correct way to use a thermometer, turn to Skill Focus 5.

4 With a stirring rod, stir the contents of each beaker for several seconds, and then **measure** and **record** the temperature. Lift the thermometer off the bottom of the beaker to ensure that you are measuring the temperature of the contents, not the container.

5 Repeat the temperature measurements every 3 min. For a fair test, make sure that you stir and measure exactly the same way each time. **Record** each result.

6 Stop heating the boiling water *before* it all boils away. Unplug the hot plate, and carefully set aside the hot beaker to cool.

Skill
F O C U S

For help in drawing your line graphs, turn to Skill Focus 10.

Analyze

1. In this activity, you measured time and temperature.

   (a) What was your responding variable? (Which value was unknown until after you made an observation?)

   (b) What was your manipulated variable? (What value did you select before making an observation?)

2. **Draw two line graphs** to show your temperature/time observations: one for the melting ice and one for the boiling water. Instead of joining the points, draw a smooth line or curve that passes through or between the points (a best-fit line).

3. On your hot-water graph, mark where

   (a) the water was hot but not yet boiling

   (b) the hot water was boiling vigorously

4. Label any plateaus (flat, horizontal segments).

5. Compare the temperature of your melting slush with the "official" temperature you learned in Topic 2.

   (a) If the two temperatures are almost the same, any small difference might be caused by errors in your equipment or measurements. Suggest at least two specific errors of this sort that might occur.

   (b) If the two temperatures are quite different, the conditions in your laboratory or your sample may be responsible. Suggest at least two specific conditions that might cause this type of error.

6. Imagine that you combined both parts of this investigation. **Sketch a third graph** that shows what would probably happen if you heated one sample from ice to water and then to water vapour.

7. On the temperature scale of your third graph, mark the melting point and the boiling point of your samples, according to your **observations**.

8. Combine all the results from your class to find the average melting point and the average boiling point for water. Compare these values to the "official" values. Are they closer than your individual group values? If they are closer, explain why.

Conclude and Apply

9. From your observations, write a clear answer to the question at the beginning of this investigation.

10. How well do your **observations** support your **hypotheses**?

11. **(a)** Identify any problems you had with apparatus, procedure, or the way you organized and worked together in your group.

    (b) Describe one improvement your group could make the next time you work together.

The Particle Model and Changes of State • MHR **223**

How Low Can It Go?

Alcohol evaporates more rapidly than water. If you compare the temperature change when the two liquids evaporate, the results may surprise you.

Materials

lab thermometer or computer temperature sensor

electric fan

2 strips of cloth or paper towel

room-temperature water

room-temperature alcohol

Safety Precautions

Pure alcohols are harmful to the body. Do not taste these chemicals, and do not breathe their vapours. Do not use alcohols near open flames, as the alcohol vapours may catch fire or explode.

Procedure ✳ **Performing and Recording**
✳ **Communication and Teamwork**

1. Measure and record the temperature of the liquid water and alcohol.

2. Wrap the cloth strip around the thermometer bulb, and soak it in the water. Hold the thermometer near the fan to speed up evaporation from the wet cloth. Record the temperature every 30 s until it stops dropping.

3. Repeat step 2, using a second cloth strip and alcohol.

4. To compare your observations for the two liquids, draw a graph with temperature on the vertical axis and time on the horizontal axis. Plot both sets of data on the same graph.

What Did You Find Out? ✳ **Analyzing and Interpreting**

1. In which liquid were the particles evaporating faster? How do you know?

2. Which of the two cloths would take longer to dry completely? What would happen to temperature of the cloth after all of the liquid had evaporated?

Skill
F O C U S

To learn about graphing, turn to Skill Focus 10.

Why the Temperature Stays the Same

What, exactly, is happening to particles of a substance during a phase change? For example, what happens to water particles in ice crystals as the ice melts? Recall that, according to the particle model, the average speed of the particles cannot be changing because temperature stays constant during a phase change. If the speed of the particles changed, the temperature would have to change, too.

What does change, according to modern particle theory, is the *arrangement* of the particles. Study Figure 3.21 to visualize how this happens. Particles become *less* organized as their energy increases, so the substance changes from a solid to a liquid, and then to a gas. Particles become *more* organized as their energy drops, so a gas will change to a liquid and then to a solid.

During a phase change, the total energy of a substance increases or decreases. This occurs because the particles no longer increase or decrease their speed; the arrangement of the particles changes. The average energy of the particles, however, does *not* change. Therefore, the temperature of the substance stays constant. The energy change is hidden from thermometers, so it is called "hidden heat" or "latent heat."

Pause& Reflect

When you take a shower, beads of water may form on the bathroom mirror and other cold surfaces far from the shower.

(a) Where did the water in the beads come from?

(b) In what state was the water that formed the beads as it travelled to the mirror?

(c) What change of state is occurring when the beads of water form?

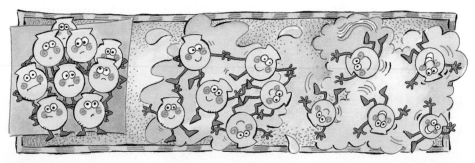

Figure 3.21A Particles in many solids have a regular arrangement. They move by vibrating in the same spot.

Figure 3.21B Particles in a liquid move freely, but they are still held loosely together. They can vibrate and rotate, but they can only move a short distance before colliding with a nearby particle.

Figure 3.21C Particles in gases move independently and are separated by large spaces. They can vibrate, rotate, and travel longer distances between collisions.

TOPIC 5 Review

1. Name a change of state in which particles become
   (a) more organized
   (b) less organized
   (c) able to move more freely

2. Imagine that you can see the moving particles in a drop of liquid on your skin. Describe
   (a) the speed of the particles that are able to escape from the surface of the drop
   (b) the speed of the particles that are left behind in the drop
   (c) the temperature change of the drop as particles continue to escape
   (d) the change of state that is occurring

3. Use Table 3 on page 221 to find a temperature at which
   (a) oxygen is a liquid
   (b) table salt is a gas
   (c) tin is a liquid

4. From memory, list six changes of state, and give a name for each one.

5. **Apply** Anyone who falls into a lake fully clothed may develop hypothermia (dangerously low body temperature) after being rescued. No matter whether the water and the weather are warm or cold, first-aid experts say that the victim's wet clothing should be removed immediately. Use your knowledge of energy and change of state to explain why.

TOPIC 6 Transferring Energy

Imagine holding your hand near a light bulb or in front of a hot fire. You can feel the warmth. Your skin warms up because it receives thermal energy from the bulb. The light bulb is an **energy source**: an object or material that can transfer its energy to other objects. In this section, you will study three ways in which energy can be transferred: radiation, conduction, and convection.

Radiation Transfers Energy

Figure 3.22 A tsunami carries enormous amounts of energy from its source, an underwater earthquake, across thousands of kilometres of ocean. When the wave hits land, the energy can devastate buildings and the natural environment, and can cost thousands of lives.

Figure 3.23 The ripples in this pond are evidence of energy transfer.

The Sun shines. Millions of kilometres away, sunshine may strike a solar cell that runs your calculator or a solar-powered radio or toy. Energy has been transferred, even though no material — no *thing* — has travelled from the Sun to the solar cell. Scientists call this form of energy transfer **radiation**. Radiation is the transfer of energy without any movement of matter. Energy that is transferred in this way is called **radiant energy** or **electromagnetic radiation** (EMR for short).

Exactly how does radiant energy travel through space? After many years of study, scientists found that radiant energy travels and behaves like a wave. Like the ripples and tsunami in the illustrations, electro-magnetic radiation transfers energy. Unlike other waves, EMR can travel through empty space, as well as through air, glass, and many other materials.

There are many different forms of EMR, including radio waves, microwaves, visible light, and X-rays. If the energy source is a warm object, such as the Sun, some of its thermal energy is transferred as a type of EMR called infrared radiation (IR) or "heat radiation." All of the different forms of radiant energy share several characteristics:

- They behave like waves.
- They can be absorbed and reflected by objects.
- They travel across empty space at the same very high speed: 300 000 km/s.

Absorb That Energy

If an object absorbs radiant energy, what happens to its temperature?

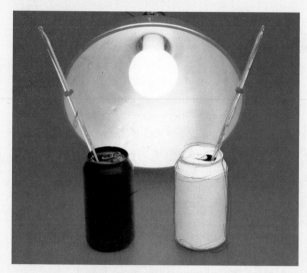

Materials

2 empty pop cans

2 thermometers

light (at least 100 W)

ruler

dark- and light-coloured cloth, or black and white paint

aluminum foil

200 mL cooking oil

tape or rubber bands

Procedure ✳ Performing and Recording

1. Think of summer sunlight beating down on different materials. Use your own experience to write a prediction about which type of surface absorbs the radiant energy best:

   (a) dark or light

   (b) shiny or dull

2. Use an appropriate choice of materials to cover the pop cans so that you can test one of your predictions.

3. Pour 100 mL of cooking oil into each can. Place the cans an equal, short distance from the light. (Try 10 cm.)

4. For each can, record the initial temperature of the oil and the temperature of the oil every 5 min for 15 min.

5. Calculate the temperature change of the oil in each can by subtracting the initial temperature from the final temperature.

What Did You Find Out? ✳ Analyzing and Interpreting

1. Compare the temperature change of the oil in the two cans. Do your observations support your prediction?

2. If several groups tested the same prediction, how well did their results agree?

3. What other factors, besides the one that you tested, may be affecting the temperature change in the oil?

4. According to scientific theory, the same materials that absorb radiant energy well should also radiate energy well. Suppose that you have pairs of similar objects with different surfaces, as listed below. You heat them to the same high temperature. Which type of surface radiates energy better and thus cools down more quickly?

   (a) a light-coloured surface or a dark surface

   (b) a dull surface or a shiny surface

You know, from your own predictions or from the activity above, that some materials absorb radiant energy well, and some materials reflect well. Do the same materials make good reflectors and bad absorbers of radiant energy? In the next investigation, you can think about this and similar questions, and infer some everyday-life consequences.

INVESTIGATION 3-G

Comparing Surfaces

Think About It

From your own experience, can you think of examples of the following scientific observations?

- Dark-coloured surfaces absorb and radiate energy better than light-coloured ones.
- Dull surfaces absorb and radiate energy better than shiny ones.
- Shiny surfaces reflect radiant energy better than dull ones.
- Light-coloured surfaces reflect radiant energy better than dark-coloured ones.

How can you use this knowledge to make wise choices about materials you use?

Procedure

1 In your notebook, make a table like the one below. Give your table a title. Complete the table by writing "better" or "worse" to describe the behaviour of each surface compared to its opposite.

Surface	Ability to absorb	Ability to radiate	Ability to reflect
light-coloured			
dark-coloured			
shiny texture			
dull texture			

2 Identify the combination of colour and texture that would be

(a) the best reflector (b) the worst reflector

(c) the best absorber (d) the worst radiator

 People radiate energy. Have you ever been cool and comfortable at the start of a concert or school assembly and then, after an hour or so, found yourself getting unbearably hot? Thermal energy from the crowd of warm bodies was probably to blame. Each person acted like a miniature furnace, warming nearby air and furniture. Without air conditioning to transfer the thermal energy elsewhere, a crowded room can quickly become uncomfortable.

Analyze

1. Use your answers in steps 1 and 2 to:

   (a) recommend that a car owner cover black seats with light-coloured fabric in summer

   (b) suggest to a dairy truck manufacturer that the milk-holding tanks be shiny white or silver-coloured

   (c) explain why you carry your dog across a dark asphalt road in summer and let it walk on the concrete sidewalk

   (d) persuade tennis players to wear white or light-coloured clothing

2. The Russian government once experimented with a method to speed up the melting of snow on northern farmland, so that crops could be planted earlier in the spring. Black coal dust was dropped on the snow from low-flying aircraft.

   (a) Explain why the coal dust was expected to speed up snow melt.

   (b) The snow did melt sooner, but the method was never actually put into use. Think of some reasons why it would be impractical.

3. Write a brief statement explaining how these observations can lead to energy-saving actions.

Conducting Energy Through Solids

In solids, where particles are close together, thermal energy can be transferred directly from one particle to the next. **Thermal conduction** is the process of transferring thermal energy through direct collisions between particles. Study Figure 3.24 to see how conduction transfers energy.

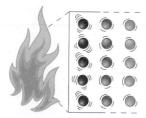

Figure 3.24A Particles near the heat source absorb energy from it and begin moving more rapidly.

Figure 3.24B The fast-moving particles bump into neighbouring particles, increasing their energy and motion.

Figure 3.24C In this way, thermal energy is transferred throughout the material.

Most metals, especially gold and copper, are excellent heat conductors. A hot stove burner touching one part of a copper saucepan, for example, soon heats the entire pan. Other solids, such as glass and wood, are much less efficient at transferring thermal energy by conduction. Poor conductors are called **heat insulators**. When insulators are wrapped around an object, they slow down the transfer of thermal energy to or from the surroundings. The object stays warm or cold longer. Think of some good insulators!

Find Out ACTIVITY

The Super Stirrer

Can you predict how well a substance will conduct heat? Find the material that will make the best stir stick.

Materials

equal-length pieces of plastic from a pen, pieces of copper wire, long iron nails, wooden craft sticks or wooden pencils

plastic cup of very hot water CAUTION
Handle the hot water with care.

Procedure ✶ Performing and Recording

1. Predict which of your sample stir sticks will be the

   (a) best conductor   **(c)** best insulator

   (b) worst conductor   **(d)** worst insulator

2. Place one end of each sample in the hot water. Wait 1 min.

3. Touch the inside of your wrist to the top of each sample to identify the warmest one (the best conductor). Remove it from the cup and record which materials made the best conductor.

4. Wait another minute. Then repeat step 3 to find the second-best conductor. Continue to repeat step 3 until you have ranked all of the samples in order, from the best to the worst conductor.

What Did You Find Out?

✶ Analyzing and Interpreting

1. Explain which of your samples would be the best for making
   (a) a stir stick
   (b) the bottom of a frying pan
   (c) the handle of a frying pan
   (d) a container for delivering hot pizza

2. How might the particles in your best insulator differ from the particles in a conducting material?

Convection, Energy on the Move

Thermal energy can be transferred in a third way by **fluids**: materials that can be poured or that flow from place to place. A hot fluid may force its way up through a colder fluid. In **convection**, the warm fluid, itself, moves from place to place, carrying the thermal energy with it. The moving fluid is called a **convection current**. Study Figure 3.25 to identify the different parts of a convection current. Then read on to learn the details of how a convection current operates.

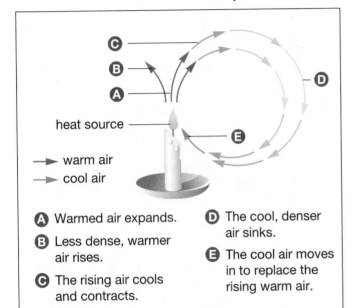

A Warmed air expands.

B Less dense, warmer air rises.

C The rising air cools and contracts.

D The cool, denser air sinks.

E The cool air moves in to replace the rising warm air.

Figure 3.25 All convection currents display the features shown here.

Why do fluids, at different temperatures, rise, sink, and create convection currents? Remember that materials expand as they warm up. Their particles move farther apart. Each section of the warmed material is left with fewer particles than when it was cold, so each section is a bit lighter than it used to be. In other words, the warmed material becomes less dense. Colder, denser fluid sinks down and pushes nearby warmer fluid upward. Then this cold fluid, too, is warmed and pushed upward.

As warm fluid rises and moves away from the heat source, it cools. It contracts as its particles move closer together. It becomes denser and sinks back down toward the heat source, where it is warmed and forced upward. As the whole process repeats, a continuous movement — a convection current — forms.

Displaced Drops

You can create a small-scale model of parts of a convection current. Observe what happens in this activity, and compare it with the explanation you have just read.

Materials

dropper
250 mL beaker of room-temperature water
100 mL beaker of coloured, ice-cold water
100 mL beaker of coloured, very hot water

CAUTION Handle the hot water with care.

Procedure ✳ Performing and Recording

1. Make sure that the beaker of room-temperature water is completely still.

2. Fill the dropper with ice-cold water, and hold it just above the surface of the room-temperature water. Gently squeeze out one drop of cold water. Watch to see if it can force its way to the bottom of the beaker.

3. Repeat step 2 several times. Then make a careful diagram showing what usually happens to the drop of cold water.

4. Repeat steps 2 and 3 using very hot water in the dropper.

What Did You Find Out? ✳ Analyzing and Interpreting

1. Did the drops of very hot water appear to be more or less dense than the room-temperature water around them? How do you know?

2. How did the density of the drops of ice-cold water compare with the density of the room-temperature water? How do you know?

3. In what way do your observations agree or disagree with the text description of what happens to warm and cold fluid in a convection current?

4. Why did the drops of hot or cold water not move in a complete convection current?

Analyzing Energy Transfer Systems

A volleyball rockets across the net. This fast movement means a large amount of energy. The source of the energy was Carrie's hard-swinging fist. The impact of her fist on the ball transferred energy to the ball.

Most of the energy of Carrie's fist ended up as the energy of the ball — most, but not all. The other players heard the smack of Carrie's spike and the thud of the ball hitting the floor. If you asked Carrie, she would report that her fist stung and felt warmer after her shot. The part of the ball that she hit also warmed up a bit. When the ball hit the floor, the ball warmed up a bit more. So did the spot on the floor where the ball landed. A few moments later, the floor nearby and even the air above it was a tiny bit warmer.

Can you explain what is going on in this energy transfer system? Examine Figure 3.26 below without reading the information below it. Try to explain what is happening at each letter, in terms of energy, particle movement, and temperature. Then check to see if your explanation included everything in the caption.

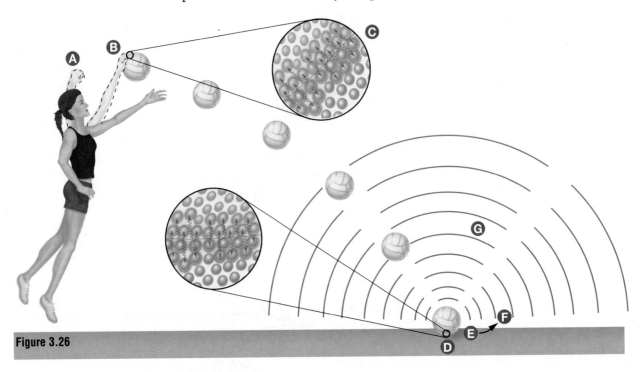

Figure 3.26

Ⓐ The moving fist (energy source) has a large amount of energy.

Ⓑ Most of the energy is transferred to the entire volleyball, which moves away rapidly.

Ⓒ Some energy is transferred to individual particles in the skin and the volleyball, which vibrate more rapidly, producing a temperature increase.

Ⓓ Energy is transferred from the ball to the floor. Particles that make up the floor vibrate more rapidly, producing a temperature increase.

Ⓔ Energy is transferred by conduction to nearby particles in the floor.

Ⓕ Convection currents transfer energy through the air.

Ⓖ Energy is also transferred to air particles by compressing them and starting a sound wave. The sound wave distributes this energy throughout.

Features of Energy Transfer Systems

All energy transfer systems have similar features. Hair dryers, bicycle brakes, weather systems, and ocean currents — like Carrie's volleyball spike, they all have five things in common. As you study each point below, find an example of it from Figure 3.26.

• *Energy Source* Some part of the system acts as an energy source, supplying energy to the rest of the system. Some systems have *mechanical* energy sources, such as a tightly wound spring in a toy. Cars, trains, and even humans and animals depend on *chemical* energy sources, such as gasoline, diesel fuel, or food. Stars, atomic bombs, and nuclear power plants use *nuclear* energy sources: substances whose smallest particles can fuse together or break apart, releasing large amounts of energy. Radios, power tools, and plug-in appliances use *electrical* energy sources: batteries or generators in a power station. (You will find out more about sources of energy in Topic 7.)

- *What is the energy source for Carrie's volleyball spike?*
- *Direction of Energy Transfer* Energy is always transferred *away* from concentrated sources. Changes in non-living systems always spread energy around more evenly.
- *At which point in Figure 3.26 is energy most concentrated?*
- *Name three things that end up sharing part of Carrie's original energy.*
- *Transformations* Energy does not necessarily keep the same form as it is transferred from place to place. When Carrie hit the volleyball, only part of the original energy of her fist became energy of the ball.

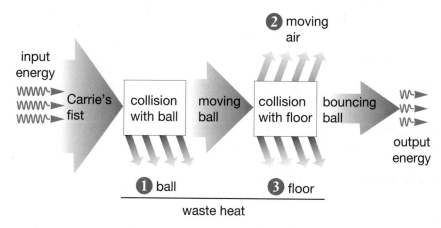

Figure 3.27 These are the energy transformations that take place when a volleyball is spiked.

- *Waste Heat* Almost all energy systems transfer at least a little thermal energy into the surroundings. Some of this can be prevented by using a thermal break. For example, the two outer metal sections of a door or window frame are separated by a layer of solid wood or plastic. This thermal break is a poor conductor, so it prevents heat transfer through the metal.
- *Identify two things which were warmed by waste heat from Carrie's volleyball spike.*
- *Control Systems* The furnace in your home transfers thermal energy to the air, but it does not run all the time. A thermostat controls the energy transfer by turning the furnace on and off. Many other systems include some way of adjusting energy transfers. Warm-blooded animals, for example, are able to warm themselves in winter and keep cool in the summer. Their body temperature stays almost the same despite changing weather conditions.
- *Which item in Figure 3.26 includes an energy control system?*

Making a Transfer

You know more about energy than most people who have ever lived! Almost all of the ideas you have been studying were developed in the last 200 years. Can you apply all this new knowledge in a practical way?

Challenge

Design and build a simple but efficient device to harness and transform energy: a candle-powered water heater.

Safety Precautions

- All nonflammable materials must be approved by your teacher.
- During and after heating, handle the apparatus with care. It may be hot enough to burn you.
- Candle flame soot is hard to wash off clothing. Wear an apron, and wash your hands immediately with soap and hot water if you get soot on them.
- Have water or a fire extinguisher nearby.

Materials

thermometer
birthday candle
100 mL room-temperature water
nonflammable containers, fasteners, and insulation
matches

Specifications

A. Your goal is to raise the temperature of the water as much as possible.

B. The water may be heated directly with the candle or indirectly using the candle to heat something else, which will then heat the water.

C. Your energy transfer device must be nonflammable and movable so that it can be safely placed over the candle after the candle is lit.

D. The candle will be allowed to burn for only 3 min during your demonstration.

Plan and Construct

1. Brainstorm ideas about how to build the most efficient heater. Think about

- energy transfer by convection, conduction, and radiation
- prevention of heat loss to the surroundings
- specific heat capacity (you will need to make sure that the heater itself does not absorb too much energy)
- possible materials to use (remember that paints, plastics, glues, and tape are flammable, so they do not meet the design criteria)

2. Choose the most practical ideas, and write a design proposal for your teacher that includes

- a list of materials
- a labelled sketch of your device
- a task list and a time line to show how each group member will contribute to the project

3. Assemble the materials, and build your device. You may test and modify it, but the candle can be burned for only 1 min during a test. Keep a written record of any design changes you make.

4. For the demonstration, be ready to give a brief explanation of the design features of your device. Then show how it works!

Evaluate

1. What knowledge from this unit did you use when designing your device?

2. How could your device be improved if you had more time to work on it?

3. What extra resources would have helped you to do a better job on this project?

4. What could your group do differently in the next design project to be more efficient?

Keeping in the Warmth

In a home, some of the thermal energy produced by a furnace is lost to the outside air through chimneys, walls, windows, etc. (see the diagram). We can reduce this loss by using high-quality insulation in new houses that are built.

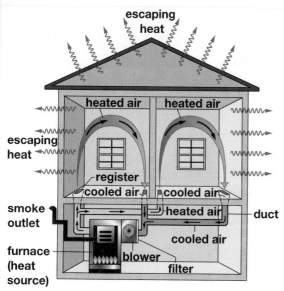

Fuel is burned in a furnace.

- It heats air that then travels through ducts to various rooms. The air circulates from heat registers throughout the room.

- A fan helps to pull air back into the furnace.

- A filter helps clean the air of dust and other particles before the air returns to the furnace.

Insulation materials that are used in building construction are rated by their RSI value. This value describes the resistance of a 1 cm thickness of a material to heat conduction. Materials with higher values are better insulators. Some typical values are given in the table below.

Material	RSI per cm
blue plastic foam panels	0.35
white plastic foam panels	0.29
fibreglass	0.24
vermiculite	0.16
plywood	0.087
glass	0.017

Extra thickness increases the RSI value. For example, a 3 cm thickness of fibreglass would have an RSI value of 3 x 0.24 = 0.72. Only 2 cm of blue plastic foam would provide about the same resistance to heat conduction (2 x 0.35 = 0.70).

Procedure * Performing and Recording

List each type of insulation material used in your home and how thick it is. Then calculate its total RSI value. If the material is not listed in the table, check with a building materials store, in the library, or on the Internet to find its RSI value.

Extension

You have probably noticed that the area around windows and doors feels cooler in winter than other parts of the room. Windows and doors allow heat to escape, reducing the efficiency of a home's heating system. How could you reduce the heat loss through windows? With your group, think about this question. Brainstorm some methods of cutting heat loss through windows, and design an investigation to test at least one of your methods. State the question your experiment is intended to answer. Describe your variables and how you will control them. List the materials your experiment will require and the steps you will follow. Have your investigation approved by your teacher, and if possible, carry out the experiment.

Fibreglass building insulation

In the 1970s, the price of fuels rose suddenly. People and governments became very concerned about conserving energy and using fuels efficiently. The auto industry started making vehicles that travelled much farther on each litre of gasoline. Architects designed buildings with more insulation and better seals around windows and doors. Today there is less emphasis on energy conservation. Few headlines or television newscasts focus on this topic. Do you think people should still be concerned about energy conservation? Why? Find out about the United Nations Earth Summits, held every five years.

TOPIC 6 Review

1. Define the term "energy source," and list four common types of energy sources. Give an example of each type.

2. List five features of all energy transfer systems.

3. **Apply** 100 mL of hot water (50°C) is mixed with 100 mL of cold water (10°C).

   (a) Predict the temperature of the mixture after it is well stirred.

   (b) In which direction was energy transferred?

4. **Apply** In the winter, pioneer families spent much of their waking time in the kitchen because it was the warmest room in the house. A wood box beside the large cast-iron stove held the fuel for the stove. The stove pipe passed through a hole in the ceiling and went up through the upstairs hallway and out through the roof.

   (a) What was the source of heat for the house?

   (b) How was thermal energy released from the source?

   (c) Explain how thermal energy was transferred to

   • the iron stove

   • the kitchen

   • the bedrooms

   • the rest of the rooms in the house

   (d) How did this heating system release waste heat to the surroundings?

   (e) How is this heating system an example of thermal energy spreading out?

If you need to check an item, Topic numbers are provided in brackets below.

Key Terms

expand	freezing	sublimation	fusion	radiation	heat insulators
contract	condensation	boiling	evaporative cooling	radiant energy	fluids
melting	solidification	evaporation	energy source	thermal conduction	convection current

Reviewing Key Terms

1. Copy and complete the crossword puzzle below using new terms you learned in these Topics.

Across

1. cooling caused by a wet blanket (6)

2. increase in size (4)

5. phase change involving no liquid (5)

8. energy from the Sun (6)

9. another word for melting (5)

10. cannot be compressed (4)

Down

1. a drying puddle (5)

3. state not found on Earth (4)

4. happens when ice is heated (5)

6. opposite of evaporation (5)

Understanding Key Concepts

2. Carbon dioxide gas sublimes at –78.5°C.

   (a) If you cool carbon dioxide below –78.5°C, in what state will it be?

   (b) Could you produce liquid carbon dioxide by cooling the gas or by warming the solid? (Hint: What does *sublimation* mean?) (5)

3. You pour 100 mL of hot water at 50°C into 200 mL of cold water at 10°C. (6)

   (a) In which direction is thermal energy transferred?

   (b) Which methods of energy transfer occur?

   (c) What happens to the temperature of the hot water and the temperature of the cold water?

   (d) If you leave the water mixture in a glass beaker for 24 h in a room with a temperature of 20°C, what will happen? What general feature of energy transfer does this illustrate?

4. The two graphs below show the volume of liquid in a laboratory thermometer during a temperature measurement. (4)

   (a) Which graph is a warming curve, and which is a cooling curve? Explain how you know.

   (b) Which graph shows what happens when the thermometer is placed in water in a pot on a stove and the burner is turned on? Which shows what happens when the thermometer is placed in a jug of water that was just put in a refrigerator?

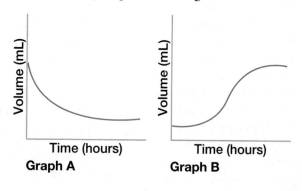

Sources of Thermal Energy

In Topic 1, you thought about common sources of energy in the activity Using Energy. You probably found that much of the energy for cooking and heating was either natural gas or electricity. Gas and electricity have to be transported from where they are found, and they might result from a series of energy transformations. For example, gravity causes the water in a waterfall to fall downward. This energy of the moving water can turn a turbine. The mechanical energy of the spinning generator is changed to electrical energy.

If your home uses natural gas for heating and cooking, you are changing energy stored in the gas into thermal energy. Unlike hydro-electric power, natural gas requires few energy conversions before it can be used as a fuel.

Figure 3.28 Energy of moving water turns a turbine which causes a generator to spin.

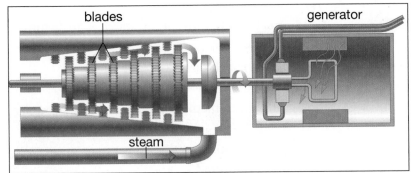

blades   generator

steam

Find Out ACTIVITY

Energy Inputs for Energy Outputs

Some energy resources require considerable treatment before they can be used by consumers. When oil is pumped out of the ground, it goes through a process called fractional distillation that turns it into various petroleum products. Natural gas needs less treatment, but it does require the building of pipelines and networks of pipelines to deliver it to homes and industries. How many energy inputs does firewood require?

Procedure

1. With your partner, brainstorm everything that can happen in order for energy to be obtained from firewood.

2. Suppose you were setting up a small business to obtain and sell firewood. Think about how you would obtain the wood, prepare it for sale, get it to its selling point, and find customers. List the steps that you would have to take in order to sell a bundle of firewood.

3. ❋ **Performing and Recording** Beside each step, write any energy input that would be required for this step to be completed.

4. Compare your ideas with those of other students.

What Did You Find Out? ❋ **Analyzing and Interpreting**

1. How many steps did you and your partner think of? How many energy inputs did you find?

2. Wood requires no treatment in order to be burned in a fireplace or wood stove. Why would it be inaccurate to think of it as a "free" energy source?

3. What are some energy inputs that allow us to use natural gas in furnaces and stoves?

Chemical Energy

Humans began using chemical energy long before they understood much about it. Cave dwellers collected wood for their fires, unaware that stored chemical energy was released in the form of thermal energy when the wood burned. Coal also contains stored chemical energy that needs no further treatment to produce thermal energy as it burns.

Electrical Energy

Electricity can be produced in many ways. Hydro-electric dams, like waterfalls, change the energy of falling water to electrical energy. Dams are usually impressive to look at, so they often become attractions and contribute to the tourism industry. Because the river on which a dam is built no longer flows naturally, wildlife in the area is usually affected. Plants that used to grow can no longer do so, and organisms that used to eat them have to move to other areas. The livelihood of people who have fished and hunted in the area for generations is also affected.

Figure 3.29 Dams use the energy of falling water which is transformed into electrical energy.

Electricity can also be produced at generating stations that burn fossil fuels. Where large waterfalls or good locations for dams do not exist, thermo-electric (fuel-burning) generating stations are common. They can provide electrical energy to large populations that have no other means of obtaining it. Heated water is a by-product of thermo-electric plants, however. If it is released into lakes or rivers, many living organisms can be affected by changing temperatures or water levels. Chemicals released by the burning fuel can cause more environmental damage.

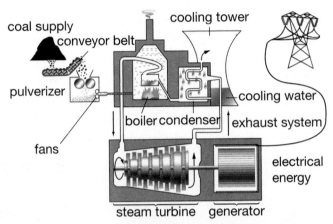

Figure 3.30 Burning fuel converts chemical energy to thermal energy. The thermal energy boils water. Steam from the boiling water spins the turbines. Mechanical energy from the spinning turbines turns a generator. The generator converts mechanical energy into electricity.

Mechanical Forces

Have you ever pounded a nail into a piece of wood and then noticed that the nail felt warm? Thermal energy was released by the impact of the hammer and by the friction of the nail rubbing against the wood as you pounded it into place. Mechanical forces that push or pull objects often release thermal energy. Car brakes, bicycle brakes, skidding tires, and shoes release thermal energy in this way.

Mechanical forces release thermal energy in other ways, as well. You may have noticed that the valve on a bicycle pump becomes warm as you energetically pump up the bicycle's tires. As you compress the air in the pump, it warms up.

Geothermal Energy

Volcanoes, hot springs, and geysers are indications of extremely hot materials that exist inside Earth's crust. (You will learn more about volcanoes in Unit 5.) The hot material inside Earth that shoots or oozes out during a volcanic eruption can also produce hot water or even steam which moves through cracks in the rock. This boiling water or steam can be piped to a power plant at the surface. There it is channelled through a control system to turbines, and is transformed into electrical energy. Energy that we harness from Earth's interior is called **geothermal energy**.

Another technique for using geothermal energy is called HDR (hot, dry rock). Using this technique, engineers pump water into rock that has been cracked (see Figure 3.31). The heated water returns to Earth's surface as steam, where it is used to generate electricity.

Geothermal energy is clean, and the power plants that convert it to electrical energy are reliable. It is a good alternative to the dwindling supply of fossil fuels. Using more geothermal energy could help reduce wastes resulting from the mining of fossil fuels, as well as pollutants caused by burning fossil fuels.

Looking Ahead

Can geothermal energy be used to heat individual homes? Research this on the Internet. You might want to consider combining geothermal energy with solar heating for your Unit Issue.

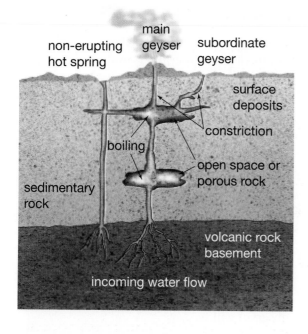

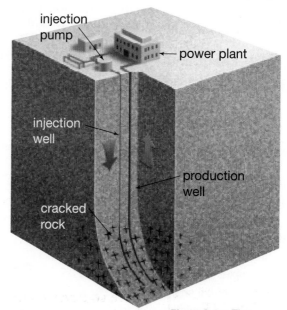

Figure 3.31 The illustration on the left shows a cross-section of a hot spring and a geyser. Both could be harnessed for geothermal power. The illustration on the right shows a geothermal power plant.

Solar Energy

When you hang a shirt out to dry on a sunny, breezy day, you are using **solar energy** (energy from the Sun) to dry your shirt. Solar energy is clean, and it is guaranteed not to run out. Unfortunately, there are periods of time when the Sun does not shine. Solar energy is not available through the night. Less solar energy is available in winter than in summer. How can these problems be overcome?

Passive Solar Heating

There are two basic ways of using solar energy to warm buildings. **Passive solar heating** uses the materials in the structure to absorb, store, and release solar energy. For example, a home that uses passive solar heating might have a wall of windows on the south side of the house. The remaining exterior walls are well insulated and have few windows. Energy from the Sun is absorbed by materials such as concrete in the floor or water in a storage tank. During the night, this stored energy is released and warms the air in the house. **Active solar heating** uses mechanical devices like fans to distribute stored thermal energy.

PROBLEM-SOLVING

INVESTIGATION 3-1

SKILLCHECK

✿ Initiating and Planning

✿ Performing and Recording

✿ Analyzing and Interpreting

✿ Communication and Teamwork

Passive Paint

Can paint help to keep your home warmer in winter and cooler in summer? Use your knowledge of the transfer of thermal energy to design an investigation to test this claim.

Challenge

Can you change the solar heating of a model room by changing the way its walls are painted?

Safety Precautions

- Use care when working with paint. Avoid inhaling fumes. Use in a well-ventilated area.
- Avoid contact with eyes. If contact occurs, flush eyes immediately and thoroughly with water.
- Wear disposable gloves.
- Dispose of your materials as your teacher directs.

Materials

disposable gloves

two shoe boxes

a source of thermal energy

sheets of heavy, insulating plastic

heavy-duty adhesive tape

2 paint samples (sample A is treated for greater thermal energy efficiency; sample B is untreated)

2 paintbrushes or sponges

2 thermometers

other materials

Specifications

A. Your investigation should investigate how differences in paint affect solar heating in a model room. Your two paint samples will differ in only one way.

B. To test room temperature rather than the temperature of a wall or floor, you will need to avoid or minimize thermal energy conduction. Your design should show the materials and method you will use. Your notes should explain why you think your materials and design will avoid or minimize conduction.

Plan and Construct

1. Write a prediction that relates the likely results of your experiment to the paint property you are investigating. For example, you could complete the following sentence: "We think that painting the model room with Sample A paint will increase the effect of solar heating because …"

2. Decide how you could use the suggested materials to set up an experiment to find out whether differences in paint affect the amount of solar heating in a model of a house room.

3. Write your procedure in point form and list the variables. For example you might write:
   The responding variable (the feature we observe) will be …
   The manipulated variable (the feature we change) will be …
   Controlled variables (features we keep the same) will be …

4. Show the procedure to your teacher. When it has been approved, construct your model.

5. Conduct your experiment, keeping a careful record of your observations. Wash your hands after completing the experiment.

6. Prepare a report, with diagrams, to help explain your findings.

Evaluate

1. Did your findings support your prediction? If not, how might you modify the investigation in order to re-test your hypothesis?

2. How did other groups conduct their experiment? Were their results similar to yours? If not, what explanation might there be for the differences?

Active Solar Heating

Figure 3.32 illustrates an active solar heating system. Active solar heating systems involve fairly complex mechanical systems and devices called **solar collectors**. These collectors, usually on the roof or the south side of a building, contain water or air. The Sun heats the water or air, which is then pumped through the building by the mechanical parts of the system.

Looking Ahead

In your Science Log, list some materials you could use to build a model of an energy-efficient solar home. You could use these ideas for your solar house in the Unit Issue.

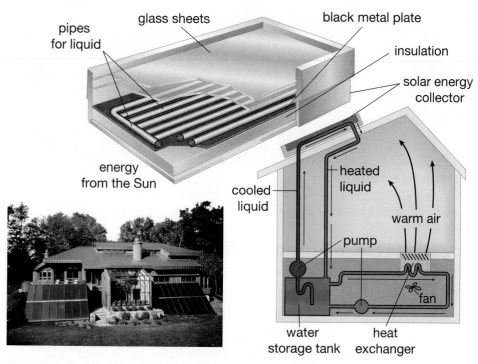

Figure 3.32 Radiant energy from the Sun passes through the glass, which traps the energy in the solar collector. The black metal plate absorbs the radiant energy. The solar energy is converted to thermal energy, warming the metal. This thermal energy is transferred to the water in the pipes just beneath the plate. The water flows through pipes to a basement pump that circulates water to radiators throughout the system. A fan helps the air, heated by the water, to circulate through the rooms. The cooled water is pumped back up to the collector to be reheated. Some active solar heating systems include large, insulated tanks for storing heated water for later use.

Wind Energy

Remember that shirt you hung out to dry? You know that the Sun's radiant energy will cause moisture to continue to evaporate from your shirt until it is dry. The process is speeded up by a breeze.

Wind energy is the energy of moving air. Wind energy is a result of solar energy. As the Sun heats the air, the warmer air rises and cools off. Cooler air falls, creating a convection current. These currents, on a global basis, form our wind systems.

Wind has more uses than simply drying your shirt. Scientists and engineers have been able to harness wind energy to produce electricity. The windmill is a turbine (a wheel with fan blades). When the wind makes it spin, it rotates an electrical generator to produce electricity. Throughout the world there are windmill farms that function in this way.

Figure 3.33 If you have ever ridden a bicycle into a strong headwind, you know how much of your energy is required to work against the wind's energy.

Figure 3.34 The use of wind energy is increasing in Alberta. The Cowley Ridge Project in Cowley Ridge in southern Alberta has been producing electricity since 1994. Since then it has averaged 55 million kilowatt hours of electricity annually.

More Sources of Thermal Energy

Have you thought about your own body as a source of thermal energy? Burning fuels such as natural gas and oil releases thermal energy in a furnace or a car, for example. In a similar way, food you eat is digested and releases energy for your body's growth and activity. Some of that energy maintains your body's internal temperature at about 37°C. Some of your body's thermal energy is tranferred to the air and objects around you. Have you ever been out in the cold watching a sports event? If you huddled together with your friends, you were taking advantage, to some extent, of thermal energy that all of you were releasing. Litters of warm-blooded organisms such as mice, kittens, and puppies huddle together for warmth when they are very young. A composter is another source of thermal energy. In a composter, organisms called decomposers break down food. Chemical changes occur, like burning or digesting food. As these changes occur, they release thermal energy. The thermal energy in turn helps in the process of decomposition.

Figure 3.35 This photograph shows red wrigglers in an indoor composter.

How about heating your household water with a composter? It has been done! A large composter (approximately 3 m in diameter and 1.2 m high) has provided hot water to a family on a 24 h basis. A smaller mass would not have provided enough pressure to release the amount of thermal energy required. A plastic coil buried in the compost contained cold water that flowed in at one end. Thermal energy was released by decomposition of the large mass of materials in the composter. It raised the temperature of the water in the pipe. The hot water flowed out of a tap at the other end of the pipe, when needed. Incoming cold water replaced the heated water. Users then had to wait until the water warmed up again.

Fossil Fuels

You have been examining some alternative sources of energy. An **energy resource** is anything that can provide energy in a useful form. Fossil fuels are the main energy resource in Alberta and throughout the world. **Fossil fuels** are chemicals from plants and other organisms that died and decomposed millions of years ago and have been preserved deep underground. Fossil fuels normally form when oceans and silt exert pressure on the cells of dead organisms. Natural gas and petroleum oils are fossil fuels.

Figure 3.36 Furnaces in buildings use fossil fuels. Airplanes, trucks, and automobiles burn fossil fuels. Thermo-electric generating stations produce electricity by burning fossil fuels.

INTERNET CONNECT

www.mcgrawhill.ca/links/sciencefocus7

The cruise ship *Queen Elizabeth II* travels only about 4 cm for each litre of fuel it burns. Go to the web site above for information about how much fuel other forms of transportation require. Click on **Web Links** to find out where to go next. Make a chart to show amount of fuel used and average distance per litre for each form of transportation.

Fossil Fuels: Two Problems

Our society's use of fossil fuels has continued to increase rapidly since the Western world became industrialized in the 1800s. We have been using fossil fuels for only a very short time compared to Earth's age, but we have already used up about half of the known easy-to-obtain fossil fuels (see Figure 3.37). New technology is enabling us to extract the fuel from oil sands and underwater deposits. At our present rate of use, these too will likely be used up in a relatively short time. As a result, fossil fuels will become more difficult and more expensive to obtain. Since fossil fuels take millions of years to form, we refer to them as **non-renewable resources**. Energy resources that can be recycled or replaced by natural processes in less than 100 years are called **renewable resources**. Trees and food crops are renewable resources that can usually grow at about the same rate as they are used up.

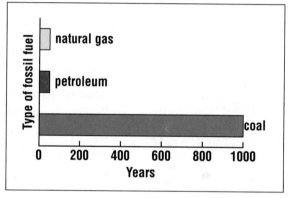

Figure 3.37 This graph shows how long our obtainable supplies of fossil fuels will last if our use of them continues at the current rate.

Another problem occurs when fossil fuels burn and produce carbon dioxide gases. Carbon dioxide is required by green plants, as you saw in Unit 1. It occurs naturally in the atmosphere. You add carbon dioxide to the air every time you breathe out, because as your body uses food, it produces carbon dioxide as a waste product. With ever-increasing numbers of planes, trucks, and automobiles meeting the demands of industry, natural carbon dioxide recycling systems are becoming badly overloaded. What happens then? Heat from Earth is unable to escape into space because it is trapped by greenhouse gases (largely carbon dioxide) in the atmosphere. You can observe the effect of **greenhouse gases** in the next activity.

Looking Ahead

In your Science Log, write some notes about why energy conservation is necessary. Use them as you develop your presentation for the Unit Issue Analysis.

Simulating the Greenhouse Effect

In this investigation, you can model the greenhouse effect and make an inference about its impact on life on Earth.

Question

How can you simulate the greenhouse effect?

Prediction

Use what you know about the greenhouse effect to predict what will happen to the temperature in a closed container in a sunny location.

Safety Precaution

- Always be careful when handling glass thermometers.
- If a thermometer breaks, do not touch it. Have your teacher dispose of the glass.

Apparatus

2 empty aquariums, the same size

glass lid to cover one of the aquariums

3 test-tube racks

3 thermometers

Materials

3 large index cards or other cardboard

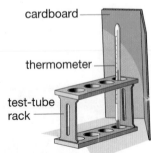

cardboard

thermometer

test-tube rack

Procedure

1 Arrange the aquariums side by side in a sunny window. Leave about 30 cm of space between them.

2 Place a test-tube rack in each aquarium and one rack between the two aquariums. Gently place a thermometer in each rack. Shade each thermometer by making a small wall with the folded cardboard as shown in the diagram.

3 Immediately **record** the temperatures of the three

thermometers in your notebook. (The temperature reading on all three should be the same.)

4 Place the glass lid on one aquarium.

5 Record the temperatures of all three thermometers at the end of 5, 10, and 15 min.

Analyze

1. Why did you place a thermometer between the two aquariums? Why is this called a control? Which variable did you change? Which feature did you **observe**? Did your observations support your prediction?

2. Which thermometer indicated the greatest temperature change? Explain why.

3. Assume that this model is truly like Earth. What can you infer about what will happen if Earth's system becomes overloaded with greenhouse gases?

Conclude and Apply

4. How was the glass lid like greenhouse gases in the atmosphere?

5. **Make a line graph** that shows the temperatures of the three thermometers for the 15 min of the experiment.

Skill FOCUS

For help with line graphs, turn to Skill Focus 10.

For tips on using models in Science, turn to Skill Focus 12.

Global Warming

Normal amounts of carbon dioxide in the atmosphere help to keep Earth warm enough to support life. Many scientists believe that increased amounts of carbon dioxide and other greenhouse gases are trapping thermal energy, warming Earth at a fairly rapid rate. Even a rise in temperature of a few degrees can make a big difference. It can change climatic zones and their plant-growing abilities, dry up rivers and lakes, and even melt the polar ice cap.

Canadians are among the highest producers of greenhouse gases (per person) in the world. Canada's physical size, small population, and fairly cold climate mean that materials have to be transported over large distances. Our energy use produces many economic benefits for ourselves and other countries. It also contributes to global warming.

Cogeneration

Engines in cars, trucks, trains, and aircraft, and furnaces in buildings, generating stations, and large industries, get hot. They release a lot of thermal energy into the environment. This accidental warming of the environment is called **thermal pollution**. **Cogeneration** uses this waste heat to generate electricity or heat buildings, or do other useful tasks.

For example, waste heat could be transferred from a factory to a downtown area (or to another factory), to heat and power buildings. Waste heat can be collected and transported using hot water running through a heat exchanger (like a huge car radiator). A pipe can run from the place where the heat is collected to where the waste heat is used. All along the pipe, buildings can use smaller exchangers connected to the pipe to obtain the thermal energy they require.

When fuel burns in a thermo-electric power plant, only about one third of its energy is usually converted to electricity. Cogeneration is efficient because it uses some of the remaining two thirds of the energy released from the fuel.

Figure 3.38 Some companies, such as Canada's Bombardier, are becoming more environmentally conscious. The aircraft shown here was designed to burn less fuel than other aircraft in its class. As a result, it releases less greenhouse gas into the atmosphere and causes less thermal pollution.

DidYouKnow?

In Antarctica, ice shelves are melting at an increasingly rapid rate. Ice shelves are floating extensions of the ice sheets that cover the Antarctic land. Over a few days in 1995, 1300 km^2 of one ice shelf broke up. Average temperatures in the area have risen by 2.5°C in the past few decades. Although it has not yet been proved, researchers suspect the break-ups are related to global warming.

TOPIC 7 Review

1. Describe two ways of producing electricity, and give an advantage and a disadvantage of each.

2. Describe two ways of converting mechanical energy to thermal energy.

3. Define active and passive solar energy.

4. What is the greenhouse effect, and why does it pose a problem?

5. **Thinking Critically** Why have Albertans not taken greater advantage of their geothermal energy sources like the hot springs near Banff?

TOPIC 8 Conserving Our Fossil Fuel Resources

There are so many disadvantages to burning fossil fuels, but we still use them. Fossil fuels form a key part of Alberta's economy. Coal, for example, is burned in generating stations to produce about 80 percent of the province's electrical energy. That energy is used in homes and in industries that provide employment for people who live here.

At the beginning of the last century, horses and wagons were so plentiful in New York City that horse manure caused a serious pollution problem. When it dried, small particles of manure would fly into the air, land on food displayed outside stores, and be inhaled into people's lungs. When the automobile was intro-duced, people hailed it as a wonderful, pollution-free device.

Figure 3.39 Has our air become overloaded with gases produced by burning fossil fuels?

Other fossil fuels, like oil and natural gas, are also readily available in Alberta. Fossil fuels have been so plentiful that people have assumed until recently that they would always be available. As well, when people first began to use fossil fuels, they believed that the unwanted gases they produce would simply be absorbed by the atmosphere. Fossil fuels were firmly established as an energy source and as a major part of Canada's and the world's economy before scientists began to observe some of the problems associated with them.

Find Out ACTIVITY

Timing Is Everything!

How long does it take to bring water from room temperature to boiling in a microwave oven? Plan a class project to find out and consider what your findings might mean in terms of energy conservation.

Safety Precaution

Handle hot water with extreme care. The boiling water and the container can cause painful burns. Enlist the help of an adult to do this activity.

Procedure * Performing and Recording

1. If you do not have a microwave oven, try to do this test with a friend whose home does have one.

2. Measure 250 mL of water and leave it at room temperature for an hour or so.

3. Place the container of water in the microwave oven. Set it at high power. Start timing as soon as you press the "Start" button. Continue timing until the water is bubbling.

What Did You Find Out? * Analyzing and Interpreting

1. Report your findings to the class. Did you find a wide variation in results? What might have caused these variations? How might they be eliminated?

2. If you can, try your test again to see if you can obtain more consistent results. Keep your notes so that you can compare your findings with a variety of cooking methods in the investigation on page 253, How Much Energy?

DECISION-MAKING

INVESTIGATION **3-K**

SKILLCHECK
☼ Initiating and Planning
Performing and Recording
☼ Analyzing and Interpreting
☼ Communication and Teamwork

You Choose!

Think About It

Opportunities to be energy-efficient are all around you. For example, the diagram below shows some features of the hot water system in many homes. It also suggests some possible ways to make this system more energy-efficient. This investigation will give you a chance to practise making energy-conserving choices in everyday life.

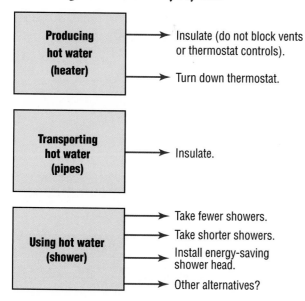

Procedure

1. In your notebook, write whether you would or would not take each action in the illustration. Give a reason for each choice.

2. Share your ideas and your reasons with the class.

3. **Estimate** how many minutes you spend when you shower.

4. An average shower uses 15 L of water per minute. **Calculate** how much water you use each time you shower.

5. An average bath uses about 220 L of water. Calculate how long you would spend in the shower to use this much water.

6. How many showers would you need to take to use the same amount of water as one bath?

Analyze

1. In your class discussion, which two energy-conserving actions were the most popular? Which two actions were the least popular?

2. Suppose that for one week you showered, and for the next week you took baths. Which method would be more energy-efficient? Give reasons to support your answer.

3. Why might your answers to procedure steps 5 and 6 be inaccurate?

4. What problems could be caused by setting your hot-water heater thermostat to a lower temperature in order to be more energy-efficient? Why might a too-high setting be dangerous?

5. What are the positive effects on your household of taking at least some of these actions? What are the effects on your community?

Extension

1. Next time you take a shower at home, time yourself. How accurate was your estimate in step 3?

2. Consider any hair products you use, such as shampoo or conditioner. In what way do they affect the amount of time you spend in the shower?

3. List other activities in your house that involve hot water use; for example, washing clothes. For each activity, suggest some energy-efficient choices you could make.

Keep It Warm

Imagine that you are a researcher working for a company that develops products that will keep people warm in the winter. Before you can begin your research, however, you need to answer a basic question about insulating material.

Question

What is the effect of increasing the thickness of an insulating material on the amount of energy transferred through the insulation?

Hypothesis

Write a hypothesis about thickness of insulating material and transfer of thermal energy.

Safety Precautions

Use care when handling the hot water and when working around the heat source.

Materials

tin can (284 mL)

200 mL water

newsprint (One half of one sheet of newsprint will be considered one piece.)

masking tape

Apparatus

heat source

thermometer

retort stand

clamp

beaker (500 mL)

Procedure

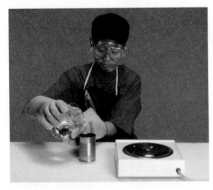

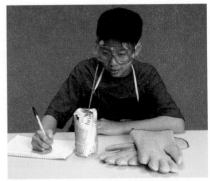

① With your group, heat a 200 mL sample of water to above 80°C. Carefully pour the water into your tin can.

② Carefully and quickly insulate the tin can by wrapping it in newsprint, as demonstrated by your teacher. The amount of newspaper to be used by each group is shown in the following chart.

③ Insert the thermometer into a small hole, made by your teacher, in the top of the paper. Immediately, start taking the temperature of the water. Continue to **record** the temperature every minute for 15 min (or for as long as your teacher directs). **Make a chart** to record this temperature.

④ Carefully dispose of the hot water down the sink and clean up your work station.

⑤ **Record** the final temperature of your water in the chart or data base provided by your teacher.

⑥ **Draw a graph** to compare the results within the class.

Group number	Amount of paper	Temperature After							
		1 min	2 min	3 min	4 min	5 min	6 min	...	
1	0 sheet (s)								
2	1								
3	2								
4	3								
5	4								
6	5								
7	6								
8	7								
9	8								
10	9								

Ask an Expert

Turn to page 258 to find out why Mario Patry needs to understand how insulating materials work.

Analyze

1. What scientific name should be given to the first group in the chart? What is the purpose of this group?

2. Which variable (manipulated variable) did you change? Which feature (responding variable) did you observe?

3. If you repeated this activity, do you suppose you would get exactly the same results? What might make the new results different?

4. How was heat lost through each of the following?
   (a) conduction
   (b) convection
   (c) radiation

Conclude and Apply

5. What is the effect of increasing the thickness of an insulating material on the amount of energy transferred? Did your observations support your hypothesis?

6. Would newsprint make a good insulator in your home? Explain your answer.

7. Describe three areas in which you could apply what you have learned about energy conservation.

8. During the winter, house owners often compare the amount of snow on their roof to that of their neighbours to determine if they have enough insulation in their attic. Explain how a homeowner would be able to tell if more insulation were needed.

9. **Design Your Own** With your group, brainstorm other materials that could be used for insulation. Think about different applications: clothing, home insulation, keeping foods warm or cold. What features will each application require? Choose one application, and design an investigation to test at least two insulating materials in that application.

Extension

10. Use library and Internet resources to research survival and other clothing that helps protect people from very cold weather and from the danger of hypothermia (dangerously low body temperatures). Find out what kinds of materials and fillings are used in cold-weather clothing. What design specifications do these articles need to meet? What criteria are used to rate them? How do clothing manufacturers reduce fossil fuel use and pollution at their factories? Prepare a report for presentation to the class. Use informative visuals and, if you can, obtain samples of each material for display. Evaluate the usefulness of these products.

It's Hot in Here!

Programmable thermostats and other technologies have provided many ways to save energy (and money) at home. If you turn on a hot water tap at school, is the water hot right away, or do you have to wait for it to warm? If it is instantly hot, it is probably produced by a recirculating hot water system. Examine Figure 3.41 to see how a recirculating water system works. The system saves energy and provides instant hot water at all times.

Figure 3.40
Programmable thermostats can be set to adjust the temperature so that a home is cooler when its occupants are away or sleeping.

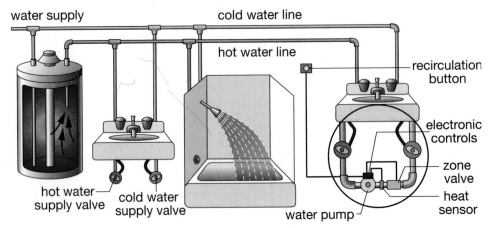

Figure 3.41 This recirculating system pumps hot water to a zone valve. When the system is filled with hot water, the zone valve shuts off the pump.

It's Cold in Here!

What do a refrigerator and an air conditioner have in common? Both are thermal energy movers. A thermal energy mover is a device that transfers thermal energy from one location to another location at a different temperature. How does it do this?

The operation of a refrigerator or an air conditioner depends on the processes of evaporation and condensation. Examine Figure 3.43. Refrigerators use **refrigerants** (liquids that evaporate easily at low temperatures) to remove thermal energy from food. The refrigerant is pumped through coils inside the refrigerator. As the refrigerant evaporates, it absorbs thermal energy from the items inside the refrigerator, so they cool down. The warmed gas is pumped to a compressor at the back or bottom of the refrigerator. When the gas is compressed, its temperature rises until it is above room temperature. Then it loses thermal energy to the air in the room and condenses again into a liquid.

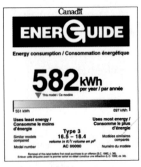

Figure 3.42 The EnerGuide label, found on most household electrical appliances, tells the consumer how much electricity, in kwh/year an appliance uses in one year under normal use. Check the energy ratings of large appliances in your home.

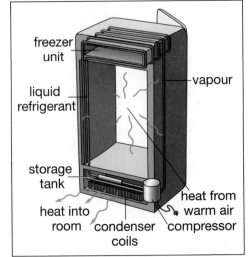

Figure 3.43 A refrigerator is a thermal energy mover.

INVESTIGATION 3-M

How Much Energy?

Think About It

What is the effect of the choice of cooking method on energy use?

How Can Science Help?

Your knowledge of thermal energy transfer and your science skills in conducting fair tests will help you in this investigation.

Procedure

1 With your group, examine the graphs. They tell you how long it took to bring 900 mL of water from room temperature (20°C) to boiling and the cost of the energy it required.

2 Discuss the variations in times with your group. Think about why such variations would occur, and make some notes about your ideas.

3 Trace and record as many energy inputs as you can for each method.

4 Examine the photograph of the solar cooking device shown below. Although such devices cost nothing to operate, they are complicated to construct. The cooker has to point directly at the Sun, so it must be turned as the Sun's position changes. A solar cooker can get hot, but, depending on the weather, it may take considerably longer than the other methods you have investigated.

5 Share the ideas you recorded in step 2 and the inputs you recorded in step 3 with the rest of the class.

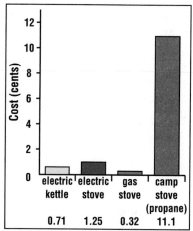

Boiling Water (Cost)

	electric kettle	electric stove	gas stove	camp stove (propane)
Cost (cents)	0.71	1.25	0.32	11.1

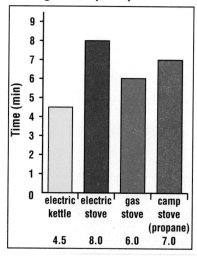

Boiling Water (Time)

	electric kettle	electric stove	gas stove	camp stove (propane)
Time (min)	4.5	8.0	6.0	7.0

Analyze

1. What does it mean to say that some heating methods are more energy-efficient than others?

2. If you look only at the graphs of experimental results, which method of heating required the smallest energy input?

3. If you look at the "total" energy inputs required for the different heating methods, which method appears to be the most energy-efficient? If you cannot decide, what additional information would help you to answer the question?

Turn It Down!

Find Out **ACTIVITY**

You have been examining ways to conserve energy. One idea is to turn down the thermostat on your home hot water heater. Would others in the household notice any change if you did?

Safety Precautions

Hot water heaters are dangerous if not handled carefully. Have an adult turn down the thermostat while you observe. Use care when testing the hot water temperature.

Procedure ✷ Performing and Recording

1. Fill the kitchen sink with hot water, and use a thermometer to measure the temperature. Record the temperature. Ask an adult to change the setting on the water heater.

2. A day or so later, fill the same sink with hot water and check the temperature. How does it compare to the first measure you took? After turning down the thermostat, what difference (if any) do you notice?

3. Check to see if members of the household find that the water is not hot enough or if they ever run out of hot water.

What Did You Find Out? ✷ Analyzing and Interpreting

1. How did your results compare with the results of other class members?

2. What scientific knowledge have you learned in this unit that you could use to explain to someone how turning down the water heater thermostat saves energy?

3. If you live in an apartment building, get the permission of an adult to speak to the superintendent about the temperature setting on the building's hot water heater. Compare it with the temperature of hot water heaters in houses.

Danger: Thermal Energy

Figure 3.44 Care must be taken with the use and storage of fossil fuel products in order to avoid situations like this.

Many of the harmful effects of thermal energy are obvious. A burn caused by touching a hot metal pot is painful. The effects of a forest fire are devastating. Thermal energy does indeed have the power to hurt and destroy us, our belongings, and our environment.

Look again at the photograph on page 186. It is just one example of a problem with the storage of petroleum products. Storage of fossil fuels presents a fire hazard, but there are other risks, as well. Industries are sometimes charged with unsafe storage of materials that pollute the environment. Large storage tanks buried underground may leak harmful chemicals into the soil. Industries that produce petroleum products use chemicals in their manufacturing processes. These chemicals end up in the soil and water. Many millions of dollars are spent in reclamation programs — programs that attempt to restore the soil to its original state. Until the soil is restored, it cannot be used for other purposes.

Individuals, as well as industries, need to take proper care with the storage and use of fossil fuel products, even when those products are used in small quantities.

Store it Safely

People sometimes mix paint and clean paint-brushes in their basements because they do not need to worry about staining the floor with any spilled paint. For certain types of paints, though, this can be a real danger. Fumes from the paint or paintbrush cleaner can be ignited by the flame of a furnace or hot water heater.

What to Do

1. Find out how to use and store paint safely. Read the labels on paint tins. With your group, decide if those labels present the dangers clearly enough for consumers.

2. **Performing and Recording** Contact paint store employees to find out what they can tell you about these dangers and if there is anything consumers can do to reduce

Find Out ACTIVITY

them. Find out what the store does in order to handle large quantities of paint safely.

3. **Performing and Recording** Find out what the difference is between water-based (latex) paint and solvent-based (oil) paint. Identify which type presents a greater fire hazard.

4. **Performing and Recording** Contact your fire department to find out other dangers of burning paint. Ask the firefighters to describe how they would put out a fire in a paint store.

5. **Communication and Teamwork** Design your own visual safety label for a paint tin and use it in a poster in which you include your recommendations for the safe use and storage of paint products.

DidYouKnow?

It is possible that the largest fire on Earth occurred about 66 million years ago. There is evidence that at that time an asteroid smashed into the Gulf of Mexico close to the Yucatan peninsula. White-hot and molten rock from the impact sprayed across North America. This may have set most of the forests on fire and killed almost all of the living creatures on the continent. Many scientists believe that this type of catastrophe caused the extinction of the dinosaurs.

Figure 3.45 In Canada, many thousands of square kilometres of forest burn each year. Most forest fires are set off by lightning. However, some are caused by careless use of fire in the wilderness.

Figure 3.46 Copper is a good heat conductor, so the coating on this pan cooks the food evenly and prevents burning and scorching. The material in the oven mitt is a poor conductor, so thermal energy cannot be transferred from a hot pan to your hand.

By-Products of Thermal Energy Use

Not all the dangers of using thermal energy are as obvious as house or forest fires. One problem comes from the products released during burning. You may recall that carbon dioxide, which all fossil fuels give off as they burn, is a greenhouse gas. This means that it helps to trap heat energy in our atmosphere and so leads to global warming. But many fuels, like coal and sulfur-containing natural gas or oil also release other gases while they burn. One of these is sulfur dioxide. This gas is extremely irritating to the eyes, nose, and throat. People with asthma suffer greatly from this pollutant. Hydro-electric companies invest large amounts of money into researching and developing technology that will remove or reduce emissions of sulfur dioxide.

When a fire burns without enough oxygen, a gas called carbon monoxide is produced. It is colourless, odourless, and lethal. The symptoms of carbon monoxide poisoning begin with dizziness and confusion. Because it hinders the brain's reasoning ability, people often do not notice when they are being affected by carbon monoxide. Many people have died in houses or in stranded cars from inhaling this gas. That is why governments in Canada recommend that every house contain carbon monoxide detectors, as well as smoke detectors.

Large-scale use of any type of energy has both benefits and problems. Thermal energy is no exception. Your knowledge of thermal energy and how it is released and transferred will help you to make choices that will preserve both our resources and our environment.

Technological advances now use thermal energy to help drivers avoid danger. An infrared beam senses thermal energy in an object in front of a car at night time. The infrared beam reaches up to five times beyond the headlights. It translates the thermal energy into a black and white image that is projected onto the lower part of the windshield, enabling the driver to take action and avoid a collision.

TOPIC 8 Review

1. In what ways are fossil fuels important to Alberta?

2. Describe some of the dangers involved when thermal energy is used.

3. Why is it necessary to remove sulfur dioxide gas from the gases given off by a coal-burning hydro generating plant?

4. (a) When is carbon monoxide produced?

   (b) Why is carbon monoxide so dangerous?

5. **Apply** A fire produces hot gases. Using what you know about the behaviour of gas when it is heated, answer the following:

   (a) Where should you place fire detectors and carbon monoxide detectors in the house?

   (b) Where is the air safest to breathe in the corridors of a burning building?

Figure 3.47 Carbon monoxide detectors should be installed in all homes for the safety of the occupants.

If you need to check an item, Topic numbers are provided in brackets below.

Key Terms

geothermal energy

solar energy

passive solar heating

active solar heating

solar collectors

wind energy

energy resource

fossil fuels

non-renewable resources

renewable resources

greenhouse gases

thermal pollution

cogeneration

refrigerant

Reviewing Key Terms

1. Copy the following list of terms into your notebook. Match each with the correct definition. Write a definition of terms that are not defined.

   (a) active solar heating

   (b) non-renewable resources

   (c) thermal pollution

   (d) refrigerant

   (e) solar energy

   (f) fossil fuels

   (g) resource

   (h) cogeneration

   (i) wind energy

   (j) greenhouse gases

   (k) solar collectors

   (l) renewable resources

   (m) passive solar heating

   (n) geothermal energy

   energy that will never run out (7)

   energy that depends on the Sun (7)

   an important resource in Alberta (7)

   prevent heat from escaping into outer space (7)

   undesirable effect of thermal energy (7)

   solar heating without fans or motor (7)

   technique for using unwanted thermal energy (7)

   a means of trapping the Sun's energy (7)

   liquid that easily evaporates at cold temperatures (8)

   fossil fuels are this kind of resource (7)

   energy inside Earth (7)

Understanding Key Concepts

2. Classify the sources of energy you have studied in these Topics as renewable or non-renewable. Explain what it means to say an energy resource is non-renewable. (7)

3. What is another name for a windmill? How does it produce electricity? (7)

4. In your notebook, draw a diagram showing how cogeneration works. (7)

5. Explain why you should never leave a pet inside a closed car in warm weather. (7)

6. List several advantages and disadvantages of a solar cooker. (7)

7. Is any energy resource "free"? Explain. (7, 8)

8. Why is a refrigerator called a thermal energy mover? On what scientific principles does it work? (8)

9. Look up the word "combustible" in the dictionary and explain how it applies to fossil fuels. (8)

10. Is it possible to change people's attitudes so that they will make wise environmental choices? How can you do it? (8)

UNIT 3

Ask an Expert

Planning a camping trip? Talk to someone like Mario Patry. Mario, who works at a camping equipment store, knows a lot about outdoor equipment. He can help you figure out which of the store's 30 different sleeping bags you will need to keep you warm. Mario knows a lot about insulation and energy transfer—the same topics you studied in Investigation 3-L (page 250).

Q **How do you help a customer choose a sleeping bag?**

A The first question I ask is where and when they intend to use the bag. If you are backpacking in southern Canada in July, you will want a very different bag than if you are backpacking in Yellowknife in April.

Q **Can a sleeping bag really keep you warm in Yellowknife in April?**

A The right kind of sleeping bag can. Not all of the bags we sell would be warm enough in that situation, especially those designed for summer camping. Our warmest bag, though, has a tem-perature rating of –40°C. It can keep you warm on very cold nights, if you use it in a tent for protection from the wind and on top of a sleeping pad for insulation from the cold ground.

Q **What makes these bags so much warmer than the summer ones?**

A Many factors affect how well a sleeping bag can keep the sleeper warm. Probably the biggest factor is what kind of insulation it uses. By that I mean what the bag is filled with. There are two main types of sleeping bags: those that are filled with down (the fluffy layer under the feathers of water birds) and those that have synthetic fills (fibres made by machine).

Q **Which type of fill keeps you warmer?**

A If you compare a down sleeping bag with a synthetic sleeping bag of the same thickness, the down bag is warmer.

Q **Why is that?**

A Down puffs up very high — we call this effect "loft" — because of the many, many tiny air pockets in-between the bits of down. These air pockets are excellent insulators. They warm up with heat from your body and hold on to this warmth instead of letting it seep out of the sleeping bag. If you unroll your sleeping bag when you first set up camp, it has a chance to puff up with as many air pockets as possible before you sleep in it.

Q **What about synthetic bags?**

A Synthetic fill doesn't have as much puffiness, or loft, as down because synthetics have fewer air pockets. Fewer air pockets mean less trapped heat.

Q **Why would a customer choose a synthetic bag, then?**

A For any of several good reasons. Down is very expensive, sometimes twice the price of a comparable synthetic bag. Also, synthetic is a better choice if there's a chance your sleeping bag will get wet. A down bag takes much longer to dry out than a synthetic bag. While it's wet, the feathers are stuck together. That means fewer air pockets and not as much warmth. And, of course, people who are allergic to down need to buy synthetic bags.

Q How did you learn so much about sleeping bags?

A A lot of what I know about equipment I've learned from reading backpacking books and magazines and from trying out the equipment myself. I've been cycling, skiing, and winter camping for years. When I began working here, I completed two weeks of training to learn about the specific products the store offers.

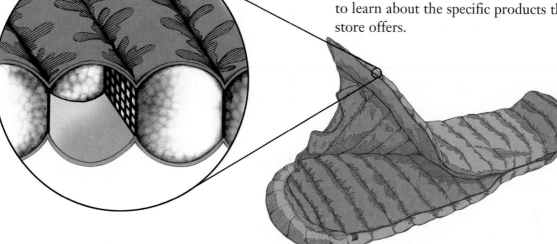

Cross section of synthetic sleeping bag insulation

EXPLORING Further

Who Is Warmer?

Imagine this situation. Sydney and Yasmine arrive with their school group at a camp site cold and damp from a day of canoeing. Luckily their equipment is dry. Yasmine unpacks her synthetic sleeping bag, pad, and one-person tent, and quickly sets up camp. Sydney ignores her down sleeping bag and gets the stew cooking. As the Sun sets, they feel the temperature dropping. After supper is cleared away, Sydney unrolls her sleeping bag on the ground. Then both campers climb into their sleeping bags and go to sleep.

If Yasmine's and Sydney's sleeping bags are both rated to –10°C, who do you think will be warmer during the night? Why?

An *Issue* to Analyze

Using Thermal Energy Efficiently

Background Information

Imagine that you and your team are a planning committee. Your task is to suggest alternative energy-efficient home heating systems for city council to examine. You believe that passive solar energy should be part of the system you recommend. Because you know that it will not be possible to use passive solar heating all year, you plan to combine it with another heating method. Some people on city council see no need to make home heating more energy-efficient and are not convinced that passive solar heating works. How can you persuade them to your point of view?

Think About It

How will you and your group effectively do the following?

(a) identify features of a solar heating system that increase its efficiency

(b) research alternative heating methods to combine with passive solar heating

(c) decide which is the best combination of heating methods and recommend it in a presentation.

How Can Science Help?

In order to prepare for your presentation, you need to understand the particle model and its relationship to thermal energy. You need to understand how thermal energy is transferred and how to prevent its transfer. If you recommend a fossil fuel resource, you must be able to explain why you are recommending one resource over another.

Skill
FOCUS

For tips on scientific decision-making, turn to Skill Focus 8.

Materials

paper

Internet access/
library research materials

coloured markers

notebooks

Procedure

Identifying Features

1 Think about what you already know about solar heating and how it works. Think about features that might make a house more efficient. You could consider features such as; the size and location of windows

insulation

colour of the outer walls

types of interior fabrics

any other relevant features, based on what you have learned in this unit

2 Examine the material you have been collecting in your Solar Centre and your Internet bookmarked sites. You might look for other features that you haven't yet considered. You might also look for new information that will improve on features you have considered. (For example, you might not have considered the overall layout of the house. You might not have thought about how landscaping can help with the house's efficiency.) Think about the cost and availability of materials as you consider various features. You might want to make a table for each feature with headings such as the following:

Feature
How/Why It Works
Cost/Availability
Pros/Cons

3 Conduct a careful discussion of the features you have been examining. Obtain agreement about the ones you want to include. They should be features that each person thinks will make the house more efficient. Make sure that everyone understands why each feature has been chosen, and that each person sees the reason for the choice, even if he or she disagrees.

4 Prepare a labelled diagram of your model house design. With your diagram, include a reference list of books, magazines, periodical, and web sites that you consulted during the research stage.

Researching Alternatives

5 With your group, research possible heat sources that could be combined with passive solar heating. Earlier, you investigated the cost of different energy sources. Find out about the cost of wood so that you can be prepared to consider the alternative of heating a house without natural gas or fuel oil. Find out about geothermal energy possibilities.

6 Discuss your findings with your group. Think about what else, besides cost, you need to consider in choosing a heating system. Develop a way to compare the systems under consideration. Through discussion decide which you prefer, stating your reasons.

Suggesting Alternatives

7 Prepare a presentation for city council. Make your presentation as effective and interesting as you can. You should consider:

(a) what understanding of science you will need in order to persuade city council that more energy efficient methods are necessary

(b) what understanding of science you will need to explain how passive solar heating works

(c) how and why the supplementary heating method you recommend will work

(d) why you feel the supplementary method is the best choice.

8 Your report on your model house should include solar energy features, landscaping material, and a description of the heating system. Use specific data to make it very clear to city council how your system could cut costs and save non-renewable resources.

9 You and your teacher will act as city council members as you listen to and observe the presentations made by other groups.

Analyze

1. As a class, discuss each system and select the one you think is most efficient. Think about it from an energy-saving viewpoint. Think about it from the consumer's point of view: its cost, its convenience, its comfort. Explain why you consider that system the most efficient and how you reached your decision.

2. If the class disagrees about which is the most efficient system, those of you who have voted for that system should meet and discuss how you can persuade the rest to your point of view.

3. If you were to do this Issue Analysis again, how might you do it differently? What parts of it could you improve upon? In what way?

Unit at a Glance

- Humans use thermal energy to meet increasing needs. In order to monitor thermal energy, we need to know how to measure temperature. We make use of a variety of technological devices and systems that help us in our use of thermal energy.

- The particle model of matter helps to explain:
  - why gases are compressible, while solids and liquids are nearly incompressible
  - why solids are rigid, while liquids and gases can flow
  - the relationship between thermal energy, heat, and temperature
  - how heat is involved in melting, freezing, vaporization, condensation, and sublimation
  - thermal expansion and contraction

- Thermal expansion and contraction is the basis for many devices such as thermometers and thermostats. An energy transfer system consists of an energy source; direction of energy transfer; control systems; and waste heat.

- Some sources of thermal energy are: chemical energy, electrical energy, mechanical forces, nuclear energy, geothermal energy, solar energy, wind energy, and fossil fuel resources.

- Fossil fuels are advantageous because they are plentiful. However, over-use has led to dwindling supplies. Fossil fuels have also created problems due to thermal pollution and the production of greenhouse gases.

- New technologies and new strategies are now being developed to help us to conserve our fossil fuel resources and to use them safely.

Understanding Key Concepts

1. A block of ice is placed on the pavement of a parking lot on a sunny day. Make some inferences based on your observations. What do you think would happen after one hour? What would happen after two hours?

   (a) List the thermal effects that occurred in this story.

   (b) The thermal effects in (a) involved adding energy. Explain where the energy came from in each case.

   (c) For each thermal effect in (a) explain where the energy went.

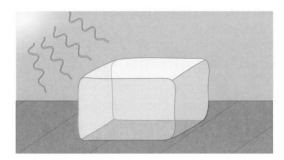

2. A new "super insulation" is made from plastic foam with a shiny, metal foil covering. All the air is pumped out of the holes in the plastic foam, so it is a vacuum. The foil prevents air from entering the foam again. This insulation could be used to insulate houses, refrigerators, vending machines, and refrigerator trucks and train cars. Experts estimate that it could save as much as $1 billion worth of fuel each year.

   (a) Explain how the super insulation prevents heat transfer by
   convection   conduction   radiation

   (b) Suggest one problem that might occur with the new insulation.

Developing Key Skills

3. The diagram below describes what happens to a large ice cube as it falls into a saucepan of hot soup boiling on a stove. Copy the diagram onto a full sheet of paper. Add information to each section about particle motion, temperature, and thermal energy.

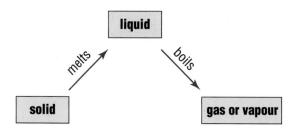

4. Imagine hitching a ride on a particle of candle wax as it melts and then evaporates in the candle flame. Describe what the ride would be like. Include as many details as you can about the changes in position and motion of the particle.

5. In your notebook, copy and complete the following concept map.

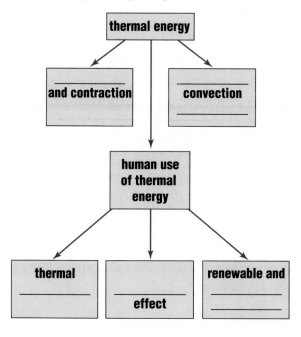

6. Draw a diagram that traces the path of energy through one of these systems: a person riding a bicycle, the hot water system that supplies your shower, a pet. Start with the source of almost all energy on Earth — the Sun. Remember to include waste heat. Label different energy transformations and transfers using the vocabulary you have learned in this unit.

Problem Solving/Applying

7. What type of thermometer would be appropriate for measuring temperature in each situation below? Give a reason for your answer.

    (a) measuring very low temperatures in the Arctic

    (b) regulating the temperature in a hot oven

    (c) finding if the temperature of a flame is high enough to melt the metal parts above it

8. Write a short story in which you imagine that you are a particle of water living with many friends in a pitcher in a refrigerator. Describe how you and your friends are behaving and how your behaviour changes in the following situations. You are taken out of the refrigerator, heated in a microwave oven, and left to cool on the kitchen counter.

9. One way to preserve fruit is to "can" it. Fruit and syrup are placed in a clean glass jar and then heated in boiling water to kill harmful bacteria. An airtight lid is fastened onto the jar, which is then left to cool.

    (a) Should the jar be filled completely to the brim before it is heated? Explain your answer.

    (b) After the jar cools, there is always some empty "head space" at the top. Does this mean that the contents leaked out during the canning process? Explain your answer.

10. Fruit farmers sometimes spray water over their orchards on cold, frosty evenings. As the water freezes, it protects the fruit from frost.

   (a) When the water freezes, does the energy of the water particles increase or decrease?

   (b) Explain how a change in the energy of the water particles can protect the fruit that the water is covering.

11. Identify the signals that your body's temperature control system would probably receive and send out while you spent an afternoon

   (a) playing beach volleyball

   (b) ice fishing

12. **Design Your Own** Use what you have learned about solar energy to design a solar cooker. You might want to try two designs and then test them to find out which is more efficient.

13. Look at the picture of the girl by the campfire. Describe all the energy transformations you can see in this picture.

14. A solar heating system for a home is designed with dark-coloured roof panels containing liquid-filled pipes to absorb solar energy. The heated liquid then transfers energy to the interior of the house.

   (a) What liquid would be best for the system: water, alcohol, or a mixture of water and antifreeze? Explain your choice.

   (b) Extra thermal energy can be used to warm an underground water tank, an underground bin of gravel, or a big brick wall in the middle of the house. Which energy storage method do you think would be best? Why?

Critical Thinking

15. The particle model of matter tries to explain everyday happenings by describing the behaviour of things that are too small to see clearly.

   (a) Why are scientists convinced that the particle model is correct?

   (b) Which parts of the particle model seem reasonable to you? Which parts do you find hard to accept?

16. To loosen a very tight lid on a glass jar, people often hold the jar and lid under hot running water. After a minute, the lid twists off easily.

   (a) What must be different about the behaviour of the metal and the glass to explain why the lid loosens?

   (b) What would probably happen if a jar with a loose-fitting lid were placed in a freezer? Explain why.

17. A large body of cool water can easily have higher total thermal energy than a small amount of hot water (for example, the amount of water in a hot water bottle). Explain how this is possible.

18. **(a)** How does the game of bowling model energy transfer by conduction?

(b) How does swimming model energy transfer by radiation?

(c) How does dancing model energy transfer by convection?

19. Birch bark and paper both burn well. Yet water in a paper bag or a birch bark container can be warmed and even boiled over an open flame without catching fire. How is this possible?

20. Plants and trees need carbon dioxide, and use it to produce oxygen, which people and animals need. Why might this fact make many people object to destroying a park to build a housing development?

21. Which type of temperature-measuring device is shown in the photograph below? Describe how this device works, and suggest a situation in which it could be used. Do you know any other scientific device that has similar features, and what it is used for?

22. You pour 100 mL of hot water at 50°C into 200 mL of cold water at 10°C.

(a) In which direction is thermal energy transferred?

(b) Which methods of energy transfer take place?

(c) What happens to the temperature of the hot water and the temperature of the cold water?

(d) If you leave the water mixture in a glass beaker for 24 h in a room with a temperature of 20°C, what will happen? What general feature of energy transfer does this illustrate?

23. Barbecues produce carbon monoxide when they are in use. Should they be banned? Write a list of pros and cons and be prepared to debate the issue.

24. Why is energy a useful characteristic to measure or calculate when you are preparing a scientific description of an object or a system?

Pause& Reflect

Go back to page 186 at the beginning of this Unit, and check your original answers to the Focussing Questions. How has your thinking changed? How would you answer those questions now that you have investigated the Topics in this Unit?

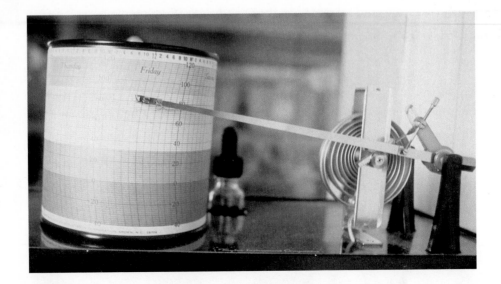

Structures and Forces

Have you ever been on an amusement park ride that is similar to one shown in this photograph? Did you find yourself wondering about the safety of its various parts — the cables, the towers, or the concrete on which the structure rested?

All of us trust our lives to structures every day. Some structures, such as dams and skyscrapers, contain such enormous amounts of materials that their weight distorts the ground beneath them. Other structures, such as amusement park rides and gymnastics apparatus, have carefully arranged parts that hold them up and support whatever they must carry. All structures, no matter how they are built, must keep their shape and do a particular job.

Small or large, structures are designed using similar principles. Professional architects and designers understand the scientific principles behind the reasons and the ways structures fail. This knowledge allows them to solve design problems so that structures meet specific needs. Some structures need to withstand extreme weather conditions. Some must be beautiful to look at. Others need to be as light and strong as possible. Still others need to be as inexpensive as the manufacturer can make them, while still being strong, beautiful, or light enough to do the structure's other jobs.

By learning the principles that designers use, you can do a better job of designing and building your own projects. As well, you will have a better understanding of how a ski lift or an amusement park ride can be safe, and why you can depend on the apparatus in gym class!

Unit Contents

Preview

- What features do structures have?

- What makes structures fail?

- What design choices make strong and stable structures?

This jellyfish and the amusement park ride on the previous page are very different. As structures, they may have similar properties. In Topics 1–2, you will learn how to classify and describe structures to understand their function and properties.

You can learn a lot by examining why something did not work. What caused the *Titanic* to sink? What have scientists learned by studying broken, collapsed structures? In Topics 3–5, you will use what you know about forces to find out what causes structures to fail—and why some stuctures are designed to do just that!

How did demolition experts know how to tear down Calgary's General Hospital? They used their scientific knowledge of forces. In Topics 6–7, you will learn how forces are used in structural design. You will also investigate common methods of strengthening structures to help them resist destructive forces.

Looking Ahead

Read pages 344–345 about your unit project, the Reverse Bungee Drop of Doom. This is your chance to apply your scientific understanding of what makes structures strong. Keep in mind the questions below as you work through the unit.

- How will you make your structure strong and lightweight?

- How can you make sure your ride is stable and safe without anchoring it permanently?

- Besides materials, what other design choices will ensure a strong, stable ride?

- What useful information can you add to your project file?

TOPIC 1 Types of Structures

Have you ever made a sand castle or an ice sculpture? What about building an igloo or assembling a tent? Have you peered through a telescope at another planet, or examined a snowflake under a microscope? All these objects are examples of **structures**: things with a definite size and shape, which serve a definite purpose or **function**. To perform its function, every part of the structure must resist **forces** (stresses such as pushes or pulls) that could change its shape or size. For example, a brick wall must be able to stand up to the force of the wind. The bricks at the bottom must support the weight of the bricks above. If a person climbs on top of the wall, the bricks must support that **load** (the weight carried or supported by a structure) as well.

Many different structures are pictured on these two pages. Look around your classroom for a moment. Pick out other things you think could be called structures. In what ways are they similar to each other? What can you think of that should not be called a structure? Why not? Write answers to these questions before reading further.

There are so many different structures that it is difficult to form a definition that fits them all. Instead, we will concentrate on describing a structure's origin, its function, its form, its design, the materials and parts it is made of, and the ways it is held together. Before reading further, get together with a partner to develop your own classification system for the structures pictured on pages 270–271.

Classifying Structures

It would be inefficient to learn about structures by studying them one at a time. There are far too many! It is much more efficient to group, or classify, structures by picking out those that share common features.

One common classification divides structures into groups according to their origin. In this system, structures are divided into natural and manufactured objects.

Natural Structures

Natural structures are not made by people. Examine the photo of a bird's feather, for example. It has a definite shape, and it is made of many parts held together in a complex pattern. Feathers serve many purposes: they insulate birds in cold weather, protect them from rain, and allow them to fly. Feathers, like many familiar things in the natural world, are structures.

Non-living parts of the natural world may also have some structural characteristics. Think of sand dunes, for example. They have a characteristic shape and are made of many parts (sand grains) arranged in a

Pause& Reflect

You will learn a lot about functions, forces, and loads in this unit. What do these words mean to you now? In your Science Log, write a brief definition of each word, using your own words. Then write a sentence that uses each word correctly.

particular pattern. They provide a home for small animals and insects and play a role in a desert ecosystem. What other natural, non-living structures can you think of?

Manufactured Structures

Many things built by people are **manufactured structures**. The largest buildings, the tiniest beads, a complicated jigsaw puzzle, and a simple spoon are all manufactured structures. Many manufactured structures are modelled after natural structures. A fishing net, for example, has a design similar to that of a spider web. Suggest natural structures that resemble a parachute, an umbrella, and a Velcro™ fastener.

Figure 4.1 Canadian wheelchair athlete Stacy Kohut competes in mountain bike competitions with his four-wheel bike.

Figure 4.2 Kayhan Nadji, the designer of this tipi house in Yellowknife, combined elements of the traditional Inuit Igloo and Dene tipi with modern technology such as central heating and electric lights.

You can also classify structures by the way they are built. How a structure is put together, how it is shaped, and the materials making up the structure are all part of its **design**. You will study three kinds of designs: mass, frame, and shell structures.

Mass Structures

To build a sand castle, you start by making a big pile of sand. A sand castle is a mass structure, as is a brick. A **mass structure** can be made by piling up or forming similar materials into a particular shape or design. Mountains and coral reefs are natural mass structures. Snow sculptures, dams, and brick walls are manufactured mass structures. So are foods such as omelettes, cakes, and breads.

Figure 4.3 This dam, a mass structure, was built by beavers making a large pile of wood and mud.

Making something from a lot of building materials has advantages. The structure is held firmly in place by its own weight. If small parts are worn away or broken, this usually makes very little difference. Mass structures like Hadrian's Wall in England have been eroding for thousands of years without being destroyed.

A Layered Look

Figure 4.4 The pattern in these bricks is called a "running bond." It is used for strength.

All around you there are mass structures made of carefully arranged pieces. Have you ever noticed the pattern of bricks in a brick wall? The centre of each brick is usually placed over the ends of two bricks in the row below, as Figure 4.4 shows. Bricks and concrete blocks are often arranged in other ways, however. Look at several outside and inside walls made of bricks or blocks and compare the patterns used. Look around doors and windows to see if the arrangement is different there.

DidYouKnow?

What is the largest amount of material ever used in a dam? The dam that was built to create the tailings pond at the Syncrude Oil Sands project in northern Alberta contains over 540 million m^3 of material! Some of the world's largest heavy equipment was used to build the dam.

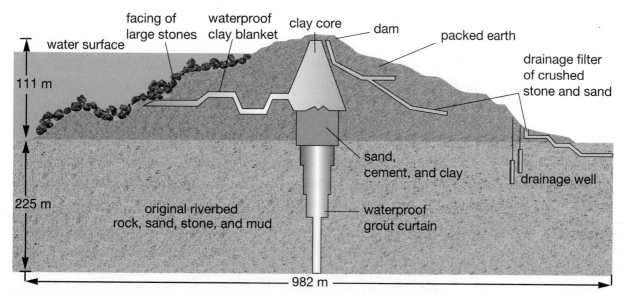

facing of large stones · waterproof clay blanket · clay core · dam · packed earth

water surface

drainage filter of crushed stone and sand

111 m

225 m

sand, cement, and clay

drainage well

original riverbed rock, sand, stone, and mud

waterproof grout curtain

982 m

Figure 4.5 A dam is an example of a mass structure.

Take a look at the dam in Figure 4.5. Try to guess the purpose of each type of material.

Mass structures are not always solid. Inside many power dams are enormous rooms that hold electric generators. Bricks and concrete building blocks are often hollowed out so that wires and pipes can pass through them.

Because of their large size and weight, mass structures must be carefully designed. Think of a wall of sandbags holding back a flooding river. There will be big problems if the wall fails! There are four main ways that a sandbag wall structure can fail.

- The wall may not be heavy enough to stay in place. The whole structure is pushed out of place by the force of the water against it.

- The wall may be so heavy that the earth beneath it is pressed down unevenly. The structure becomes unstable and tips over or falls apart.

- The wall may not be thick enough or fastened tightly together, so parts of it are pushed out of place. Then the structure breaks apart.

- The structure may not be anchored firmly to the ground. If very large forces press against the top, the structure may tip over.

The Great Pyramid in Egypt contains passages and rooms that once held everything that ancient Egyptians believed the dead Pharaoh would need as he journeyed to the spirit world.

DidYouKnow?

Flying passenger aircraft across the oceans seemed almost impossible in the 1930s. The trip required too much fuel. Canadian inventor Frederick Creed designed and built models of huge floating islands where planes could land and refuel in the middle of the ocean. During the Second World War, another inventor, Geoffrey Pyke, suggested building these artificial islands, or even aircraft-carrying ships, out of ice! A trial project in Alberta found that a frozen mixture of water and wood pulp was strong enough to build a refuelling island or a ship. Building with the new material was as expensive as using steel, however, so the project was dropped.

Frame Structures

Human dwellings and office buildings are not usually mass structures made by hollowing out piles of building materials. **Frame structures**, like the body of most buildings, have a skeleton of very strong materials, which supports the weight of the roof and covering materials. Most of the inside of the building is empty space. Extra partition walls can be built to separate different rooms, but they do not need to be particularly strong because the load-bearing framework supports the structure and everything in it. Can you identify load-bearing walls and partition walls in Figure 4.6?

Career CONNECT

Many different people work together to construct a building. Getting the foundation in the photograph built to this stage required the work of an architect, a contractor, a surveyor, an excavation team, and foundation builders. What was the responsibility of each member of the team? Which members of the team were responsible for the house's stability? Brainstorm the types of workers who would be involved in the next stages of construction for the house. Choose one, and find out about the kind of work this worker does.

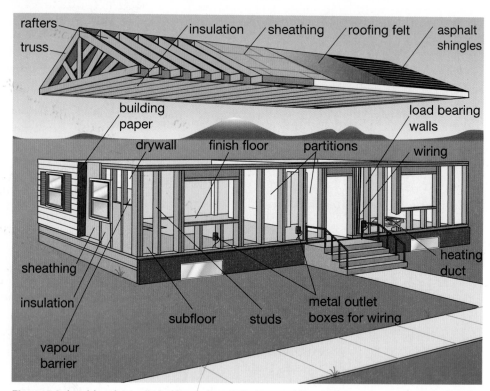

Figure 4.6 Load-bearing walls hold up a frame structure, while partition walls simply divide rooms.

Some objects, such as ladders, snowshoes, and spider webs, consist of only a frame. More complex objects may have other parts added to the frame, such as the pedals, gears, and brakes of a bicycle. The frame may be hidden beneath covering materials (as in umbrellas, automobiles, and boats) or left exposed (as in drilling rigs and steel bridges). Frame structures are relatively easy to design and build, making them one of the least expensive construction choices. Whether simple or complex, hidden or exposed, all frames must overcome similar problems.

Do you remember building frame structures in other science classes? How did you fasten the parts together? How did you make your frames strong without using too much material? How did you shape or brace them so that they would not bend or collapse?

Certain kinds of frame structures present special design challenges. Tents and other lightweight structures need some type of anchor to fasten them securely to the ground. Very tall frame structures, such as communications towers, can easily become unstable unless they are carefully braced. Large, complicated projects, such as buildings and bridges, have many parts that all have to fit together perfectly when they are finally assembled at the building site. This can happen only if every detail of the design is calculated in advance.

Picture a Frame

Procedure ✳ **Analyzing and Interpreting**

1. The diagrams show a manufactured and a natural example of frame structures. Sketch the two structures, or study the sketches that your teacher gives you.

2. Find at least one place or part on each structure that illustrates

    (a) rigid joint: fastens parts of the frame together so that they cannot move

    (b) mobile joint: holds parts of the frame together but allows them to move or turn

Find Out ACTIVITY

(c) brace: strengthens a joint or another part that must support a heavy load

(d) rigid shape: will not collapse or change shape even when large forces push or pull on it

(e) thin, lightweight material: does not have to be an especially strong part or place

(f) part that uses extra material for strength

3. Describe the primary purpose or function of each frame and the primary materials from which it is made. Explain why each material is well suited for the function it is intended to carry out.

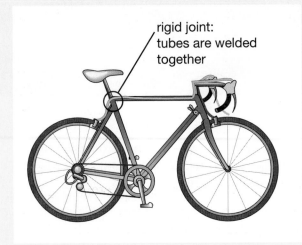

rigid joint: tubes are welded together

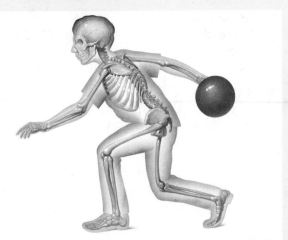

Golf Ball Bridge

Designers face many challenges when planning a new project. One of the first is that their design must fulfil specific criteria or specifications for the job. For example, the specifications for a bridge might be that it needs to be 20 m long. If the final bridge is only 19 m long, it would be useless. In this activity, you will test your ability to solve a design challenge based on a set of specifications. You will use your skills in solving problems, evaluating and testing prototypes, and applying results to practical problems.

Challenge

Build a free-standing frame bridge that supports a track capable of supporting a rolling golf ball.

Skill
F O C U S

For planning steps to solve problems, see Skill Focus 7.

Safety Precautions

Handle sharp objects with care.

Materials

15 to 20 large, thick plastic straws
15 small paper clips
60 cm masking tape
1 golf ball
scissors

Design Specifications

A. The bridge must span an opening between two desks or tables that are 30 cm apart.

B. The bridge must be free standing. It may not be attached to the desks or to anything else.

C. The bridge must support a track at least 5 cm above the surface of the desks.

D. The track must support a golf ball as it rolls from one end of the bridge to the other.

E. One end of the bridge must be higher than the other end so the golf ball will easily roll across the bridge.

F. You may use only the materials provided by or approved by your teacher.

G. You must construct the bridge in 40 min or less.

H. In at least three of five trials, the golf ball must successfully roll from one end of the bridge to the other without falling off.

I. The golf ball must roll on its own without being pushed.

J. The bridge must not fall over during testing.

Plan and Construct

1. With your group, brainstorm ideas for the design of your bridge. Each group member should contribute at least one alternative design. All designs must meet the specifications stated.

2. Based on your group's ideas, choose a plan for the bridge that you intend to build. Each group member should draw and submit a labelled diagram of the bridge to your teacher.

3. When your teacher has approved your group's design, begin to construct the bridge.

4. If, at any time during the construction process, your group agrees that the bridge will not function properly, make adjustments in the design.

5. When you have finished constructing your bridge, set it up at the designated test site. Carry out five trials.

Evaluate

1. Did your bridge pass the golf ball test? If not, explain what happened.

2. Did your bridge meet all of the structural specifications? If not, explain why it did not meet the specifications.

3. Which design specifications did you find the most difficult to meet? Explain why.

4. Describe at least three changes you would make if given the chance to re-construct the bridge. Explain the reason for each change.

Extend Your Knowledge

5. If your bridge was actually being built across a deep river gorge and the track had to support a heavy freight train rather than a golf ball, what additional things would you have to consider? List as many considerations as you can think of. For each consideration, explain why it would be important to the design and construction process.

DidYouKnow?

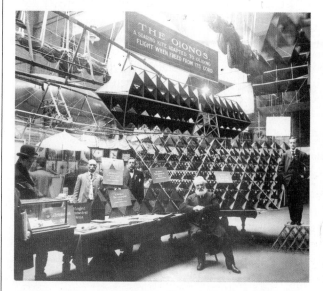

Alexander Graham Bell, the inventor of the telephone, was also very interested in flying machines. Bell experimented with many different kinds of kite frames, trying to find one that would be strong enough and light enough to lift a person and a gasoline-powered motor. The most promising kites used bamboo or aluminum frames made of many tetrahedral (pyramid-shaped) sections or cells covered in silk. In 1905, at his summer home in Baddeck, Nova Scotia, Bell demonstrated a 1300-cell kite named *Frostking*, which could lift a person into the air in only a light breeze!

Bell was certain that a practical flying machine could be built from his kite designs, but he could not do it alone. He and his wife Mabel Hubbard gathered a small troop of skilled helpers who called themselves the Aerial Experiment Association, shown here. They were one of the first modern research groups.

Figure 4.7 The dome of the Taj Mahal in Agra, India, is one of the most famous shell structures in the world.

Shell Structures

Think igloo. Think egg. Think cardboard box. All of these objects are strong and hollow. They keep their shape and support loads even without a frame or solid mass of material inside. Egg cartons, food cans and bottles, pipes, and clay pots are other examples of **shell structures**: objects that use a thin, carefully shaped outer layer of material to provide their strength and rigidity. Flexible structures, such as parachutes, balloons, and many kinds of clothing, are a different type of shell. Even the bubbles in foams and cream puffs can be thought of as shell structures.

Shell structures have two very useful features. They are completely empty, so they make great containers. Because they have only a thin outside layer, they use very little building material.

You might think that the material in a shell structure would have to be extremely strong, but this is not always the case. The shape of a shell spreads forces through the whole structure. Each part of the structure supports only a small part of the load, and the complete structure can be amazingly strong.

Canoes are shell structures that are built from birch bark, aluminum, or fibre-glass. Did you know they can also be built from concrete? Some engineers believe that concrete shells could be used to build the floating ocean platforms used for offshore oil drilling. They believe that concrete shells would perform better than the steel construction now used.

INTERNET CONNECT

www.mcgrawhill.ca/links/sciencefocus7

Find out more about concrete canoes by going to the web site above. Click on **Web Links** to find out where to go next. Write a short newspaper report telling who builds concrete canoes and why they do it.

Constructing strong shell structures can be tricky. Builders face problems like these:

- Tiny weaknesses like scratches on a glass jar can cause the whole structure to fail. Bubbles pop, balloons burst, and glass seems to explode when forces are not resisted equally by all parts of the shell.

- If a shell is formed from hot or moist materials, such as melted plastic or clay, uneven cooling or drying can cause some areas to push and pull on nearby sections. Strong forces build up inside the shell, as in Figure 4.9. If any extra force, even a small one, acts on the shell, the stressed places may break unexpectedly.

- Flat materials, such as sheets of plywood, are not easily turned into the rounded shape of a shell structure. Imagine building a plywood igloo! Each piece would need to be shaped and fitted into place individually, so construction would be slow and difficult. If you were paying a builder, the cost would be higher than for a frame structure.

- Assembling flexible materials into a shell is also tricky. Garment pieces need to be pinned into position before sewing. Afterward, the fabric edges must be specially finished so that the cloth will not pull apart along the seams.

Figure 4.8 A turtle's shell is a shell structure. It is made from a very strong, natural material called keratin. Your fingernails are made from the same substance.

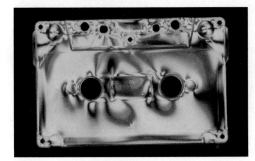
Figure 4.9 When polarized light (light waves of only one direction) passes through transparent materials, such as this cassette tape, the stressed areas appear as coloured fringes.

Across Canada

Dr. Marie-Anne Erki

As a child, Marie-Anne Erki often took apart her toys. Now she is a professor of civil engineering at the Royal Military College of Canada in Kingston, Ontario. These days, she is more concerned with putting structures together than taking them apart!

Dr. Erki works with high-strength fibres embedded in a polymer (plastic). They are called Fibre Reinforced Polymers (FRP). FRPs are as strong as steel but much lighter. "My field is making existing structures like bridges and buildings stronger using carbon tape. It's just like taping up a hockey stick," she says. In Canada and other cold-weather countries, road salt eats away at the steel bars that reinforce concrete bridges. FRP tape can patch and wrap these weak, rusted bridge columns and beams in order to strengthen them. Also, new concrete bridges can be reinforced with FRP bars instead of steel reinforcements so they will never rust.

In her work for the Canadian Forces, she is developing materials to make lightweight bridges that can be transported by airplane. This technology will be helpful when there is a natural disaster, such as a hurricane or a flood. It will enable washed-out bridges to be quickly and inexpensively replaced so that people are not cut off from food or medical aid. When she is not developing improved materials for construction, Dr. Erki helps university students with their research projects.

Mix and Match

Football helmets are shell structures, but the opening in front is covered with a strong frame. The combination of frame and shell construction protects the player while also allowing good visibility and ventilation. The helmet's designers combined different designs to improve the structure. Many structures, such as those below, combine designs.

Figure 4.10 What makes this building's shape unusual?

- Hydro-electric dams are mass structures, but inside they contain enormous rooms filled with electric generators. The walls and ceilings of the generator rooms are built with very strong frames. Otherwise, they would collapse from the enormous pressure of the rock, earth, or concrete that forms the dam.

- Airplanes are built around a metal framework, but the frame is not nearly strong enough to support the weight of the engines, fuel, and cargo. The metal "skin" that covers the framework is stretched tightly and acts like a shell. Stresses are spread through the whole frame, and the finished aircraft is strong, lightweight, and flexible.

Figure 4.11 A flimsy framework of balsa wood, covered with painted tissue paper or plastic film, makes a model aircraft strong enough to take off, do complicated stunts, and land safely.

- Domed buildings usually combine frame and shell construction. The dome forms a shell, which gains strength from its curved shape. The dome itself is often a thin layer of cloth, metal, wood, or concrete stretched over a wood or metal frame. Sometimes only the roof of a domed structure is a shell, placed on top of framed walls.

- Warehouses and other large, single-storey buildings are often built with steel columns that support the roof. The columns form a framework, but there are big spaces between them. The spaces are filled with walls of concrete blocks, which stay in place because of their weight. The walls are mass structures, but they are too tall and thin to be strong by themselves. When the walls are fastened to the steel framework, however, the combination forms a strong, easily constructed structure.

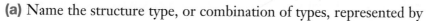

1. What type of structure (mass, frame, or shell) is each object listed below?

   (a) a backpacking tent

   (b) a pop can

   (c) a concrete barrier in a parking lot

   (d) the "jewel box" in which a CD is packed

2. Name the type of structure that is most likely to fail because

   (a) the material it was built from has small cracks or weaknesses

   (b) the weight of the structure caused the ground underneath it to shift

   (c) the outside walls were tilted slightly by an earthquake

3. **Apply** Model airplane wings are sometimes built by shaping solid pieces of foam plastic with a hot wire. They can also be made from many pieces of lightweight balsa wood glued together and covered with paper, plastic, or cloth. Full-sized, modern aircraft wings have a metal frame, but the frame is quite weak until a metal covering is stretched over it. Then the wings become strong enough to support the weight of the plane, as well as the weight of its fuel, which is carried in tanks inside the wings.

   (a) Name the structure type, or combination of types, represented by

   - a foam plastic wing
   - a balsa wood wing
   - a real airplane wing

   (b) Explain which of the two types of model airplanes would be easier to build.

4. **Design Your Own** Choose a small frame structure to test, perhaps one that you have already designed and built. Design an experimental procedure to determine the point at which the structure will fail. For example, how many golf balls can your straw bridge (from Problem-Solving Investigation 4-A) hold at one time? If you find the point at which your bridge will break, you will find what engineers call the *ultimate strength* of the structure. Predict the ultimate strength of your structure. If your teacher agrees that your chosen frame structure is safe to test, carry out your procedure.

Designers need to be able to visualize how the parts of a project can be arranged to create the final structure. Imagine that you are designing a small orchard. The owner wants the trees to be arranged in certain patterns.

1. How can ten trees be arranged in five rows, with four trees in each row?

2. If nine trees are arranged in rows of three, what is the largest possible number of rows you can make?

Describing Structures

Imagine discussing the bridge in Figure 4.12 with the engineer who designed it.

You: Wow! That's a fantastic piece of engineering!

Designer: Thank you. When I designed it almost a century ago, trains were much smaller than nowadays. I had no idea how enormous they would become, but my design had a good safety margin. It's still strong enough.

You: It must have cost a lot to build.

Designer: Yes, it was expensive for the time. The company tried to find other places to cross the river valley where it isn't so wide and deep. But when they added up all the costs, this was the still the cheapest. I used a very efficient design. There's no wasted material. Every piece of steel helps carry the load.

You: It doesn't look a century old. In fact, it looks really good.

Designer: Well, the railway company paints the structure frequently. It wouldn't last long without regular maintenance.

You: I was thinking more about the shape. It just looks strong and stable.

Designer: That's probably because of the symmetrical way the towers are designed and arranged. Most people find that very attractive. Did you notice that every tower is divided into triangular sections that make it strong and rigid?

You: That's right. You thought of everything!

Designer: Well, I tried to, but something unexpected always happens on a large project. I had to modify my design when the ground under one of the towers became unstable.

You can work like an architect or engineer. If you plan a project carefully, your final design will be improved. In this Topic you will learn about some things a designer must consider when planning a new project: function, aesthetics, safety, materials, and joints.

Looking Ahead

After reading the conversation on this page, make a list of questions and challenges the designer considered when building this bridge. Think about these challenges in terms of your upcoming unit project that will ask you to build a reverse bungee ride prototype. How many challenges will be similar?

Figure 4.12 This trestle bridge in Lethbridge, Alberta, was the longest structure of its height in the world when it was built in 1909. It carries trains 97 m above the valley of the Oldman River, for a distance of 1.6 km.

Figure 4.13 Fantastic devices like this were made famous by a cartoonist named Rube Goldberg.

RUBE GOLDBERG reprinted by permission of United Feature Syndicate, Inc.

INTERNET CONNECT

www.mcgrawhill.ca/links/sciencefocus7

To find out more about Rube Goldberg, go to the web site above. Click on **Web Links** to find out where to go next. Design your own Rube Goldberg™ device, and write a brief description of it.

Word CONNECT

Here are a few words that describe common functions of structures:
- containing
- transporting
- sheltering
- supporting
- lifting
- fastening
- separating
- communicating
- breaking
- holding

Examine Figure 4.14 and list as many functions of a running shoe as you can.

Function

What is this thing supposed to do? The answer to this question will guide all of your design decisions. Simple? Not really. Most structures have several functions. Think of a bridge. Its job is to support … what? Vehicles and people, of course, but the steel and concrete the bridge is made from can weigh many times more than the cars and trucks travelling across the bridge. Thus one very important function of any structure is to support its own weight.

Structures do more than just support loads. For example, a running shoe, such as the one in Figure 4.14, grips the ground or gym floor and cushions your foot bones from the impact of running. But it has many other functions, too. The words in the Word Connect on this page may suggest some of them.

Designers have a hard time creating structures that perform all of their functions equally well. Plastic-covered running shoes certainly keep water *out* when you run through a puddle. But they also keep perspiration *in*, so your feet soon get hot and sweaty. Most runners have rubber and plastic soles and cloth uppers. This compromise does not let much puddle water in but does let most perspiration out.

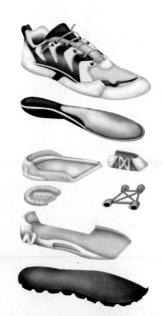

Figure 4.14 Running shoes have much more to them than meets the eye.

DidYouKnow?

Symmetrical shapes can be turned or folded to fit exactly on top of themselves. Most people's faces are quite symmetrical, as are many other natural and manufactured structures. Because symmetry looks very pleasing, it is a powerful element of good design. Symmetrical parts, braces, and decorations on an object help it look attractive. If you start watching for symmetry in structures you observe every day, you might find ways to use this principle in your next design project. Find the axis of symmetry — the line that divides the butterfly into two parts with almost identical shapes.

How well must a structure perform its functions? Designers work to a set of specifications that give precise, measurable standards their structure must meet. Specifications for a running shoe might be:

• sole must flex 100 000 times without cracking

• materials must not contain chemicals that could irritate the skin

Aesthetics

One very important design specification is seldom written down. The best designs look good. Designers refer to such designs as "aesthetically pleasing." (**Aesthetics** is the study of beauty in art and nature.)

Think of an attractive car, building, or butterfly. It might feature shapes that are repeated or carefully arranged. There might be interesting textures and colours that are carefully chosen to be harmonious or contrasting. Sometimes the choice of materials and the methods used to make a structure can have a huge impact on aesthetics. The marble columns used in classically designed Greek buildings are beautiful, functional, strong … and expensive! The concrete columns under a highway overpass are functional, strong, and relatively inexpensive. Check with your art teacher for other principles of design that can help your projects look attractive.

Above all, architects and engineers try to keep their designs simple. Clean designs look better than over-complicated, busy ones. So remember to keep it simple!

Figure 4.15 The Museum of Civilization in Hull, Québec, echoes a seashell in its design. The building was designed by Métis architect Douglas Cardinal, who is known for his ability to combine aboriginal design aesthetics with modern technology. Many aboriginal structures echo elements of nature in their designs.

Designing for Safety

Have you ever been in an elevator and looked at the safety notice on the wall? What do you suppose would happen if extra people crowded into the elevator, so it was carrying more than the greatest permitted load? The answer is: probably nothing. The elevator is strong enough to be able to carry a much larger load than could ever be squeezed into it. It was designed with a large **margin of safety**. This means it has extra strength that allows it to withstand much larger loads than it would normally need to carry.

Almost all structures are built with a margin of safety. In Canada, for example, building roofs are designed to support enormous weights, so they do not collapse under the weight of snowdrifts that develop in the winter. Bridges are designed to carry much larger loads than would ever occur, even if a traffic jam stalled a convoy of transport trucks on them.

Figure 4.16 Extreme weather conditions can cause both natural and manufactured structures to fail.

Balancing Safety With Cost

Making structures stronger usually makes them more expensive. Bigger, stronger parts use more material. Skilled crafts-people may cost more than inexperienced workers. Good design is a compromise between a reasonable margin of safety and reasonable cost.

Designers plan their structures to withstand conditions they imagine might occur. Totally unexpected conditions, or very rare events, may cause even well-designed structures to fail. Bridges, for example, are always designed to be strong enough to withstand the force of flood waters and the impact of floating debris. But the designers of the Groat Bridge in Edmonton failed to make the temporary forms and braces that were used during construction equally strong. In 1954, the partially completed bridge was seriously damaged by the flooded North Saskatchewan River.

Figure 4.17 Edmonton's Groat Bridge was damaged by flood waters during construction.

Materials

Choosing building materials is another important design decision. The **properties** or characteristics of the materials must match the purpose of the structure. Different materials can be combined to give the exact properties needed.

Composite Materials

There are different kinds of strength. Steel rods and cables can support very strong tension (pulling) forces, but they bend and twist if you compress them (push them together). Concrete is just the opposite: it resists large pushing forces, but breaks if it is pulled or twisted. The workers in Figure 4.18 are pouring concrete around steel rods and mesh. This produces reinforced concrete, a **composite** made from more than one kind of material. If reinforced concrete breaks, the steel rods help to support the structure.

Other composites have different properties. Fibreglass cloth embedded in rigid plastic is moulded into boat hulls. Flexible plastic formed around a nylon mesh is used in lightweight garden hose to strengthen it against the pressure of the water.

Figure 4.18 Reinforced concrete can withstand both tension and compression. It is used to make buildings, bridges, and other large, strong structures.

Layered Materials

Use a fingernail to separate the edge of a TetraPak™ beverage container. Can you see the thin sheets of paper, plastic, and aluminum foil that make the container waterproof, airtight, lightweight, easily transported, and inexpensive? Layers of different materials, pressed and glued together, often produce useful combinations of properties. Inside the safety glass of car windshields is a plastic film that helps the glass resist shattering. Drywall panels on the walls of a room, and tiles or linoleum on the floor, contain **laminations** (layers) of different materials. Even layers of one substance can be more useful than a single thick piece. Examine Figure 4.19 and pick out the layers of wood that make up a sheet of plywood. Compare the diagram to a real piece of plywood. What differences can you find?

Figure 4.19 How do plywood laminations add strength to the wood?

Woven and Knit Materials

Use a magnifying glass to examine a piece of cloth. Can you see the hair-like fibres that have been spun (twisted together) into long, thin strings called yarn? A loom is used to weave two or more pieces of yarn together in a crisscross pattern to make cloth. Yarn can also be looped and knotted together to make knit materials. Figure 4.20 shows how each section of the knit is interlocked with many other sections. Knit materials stretch in all directions, so they fit well over complex shapes, such as human bodies.

Weaving and knitting are not the only ways to make flexible materials. Paper and felt are made from fibres that have been pressed and matted together. Aluminum foil and plastic wrap are made by melting and dissolving a substance and then letting it harden into thin solid sheets. No matter how they are made, materials that can be folded or rolled are extremely useful for lightweight structures that must be easily transported and stored, such as clothing, tents, and parachutes.

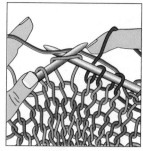

Figure 4.20 Interlocking yarn in a knit material spreads the forces throughout the fabric.

Find Out ACTIVITY

Sneezeproof Strength

Look closely at a facial tissue. Use the information in the previous section to infer why such thin material has enough strength to resist sneezes.

Materials

facial tissue
magnifying glass
pencil

Procedure ✷ Performing and Recording

1. Partly separate a facial tissue into its layers. Look at the fibres through a magnifying glass. Record your observations. Use diagrams if necessary.

2. Put one layer of the tissue flat on a desk. Gently pull the two top corners apart. Record how much force is needed to tear the tissue.

3. Now turn the tissue 90 degrees, and try pulling apart the same layer again. Record your observations.

4. Mark the grain of the layer along the direction that pulls apart more easily.

5. Repeat steps 2 to 4 for the other layer.

What Did You Find Out? ✷ Analyzing and Interpreting

1. Are the layers arranged with their grains pointing in the same direction or in different directions? Which arrangement would be stronger? Which arrangement would be easier to tear apart? Include sketches to make your answers clearer.

2. Are the fibres pressed or woven together?

3. In which direction is the tissue easier to tear? Explain.

Extension

4. Facial tissues are made from wood pulp. So are writing paper, newsprint, paper towels, and paper napkins. Find out if these other products have a grain and, if they are arranged in layers, whether the grains of different layers are aligned or not.

Pause & Reflect

Which shirt would you choose? Why? How would you balance the different properties of the different materials? Write answers to these questions in your Science Log before reading on. Write a list of questions about materials that you will use for your unit project.

Choosing Materials

Have you ever shopped for clothing, redecorated your bedroom, repaired a broken bike or chair, or patched a torn pair of jeans? All of these tasks, and many others, involve choosing among different materials, most of which could probably do an acceptable job. Choosing one material from many means balancing the advantages and disadvantages of each possible choice. Higher quality, stronger materials are often more expensive than weaker alternatives. Study the scenario below to discover some of the things to consider when making this design decision.

Choosing a Shirt

Figure 4.21 Choosing the right shirt

Jacob is shopping for a new shirt. He finds several that fit well and have colours and designs that he likes. To help choose, Jacob checks the labels to see what material each shirt is made from. One, which is very comfortable, is 100 percent cotton, a natural fibre made from the fluffy seeds of cotton plants. The care label says the garment should be washed with cool water, dried at low temperature, and ironed.

Another shirt, which is a bit less expensive, is labelled 100 percent polyester, a synthetic plastic fibre. The care label says to machine wash and dry, and hang up immediately. The third choice is also polyester, but it is labelled "Contains recycled materials." A card tied to the garment explains that the polyester is partly made from recycled pop bottles.

Jacob asks the store's sales clerk what else he should consider. The clerk tells him that cotton garments tend to shrink if they are washed in hot water, and that stains can be difficult to remove. Polyester is easier to care for, and much stronger than cotton, but it is less comfortable in hot or cold weather. Jacob now feels ready to make his choice.

To pick the most suitable materials for a structure, architects, engineers, and designers need to organize their information about possible choices. They might consider the following:

- **Cost:** The lowest-cost materials may not be a bargain. If they are of poor quality, making the structure may be difficult and much material may be wasted. Cheaper materials may wear out quickly or require a lot of maintenance. On the other hand, less expensive material may do an acceptable job.

- **Appearance:** Structures like buildings and bridges last a long time. The materials they are made from need to remain attractive and strong without requiring expensive maintenance.

- **Environmental impact:** Using recycled materials, or materials made from renewable resources, helps preserve Earth's resources. You can choose not to use materials that are produced in ways that damage the environment. You can also avoid materials that require construction techniques that use harmful chemicals, or materials that are difficult to dispose of or to recycle.

- **Energy efficiency:** The cost of many structures includes more than just materials and construction. Buildings need to be kept warm in winter and cool in summer. Refrigerators and freezers use electricity to stay cold. Washing machines and clothes dryers use water and air that has been heated by electricity or natural gas. Your choice of materials can reduce the amount of energy a structure requires. This reduces its operating costs, and also preserves Earth's limited supply of energy sources.

Find Out ACTIVITY

Tough Tissue Test

Tissue manufacturers often boast about the strength and quality of their product. In this activity, you will evaluate the properties of different kinds of tissues.

Materials

2 sheets of several brands of facial tissue (both one- and two-ply)
large empty container
600 to 800 pennies (or washers)

Procedure ✳ **Performing and Recording**

1. Prior to testing the tissues for strength, examine all brands carefully and write down as many properties as you can observe. Write a hypothesis about which brand will be strongest.

2. Put the empty container on a desk. Place a one-ply tissue over the open end of the container. (For thicker tissues, carefully separate the two plies and place one over the container.)

3. One partner holds the tissue firmly over the container, by holding it at the sides of the container. The other partner adds pennies to the centre of the tissue. Be sure that the tissue does not droop in the middle.

4. Continue adding pennies until the tissue tears and the pennies fall into the container.

5. Count the number of pennies the tissue held prior to tearing and record this value, along with your other observations about the tissue. The pennies collected could also be weighed.

6. Repeat the above steps for all of the brands of facial tissue.

What Did You Find Out? ✳ **Analyzing and Interpreting**

1. Which tissue was strongest?

2. What features do you think make a tissue stronger?

3. Describe other properties of tissues that could affect their function or sales.

4. Which of the tissues tested would you buy? Use your list of properties to explain your choice.

Extension

5. If time permits, the above test could be repeated with damp samples of each brand of tissue. Would testing damp or wet tissues be a fairer test of a tissue's strength? Explain your answer.

Joints

How should we fasten this structure together? That is a critical decision because structures are often weakest where their parts are joined together.

Mobile joints are joints that allow movement. Door hinges, elbows, and the pins in a bicycle chain are examples of mobile joints. They hold parts together while still allowing some movement. Their complicated shapes are tricky to make, and they must be coated with a lubricant (a slippery substance) so that they move smoothly. Without lubrication, door hinges squeak, bicycle chains wear out, and human joints develop arthritis and similar painful diseases.

Compare the functions of the mobile joints in Figure 4.22. Look around your classroom and your home to see how many types of mobile joints you can find. What is the most common material that is used to make mobile joints?

Many structures consist of hundreds, even thousands of parts. Each one of these parts must be securely held together to form a sturdy structure. **Rigid joints** attach these parts together. Most rigid joints fit into five categories: fasteners, ties, interlocking shapes, adhesives, and melted joints. These categories are discussed separately below.

Figure 4.22 Examine each of these mobile joints. What are the requirements of the materials used in making mobile joints?

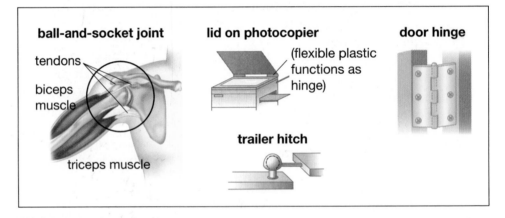

Fasteners

Nails, staples, bolts, screws, rivets, and dowels (shown in Figure 4.23) are used to hold many structures together. Unfortunately the holes that fasteners make also weaken the materials they fasten. Staples and nails are usually forced into the parts they join, which can crack and separate the material. Drilling holes for bolts, screws, and dowels does not weaken the material as much, but the holes are time-consuming to position and cut.

Figure 4.23 Dowelled joints are used by cabinetmakers to hold pieces of furniture together. How are the rivets in the steel beams similar to the dowels? How do they differ?

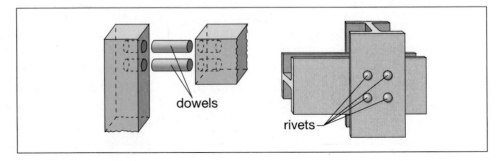

Attaching parts with just one fastener allows the parts to twist around it when they are pushed or pulled. Several fasteners make a more rigid joint, but the extra holes weaken the material more. So making a strong joint does not mean simply pounding in a bunch of big nails! Both the kind and number of fasteners must be carefully planned.

Interlocking Shapes

Carefully shaped parts can hold themselves together. Lego™ bricks and some paving stones fit together and stay together because of their shape. The fronts of wooden drawers are often locked to the sides with dovetail joints. Dentists shape the holes they drill in teeth to keep the filling material in place.

The joints in flexible materials are also carefully shaped. The sheet metal in the furnace and heating ducts of your home is overlapped or folded to strengthen the places where it is joined. Folded seams protect the cut edges of pieces of cloth and give a neat, finished appearance to the joints in clothing. Figure 4.24 shows some of the different kinds of interlocking joints.

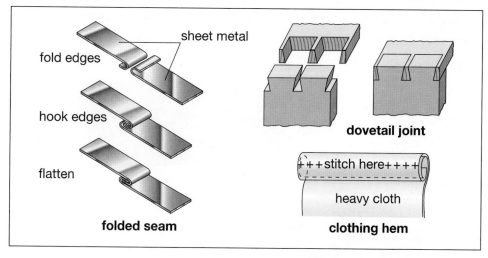

Figure 4.24 Various kinds of interlocking joints can be used to strengthen different types of structures.

Ties

Thread, string, and rope can also fasten things together. Shoes are tied with laces. Jacket hoods are tightened with drawstrings. Seams in clothing are "tied together" with a sewing machine. Figure 4.25 shows how the needle and bobbin thread are intertwined to tie the seam in place. Before sewing machines were invented, people sewed all of their clothing, including their shoes, by hand.

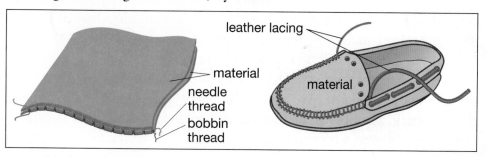

Figure 4.25 Sewing machines tie two threads together as they stitch a seam. Moccasins are sewn by hand with a strip of leather.

Adhesives

Sticky substances, called **adhesives** or glues, can hold things together. Figure 4.26 shows how glue flows into tiny rough areas on the surface of the pieces it joins. When the glue hardens, it locks the pieces together. *Thermosetting glues* like those used in glue guns harden when they cool. *Solvent-based glues* harden as they dry out. The strongest glues also create a special kind of force between the tiniest particles of the pieces being joined. Because of these forces, epoxy resins and super glues are strong enough to hold pieces of car bodies together.

Even the strongest glued joints fail under extreme conditions. Glues may soften in water or under very hot conditions. If a glue is stronger than the substances it joins, the material next to the joint may break.

Adhesives can be a health hazard. Some glues start to harden as soon as they touch moisture. If a drop gets on your fingers or in your eye, it can stick your fingers or eyelids together almost instantly. Other glues, such as those used to make plywood and particleboard, release powerful chemicals into the air as they harden. These gases collect between walls, in basements, and in other places that have poor air circulation. If people with asthma and allergies live or work in these areas, the gases may trigger breathing difficulties, skin problems, headaches, and other health problems.

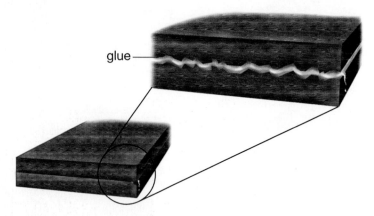

glue

Figure 4.26 Glue creates a bridge between two surfaces and locks them together.

Melting

Pieces of metal or pieces of plastic can be melted together. **Welding** melts the pieces themselves. **Soldering** (or brazing) surrounds pieces with a different melted material, which locks the pieces together as it cools and hardens. To increase strength, the pieces to be joined may be twisted or folded together. The pieces must be carefully cleaned before joining, and the melted material must be cooled slowly and carefully. Otherwise, the joint will be brittle and weak.

There are many ways of melting materials to make welded joints. Torches use a hot flame. Arc welders and spot welders use heat from an electric spark. Plastics can be melted and welded together with strong chemicals and even with sound waves.

Figure 4.27 Welders use a dark mask to protect their eyes and to see white-hot joints clearly.

STRETCH Your Mind

Builders need to avoid waste when cutting large pieces of building materials. How can you make one straight vertical cut and one straight horizontal cut to divide the cross shape below into four pieces that can be reassembled into a square?

Design Detective

Procedure ✳ Analyzing and Interpreting

1. At home, search for a small device with several parts that you can bring to school. Look for something with a clear function. A device made from unusual materials or fastened together in an interesting way would also be a good choice.

2. Print your name on one side of a small index card. On the other side, list the following details about the device:

   (a) name

   (b) function

   (c) material(s) from which it is made

   (d) how it is fastened together

3. Bring your device to class. Display it with the index card beside the device with your name facing upward.

Find Out ACTIVITY

4. Examine each device on display. Observe what it is made of and how its parts are fastened together. Guess its function and what it is called.

5. At your teacher's signal, compare your ideas with the information on the hidden side of each object's display card. Give yourself one point for every correct answer, so you can earn up to four points per device.

What Did You Find Out?

Choose one device and write a short paragraph analyzing why its particular materials and fastening methods were selected. What advantages do they have over other possible materials and fastening devices? What disadvantages do they have?

Traditional Structures

Think About It

People have been building useful structures for thousands of years. Early builders probably chose their designs out of necessity. For example, they had to use materials that were available in the areas where they lived. Their structures had to be appropriate for the climate or the area. As new technologies became available, builders modified their structures. Often, the design of a structure reveals its purpose. You can sometimes determine whether a structure was determined to protect the people inside from dangerous enemies or from the ravages of winter. What type of structure attracts your attention and makes you want to learn more about it?

Procedure

1. As a group, choose a structure that you would like to research. For example, it could be a famous historical building in your area or a famous building somewhere else. It might be a type of structure used by Aboriginal peoples or European pioneers in Canada. As a guide for your research, read the Analyze questions on the following page. You might also collect information about the original builders. Include any information about their lifestyle that could relate to the structure's design and function.

2. Divide up the questions among your group members. After your group receives teacher approval, research the structure you have chosen. Use resources such as the Internet, encyclopedias, and library books.

3. On the left side of a large piece of poster paper, make a scale drawing of the structure you have chosen to study. Pay as much attention to detail as possible. Label significant structural features.

Skill
FOCUS

For tips on using the Internet and other communication technology for research, turn to Skill Focus 9.

Analyze

1. Within your group, discuss the answers to the questions and other information that you found in your research. Prepare a report to go on the right side of your poster. If some information applies directly to a part of your scale drawing, you may wish to put that information beside the label.

   (a) What type of structure is it (mass, frame, shell)? What is it called? Who built it?

   (b) What materials were used in your structure's construction. Why were they chosen?

   (c) Describe the intended function of the structure and why the original builders chose this design. If possible, relate the design and function to the lifestyle and culture of the builders.

   (d) What features of your structure are designed to enhance its appearance (aesthetics)?

   (e) What sales techniques would real estate salespeople of the time use to promote the structure?

   (f) Describe the steps followed by the builders during the structure's construction.

2. Were there questions you could not answer in your research? Explain what they were and why you might have trouble finding the answers.

3. What scientific knowledge did the builders apply in designing and building their structure?

Extend Your Knowledge

4. Display the information compiled by each group for the whole class to see. Study the variety of structures, then construct a chart to compare the structures based on similarities and differences. Try to explain why the differences and similarities exist.

1. Imagine that you are stranded on a tropical island with very few supplies. Among your supplies is a roll of heavy plastic sheeting. Describe five possible functions the plastic could have. Be creative!

2. Suggest examples of
   (a) a woven material
   (b) a laminated material
   (c) a composite material
   (d) a glued joint
   (e) a structure that is tied or sewn together
   (f) something that is welded together

3. **Apply** Imagine that you are the architect for a new arts centre in your province's capital city. What kind of information would you need before you could begin your initial design? Write a list of questions you would ask your clients about their needs and expectations for the building.

4. **Apply** Your foot is a wonderful, complex structure. Use what you have learned in this section to analyze the structure of your foot and answer the questions below.
   (a) Name three functions of your foot.
   (b) Identify three materials that make up your foot. For each material, describe one particular function that it has and one property that allows it to perform this function.
   (c) What type of structure is your foot (mass, frame, or shell)?
   (d) What type of fastening method holds the parts of your foot together? How many parts does your foot have? (You may have to do some extra research to answer this!)

Looking Ahead

Write down ideas from Topic 2 that might be useful for your unit project to build a reverse bungee ride prototype. Select your best ideas for the group file or notebook.

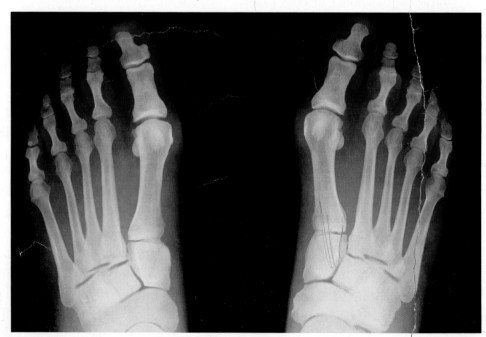

If you need to check an item, Topic numbers are provided in brackets below.

Key Terms

structures
function
forces
load
natural structures

manufactured structures
mass structures
frame structures
shell structures
design

aesthetics
margin of safety
properties
composite
laminations

mobile joints
rigid joints
adhesives
welding
soldering (brazing)

Reviewing Key Terms

1. Write down at least three pairs of natural and manufactured structures that share a similar form or function. Explain how they are similar or different. (1, 2)

2. Think of examples of
   (a) four mass structures (1)
   (b) five frame structures (1)
   (c) five shell structures (1)

3. What is the difference between a welded joint and a joint held together with adhesives? (2)

Understanding Key Concepts

4. Think about a glass filled with orange juice. (1)
   (a) Is the juice a structure? Explain your answer.
   (b) Is the glass a structure? Explain your answer.

5. Describe one property of glass that makes it
   (a) a good material for making beverage containers (1, 2)
   (b) a poor material for making beverage containers (1, 2)

6. People have invented many different types of foot gear. Four examples are wooden shoes, soft leather moccasins, sports sandals, and downhill ski boots moulded from strong, rigid plastic.

   (a) What is the main function of each of these types of foot gear? (2)
   (b) What type of structure is each type of foot gear? (1)
   (c) How is each type of foot gear fastened together? (2)

7. You are stranded on an island covered in vegetation. To escape, you decide to build a raft out of layers of reeds and small branches. (2)
   (a) Would it be better to line up the reeds in each layer and tie them together, or to crisscross them and weave them together? Explain.
   (b) Would it be better to line up the reeds in each layer in the same direction as the layer below, or should the reeds in each layer point in different directions? Explain.

8. Describe how the material in a structure can be weakened when pieces are held together by
   (a) ties, such as shoelaces (2)
   (b) welded joints (2)

TOPIC 3 Mass and Forces

Not long ago, circus elephants were trained to balance on tiny stools. The stool had to be very strong or it would collapse under such an enormous load. However, if an elephant were taken to the Moon, even a flimsy stool would support it. The elephant's matter — the amount of material in the elephant — would be the same in both places. The load force (weight) that the elephant exerted on the stool would be very different.

If you understand how mass causes a load force on a structure, you will find it easier to make strong, efficient designs.

DidYouKnow?

The metric system of measurement was created in 1795 in France. It replaced many traditional systems of measuring with just one system. The modern International System of Units (in French, *Le Système International d'unités* or SI) is based on the original metric measures. Standard SI units were set up in 1960 by an international committee called the General Conference on Weights and Measures. Experts meet regularly to review and revise SI.

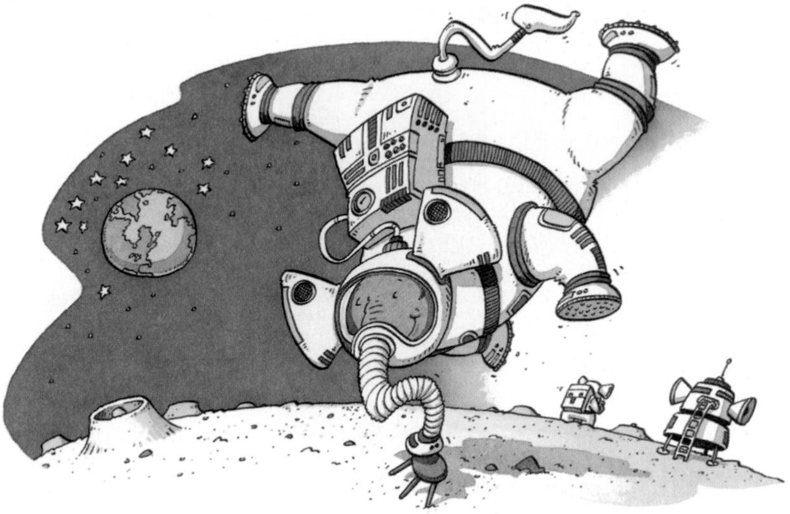

Figure 4.28 If an elephant was on the Moon, what would stay the same? What would change?

Mass

The **mass** of an object is the measure of the amount of matter in it. As you learned in Unit 3, all objects are made of tiny particles. An elephant is made of a very large number of particles, so it has a large mass. An egg-sized lump of lead contains fewer particles than an elephant, so it has less mass.

When the metric measuring system was first designed, scientists decided to measure mass by comparing objects to a particular small cylinder of metal. They called this cylinder the **primary standard** of mass, and the amount of material in it was called one **kilogram (kg)**. Exact copies of the primary standard kilogram are kept in various countries, including Canada.

Smaller masses are usually expressed in grams (g). "Kilo" means "thousand," so one kilogram (1 kg) is just another way to say one thousand grams (1000 g). Very small masses are usually expressed in milligrams (mg). "Milli" means "one thousandth," so a milligram is one thousandth of a gram (0.001 g). How many milligrams would be needed to make one gram (1 g)?

Skill FOCUS

To find a summary of basic SI units, turn to Skill Focus 4.

A **balance** is the most common type of measuring instrument for mass. Many balances compare the pull of gravity on the object being measured with the pull of gravity on standard masses. If the pull of gravity is equal, the masses must be equal, too. Figure 4.29 shows a common type of laboratory balance.

Mass is a very useful property to measure because it stays the same no matter where an object is located. An elephant has a mass of about 5000 kg whether it is on Earth, on the Moon, or in space. Its mass will change only if it gains extra matter (by eating a large meal, for example) or if it loses matter (perhaps by converting body fat into energy through exercise).

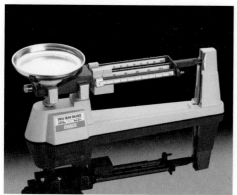

Figure 4.29 Triple-beam balance

Figure 4.30 The standard kilogram has about the same mass as 1 L of water, milk, or juice.

Forces and Weight

You have just learned that the elephant's mass of 5000 kg would not change whether it was on Earth or on the Moon. This is because the amount of matter making up the elephant would be the same wherever it is in the universe. So why does its weight change? To understand how mass and weight are different, you must first learn more about forces. In Topic 1, you learned that **forces** are stresses such as pushes or pulls.

The standard SI unit of force is called a **newton (N)**. One newton (1 N) is only a small force, just enough to stretch a thin rubber band a bit. Some other examples are shown in Figure 4.31. To understand and predict how forces affect structures, you need to find the size of the force.

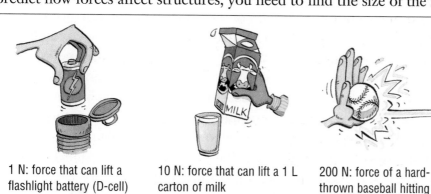

1 N: force that can lift a flashlight battery (D-cell)

10 N: force that can lift a 1 L carton of milk

200 N: force of a hard-thrown baseball hitting your hand

Figure 4.31 Some forces of different sizes

Study Figure 4.32 to find out how to use a **force meter**, or spring scale, a common laboratory instrument for measuring forces. Force meters are not very accurate, but they are less expensive and more sturdy than electronic sensors. Some forces are very large or otherwise difficult to measure, such as the force exerted by a rocket engine. Forces like these can often be calculated by observing their effect on the motion of an object.

To completely describe a force, you need to determine both its direction and its size. To lift a box, for example, you might have to exert a force of 50 N upward. A book falling on your toe might exert a force of 15 N downward.

Figure 4.32 A force can be measured by seeing how far it stretches the spring in a force meter.

Weight

Weight is a force and, like other forces, it is properly measured in newtons. Did you notice that we said the elephant's *mass* is 5000 kg, not the elephant's *weight*? Weight was carefully investigated by Isaac Newton in the seventeenth century. According to a famous story, Newton once sat under an apple tree and began to wonder why the apples always fell down, toward Earth. They never fell up into the sky or just floated in mid-air. Newton realized that there is a force between any two objects, anywhere in the universe, that tries to pull them together.

Using his mathematical skills, Newton analyzed the size of this force, which he called gravity. He found that the **gravitational force** between two objects depends on the masses of the objects and the distance between them. The force of gravity is very small between ordinary-sized objects. You do not notice gravity pulling you toward trees or other people as you pass by them, but the force is there. If objects are very massive, however, the gravitational forces near them become much larger.

Earth is big enough for the gravitational force between it and nearby objects to be important. In everyday language, we call this force **weight**. Instead of saying that there is a gravitational force of 10 N between a 1 kg mass and Earth, we would say that the mass has a weight of 10 N. (It actually has a weight of 9.8 N, but we will use the rounded value of 10 N to make calculations easier.)

Skill FOCUS

For tips on measuring mass, turn to Skill Focus 5.

Because gravitational force depends on the distance between objects, an object's weight changes depending on where it is. In an airplane or on a high mountain, where you are farther from the centre of Earth, your weight is a little bit less. However, your mass remains the same. Gravitational force also depends on the mass of an object. On the Moon, your weight would be about one sixth what it is on Earth, because the Moon's smaller mass exerts less gravitational force than Earth's mass. In space, very far from Earth or any other large body with a gravitational force, you would be essentially weightless!

It is easy to confuse mass and weight. As you have just learned, mass is the amount of matter that an object is made of, while weight is the force with which gravity pulls on an object. Read the following sentences and decide whether the terms and units of mass and weight are used correctly:

- The spring scale in the super-market was used for finding the mass of the fruit to be purchased.

- After a rigorous exercise program, Bob's weight decreased by 5 kg.

- As the space shuttle returned to Earth, the mass of the astronauts' bodies returned to normal.

- The Olympic weight lifter competed in the 100 kg weight class.

Figure 4.33 A standard bathroom scale is a type of spring scale. Springs within the scale are stretched when a person stands on the scale. The springs are connected to parts that move a numbered scale below a fixed needle.

How Forceful!

Procedure

Stretch a rubber band between two fingers. Do you feel a pulling force on just one finger, or on both?

Find Out ACTIVITY

What Did You Find Out? ✳ **Analyzing and Interpreting**

Now think about gravity. Like the rubber band, it acts between two objects. So — does it pull on both objects, or just one? If your weight is 400 N, is that just the force pulling you toward Earth? Is there also a force of 400 N pulling Earth toward you?

Why do we always see things falling down toward Earth? Why is Earth not pulled up toward them? Or is it? These are the kinds of questions Newton tried to answer 300 years ago. Write a short paragraph to explain your ideas about them.

Crush It!

You can find out about a structure's strength by gradually adding weight to a structure until it breaks. In doing so, you observe the ability of the structure to withstand a force. Observations of when and how a structure fails can help a scientist understand the strength of a particular material or design. In Topic 1, you learned that this point of failure is called the ultimate strength of a structure. In this next investigation, you will use your skills in making a hypothesis and prediction, performing tests with controlled variables, recording data, and analyzing results.

Question

Which types of shell structures can withstand the most force before they fail?

Hypothesis

Before beginning your investigation, form a hypothesis about which structures will withstand the most force before they fail.

Safety Precautions

- Work on newsprint or a plastic drop cloth to simplify clean-up.
- Wear safety goggles and an apron during this investigation.

Apparatus

15 x 30 cm piece of wood

assortment of objects to use as weights (i.e., bricks, masses from mass kits, pennies, washers, ceramic tiles)

force meter

Materials

newspaper; 3 or 4 shell structures to test: ice-cream cone (flat bottom); styrofoam cup; section of a cardboard or foam egg carton; paper muffin tin liner; small section of celery stalk; half an orange, eggshell, or Ping-Pong™ ball; plastic blister packaging; pieces of breakfast cereal in shell shapes; shell-shaped pasta; walnut or peanut shells; red or green pepper halves; cones made of paper

Procedure

❶ Before starting your investigation, **predict** which materials will be weakest and strongest. **Rank** your test materials in order from weakest to strongest. Be sure you are testing some natural and some manufactured structures. **Explain** your ranking based on your hypothesis.

❷ Copy the table shown below into your notebook.

❸ **Record** the names of the structures you will be testing and **classify** them as natural or manufactured.

❹ Use the force meter to **measure** the weight of the objects you will use to test the strength of the shell structure. Find the weight of the board you will use in your test.

❺ Place a shell structure on a flat surface covered with newspaper.

❻ Balance your piece of wood on the structure.

Force to Crush the Shell Versus Type of Shell

Shell structure tested	Type of structure (manufactured or natural)	How does the structure fail?	Force needed to break the structure (N)

7 Place your weights one at a time on top of the wooden platform until the structure fails. **Observe** how the structure fails. (Does it bend first or just crack? Do small cracks appear and then spread, or does it crumble all at once? Where does it fail first?) **Record** your observations in your table.

8 **Record** the weight of all materials placed on the shell structure prior to collapse. Remember to count the weight of the board.

9 Repeat steps 5 through 8 for all shell structures to be tested.

10 Clean up your work area.

Skill
F O C U S

To learn how to make a bar graph, turn to Skill Focus 10.

Analyze

1. What was the manipulated variable (the feature you changed for each test)? What was the responding variable (the feature you observed in each test)? What variables did you control for each test?

2. **Rank** the objects from weakest to strongest.

3. **Draw a graph** that clearly shows the strengths of the different objects. A bar graph would show these data clearly.

Conclude and Apply

4. **(a)** Did any shapes seem stronger than the others? Give examples and **explain**.

   (b) Did any materials appear stronger than the others? Give examples and **explain**.

5. What might have happened if you had suddenly increased the weight on the test object, or put all the weight on a tiny part of it? How can the way in which you apply force affect the results?

6. Think of a shell structure in which strength would be

   (a) very important

   (b) not particularly important

Math CONNECT

Forces are measured in newtons, but most bathroom scales are marked in kilograms or pounds. (A pound is a unit of force but it is not an SI unit.) Each kilogram represents a force of almost 10 N and each pound represents a force of about 4.5 N. Using the results of your investigation and your weight in newtons, calculate how many ice-cream cones (or egg cartons or styrofoam cups) would be needed to support your weight. If you have enough materials, try this out to check your calculations. (Remember to distribute your weight evenly over all of the objects.)

Picturing Forces

Math CONNECT

Very precise measurements show that the gravitational force at Earth's surface is a bit smaller than 10 N on each kilogram of matter. (The actual figure is close to 9.81 N.) Try recalculating the predicted weight of each object you measured in *Cool Tools* on page 301, using 9.81 N as the force on each kilogram instead of 10 N. Are these predictions closer to your measurements than your original predictions?

A **force diagram** is a simple picture that uses arrows to show the strength and direction of one or more forces. As you can see in Figure 4.34, a circle or rectangle stands for the object on which the forces act. Each force is shown by an arrow. The length of the arrow shows the size of the force: a longer arrow represents a larger force. The direction of the arrow shows the direction of the force. The arrow is usually drawn pointing away from the place where the force is acting, like a rope pulling an object.

Diagrams are especially useful to find the combined effect of several forces acting on the same object. A neat sketch is often enough to solve a simple problem. Even when many forces are acting together, mathematicians have found ways to use exact scale drawings and calculations to predict what will happen.

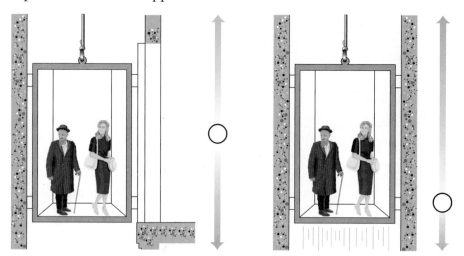

Figure 4.34 When the elevator is standing still, the force of the cable pulling it up is the same as the force of gravity pulling it down. When the force of the cable becomes greater than the force of gravity, the elevator begins to rise.

TOPIC 3 Review

1. Suppose you want to measure the weight of a pencil.
   (a) What measuring instrument should you use?
   (b) What units should you use for your answer?

2. In a lab report, two students reported that they had applied a force of 6.5 N to a brick. Their answer received only half marks. What extra information should they have reported?

3. Write three sentences that show you know how to use the terms "mass" and "weight" and the units of mass and weight.

4. **Apply**
   (a) Express the mass of a 125 g tube of toothpaste in kilograms.
   (b) Calculate the weight of the tube of toothpaste.

Figure 4.35 A train derailment produces a number of effects on the cars that collide with each other.

You do not have to witness a train crash to know that it creates dangerously large forces. Look closely at Figure 4.35. What effects did the forces in this collision have on the colliding objects? List as many effects as you can.

Now imagine a smaller "collision," such as kicking a soccer ball. When your foot applies a force to the ball, or any small object that is free to move, three things can happen. The object's motion can speed up, slow down, or change direction. When you kick something larger, such as a building, it does not usually move, but the force still has an effect. A force, such as your kick, on the outside of the building is called an external force. **External forces** on structures are stresses that act on a structure from outside it. These forces produce **internal forces**, or stresses, within the materials from which a structure is made. Such internal stresses can change the shape or size of a structure. This change to the shape or size of the structure is called **deformation**. Deformation can lead to either repairable damage or the complete failure of a structure. Engineers must design structures strong enough to withstand damaging changes. Therefore, they must understand external forces and the internal forces that they cause.

Ask an Expert

Read about Alan McColmon, on pages 342–343. Alan uses forces to tear down and demolish structures.

External Forces

Engineers divide the forces that affect buildings into two groups.

A **dead load** is a permanent force acting on a structure. This includes the weight of the structure itself. Over time, this gravitational force can cause the structure to sag, tilt, or pull apart as the ground beneath it shifts or compresses under the load.

A **live load** is a changing or non-permanent force acting on a structure. This includes the force of the wind and the weight of things that are in or on a structure (people, furniture, and snow and rain on the roof). Impact forces, caused by objects colliding with the structure, are another type of live load. Most structures are designed to withstand forces at least two or three times larger than their expected live load. Sometimes, though, live loads become extremely large for a short time, as in a storm or a collision, and the structure can be damaged.

When you act as a live load on a teeter-totter, you create forces that spread through the whole apparatus. Your weight pushes down on the seat and the bar to which the seat is fastened, but the opposite seat is lifted up. The centre of the teeter-totter twists around its pivot. One external force (your weight) creates several internal forces. These stresses affect different parts of the structure in different ways. Study Figure 4.36 on the next page to learn about four of the most important internal forces.

INTERNET CONNECT

www.mcgrawhill.ca/links/sciencefocus7

For information about how the CN Tower was designed and built, and some of the records it has set, go to the web site above. Click on **Web Links** to find out where to go next. Or submit "CN Tower" to an Internet search engine. Compare your findings with facts about other tall buildings around the world.

INTERNET CONNECT

www.mcgrawhill.ca/links/sciencefocus7

Find out more about the Leaning Tower of Pisa by going to the web site above. Click on **Web Links** to find out where to go next. Based on what you learn, how would you suggest the city of Pisa prevent further leaning?

Internal Forces

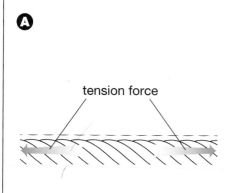

A

tension force

Tension forces stretch a material by pulling its ends apart. **Tensile strength** measures the largest tension force the material can stand before breaking.

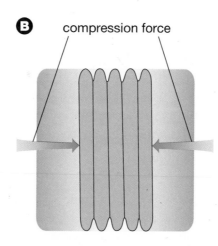

B

compression force

Compression forces crush a material by squeezing it together. **Compressive strength** measures the largest compression force the material can stand before losing its shape or breaking into pieces.

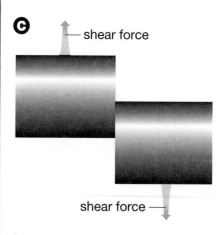

C

shear force

shear force

Shear forces bend or tear a material by pressing different parts in opposite directions at the same time. **Shear strength** measures the largest shear force the material can stand before ripping apart.

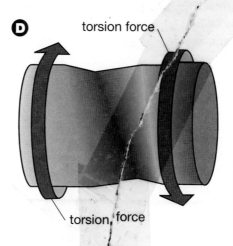

D

torsion force

torsion force

Torsion forces twist a material by turning the ends in opposite directions. **Torsion strength** measures the largest torsion force the material can stand and still spring back to its original shape.

Figure 4.36 Internal forces

Pause & Reflect

In your Science Log, write a short paragraph explaining the difference between external forces and internal forces. To illustrate your explanation, give an example of each type of force when a strong wind blows on a flag.

Word CONNECT

The same words that name internal forces are used in other situations.

- How is a metal pair of cutting *shears* similar to a *shear* force?

- How is a *tension* headache similar to a *tension* force?

- How is a *compressed* computer file similar to a *compressive* force?

camber

Figure 4.37 Cross-country skis are designed to bend when a force is applied. Bending allows the middle, or camber, of the ski to contact more snow and give the skier a better grip when pushing off.

Hold a ruler with one hand at each end and bend the ends gently toward the ground. (You will find this easiest if you begin by holding the ruler flat in front of you.) Describe the kinds of forces that are acting on a ruler when you exert a **bending force**. Draw a diagram with arrows showing how the forces are acting on the ruler. Bending is a combination of tension and compression forces. In Topic 5, you will learn how shear and torsion forces are also a combination of tension and compression. You will also learn why bending the ruler in one direction is much easier than bending it in another!

Find Out **ACTIVITY**

Bend That Bike!

If you know the types of internal forces that stress part of a structure, you can design that part with the kind and amount of strength it needs to support the forces efficiently. In this activity, you will identify the forces acting in a bicycle and the effect each force has.

Procedure ✳ **Performing and Recording**

1. Set up a data table to record your observations for five parts of a bicycle. Include columns for the name of the bicycle part, its letter on the diagram, the force acting on it, and the type of strength it needs. Give your table a title.

2. Study the diagram of the bicycle.

   (a) Read the descriptions of the forces acting in each part of the bicycle.

   (b) Fill out one row of the data table for each labelled part of the bicycle.

What Did You Find Out?

Identify one more part of the bicycle that might fail because it has too little

- tensile strength
- compressive strength
- shear strength
- torsion strength

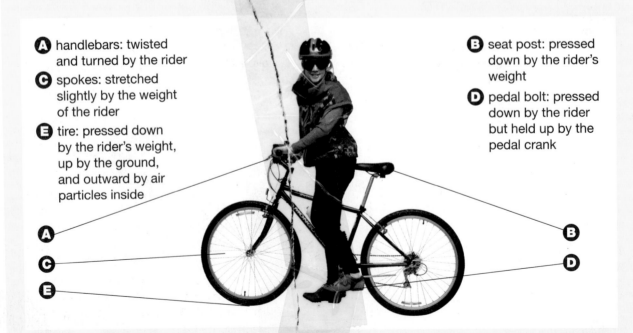

A handlebars: twisted and turned by the rider

C spokes: stretched slightly by the weight of the rider

E tire: pressed down by the rider's weight, up by the ground, and outward by air particles inside

B seat post: pressed down by the rider's weight

D pedal bolt: pressed down by the rider but held up by the pedal crank

Figure 4.38 Examine the illustrations to find examples of live loads, dead loads, tension, compression, shearing, bending, and torsion. How many examples can you find of each?

Looking Ahead

What kinds of forces and loads will affect the reverse bungee ride you are planning for your unit project? Write down your ideas and add the best ones to the group file or notebook.

Cool Tools

Have you ever wondered how dental braces work? You probably think of your jawbone as a very solid and strong material. However, when you are young, you can stretch your jaw by applying forces to it. This is because your body's bones are still growing.

It is common for a person's jaw to be too small for its owner's teeth. If your jaw is too small, specialized dentists called orthodontists may insert a structure in your mouth that will pull on your jaw. As your body grows, your jaw will grow in the direction of the pulling force, making your jaw larger.

Most people grow fastest when they are around 8 or 9 years old. This is the best time to expand or reshape your jaw. When you are an adult, your jawbone will have hardened. By the age of 20, you may even need surgery to reshape your jaw.

Dental braces can also move your teeth. The best time to move your teeth into the correct positions is after you get your permanent teeth, when you are 12 or 13. Permanent teeth are still a bit loose when they first come in, so they are easier to move. When you are older, your teeth are more firmly set in place. You can get the same dental treatments when you are older, but it will hurt more!

The materials used for dental braces have specific performance requirements. Braces are designed to apply tension forces to out-of-line teeth, so the materials need high tensile strength. Braces also need a strong adhesive to make sure they are solidly anchored to teeth. Everything making up the braces — bands, brackets, cement, and elastics — has to be able to withstand the hostile environment of the mouth. All mouths have bacteria that produce acids that attack both metal and teeth. Even saliva is a chemical designed to break down other materials.

Examining Forces

If you know the types of internal forces that stress part of a structure, you can design that part with the strength it needs to resist the forces acting on it. In this investigation, you will identify the forces acting on a variety of structures and materials and the effect each force has.

Question

What forces create stress in various structures, and where does the stress occur?

Part 1
Stressed-out Marshmallows

Apparatus
black non-permanent overhead felt pen

30 cm ruler

Materials
5 large-sized marshmallows

Procedure

1. As shown in the photograph below, use a felt pen to **draw a grid** on 5 marshmallows. Use a ruler to draw the lines as straight as possible. The squares formed by the grid should have sides of equal length. (Do not draw rectangles.)

2. **Prepare a data table** similar to the one shown, with sufficient space to record your observations for each part of this activity.

3. Hold a marshmallow between two fingers as shown in the photograph to the right. Squeeze the marshmallow. **Observe** changes to the horizontal and vertical lines. In the appropriate section of your data table, **draw a diagram** that represents the change in the size and shape

of the grid. **Describe** the changes to the grid lines using words such as "shortened," "lengthened," or "stayed the same."

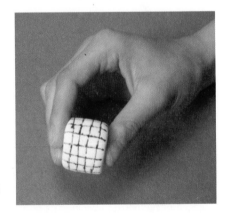

Force Versus Action

Action	Grid diagram	Description of grid changes	Type of force(s) observed
Squishing			
Stretching			
Bending both ends			
Bending one end			
Twisting			

4 As shown in the photograph below, hold a second marshmallow firmly at both ends. Pull outwards. **Record** your observations as you did in step 3.

5 Holding a marshmallow with your hands positioned as they were for step 4, bend the ends of the marshmallow upward. **Observe** and **record** any changes to the grid on your data table.

6 While holding one end of a marshmallow on the edge of a desk or table, push the other end downward over the edge of the desk. **Record** your observations.

7 Firmly grip a marshmallow on each end as you did in step 4. By turning your hands in opposite directions, apply a twisting force to the marshmallow. **Record** your observations.

Part 2
Shear Excitement
Safety Precautions

Take care using both sharp and dull scissors.

Apparatus
sharp scissors

dull scissors (or scissors with a loose central screw)

Materials
toothpicks

2 (10 × 15 cm) pieces of blue polystyrene

sheet of paper

Procedure

1 Read this procedure completely, then **draw a data table** with sufficient space to record your observations for each part of this activity. You will need a column for an observation diagram and a column for a description of your observations. Give your data table a title.

2 Slowly tear a sheet of paper from top to bottom. In your data table, **draw** and **describe** what happened to the fibres that make up the paper when it was torn. Include arrows to show the direction of the forces acting on the paper.

3 Using the sharp scissors, cut a sheet of paper from top to bottom. **Record** your observations as you did for step 2.

4 Repeat step 3, this time using the dull scissors.

5 Place the two pieces of polystyrene together and connect them by pushing two or three toothpicks through both pieces. Holding each block firmly, rapidly slide the blocks apart, snapping the toothpicks. Observe the broken ends of the toothpicks. **Record** your observations on your data table.

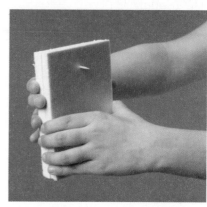

CONTINUED▶

Part 3
Twist That Towel

Apparatus
small towel or washcloth
plastic bucket or basin full of water
empty plastic bucket or basin
graduated cylinder
rubber gloves

Procedure

1 **Prepare a data table** to record your results. Headings should include Action (squeezing or twisting), Amount of water collected (mm), and Type of force(s) involved. Give your table a title.

2 Soak the towel in water. Hold the towel above the bucket of water until it stops dripping.

3 After dripping has stopped, hold the towel over the empty bucket. Squeeze, *but do not twist*, as much water as possible into the empty bucket.

4 Use the graduated cylinder to **measure** the volume of water squeezed out. **Record** your answer and the type of force or forces in the data table.

5 Repeat steps 2 through 4, but this time twist the wet towel tightly to squeeze out the water. **Record** your answer as in step 4.

Part 4
Tug-o'-war

Apparatus
2 desks or tables
retort stand bar or other strong metal bar
plastic bucket (with a handle)
paper clips
assorted masses of known weight

Materials
30 cm lengths of at least four types of materials to test (e.g., sewing thread, fine fishing line, knitting wool, crochet cotton, strips of scotch tape, masking tape, paper)

Procedure

1 **Prepare a data table** in which to record the total weight held by each material before breaking.

2 Loop the first material being tested through the handle of the plastic bucket and over the metal bar that has been placed between two desks. Securely tie or connect the loose ends of the material together.

3 Gradually add masses to the bucket until the material being tested breaks. Hold your hands just below the bucket as masses are added, to prevent the bucket from falling quickly when the test material breaks. **CAUTION** Keep your feet clear of falling buckets.

4 In your data table **record** the amount of weight supported by the material before breaking. Remember that weight must be recorded in newtons.

5 Repeat steps 2 through 4 for all materials to be tested.

6 After all materials have been individually tested, braid three pieces of one of the materials together and repeat the test.

Skill
FOCUS

To learn how to measure with a graduated cylinder, turn to Skill Focus 5. For tips on making data tables by computer, turn to Skill Focus 9.

Analyze

1. Use your observations to decide whether each statement below is true or false. In your answers, **explain** which part of the investigation gives evidence for your decision.

   (a) Only one force can act on one part of a structure at a time.

   (b) Torsion forces reduce the size of the spaces between particles in a substance.

   (c) A piece of yarn or rope made by twisting several fibres together has much higher tensile strength than a single fibre.

   (d) The top of a structure that is being bent may be placed under tension or compression.

Conclude and Apply

2. In this investigation, you tested a variety of materials for strength against tension, compression, torsion, shear, and bending. For each type of force, **list** at least two examples of materials that would be well suited to resist that particular force. Give at least two examples of materials that would be poorly suited. **Explain** your examples.

3. For each of the forces you investigated, give an example of a "real life" structure or part of a structure that must be able to resist that force. **Explain** how you think these structures have been designed to resist those forces. Hint: Think about structural features such as the type of materials used, the shape of parts, and how the parts are connected.

4. For each example below, **describe** which force(s) would cause internal stress:

   (a) playground swing set

   (b) playground seesaw

   (c) full garbage bag held shut with a twist tie

   (d) front bumper on an automobile

   (e) member of a school's wrestling team during a match

   (f) snowboard with bindings

INTERNET CONNECT

www.mcgrawhill.ca/links/sciencefocus7

Find out more about the most recent efforts to manufacture fibres as strong as spider silk by going to the web site above. Click on **Web Links** to find out where to go next. Or submit "spider silk" and "strength" to an Internet search engine. Write a brief report based on your findings.

Computer CONNECT

If you have access to a computer, you could use it to prepare data tables for the investigation.

DidYou**Know**?

One kind of spider silk is the strongest material known. Dragline fibres are spun by spiders when they make the frame of a web and when they drop from high places. Because the fibres have high tensile strength and are also very stretchy, it takes a great deal of energy to break them. The web of the golden silk spider is strong enough to trap a bird!

Measurements of the dragline fibres show that they are at least five times stronger than an equal mass of steel. That is even stronger than Kevlar™, the fibre used to manufacture bulletproof vests. If a strand of this spider silk were as thick as a pencil, it could stop a speeding 747 passenger jet! Scientists are currently using genetic engineering to develop a bacteria containing the gene for spider silk. They hope to someday produce large quantities of this "super strong" material.

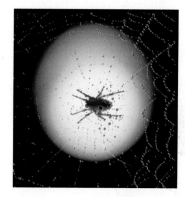

Resisting Stress—The Inside View

What determines the strength of a material? Scientists trace strength, and many other properties, to forces between the tiniest particles of the material. Examine Figure 4.39 to learn what scientists have been able to infer about particles that are far too small to see.

- Steel has high tensile strength. It has strong forces pulling its particles together. A very strong tension force is needed to separate the particles and break the material.

- Graphite (a form of carbon) has low shear strength. Its particles are arranged in layers, but the forces between the layers are relatively weak. Because the layers slide over one another easily, graphite is slippery and makes a good dry lubricant. The layers of graphite in a pencil "lead" rub off and leave a mark on the paper when you write.

- Rubber has high torsion strength. Each particle is attracted in all directions to the other particles around it. The particles hold together even when a piece of rubber is twisted out of shape.

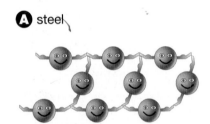

A steel

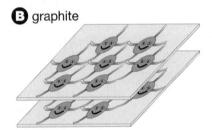

B graphite

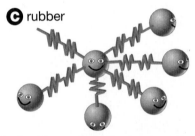

C rubber

Figure 4.39 Each metal particle attracts a few other particles very strongly. The forces are quite directional, so the particles form a regular arrangement in space.

Graphite particles attract strongly in some directions, but hardly at all in other directions.

Each rubber particle attracts many other particles in all directions.

TOPIC 4 Review

1. List examples of deformation that you investigated or read about in this topic.

2. Name three types of stress that a force can cause inside an object.

3. **(a)** What is the difference between a live load and a dead load?

   (b) Study the following loads that are acting on a tree. Classify them as "live" or "dead."
   - wind blowing against a tree
   - the weight of the tree
   - the weight of a bird in the tree

4. Identify the type of strength that is shown by
   (a) the chain that connects a ship to its anchor
   (b) a piece of very tough dried meat you are chewing
   (c) a bolt you are tightening with a wrench
   (d) the legs of the chair you are sitting on

5. How well can chewing gum withstand internal forces? Explain differences between a dry stick of gum and chewed gum.

How Structures Fail

No structure is perfect. No material is perfect. If a great enough force acts on a structure, it will begin to fail. Even small forces, acting in a vulnerable place, can cause damage. Learning how structures could possibly fail helps engineers design strong, durable structures.

Levers Create Large Forces

Frame structures that are made of long, rigid lengths of lumber or steel can fail when force is applied to them. Such failures can result from the force created by the action of a lever. A **lever** is a device that can change the amount of force needed to move an object. Some types of levers consist of a long arm that rests on a pivot, or **fulcrum**. When effort is applied as an external force to the lever, a large enough force is created to lift a heavy load. A crowbar used to lift a rock shows such forces at work (Figure 4.40).

Figure 4.41 shows how unintentional lever action can damage a structure. Strong winds can exert an external force that bends the frame structure of a flagpole. Even a slight bend can exert a large force on one side of the flagpole's base. Then, the base acts like a lever (see Figure 4.41). As the external force pushes down against one side of the base, the other side pushes up against the load of the flagpole. Eventually, the bolts holding the frame structure to the base weaken, and the flagpole falls over. Strong winds can produce other forces that can result in structural failure (see Figure 4.42).

How Materials Fail

External forces can cause internal forces in the structure (see page 305). Each type of internal force can cause certain types of damage.

- **Shear** Solid materials are never perfectly uniform. They nearly always have microscopic cracks or weaknesses. When a solid material is compressed, the crack can enlarge or break apart. One section may shear (slide over another section along the weakness). The weight of a building can compress the soil causing the soil to shear or slip sideways. The ground beneath the building sinks, and the building tilts or collapses.

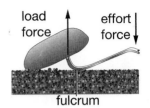

Figure 4.40 With a crowbar, you can lift very heavy objects or separate pieces of wood nailed together.

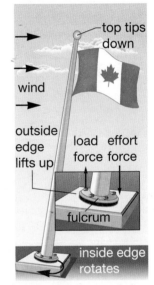

Figure 4.41 Strong winds can tip a flagpole.

Figure 4.42 Winds in a tornado produce twisting, bending, and compression forces so strong that no structure can escape damage.

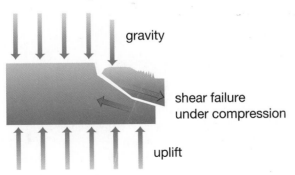

Figure 4.43 Compression causes sections of material to slide sideways, causing shear failure.

Figure 4.44 Even if the ground beneath a building was uniform when the building was constructed, shear damage can occur. An earthquake caused this damage.

Figure 4.45 How could an engineer design buildings so they would not bend or buckle during an earthquake?

• **Bend or Buckle** If you put pressure on a metal can, the thin metal folds and the can buckles (gives way) under the compressive force you apply. The same thing happens to a piece of paper when you push the ends together. All thin panels tend to bend and buckle when they are compressed. Compression forces cause material to bend on the inside of the curve, and pull and snap on the outside of the curve. Shell structures that use thin panels to support their entire load, such as boats and aircraft, are reinforced to prevent buckling. Examine Figure 4.46 to see some common methods of reinforcement.

• **Torsion** Twisting forces can cause material failure, too. Brittle structures, such as dry spaghetti and plastic cutlery, often shear when they are twisted. Sections of the structure slide past each other, and the structure cracks or breaks in two. Very flexible structures, such as rubber bands, hoses, and electrical cords, shear less easily. Instead, torsion forces make them fold up and twist into tangles and knots. Although the structure is unbroken, it has lost its shape, which is a form of failure.

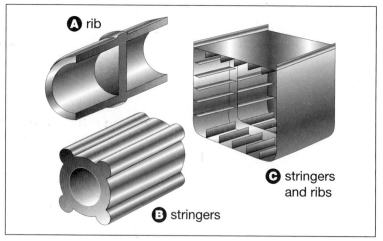

Figure 4.46 These three common designs reinforce structures in order to prevent shear, bend, buckle, and twist failure. Stringers and ribs are used to reinforce large vessels such as cargo ships, aircraft, and many rockets. Sometimes they are hidden beneath an exterior skin, so they are not easy to see.

INTERNET CONNECT

www.mcgrawhill.ca/links/sciencefocus7

Find out how engineers design structures that are resistant to earthquake damage. Click on **Web Links** to find out where to go next.

Making Use of Stress

Snap, twist, buckle, bend, and shear: that is what materials and structures do when they fail. These same behaviours can also be put to good use. You already saw bending put to good use in cross-country skis (see Figure 4.37 on page 308). Other examples include:

- *Buckle* Car bumpers and sheet metal can be designed to buckle in a collision. As the metal deforms, it absorbs some of the energy of the impact. The car may be badly damaged, but the occupants are less likely to be seriously hurt. Blades of grass on a sports field buckle as athletes land on them, absorbing some of the energy of the impact. Certain kinds of panels, such as the bellows in an accordion or the flaps on a cardboard box, are designed to buckle in specific places when you press on them.

- *Shear* In a boat's outboard motor, the propeller is held to the drive shaft with a shear pin. If the propeller becomes tangled in weeds, the shear pin will break, allowing the motor and the gears to spin freely instead of being damaged. The clutch and automatic transmission of a car are designed so that shear forces allow parts to slip past each other, speeding up or slowing down gradually until they are moving at the same speed. This produces a much smoother ride than connecting the engine directly to the wheels.

Figure 4.47 Car designers increase the margin of safety for vehicles by using principles of material failure.

- *Twist* Spinning wheels twist cotton or wool fibres tightly so that they lock together. The twisted yarn is much stronger than a bundle of straight fibres and is long enough to knit or weave into cloth. If the fibres are twisted too much, they tangle and shorten unless you keep pulling on them. That's one way to make stretchy fabrics. Controlled twisting turns hair into braids, string into ropes, and wires into cables.

◆✦◆ Across Canada

One day, Sandford Fleming (1827–1915) invited some governors to have lunch under a bridge. Fleming was chief engineer on the construction of the railroad across Canada. He was trying to convince the governors that iron was the best material for building train bridges because it would stand up well to fire, moisture, and cold. Everyone else wanted to use wood, fearing that iron beams would crack from the weight of the trains.

When a heavy train thundered across the bridge during lunch, the governors shook with fear, and some ran away from the table. Of course, nothing happened; the bridge was safe. Fleming went on to build more iron bridges across Canada.

Solving problems was always one of Fleming's passions. In his late teens, in 1845, he sketched a design for a type of rollerblade! Later he created the first Canadian postage stamp. It featured a beaver and was issued on April 23, 1851. Hard work and determination helped Sandford Fleming become one of the most respected scientists in Canadian history.

Sandford Fleming

Metal Fatigue

Looking Ahead

In your Science Log, write a point-form outline to summarize the main ideas about structural failure that you have studied so far. What kinds of failure might your reverse bungee ride design need to overcome?

Early railway cars often developed a serious problem after they had been used for several years. Their solid metal axles broke and their wheels fell off, even though the parts were designed to be much stronger than necessary. About 150 years ago, a German railway official identified the problem. Metals weaken when they are bent or twisted over and over again.

Figure 4.48 The material around this rivet shows signs of metal fatigue.

You can explain this loss of strength using the particle model, which you learned about in Unit 3. In a bent or twisted part of a metal structure, the arrangement of particles is changed. Where particles move apart, the forces holding them together become weaker. If enough particles are affected, small cracks develop. Eventually the material may fail under only a small stress, one that it could easily resist when it was new. Engineers call this weakening **metal fatigue**, and it is still a problem, especially in lightweight, flexible structures such as aircraft.

Find Out ACTIVITY

Bend and Break

Materials
2 silver-coloured metal paper clips

Procedure ✳ Performing and Recording

1. Straighten one paper clip as shown. Touch it to your inner forearm. Note the temperature.

2. Bend the paper clip back and forth quickly ten times. Can you feel it weaken? Record how many bends are needed to produce noticeable metal fatigue. Immediately touch the paper clip to your forearm again. Record whether you noticed a change in temperature.

3. Repeat step 2 until the paper clip breaks. Record how many bends are needed. Take care not to puncture your skin with the broken paper clip.

4. Straighten the second paper clip. This time, twist the ends of the paper clip back and forth. Count the number of twists needed to produce noticeable metal fatigue. Count the number of twists needed to break the metal.

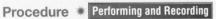

What Did You Find Out? ✳ Analyzing and Interpreting

Answer the following questions:

1. Which type of stress seems to cause metal fatigue sooner, bending or twisting?

2. Did you notice any change in temperature after bending or twisting the paper clip? If so, what provided the energy to warm or cool it?

3. Describe the force or forces that led to the failure of the paper clips. Explain your answer.

- chemical engineer
- electrical engineer
- mechanical engineer
- aerospace engineer
- civil engineer
- materials science engineer
- structural engineer

There are many different types of engineers. Using a dictionary and logic, try to guess what type of engineer each of the people below is. Note that there may be more than one person for some branches of engineering.

Stanley Arthurson: designs custom tools for assembly line industries

Tom Cardinal: developed a new metal alloy for a lighter, faster bicycle frame

Josh Cohen: oversees smelting operations at a large mining company

Tony Chung: designs and modifies equipment to lower pollution from a large processing plant

Susan Erickson: develops circuitry for stereo components

Bob Gonzales: designs and oversees construction of roads and overpasses

Karen Ouimette: oversees the operation of the equipment needed to process petroleum into its components

Sasha Salinsky: creates new wing designs for a small airplane manufacturer

Tammy Nguyen: designs building frames capable of withstanding earthquakes

Find a partner and compare your matchings. Then, as partners, devise a plan to check your accuracy. Perhaps you will look in your telephone book for information, or your local college or university course calendar. The Internet or the guidance office in your school could provide some clues as well. Keep a journal of the steps in your plan and what information you gain at each stage. Share the journal, as well as your original and revised matchings, with the other partnerships in your class.

Skill FOCUS

For tips on using the Internet to do research, turn to Skill Focus 9.

INTERNET CONNECT

www.mcgrawhill.ca/links/sciencefocus7

Find out more about engineering by going to the web site above. Click on **Web Links** to find out where to go next. Can you discover why many Canadian engineers wear a special ring, what metal it is made of, and what famous disaster it commemorates? Write a short article about your findings.

TOPIC 5 Review

1. **(a)** Identify three dead loads and three live loads that are acting on your classroom.

   (b) Explain your reasoning for deciding which loads are "dead" or "live."

2. Name three ways that materials fail, and identify the type of internal force that causes each kind of failure.

3. **(a)** Which type of structure (mass, frame, or shell) is most likely to be damaged when its parts act as levers and create very strong forces?

   (b) Why are the other two types of structures not also weakened by lever action?

4. Which type of material failure occurs when you

   (a) leave a trail of footprints in a carpet?

   (b) sprain your ankle in a soccer game?

   (c) accidentally hit a baseball through a window?

   (d) crinkle a new $5 bill as you stuff it into your pocket?

   (e) twist the lid of a partly opened tin can back and forth until it breaks off?

5. Write a technical description of a time when you knocked something down or demolished a structure. Use the terms you learned in Topics 1–5. For example, to describe kicking over a sand castle, you might begin, "I applied an external force to a small mass structure. As a result, …"

If you need to check an item, Topic numbers are provided in brackets below.

Key Terms

mass
primary standard
kilogram (kg)
force meter
gravitational force
weight
balance

forces
newton (N)
force diagram
external force
internal force
deformation
live load

dead load
tension forces
tensile strength
compression forces
compressive strength
shear forces
shear strength

torsion forces
torsion strength
bending force
bend (buckle)
twist
shear
metal fatigue

Reviewing Key Terms

1. Copy the puzzle below into your notebook. Do not write in the textbook. Use the clues to complete each line. The number of blanks gives the number of letters in the word. If your answers are correct, the letters in the box will spell the name of an important force.

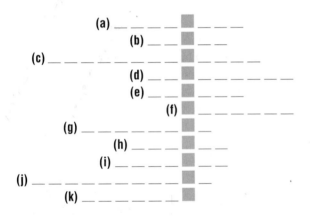

(a) primary standard of mass (3)

(b) push or pull (3)

(c) picture of forces on an object (3)

(d) force that causes extra stress on a structure (4)

(e) force that pulls you against Earth (3)

(f) force for turning off a water tap (4)

(g) forces that resist outside forces (4)

(h) standard unit of force (3)

(i) kind of strength that spider silk has (4)

(j) forces that develop when you squeeze something (4)

(k) type of material failure that occurs when you twist plastic cutlery (5)

Understanding Key Concepts

2. Classify each statement as referring to force (F) or mass (M). (3)

(a) measured in newtons

(b) stays the same no matter where the object is located

(c) measured with a balance

(d) your weight

3. Describe two ways that material failure can be put to good use. (5)

4. What two factors affect the gravitational force between two objects? (3)

5. Using the diagram below:

(a) Name the type of force stressing the top of the bookshelf. (4)

(b) Name the type of force stressing the bottom of the bookshelf. (4)

(c) Describe what might happen if more books were piled on the bookshelf. (4)

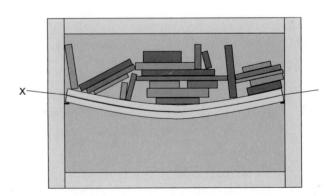

Designing with Forces

In Topic 4, you learned about the types of forces that act on structures. Then in Topic 5, you saw the ways that forces could make a structure fail. With this type of information, engineers create designs that are most likely to prevent the structures from failing. First they study the general features of the structure. Then they analyze the types of forces that are likely to be the greatest. Finally they choose details for the design that will counteract those forces. Designers often rely on one of three key methods to help structures withstand forces.

- Distribute the load throughout the structure so that no single part is carrying most of the load.

- Direct the forces along angled components so that the forces hold pieces together instead of pulling them apart.

- Shape the parts to withstand the specific type of force they are likely to experience.

Some structural problems, along with potential solutions, are described below. As you read, notice how the solutions fit into one or more of the key methods above.

Figure 4.49 What stresses is the weight of the snow exerting on the roof and the frame of this cottage? How could its owner ensure that the snow will not cause the roof to collapse?

PROBLEM 1

Rectangular frames are probably the easiest to build. However, load forces can easily push or pull them out of shape. Examine Figure 4.50 for some possible solutions.

Figure 4.50 Triangles form a sturdy shape Triangular shapes are much stronger than rectangles. A rectangle can collapse but a triangle cannot. Notice the number of triangular shapes in each truss.

Share the Load Frame structures contain many vertical supporting posts. The weight is shared by all of them. Therefore, no single part of the structure carries a large load.

As you can see in Figure 4.51, any structure with a load-bearing, horizontal beam supported only at the ends, may bend in the centre. This bending directs forces outward on the vertical beams. Sometimes it is not practical to put more supporting columns in the centre. Examine Figure 4.52 to find some solutions.

Figure 4.51 When a horizontal structure carries a heavy load, it may begin to sag in the middle.

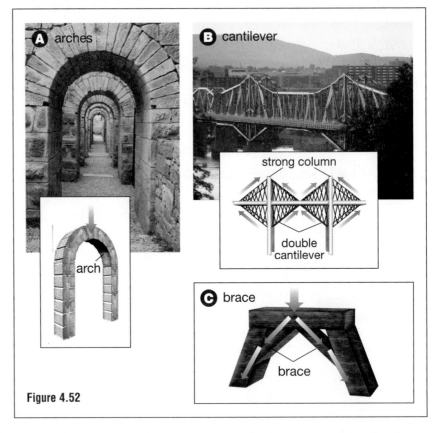

Figure 4.52

A Arches can be rounded and the stones shaped to fit. The central stone is called the keystone. It is shaped like a wedge. As it slips further down between the next two stones, the keystone presses harder against the two beside it. This shape directs the forces along the stones and down to the ground as shown by the arrows. Domes and shell structures are based on the same concept.

B A cantilever is a horizontal board or span, supported by a very strong column at one end. Double cantilever bridges are very strong structures and support heavy vehicles. Beams from the top of the columns pull upward on the ends of the cantilevers. Beams from the columns below the span to the ends of the cantilevers push upward on the ends of the cantilevers.

C Braces can be added and materials angled to direct the forces through the solid part of the structure to the ground as shown by the arrows.

Figure 4.53 (diving board) A cantilever must be able to withstand tension forces on top and compression forces underneath. Engineers must choose materials carefully, when designing a cantilever.

Large, solid beams are very strong. However, they are extremely heavy and hard to handle. As well, they use a lot of building material. Figure 4.54 shows several ways to make strong beams that are not too heavy. Nature uses some of the same tricks.

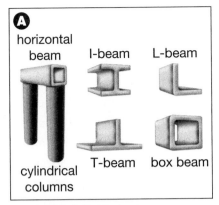

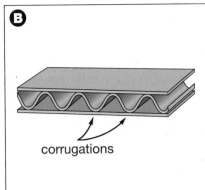

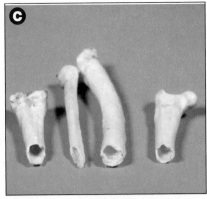

A
horizontal beam
I-beam
L-beam
cylindrical columns
T-beam
box beam

Figure 4.54 Cylindrical columns are very strong but use a little less material than square beams. Beams in the form of an I, L, T, or a box are very strong but use much less material than solid beams.

B
corrugations

The wavelike shape in corrugated cardboard gives the cardboard strength. As well, it is lighter and uses less material than solid cardboard.

C

Animal bones are often hollow. In the living animal, the bones are filled with a very lightweight, spongy material.

How did architects and builders of hundreds of years ago make majestic cathedrals so sturdy that we still enjoy their beauty today? One technique that they used is shown in Figure 4.55A. The construction of the cathedral of Notre-Dame was started in 1162. It took nearly 200 years to complete. The extremely tall sides of the cathedral are supported by columns on the outsides that connect to the building near the top. These columns are called flying buttresses. They support the outer walls in much the same way that the two sides of an arch support each other. With modern materials and techniques, these flying buttresses are no longer needed. However, nature still uses a similar structure (see Figure 4.55B).

Career **CONNECT**

With the help of an adult, contact an architect or building contractor in your area. Interview her or him to find out how architects are trained and what their work is like. Ask the architect to think of a particular building that was challenging to build. What were the functions and specifications for this building, and how did they influence its design?

Vancouver Public Library

Figure 4.55A Flying buttresses were used to support buildings hundreds of years ago.

Figure 4.55B The roots of these mangrove trees function much like the flying buttresses of the cathedral of Notre-Dame.

Strengthening Structures

In science fiction stories, you can read about wonderful imaginary materials that stand up to almost any force. Real materials are more limited. Concrete and mortar have very high compressive strength if they are made according to the correct recipe. Concrete is quite weak if it is pulled or sheared, however. Similarly, most other materials have one kind of strength but not another. That is why engineers must analyze structures in great detail to find out what types of internal forces are stressing each part. They can then choose materials and shapes with the strength to withstand each force. Even a simple swing needs to be designed in this way (see Figure 4.57).

Shear forces were a big problem for early railways. Tiny cracks inside the rails often weakened them enough that the weight of a loaded train would shear a rail in half, causing a serious accident. But the cracks could be detected only after the rails broke. In 1932 a Canadian metallurgist, J. Cameron Mackie, discovered that the cracks formed when the rails cooled too quickly during the manufacturing process. Mackie tried putting red-hot rails in a covered steel box where they could cool more slowly. He found that this eliminated the cracks completely. Within ten years, Mackie's process was being used by steel companies all over the world to produce strong, crack-free rails.

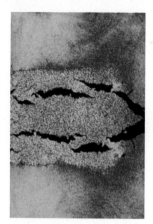

Figure 4.56 Stress cracks in metal can lead to structural failure. Rust can also lead to metal failure.

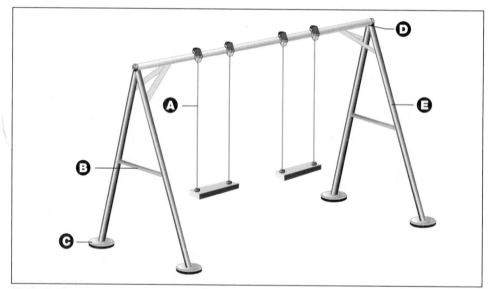

Figure 4.57

A The rope holding the person undergoes a lot of tension. Use rope or chain for high tensile strength.

B The cross bar forms a triangle that strengthens the frame. Use steel.

C The anchor beneath the posts undergoes compression due to the weight of the swings and people using them. Concrete is good and will not rot when the ground is wet.

D The joint gets twisted every time the person swings back and forth. Use a material that has high torsion strength and is not brittle.

E The frame is slanted for stability. Each time the swing moves forward, the front bar experiences compression and the back bar experiences tension. When the swing moves back, the opposite forces apply. Use steel for both compressive and tensile strength.

PROBLEM-SOLVING

INVESTIGATION 4-E

SKILLCHECK
☼ Initiating and Planning
☼ Performing and Recording
☼ Analyzing and Interpreting
☼ Communication and Teamwork

The Paper Olympics

Architects and designers are sometimes quite limited as to the materials they can use, but they still need to design the sturdiest structure possible.

Challenge

How can you use your knowledge of shape and strength to turn flimsy paper index cards into load-bearing columns, beams, and flat panels?

Safety Precautions

- Use sharp objects such as scissors with care.
- A glue gun is hot and the glue remains hot for several minutes.
- Wash your hands thoroughly after completing this investigation.

Materials

scissors
templates for beams (optional)
assorted masses of known weight
force meter (or plastic bucket and masses)
5 index cards (20 cm × 13 cm)
glue gun, white glue, or glue stick
flat plywood (20 cm × 20 cm)
string

Design Specifications

A. Use one card to build a column that is the full height of the card (20 cm).

B. Cut and fold a second card into a strong beam that will span a 15 cm gap. Use the diagrams in Figure 4.45 to decide what type of beam to make.

C. Use the last three cards to make a strong flat panel, larger than 10 cm × 12 cm. The panel must have at least three layers that are glued together, and it must be at least 1 cm thick.

D. Let the glue harden overnight.

E. Disqualify any structures that are too small or do not match the specifications.

F. Each group member should draw a diagram of the structures that have been built prior to testing.

G. In each category, the strongest structure receives 100 points, the next strongest gets 90 points, and so on. Your teacher might award extra points for aesthetics and careful construction.

Plan and Construct

1. Stand the column upright on the floor or a desk. Place the piece of plywood squarely on the top of the column. Place masses on the board, distributing them evenly. Add masses until the column fails. Record the maximum amount of weight held by the column (in newtons).

2. Place the beam across a 15 cm gap between two desks. Put a loop of string around the middle and attach the string to a force meter or a plastic bucket. Pull down on the force meter, or add masses to the bucket, until the beam breaks, twists out of shape, or bends more than 1 cm. Record (in newtons) the largest force that the beam can support.

3. Stand the flat panel on a desk or the floor. Lay the piece of plywood on top of the panel. Add masses to the panel until it collapses. Record the maximum weight held by the panel.

Evaluate

Based on your results, suggest ways in which you could improve the design of each of your structures. Draw sketches of your improved designs and explain your reasons for making the changes.

Using Frictional Forces

Press your open hand straight down hard on your desk. Keep pressing down while you slide your hand sideways. Unless your desk or hand is greasy, this is probably hard work! You are feeling the force of **friction**, which resists (works against) movement between two surfaces that rub together. That is why friction is so important in assembling structures: it can help keep pieces of the structure from moving apart.

In a brick wall, for example, each layer of bricks rests on the layer below. A thin layer of mortar between rows of bricks keeps them level and evenly spaced. No glue, fasteners, nails, or screws help to hold the bricks together, but the wall is still strong. If you push against one brick, friction between it and neighbouring bricks prevents any movement. The wall is held together by friction.

Friction is especially important in wooden frame structures. Houses and garages, for example, are often built around wooden frames (see Figure 4.6 on page 274). The pieces of the frame are usually nailed together. Friction between each nail and the wood around it keeps the nail in place and the joint rigid. Study Figure 4.59 to learn how different types of fasteners are designed to increase the amount of friction with the wood and produce tighter joints.

Figure 4.58 Frictional force holds the bricks in this wall together.

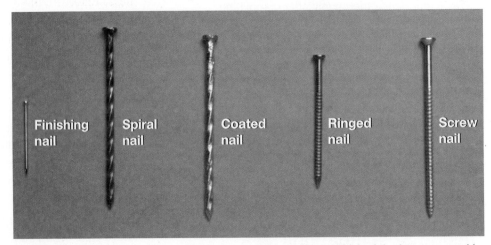

Finishing nail   Spiral nail   Coated nail   Ringed nail   Screw nail

Figure 4.59 Frictional forces are greater between rough surfaces. Which of the fasteners would have the least friction with the wood around it? Which would have the most?

If there is a squeaky place in the floor or stairs of your home, you know one effect of too little friction in a frame structure. Nails holding the plywood subfloor to the house frame have loosened. When you step on the loose spot, the plywood moves up and down a tiny bit, rubbing on the loose nail and causing the squeak. Pounding the nails down seldom helps. They just slip loose again. To really fix the noise, you would have to pull the subfloor tightly against the frame with new fasteners.

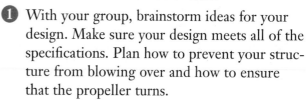

SKILLCHECK

☼ Initiating and Planning

☼ Performing and Recording

☼ Analyzing and Interpreting

☼ Communication and Teamwork

The Windproof Wonder

Some structures have moving parts that must resist friction. Can you design a structure that uses the power of the wind but is not blown over by it?

Challenge

Build a free-standing frame tower to support a working windmill propeller.

Safety Precautions

Handle electrical equipment and sharp objects with care.

Materials

scissors

2-speed hair dryer or fan

paper plates (or index cards)

wooden dowel

30 cm masking tape

2 balls modelling clay (200 g each)

fasteners/connectors (paper clips or pins)

20 plastic drinking straws

2 small sandbags (plastic sandwich bags filled with 200 g of sand)

Design Specifications

A. The windmill frame tower must be at least 50 cm tall.

B. The tower must include a propeller with at least three blades that turn when exposed to wind (from the hair dryer).

C. The masking tape cannot be used to connect the straws to each other. It can only be used in the construction and attachment of the propeller.

D. The sandbags and/or modelling clay can be used as masses to weigh the tower down, but the modelling clay cannot be used to "stick" the tower to the table.

E. After creating your initial design, you have 35 min to build, test, and modify your structure.

Plan and Construct

1 With your group, brainstorm ideas for your design. Make sure your design meets all of the specifications. Plan how to prevent your structure from blowing over and how to ensure that the propeller turns.

2 Use the most practical design ideas as the basis for a neat labelled sketch of your design. Then list the materials you need. After getting your teacher's approval, gather the materials and start building.

3 You may test your frame tower once before judging, but only with the fan or hair dryer set to low power. If you modify your original design, sketch how your structure actually looks when it is complete.

Evaluate

1. With your group, evaluate your structure. Record how well your structure met the specifications. How might you modify its design to eliminate weaknesses and improve its performance?

2. Describe the fixed and mobile joints in your structure. Explain why you chose the materials you did to connect these joints.

3. Describe the live and dead loads that were acting on your structure. How did you try to make your structure strong enough to handle these loads?

4. (a) Where is friction a force in your structure?

   (b) For each point listed in (a), describe whether friction helped your structure or lessened its effectiveness.

   (c) Where and how might you try to increase friction?

   (d) Where and how might you try to decrease friction?

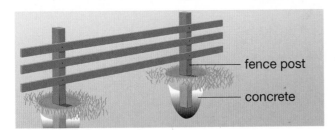

Figure 4.60 Friction between the fence posts and concrete hold the posts in place.

As you may have noticed in Problem-Solving Investigation 4-F, friction between the ground and the bottom of a structure is an important design consideration. Friction helps hold the structure in place when the wind or other forces try to lift or tip it. The bases of fences, flagpoles, communications towers, and playground swings are often made of strong metal pipes or rods driven into the ground. Can you remember playing on a "bumpy" swing set with legs that slid up and down in the ground as your weight twisted the swing frame? Frictional forces between the smooth metal and the ground were too small to hold the swing safely in place. If the swing had been set in larger holes filled with concrete, friction between the rough concrete and the ground would have been much greater, and the swing would have been more stable.

Too little or too much friction can cause problems in other types of structures, too. Chairs stick or grind across the floor if there is too much friction between their legs and the floor. Putting a smooth cloth, metal, or plastic glider on the bottom of the chair legs can help solve the problem.

TOPIC 6 Review

1. Sketch a diagram of each structure listed below:
   (a) an arch
   (b) a column and beam gateway
   (c) a double cantilever bridge

2. Name two ways that friction can be used in a structure.

3. Make a labelled sketch of a sturdy chair. Include two features that increase its strength and two features that increase its stability. Describe how these features are effective.

4. **Apply** Examine the photograph of the suspension bridge.
   (a) Which parts of the bridge are under compression? Which parts are under tension?
   (b) Describe two ways in which the bridge is being supported.
   (c) Identify two ways in which the stability of the bridge has been increased.

5. Think of one structure that has been designed to withstand
   (a) compression   (b) torsion   (c) shear force

TOPIC 7 Stable Structures

There is more than one way to collapse a structure. For the figure skaters in Figure 4.61, just a tiny mistake in the distribution of their mass would make them unstable. The force of gravity would pull them down if they lost their balance. However, almost all structures can lean a bit without falling down. A bicycle rider who is moving fast enough can even lean a lot without losing balance. Athletes make adjustments to their body position intuitively, but architects and engineers need to analyze structures to predict how or when a structure will become unbalanced. To design **stable** (less likely to tip) structures, engineers need to know what features of a leaning object determine whether it will tip over or stay balanced.

Figure 4.61 How is distribution of mass important to these figure skaters?

Figure 4.62 Why do these structures not fall over?

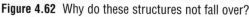

The Empire State Building in New York City is a steel frame building, 102 storeys tall. It has a mass of 365 000 t. After it was built, many people worried about the building's safety because strong winds made the top storeys sway back and forth slightly. On a foggy day in July 1945, a U.S. Air Force bomber hit the Empire State Building between the 78th and 79th floors. Fourteen people in the airplane were killed, but the building was not seriously damaged. Doubts about its safety disappeared.

THINK & LINK

INVESTIGATION 4-G

SKILLCHECK
Initiating and Planning
Performing and Recording
☆ Analyzing and Interpreting
Communication and Teamwork

Tip It!

Think About It

If you can stand or walk, your body has learned a lot about balance. Examine the pictures and answer the questions to put your experience into words.

Procedure

Figure B

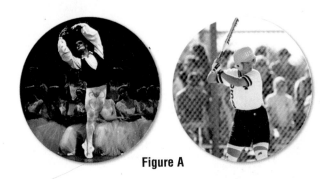

Figure A

1 To find one key to stability, examine the photographs in Figure A.

(a) Which person is in a more stable position?

(b) What difference in their positions creates the difference in stability?

(c) Based on your observations, suggest a hypothesis to explain why an opened stepladder is more stable than the same stepladder with its two legs folded together.

2 To find a second key to stability, examine the photographs in Figure B.

(a) Which athlete is in a more stable position?

(b) A large part of your body mass is in the area around your hips. What difference in the position of body mass puts one athlete in a more stable position than the other?

(c) Explain how the same principle makes balancing on stilts much harder than balancing on your feet.

Figure C

3 Football players are coached to keep their stance "wide and low" (Figure C).

(a) Explain how this advice uses both keys to stability that you have discovered.

(b) Why is it so hard to balance a pencil on its point (Figure C)? Use the ideas from steps 1 and 2 in your answer.

Balancing Act

In the last investigation, did you conclude that objects are more stable if they rest on a large area and have most of their mass close to the ground? These are useful general principles, but they are not precise enough to ensure that a particular structure, such as a bridge or a building, will be stable. Engineers need to calculate exactly how large a foundation is necessary or the best place to put heavy heating and air conditioning machinery. They also need to design structures, such as aircraft and rockets, that have to be stable even when they are not resting on the ground. To make these precise calculations, engineers must find a special point within the structure called the centre of gravity.

The Centre of Gravity — Find Out ACTIVITY

What are some characteristics of the centre of gravity?

Materials

heavy cardboard   scissors   nail   String   mass   pencil

Procedure

1. Draw an irregular shape on the cardboard, and cut it out. **CAUTION** Be careful when using sharp objects such as scissors or nails.

2. Select four or five points on the cardboard object. Use a nail to make holes at these points large enough for the object to rotate freely around the nail.

3. Put a nail through one of the holes. Tie a piece of string on the nail. Tie the mass to the other end of the string.

4. While you are holding the object up with the nail, have your partner mark the path of the string on the card board.

5. Repeat steps 3 through 5 for every hole in the cardboard object.

6. Remove the nail and string. Try to balance the object on your fingertip. Carefully adjust the position of the cardboard by moving it extremely small distances while trying to balance it.

7. Examine Figure 4.63 in which the cardboard object is rotating while it falls. Notice the path of the central point (centre of gravity.) Choose one other point on the cardboard. In your mind, picture its path as the object rotates and falls. (Do not write in this book.)

What Did You Find Out?

1. How does the point where the object balanced on your finger relate to the lines you drew on the object in Step 4.

2. Write a statement that explains what you think is unique about the point where you balanced the cardboard. Infer the meaning of "centre of gravity."

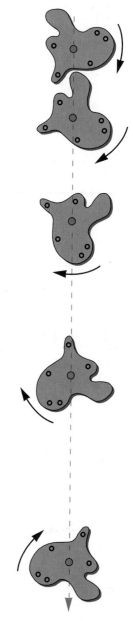

Figure 4.63 Observe the position of the central point of the rotating object while it falls.

In the activity, did you relate the point where you balanced your cardboard object with the central point that fell in a straight line in Figure 4.63? These points have the same property. In both cases, the force of gravity appeared to act directly on these points. Any point with this characteristic is called the **centre of gravity**. All objects have a centre of gravity. When an object falls, the centre of gravity falls in a straight line. All other points rotate around the centre of gravity while the object falls. Study Figure 4.65 to better understand why the centre of gravity is the balance point.

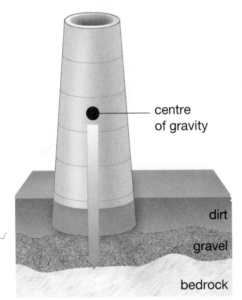

centre of gravity

dirt

gravel

bedrock

Figure 4.64A In this position, the chimney is stable. The thrust line is inside the foundation.

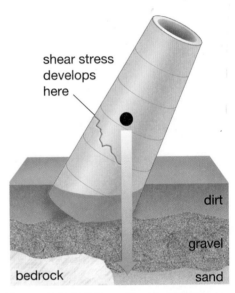

shear stress develops here

dirt

gravel

bedrock   sand

Figure 4.64B In this position, the chimney is unstable. It will tip or break apart as a result of the large shear forces near the arrow.

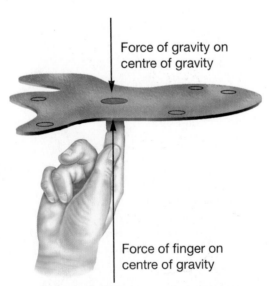

Force of gravity on centre of gravity

Force of finger on centre of gravity

Figure 4.65A When the force exerted by the finger is lined up with the force of gravity acting on the centre of gravity, the object is balanced.

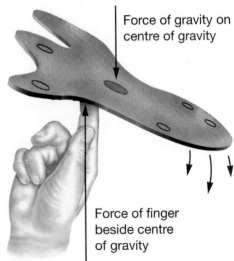

Force of gravity on centre of gravity

Force of finger beside centre of gravity

Figure 4.65B When the finger is not supporting the centre of gravity, the object begins to fall.

Unbalanced Structures

Figure 4.66 With your knowledge of the motion of the centre of gravity, explain why this chimney is falling.

Pause& Reflect

Each photograph in Figure 4.67 shows a stable structure. In your Science Log, describe

• forces which, left unbalanced, might cause instability

• how forces are balanced

To determine whether a structure is balanced or is likely to fall, locate its centre of gravity and draw a line directly down toward Earth. If the arrow points to a solid foundation, the structure is balanced as shown in Figure 4.64A. If the arrow falls beside the foundation, the structure is not stable as shown in 4.64B. If the ground beneath a structure is uneven and unstable, the structure may tip. When the imaginary arrow pointing down from the centre of gravity moves to a point beside the base of the structure, the structure will become very unstable.

Inspect each of the photographs below. Estimate the location of the centre of gravity in each structure. Figure out why each structure is stable.

Figure 4.67A A heavy mass acts as a counter-weight to keep the crane stable.

Figure 4.67B The cables on this boat keep the masts stable.

Figure 4.67C Sailors can act as a counter-weight to balance a small boat.

Figure 4.67D Symmetrical structures can also balance gravitational forces around the centre of gravity.

Building a Balanced Balcony

Whenever engineers or architects have to design a structure that is supported from only one side, such as a balcony, they are faced with a real challenge. With only one side supported, how can they make sure that the structure does not fall over when it experiences stress? As you studied earlier in this topic, centre of gravity and a balance of forces all play an important role in determining a structure's stability.

Challenge

Using your knowledge of centre of gravity and balanced forces, build a tower with a cantilevered balcony capable of supporting a load.

Materials

15 plastic straws (each at least 20 cm long)

5 (10 x 15 cm) recipe cards

30 cm masking tape

pins

paper clips

250 mL styrofoam cup

sand

250 g modelling clay

thread

30 cm ruler

scissors

Specifications

A. Only the materials supplied may be used during construction. The materials may be cut or shaped into whatever size your team thinks is necessary.

B. The tower must be free standing and at least 20 cm tall.

C. The balcony must extend at least 10 cm from the edge of the tower and must be supported only at one end.

D. Your team will be allowed a maximum of 30 min to build the structure.

E. Upon completion, the balcony must support a styrofoam cup half filled with sand for at least 30 s.

Plan and Construct

1. Write a sentence or two to describe your structure's main stability problem. List what you know about stable structures that might help you resolve this problem.

2. Each member of your design and construction team should sketch a rough blueprint of a possible design for your structure.

3. Evaluate the different designs produced by your team members and then as a group choose the best design that will best achieve the goals of this activity.

4. Draw a diagram of the design you have chosen to build and show it to your teacher for approval.

5. After your structure has been approved, begin construction using the materials provided.

6. Test and measure the structure throughout the construction process to see whether it is meeting the stated specifications.

7. Note any changes that your group makes to your initial design.

8. When your structure is complete or the building time is up, bring your structure to the testing desk for evaluation.

9. Each team member should draw a labelled diagram of the final structure prior to testing.

10. Measure the structure to determine whether it meets all specifications. Place the cup (half filled with sand) on the structure's balcony and time for 30 s. Record the performance of your structure.

Evaluate

1. Label the following on your diagram of the structure your group built:
   - all forces acting on the structure (include arrows to show the direction and if possible, the strength of the forces)
   - the centre of gravity of your structure
   - an arrow to indicate the line pointing down from the centre of gravity

2. How did you distribute the mass throughout your structure? How did this affect your structure's stability?

3. What would happen to your structure if you substantially increased the amount of sand in the cup or perhaps added a much larger cup filled with sand? What changes would have to be made to your structure in order to support this greater load?

Extend Your Skills

4. Increase the amount of sand the structure supports until the structure fails. Describe how and where the structure fails. Was the prediction you made in question 3 correct?

Skill
FOCUS
For support with the steps of the problem-solving process, see Skill Focus 7.

STRETCH Your Mind

Builders and designers must become very skilled at using flat drawings to represent three-dimensional solid objects. Try to solve the problem shown below by studying the drawings. Then test your answer by making a paper or block model.

Problem
How many cubes would be needed to make each stack below? Assume that all the blocks rest on another block when there is more than one layer.

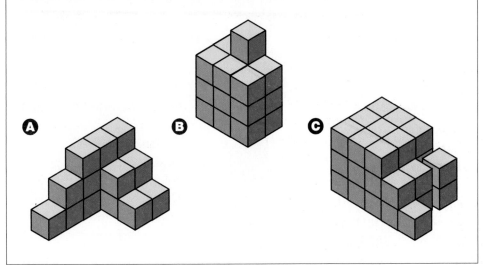

Pause& Reflect

Imagine that you have been chosen to be interviewed by the education reporter for a local newspaper or radio station. The reporter wants an explanation, in your own words, of what your class has been studying in science for the past few weeks, and why this knowledge is useful in everyday life. There is space for a paragraph of about 150 words. In your Science Log, write what you would say.

Firm Foundation

Solid ground is not always firm and stable, especially if it is moist. Water near the surface can freeze and expand (swell) in the winter, lifting the ground. In warmer weather, the melted ice water drains away, shifting tiny soil particles and leaving spaces that collapse under pressure. The soil compacts, and potholes appear. Some clay soils act in the same way when they absorb water and then dry out. Larger sections of soil can slip sideways over moist layers underground, causing sinkholes and landslides. Worse yet, very moist soil sometimes flows like a thick liquid when it is shaken or vibrated. If builders do not obtain thorough studies of the ground under a planned subdivision, many homeowners could have cracks in their walls and foundations.

Looking Below

Find Out  **ACTIVITY**

The house shown in the photograph to the right collapsed into the North Saskatchewan River because the ground underneath the house was unstable. Many homeowners in the same area are worried about the stability of their homes. Other people in places such as Richmond, a community in Vancouver, worry about their homes in case of an earthquake. The ground under their homes is full of water and could be unstable in an earthquake.

Procedure

1. Using library, Internet, and community resources, research a structure that has collapsed or may collapse.

2. Present your findings as a poster diagram showing the structure and describing the problems it faces. Show in your diagram the causes of the problem. Include details about the failure or potential failure of the structure you have chosen to study.

What Did You Find Out?

As a class, discuss the kinds of forces causing or threatening structural failure.

How do builders construct a stable structure on shifty ground? They start by creating a firm **foundation**, using one of these strategies.

Find Something Solid

Below the soil lies solid bedrock. If the loose surface soil is not too deep, builders can dig it out completely and build a stable foundation directly on the bedrock. If the loose soil is too deep, they can sink **pilings** (large metal, concrete, or wood cylinders) through the loose soil until the pilings rest on bedrock. Then the structure can be built so that its weight is carried by the pilings to the rock beneath. To support a structure such as a garage, which is not really heavy, builders might not need to dig to bedrock. In many parts of Canada, foundation walls about 1.5 m deep reach firm layers of soil that give enough support and never freeze.

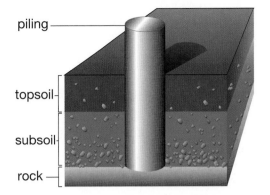

Figure 4.68A Pilings support the weight of many buildings and bridges.

Make a Solid Layer

Road builders always pack loose surface soil before paving to create a solid base for the asphalt or concrete. Later on, if the pavement cracks badly, repair crews dig out the soil and replace it with a solidly packed layer of gravel. They then repave on top of the more solid material. Packed gravel foundations are also used for dams and other mass structures.

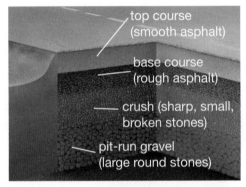

Figure 4.68B Each layer in the road base has a specific function.

Spread the Load

If the weight of a structure is spread over a large area, any particular part of the ground supports only a small part of the weight. This is why buildings are often constructed on many shallow pilings rather than on a few. Even if the pilings do not reach bedrock, the soil beneath each one is strong enough to carry its part of the load. This is also why the **footings**, the concrete foundation beneath house basement walls, are wider than the walls themselves. Spreading the weight of the walls over a larger area reduces the stress on every part of the soil beneath them.

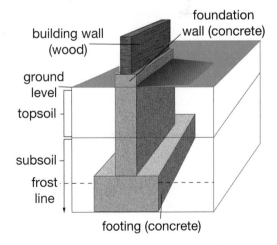

Figure 4.68C Footings beneath a foundation wall reduce stress on the soil.

INVESTIGATION 4-1

Sink the Stick

Soil testing is an early step in designing any large structure. Knowing how the soil reacts to forces helps an architect or engineer decide what type of foundation will be necessary.

Question

How does loose sand react to impact forces over different areas?

Hypothesis

Read through the procedure before you begin. Form a hypothesis about which dowel will have the greatest impact and which will have the least impact.

Skill FOCUS

For tips on making data tables by hand, see Skill Focus 10.

To develop a data table with spreadsheet functions, see Skill Focus 9.

Safety Precautions

- Do this experiment on newspaper, and have a broom handy to sweep up scattered sand.
- Handle all sharp objects with care.
- Handle the mass with care, following your teacher's instructions.

Apparatus

small tray or plastic container

200 g mass tied to 30 cm string

at least 4 wooden dowels of different diameters

table fork (for loosening the sand)

sharp pencil

ruler

Materials

500 mL of sand

1 cm graph paper

Procedure

1. **Make a data table** with four columns, headed "Object," "Base area (cm²)," "Depth in loose sand (mm)," and "Depth in packed sand (mm)." Give your table a title.

2. **Sort** your dowels according to the size of their base. **Calculate** the size of each base, and record it in your table. Test the smallest one first.

3. Fill your tray with sand so that it is at least 8 cm deep. Loosen the sand with the fork. Then level the surface.

Math CONNECT

To find the area of the base of the first dowel, use one (or both) of these methods.

1. Stand the dowel on the graph paper and trace around its base. Count the number of centimetre squares it covers. Group any half or quarter squares into whole squares, and include them in the count.

2. If you know the mathematical formula for finding the area of a circle, make the necessary measurements and calculate the area. Round your answer to one decimal place.

4. Hold the dowel gently on the sand so that it is upright but can slide through your fingers. Hold the mass about 20 cm above the top of the dowel. While holding the string, let the mass fall by its own weight and hit the dowel.

5 Mark the dowel at the level of the sand surface.

6 **Measure and record** how far the dowel is pushed into the sand.

7 Repeat steps 3 to 6 with each dowel.

8 Repeat steps 3 to 7, but this time pack the sand firmly before each test.

   (a) **Record** the results in the proper column of your data table.

   (b) If you have time, moisten the sand and repeat steps 3 to 7.

Skill
FOCUS

To find out when to use each type of graph, turn to Skill Focus 10.

Analyze

1. What type of graph (line, bar, or circle) would be most useful for predicting what would happen if you experimented with other dowels of different sizes?

2. **Draw a graph** to show the results of your tests. Use different colours, or solid and dotted lines, to show what happened in the loose and packed sand. Make a key that explains the meaning of each colour or style of line.

3. Was the blow from the falling mass an external force or an internal force on the sand?

4. Did the sand have to support a live load, a dead load, or both? Explain your answer.

5. What type of stress did your falling mass create in the sand?

6. Did you observe any signs of shearing in the sand beside the dowel? If so, describe them.

Conclude and Apply

7. Do your tests support your hypothesis? **Explain** why or why not.

8. If a load is applied to a smaller surface, what happens to the effect of the force under the surface?

9. Why are nails, drill bits, and sometimes fence posts sharpened on the bottom? In your answer, use the ideas and words you have learned in Topic 7.

10. When might a builder need the sort of soil information that you found out in this investigation?

11. Even if every group used the same dowels, sand, and mass, the results would probably not be exactly the same. What are some reasons for this?

12. How do frictional forces affect the stability of the dowels inserted into the sand?

Rapid Rotation

Every bicycle rider knows that it is harder to balance while moving slowly. The faster the wheels spin, the more the bicycle resists being tipped (see Figure 4.69A). If most of the mass of a wheel is located far from the centre, the stability is even greater. **Gyroscopes** (see Figure 4.69B), devices with heavy outer rims, can be built to spin tens of thousands of times per minute. When balanced on its axle, a gyroscope keeps pointing in the same direction, even if the structure on which it is spinning moves or turns.

Spin stabilization, the principle demonstrated by the gyroscope, is especially useful for objects that do not rest on a solid foundation. Space satellites need to keep their antennas pointed back to Earth and their instruments facing the proper location in space. Football players want the ball to travel in a stable, predictable path, so they practise for hours to throw or kick perfect spirals. If you have ever spun a toy top, a yo-yo, or a Frisbee™, you have used spin stabilization.

DidYou**Know**?

Navigation equipment can use the features of a gyroscope to detect when a ship or an airplane is wandering off course and to correct its heading (direction).

Figure 4.69A Rapidly spinning wheels stabilize a bicycle.

Figure 4.69B Spin stabilization keeps a gyroscope pointing in the same direction.

TOPIC 7 Review

1. For each pair of words below, select one item that is likely to be more stable than the other.

   (a) wet soil/dry soil

   (b) bedrock/loose soil

   (c) unbalanced forces/balanced forces

   (d) arch without a tie beam/arch with a tie beam

   (e) rapidly spinning wheel/slowly spinning wheel

2. Identify one possible cause of each event.

   (a) soil heaving up and tilting a sidewalk

   (b) soil sinking down and collapsing a driveway

3. **Apply** Early settlers built corduroy roads over muskeg by placing logs side by side over the swampy ground. Why would this provide a stable foundation for the road?

If you need to check an item, Topic numbers are provided in brackets below.

Key Terms

stable structure   centre of gravity   pilings   gyroscopes
friction   foundation   footings   spin stabilization

Reviewing Key Terms

1. In your notebook, write a sentence about structures and forces using the paired terms below.

   (a) pilings, footings (7)

   (b) stability, balance (7)

   (c) friction, resistance (6)

   (d) footings, load (7)

   (e) gyroscopes, spin stabilization (7)

   (f) brace, beam (6)

   (g) stable structure, foundation (7)

2. Draw diagrams that show how to stabilize structures using (a) pilings, and (b) footings.

Understanding Key Concepts

3. Draw a diagram that shows how part of the base of a structure is pushed up when the structure itself tips over. (7)

4. Metal or wooden fasteners can be used to hold together parts of a structure made from different materials. Explain how friction affects how well different fasteners work. (6)

5. If people balance a playground teeter-totter as shown, where is the centre of gravity in each situation? (7)

6. Describe three differences between the two structures below that make structure A more stable than structure B. (7)

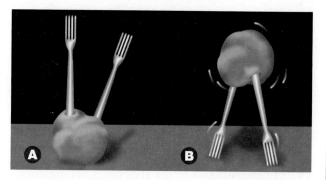

7. List five principles of stable structures that a designer might consider when planning a project. (7)

UNIT 4
Ask an Expert

There are many people in the world who make things for a living. Not Alan McColman. He's a specialist in taking things apart. Specifically, he takes apart buildings and other structures. Alan is a director of McColman and Sons Demolition in Calgary, Alberta.

Q How did you get into the demolition industry?

A When I was growing up, my father was a crane operator who demolished buildings. Then in 1979, he and my mother and brother started this business. I joined them about two years later.

Q What do you do for the company?

A When someone in the area has a demolition job to be done, I put together a bid from our company. I decide what type of demolition method is right for the project and work with my brother, Dan, to plan how that demolition would be performed. We work out the details of what equipment and how many crew members we would need, what safety issues to take into account, and that sort of thing. Then I outline our plan and include a price quote for the potential customer. If they like our bid better than ones they receive from other demolition companies, they'll hire us to do the job.

Q Are there very many different demolition methods?

A There are a few different types. For most projects we use machinery such as excavators, a wrecking ball on a crane, or bulldozers. What we use depends on the size of the structure, what it is made of, its foundation type, and its location.

Q Why does location have anything to do with it?

A Knocking down a building in the middle of nowhere is very different from knocking down a building that has an office tower on either side of it. In cases where neighbouring buildings are a concern, we often have to employ many crew members with hand tools to take the building down slowly, so we avoid damaging the other structures.

Q Let's say there is a three-storey building with no nearby structures to worry about. How would you demolish it?

A That depends on what it is made of and what type of foundation it has. Each type of building has its own cautions. If it is brick, we may do a lot of work by hand to keep the job from getting out of control. Brick buildings are very unstable when they are coming down. Concrete buildings can sometimes snap off in large sections. Steel frame buildings have more give to them and will sag and bend instead of snapping off. And each building's foundation type will help us determine which sections of the building should be brought down first.

Q Do you ever use dynamite to implode a building?

A In some cases it is necessary to implode a structure. Exploding would scatter debris. We implode so that the debris falls inward and is contained within a defined area. We don't use implosions very often, though, so when we get a job such as the demolition of the Calgary General Hospital, which we completed in 1999, we usually hire implosion experts to set the charges.

Q How long did the demolition of the hospital take?

A The implosions themselves brought down the upper storeys of all the hospital buildings in just under 20 seconds. The whole job took much longer, however.

Q What other stages were involved?

A First we had to go in and clean out all hazardous materials: asbestos, mercury, lead, biological waste, contaminated soils — that sort of thing. For the hospital project, that was the most time-consuming stage. After the implosion, we had to dispose of the debris from the upper storeys and demolish the foundations as well. The disposal stage took around five months.

Q What part of this job do you enjoy most?

A I love the variety. No two projects are exactly the same because every structure is unique in some way. I might be planning the demolition of a high-rise one week and be out on the job site of a bridge demolition the next. Every project has its own safety concerns and its own challenges. I enjoy applying my knowledge to find the solution that's just right for each one.

EXPLORING Further

Alan has explained that each demolition job is different from the next. To see more examples of demolition jobs and how they are completed, visit the web site of a demolition company. Go to **www.school.mcgrawhill.ca/resources/**, go to Science Resources, then to **SCIENCEFOCUS 7** to find out where to go next.

Imagine that you work with McColman and Sons Demolition. Choose a structure in your community and prepare a bid to demolish it. As part of your bid, you will need to explain how long you think the job will take, the special safety concerns and challenges the job poses, the methods you will use in your demolition, how many people will need to be involved and, of course, costs. You can estimate costs based on how many people you think you will need to employ for the job and how long it will take.

UNIT 4 PROJECT

Reverse Bungee Drop of Doom

Over the last decade, thousands of people have been thrilled by the exciting sport of bungee jumping, in which a person jumps from a height while attached to a highly elastic "bungee cord." The stresses placed on the bungee cord and the tower the person jumps from are of great concern to the people who design the equipment for this activity. In recent years, people at carnivals and fairs have enjoyed a "reverse bungee" experience. In the reverse bungee, participants are seated in a chair attached to a bungee cord that is stretched to the ground and then released.

Safety Precautions

- Take care when working with saws, hammers, and glue guns.
- Wear eye protection and aprons when working with tools.

Challenge

You are part of a team that needs to design, build, and test a prototype for a reverse bungee ride. Your team will compete against other teams in your class to build the safest and strongest ride for a travelling carnival. The team with the best prototype will be awarded the contract to build the ride. Your teacher will judge designs very strictly according to the specifications. The prototype, like the final ride, must have a high margin of safety since human lives will depend upon it. You want the ride to be as exciting as possible, while keeping your passengers completely safe from harm. Your structure's final mass will also be considered in the competition. The mass will reflect how much it will cost for the carnival to move the ride from city to city.

Specifications

A. The structure must be free standing. (It cannot be attached to the desk or anything else.)

B. The structure must be at least 50 cm in height at its highest point.

C. A golf ball will represent a typical two passenger load.

D. You should try make your prototype as lightweight as possible, while maintaining its stability and safety.

E. The load must be suspended at least 30 cm above the test table or desk.

F. The elastic attached to the load must be at least 10 cm long.

G. The golf ball must remain in the basket/chair during testing.

H. The golf ball cannot make contact with the structure during testing.

I. All forms and types of building materials are allowed, with the exception of materials from commercial construction kits.

J. The structure must survive having the load pulled to the surface of the test table and released at least three times in a row.

Plan and Construct

1 Each team member should independently draw a blueprint for their structure. Plans should reflect the specifications for the project.

2 At a team meeting, all members will present their plans. After discussion, the team should choose a single plan (possibly a hybrid of all of the plans).

3 A final blueprint accompanied by a list of materials and tools needed should be submitted to the teacher for approval.

4 Once a plan is approved, construction can begin.

5 Throughout the construction process, teams should test the structure to see if it is capable of meeting the specifications.

6 Teams should adjust their plan if unforeseen problems arise.

7 Once the structure is complete and meets all specifications, it is ready for testing. Give your ride an exciting name and carry it to the testing desk.

8 Draw a diagram of your prototype. Your diagram should be labelled with the following:

(a) all parts and materials used in construction

(b) strong shapes integrated into the structure's design

(c) areas of the structure placed under compression, tension, or bending during its operation

(d) the centre of gravity and thrust line of your structure

(e) a description of the live and dead loads the prototype must carry

Evaluate

1. Measure your prototype's mass, total height, load height, and elastic length to ensure that it meets all specifications. Record the measurements on your diagram.

2. Pull the golf ball down to the table and release it. Repeat the test three times. Examine the structure for signs of structural failure after each test. Record any problems on your diagram.

3. Upon completion of the tests, your teacher will score your structure based on the following evaluation scheme.

Reverse Bungee Scoring Guide

Criteria	Comments	Score (Circle one score)
Meets or exceeds all specifications		Poor 0 1 2 3 4 5 Excellent
Mass of structure compared to other successful entries		Poor 0 1 2 3 4 5 Excellent
Passing bungee test		Poor 0 1 2 3 4 5 Excellent
General appearance or aesthetic value		Poor 0 1 2 3 4 5 Excellent
Total Score		/20

4. Describe any changes your team made during the construction process. Explain why the changes were made.

5. If you were to build the structure again, would you make any changes? Explain why or why not. If your structure did not meet some of the specifications, explain how you might address these problems.

Unit at a Glance

- Structures can be classified according to their origin (natural or manufactured) and according to how they are built (mass, frame, shell).

- Many manufactured structures are similar in form or function to natural structures.

- Structural designers consider such factors as shape, function, appearance, safety requirements, environment, cost, materials, and joints in their design choices.

- Mass is the amount of matter in an object. It is measured with a balance, using kilograms.

- Weight is a measure of the gravitational force between objects. It is measured with a force meter, in newtons.

- External forces acting on structures include live loads (changing or non-permanent loads) and dead loads (the weight of the structure itself).

- Internal forces include tension, compression, shearing, buckling, and bending.

- Certain design shapes help prevent deformation in structures by strengthening them against particular kinds of forces.

- Friction can be used in structures to keep parts of the structure from moving apart.

- Materials have varying abilities to withstand internal forces. Materials can fail under pressure from forces by snapping, buckling, bending, stretching, shearing, and twisting.

- Choices in design and materials can strengthen a structure against particular kinds of forces.

- A structure's stability (ability not to tip over) depends on its centre of gravity, symmetry, and the stability of the ground upon which it sits.

Understanding Key Concepts

1. What are the key features of a mass, a frame, and a shell structure? Give one natural and one manufactured example of each type.

2. Using as many concepts as possible, write a paragraph describing key structural features of a windmill.

3. How is each of the following types of material made: composite, layered, woven, knit?

4. What are the five basic ways of fastening structures together? Give an example and a typical use of each one.

5. How are design specifications used in the construction of a structure? Give examples in your answer.

6. Give an example of something that you think is not a structure and explain why.

7. Describe the changes you might make to a bridge to increase its margin of safety. What factors might limit your ability to make these changes?

8. Name a live load and a dead load on your desk when you are doing homework on it.

9. Write directions for creating each of these internal forces in a marshmallow: compression, tension, torsion, bending.

10. Identify one external force and one internal force that act on a chair when you are sitting on it.

11. What is the difference between mass and weight?

12. Identify the shape of frame that is the most rigid. Sketch two ways of using this frame to strengthen a stepladder.

13. Draw a diagram of a shelf bending under the weight of heavy books. On your diagram, label the live load, dead load, tension, and compression.

14. Explain how you might test the flexibility of materials used in a structure. Give at least two examples of structures where flexibility is important.

15. Give at least two examples of structures that are designed to withstand compression, and two that are designed to withstand tension.

16. Why does using more nails in a joint often weaken it?

17. Explain how friction can be useful in a structure.

18. Identify the key parts of a lever and the type of structure most likely to be damaged by lever action.

19. What principle does the waiter use to carry this load successfully?

20. Describe
    (a) one way that tension forces cause deformation
    (b) two ways that compressive forces cause deformation
    (c) two ways that torsion forces cause deformation

21. Identify three ways in which builders create firm foundations for their structures.

22. Explain, using diagrams, the main factors that affect the stability of structures. Include the following terms as labels on your diagrams: mass, balance, tension, compression, gravitational force, symmetry, centre of gravity.

Developing Skills

23. Draw a concept map to summarize Topic 1. Make sure that it has a section each for mass, shell, and frame structures. Include examples, advantages, and problems for each type of structure.

24. Make a concept map to summarize Topic 2. Make sure that it has five sections, one for each of the four design features and one for other important ideas.

25. Write instructions for using each of the pieces of equipment shown in the photographs below. Explain why you would use each.

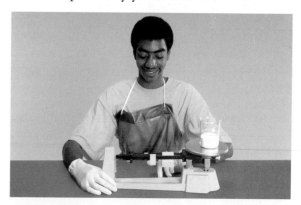

26. Study the graph below.

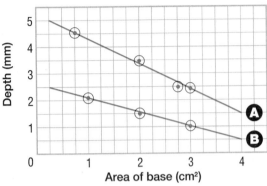

Depth an Object Can Be Driven Versus Area of Base

(a) Which soil sample was packed more tightly, sample A or sample B?

(b) How far would a wood block with an area of 2.0 cm² sink in the loose soil?

(c) A nail was driven 1.5 cm deep into the packed soil. What was its base area?

27. The graph above was produced as a result of an investigation.

(a) State the problem that the investigation was trying to solve.

(b) Identify the manipulating and responding variables in the investigation.

(c) Describe at least two variables that would need to be controlled in the investigation.

(d) Based on the data presented in the graph, write a conclusion that answers the problem.

Problem Solving/Applying

28. Suggest three specifications that need to be met by a successful design for

(a) an emergency flashlight

(b) a toothpaste tube

29. You need to store winter clothes to stay clean, dry, and free from insects in summer.

(a) Describe a simple structure to perform this function.

(b) Describe a more complicated structure for this function.

30. Polyester is a type of plastic that can be made into fibres and woven into cloth. Polyester clothing is strong, but it traps perspiration and is not very warm. To overcome these problems, clothing is often made with a blend of wool and polyester fibres. Pure wool is very warm and attractive but it is not strong, especially when it is wet. Wool shrinks unless it is washed very gently in cold water. Some people find that woollen clothing is itchy and irritates their skin.

(a) Check the labels on some of your clothing to find a garment that is mostly wool or polyester. Which of the properties described above does it have?

(b) To make warm winter clothing, would you use a cloth that was mostly polyester or mostly wool? Why?

(c) To make comfortable indoor clothing that could be machine washed, would you use a lot of wool in the blend or a little? Why?

31. Examine the table top hockey game above.

(a) List ways in which the following forces could be exerted while playing the game: compression, tension, bending, torsion, shear, friction.

(b) Could the user of the game decrease any of the above forces during its use? Explain how.

32. What type of foundation would you recommend for each structure listed below? Give a reason for each choice.

    (a) a brick garden wall

    (b) a boat dock

    (c) a roof over the patio behind a house

    (d) the concrete patio under the roof in part (c)

33. Cassette tapes and CDs are sold in brittle plastic cases that often crack and break.

    (a) What type of material failure is happening when you step on a CD case and it cracks?

    (b) Name three ways that you could strengthen the case while still making it out of the same plastic. Why do manufacturers not make these plastic structures stronger?

Critical Thinking

34. Some chairs are built from pieces of metal or wood covered with softer material. Some are made from solid pieces of foam plastic, and some are made of single pieces of moulded plastic.

    (a) Classify each type of chair according to its type of structure.

    (b) Give one advantage and one design problem for each type of design.

35. Very large structures can use a lot of materials and affect a large area. Suggest two environmental problems that designers had to overcome when planning each project described below.

    (a) The "Chunnel" is a 50 km tunnel under the sea between England and France. Three tubes, each large enough for railway trains to pass through, had to be dug through soft, water-filled rock.

    (b) The Confederation Bridge between Prince Edward Island and New Brunswick is a 12.9 km reinforced concrete structure. Icebergs and high winds are common in the area, especially in the winter. Important fishing grounds are nearby.

    (c) The Hibernia drilling platform is the largest object made by humans that was ever moved on Earth. It is the height of the Calgary tower and uses enough steel to build 15 Eiffel Towers. It took six years to build. A lake had to be drained to make room at the construction site to build it. The platform sits in iceberg-filled waters off the coast of Newfoundland.

36. Laboratory balances will not work in "weightless" conditions far from Earth. Why? A diagram might help explain your answer.

37. Copy the four situations below in order of increasing gravitational force.

    (a) two small objects close together

    (b) the same two small objects far apart

    (c) a large object close to a small object

    (d) the same large object equally close to another large object

38. A tree branch can support your weight when you stand on it near the trunk of the tree. When you move farther toward its tip, however, it bends and breaks.

    (a) Explain why your weight has such different effects on the branch.

    (b) Sketch the bending branch. Mark the part that is in compression and the part that is in tension.

    (c) Will the top of the branch snap or buckle when it breaks? Why? What happens to the bottom of the branch? Sketch the break in the branch to illustrate your answer.

39. What problem could arise in a cold climate if house foundations were not dug down deep enough to reach soil that never freezes?

Planet Earth

What forces unleash the incredible power of volcanoes and earthquakes? What processes form Earth's mountains, its rocks and boulders, and the minerals and fuels deep within it? How do we know about events that happened millions of years ago? What evidence do we have of activity in Earth's interior?

The answers to these questions lie in Earth's crust and mantle — the thin, ever-changing, outermost layers of our planet. Throughout our history, scientists have been trying to understand the forces that shape and change Earth's crust. In this unit, you will see how theories about Earth's crust were developed and then discarded. You will learn about how scientists made new observations and saw new connections between their past observations. You will consider evidence of Earth's history and of the processes still at work. Enjoy your tour of Planet Earth.

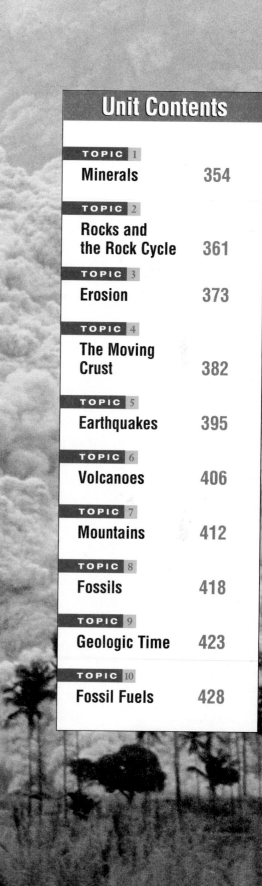

Unit Contents

Focussing Questions

- What do we know about Earth's crust?

- How did we find out?

- Why does the crust change and move?

How do beautiful crystals like this amethyst form? What is the difference between rocks and minerals? How are rocks and sediments created? Dig into the answers in Topics 1–3.

How did this car get stuck in lava? Earth's crust is constantly changing, resulting in fiery volcanoes and powerful earthquakes. What is happening inside Earth? Travel deep into Earth's crust for the answers in Topics 4–7.

Was Earth different when this Albertosaurus was alive? What deep secrets does Earth hold about its past? Which events are written in stone? Which can only be guessed? Investigate the clues in Topics 8–10.

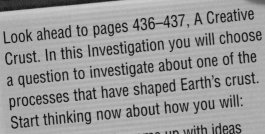

Look ahead to pages 436–437, A Creative Crust. In this Investigation you will choose a question to investigate about one of the processes that have shaped Earth's crust. Start thinking now about how you will:

- work together to come up with ideas
- set up an electronic or paper file for material you find
- represent the natural process your group investigates
- choose materials to begin collecting
- evaluate the question you investigate and the results you obtain

Minerals

What is rock made from? **Rock** is made up of one or more pure, naturally occurring, non-living crystalline materials called **minerals**.

Figure 5.1 Granite is a rock that is made up of an assortment of minerals. It is often polished and used in buildings and at the base of statues. Granite contains the minerals feldspar (sparkling grains), quartz (glassy grains), mica (grey flakes), and hornblende (dark flecks).

Most minerals are quite rare. Only a few, such as quartz, feldspar, and mica, are found throughout Earth's **crust** (the thin outermost layer of Earth). A mineral can be an **element** (a pure substance) or a compound (two or more elements combined). Quartz, for example, consists of the elements silicon and oxygen. No other mineral has these elements in the same arrangement and proportion. Sulfur, copper, gold, and diamond are each made up of a single element.

If you were a prospector digging for gold, how would you know if you had found it? "No problem," you say? We all know what gold looks like — or do we? Another mineral, pyrite, which is more common than gold, is almost identical to gold in appearance (see Figure 5.3). The value of gold is high, while pyrite is almost worthless. How could you find out if that shiny, yellow metal you found is really gold? You could investigate its properties.

The Mohs Hardness Scale

You can scratch a piece of chalk with your thumbnail, but can you scratch other rock samples the same way?

How can a substance's "scratchability" be used for mineral identification? This is a question that a German scientist, Friedrich Mohs, asked himself in 1812. He developed a scale of ten minerals with a "hardness" value of 1 to 10 (see Table 5.1).

Suppose that you have an unknown mineral that looks like talc or corundum. Scratch it with your fingernail. If it is talc, it will scratch easily, because your fingernail has a hardness value of 2.5 on the scale — much harder than talc, which has a hardness value of 1. If it does not scratch easily, it cannot be talc and must be corundum instead. The hardness of corundum is more difficult to test because corundum is so hard — it is harder than most other objects and minerals. What could you use to test the hardness of corundum?

Diamond is the hardest mineral. One of its uses is shown in Figure 5.2. Tiny rows of diamonds are used to edge surgical scalpels, razor blades, computer parts, record needles, and dental drills. Diamond-tipped drill bits can cut through steel and rock.

Table 5.1

The Mohs Hardness Scale		
Mineral	**Mineral hardness**	**Hardness of common objects**
talc	1 softest	soft pencil point (1.5)
gypsum	2	fingernail (2.5)
calcite	3	piece of copper (3.5)
fluorite	4	iron nail (4.5)
apatite	5	glass (5.5)
feldspar	6	steel file (6.5)
quartz	7	porcelain tile (7)
topaz	8	flint sandpaper (7.5)
corundum	9	emery paper (9.0)
diamond	10 hardest	carborundum sandpaper (9.5)

Crystals

There are over 3000 minerals. Other properties, such as crystal formation, help to identify them. **Crystals** are the building blocks of minerals. Crystals occur naturally and have straight edges, flat sides, and regular angles. Most of the minerals in Earth's crust grow into beautiful shapes according to the six different crystal systems shown in Table 5.2.

Figure 5.2 Although the glass-cutter wheel looks like ordinary metal, its edge is actually embedded with a hard mineral, such as diamond.

Table 5.2 The Six Major Crystal Systems

Mineral Examples		Systems	
	halite		cubic
	wulfenite		tetragonal
	corundum		hexagonal
	topaz		orthorhombic
	gypsum		monoclinic
	albite		triclinic

Other Clues to Mineral Identification

You have just seen that a mineral's crystal structure provides an important clue to its identity. What other clues can be used?

Lustre

Some minerals, such as gold and other metals, appear shiny — another clue to their identity. Others, such as talc, can appear dull. The "shini-ness," or **lustre**, of a mineral depends on how light is reflected from its surface. The surface of a mineral can reflect light in many different ways. If a mineral shines like a polished metal surface, it is said to have a metallic lustre. If a mineral has a duller shine, it has a non-metallic lustre.

Colour

Next to lustre, colour is one of the most attractive properties of minerals. The colour of a mineral can also be a clue to its identity. As in the case of gold and pyrite, however, colour alone cannot identify a mineral (see Figure 5.3). In addition, not all minerals are the same colour all the time. For example, the mineral corundum (made of aluminum and oxygen) is white when pure. However, when it contains iron and/or titanium, it is blue (and is called a sapphire). When it contains chromium, it is red (and is called a ruby).

Sometimes people grow crystals in their bodies. An excess of chemicals can form kidney stones. Mineralogists are often consulted on to indentify the contents of the kidney stones.

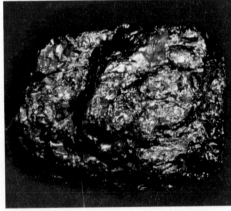

Figure 5.3 Both gold (on the left) and pyrite (on the right) are golden in colour. Which mineral properties could you use to tell them apart?

To learn how to make circle graphs, turn to Skill Focus 10.

INTERNET CONNECT

www.mcgrawhill.ca/links/sciencefocus7

Find out which minerals are used in all Canadian coins by going to the web site above. Click on **Web Links** to find out where to go next. Make a circle graph for each coin to show the percentages of different minerals it contains.

Streak

When a mineral is rubbed across a piece of unglazed porcelain tile, as in Figure 5.4, it leaves a streak. A **streak** is the colour of the powdered form of the mineral. Look-alikes, such as gold and pyrite, can be distinguished using a streak test. Gold leaves a gold streak, while pyrite has a greenish-black or brown-black streak.

Minerals with a greater hardness than the porcelain tile (hardness value of 7) will not leave a streak. Such minerals, especially the black ones, can be crushed into powder. A surprising number of black minerals have lighter-coloured powders.

Graphite is a mineral used in pencils. Pencil marks are merely graphite streaks that are soft enough to be left on a piece of paper.

Cleavage and Fracture

Hardness, lustre, colour, and streak are mineral properties that help geologists to identify many minerals fairly easily. Other properties provide further clues to their identity. Cleavage and fracture are two very useful ones.

The way a mineral breaks apart can be a clue to its identity. If it breaks along smooth, flat surfaces, or planes, it is said to have **cleavage**. Mica is an example of a mineral with cleavage (see Figure 5.5). Separating the layers of mica is like separating the pages in a book.

Not all minerals people have cleavage. Minerals that break with rough or jagged edges have **fracture** (see Figure 5.6). Quartz is an example of a mineral with fracture. When quartz is hit with a hammer it breaks like glass.

Figure 5.4 Colour is not always useful for mineral identification. Hematite, for example, can be dark red, grey, or silvery in colour. Its streak, however, is always dark red-brown.

Figure 5.5 Mica is a group of minerals with a single cleavage direction that allows it to be pulled apart into sheets.

Figure 5.6 The picture above shows both the crystal faces of quartz and the fracture on the bottom of the specimen.

Did You Know?

Transparency is another property of minerals. Hold a mineral up to the light. Can you see through it clearly? If so, it is transparent. Can you barely see through it? If so, it is translucent. If you cannot see through it, it is opaque.

A Geologist's Mystery

You are a geologist. You have just received a parcel from your company's field team in northern Alberta. The attached note reads, "New mines discovered. Enclosed are samples of minerals found there. Please identify." How can the Mohs hardness scale and the use of other mineral properties help you to solve the mystery?

Question

How can you identify different minerals? Which mineral properties will you examine, and in what order?

Safety Precautions

- Be careful when handling materials with sharp points or edges.
- Always wear safety goggles when working with acids.

Apparatus

numbered mineral samples
hand lens
iron nail
copper penny or piece of copper
utility knife
steel file
streak plate
glass plate
mineral guidebook
set of 3 or 4 local minerals

Materials

sandpaper
emery paper
Tables 5.1 and 5.2 (page 355)
10% hydrochloric acid (optional)

Procedure

1 Make a table like the one below.

2 **Record** the number of the first mineral sample in the first column of your table.

(a) **Record** the mineral's colour. You may use the hand lens to take a closer look. If you see any distinguishing crystal shapes, as in Table 5.2, record your observations under "Crystal shape."

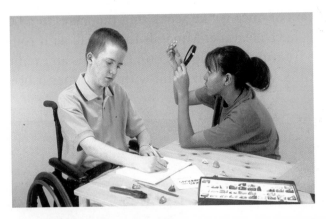

Computer CONNECT

If you have access to a computer, set up a spreadsheet to organize the data in Investigation 5-A.

Characteristics of Some Common Minerals							
Mineral number	Colour	Crystal shape (if visible)	Lustre	Streak	Hardness	Other properties	Mineral name

(b) Examine the mineral and **record** its lustre.

(c) Examine the sample, and before you test the sample, **predict** what colour its streak will be. Then scrape the mineral once across the streak plate, and brush off the excess powder. **Record** the colour of its streak. If the mineral is too hard to leave a streak, write "none" in the space under "Streak."

(d) Examine the sample, and before you test the sample, **predict** its hardness. Scratch the sample with your fingernail. If your fingernail does not leave a scratch, continue with the penny, and on up the scale, until something leaves a scratch. Use the hardness table on page 355.

(e) Record any other properties such as cleavage, fracture, and transparency under "Other properties."

(f) Your teacher may give you some 10% hydrochloric acid (HCl) to test a few of your samples. Be sure to wear your safety goggles. Rinse the specimens with water and dry them after you have used the acid.

3 Repeat all of step 2 for the remaining mineral samples.

4 Try to give each mineral a name by using a mineral identification chart provided by your teacher or information collected through your own research. Also use the Mohs hardness scale and other information from this Topic.

5 Wash your hands thoroughly after completing this investigation. Clean the streak plate. Be sure all mineral specimens are returned to their proper places.

Analyze

1. Before testing, which minerals looked the same?

2. **(a)** Which mineral was the softest? Which was the hardest?

   (b) Your predictions were based on appearance only. Were your predictions supported by your observations? Explain.

3. **(a)** Which minerals were the same colour as their streak or powder?

   (b) Which streaks surprised you?

4. Which other features or properties helped you identify samples?

Conclude and Apply

5. Were you able to identify all of the mineral samples? If not, can you suggest some other tests for further investigation?

6. **(a)** Which property was the most useful for identifying a mineral? Why?

   (b) Which property or properties were not very useful for identifying a mineral? Why?

7. How much does hardness seem to affect the similarity of a mineral's colour to the colour of its streak?

8. **Design Your Own** Write a procedure outlining the order for testing mineral properties in further investigations.

Extend Your Skills

9. Obtain a Mohs scale set of minerals. Use these minerals to test the hardness of your test samples more accurately. Based on your observations, create a definition of "hardness."

10. Your teacher will give you several minerals collected from your local area. Can you identify them?

Dig for Treasure

Where are minerals found in Canada?

Materials

mineral map of Canada

research materials

Procedure

1. Your teacher will give you a ☐ shows where minerals a Canada.

2. 👥 In a group, researc minerals found in Canada.

3. Choose one mineral, and rese characteristics: Where is it foun it mined? What is it used for?

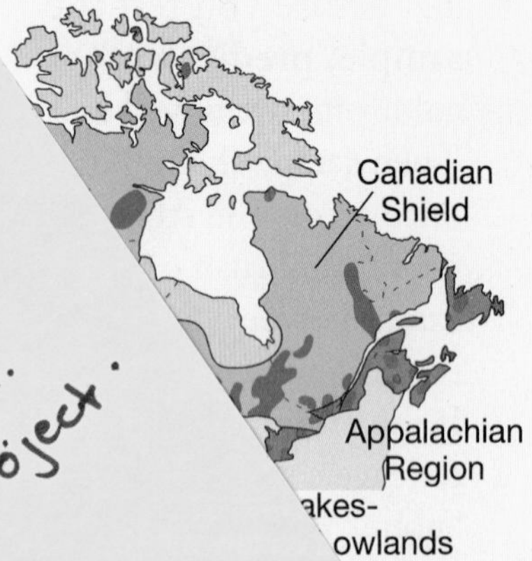

What Did You Find Out?

Suppose you were meeting with an industri representative to discuss the mineral you

Canadian
Shield

Appalachian
Region

akes-
owlands

llics, such
um, diamond,
salt

...n why Canada is a good
...op an industry that needs a
. this mineral.

Handwritten note (Topic 2):

Topic 2:
Project: presentation
and project
* Talk about Rock cycle.
* Saved model of project.
(Facebook)

Tools

How many inventions can you name that have crystals in them? Some of the varied uses for crystals include control circuits, credit cards, machines, medicine, electronics, and communication. Synthetic crystals are built into almost every electronic or optical device made today. There is a huge demand for perfect crystals. Natural crystals can contain impurities, so synthetic crystals from minerals such as silicon have been created. In fact, it is so important to have perfect crystals that experiments have been done in space to determine whether crystals form more perfectly in weightless conditions.

TOPIC 1 Review

1. Define the following: rock, mineral, element.

2. List the properties that are used to identify minerals.

3. **Apply** Suppose that you find a white, non-metallic mineral that is harder than calcite. You identify the sample as quartz. What can you infer based on your observations?

4. **Thinking Critically** Many gemstones are polished so much that you can no longer detect a crystal shape. What could you do to a gemstone to determine its crystal shape?

Rocks and the Rock Cycle

Rock Families

As you have seen, rocks are made of minerals. How do minerals combine to form rocks? Some of these processes are rapid. Others take millions of years.

Scientists have grouped rocks into three major families, or types, based on how they form. The three families are igneous, sedimentary, and metamorphic rocks. Each can usually be identified by its appearance.

Word CONNECT

The word "igneous" comes from the Latin word, *ignis*, meaning "fire." Write what you think the word "ignite" means. Then check a dictionary to see how close you were.

Figure 5.7 Basalt is an example of igneous rock formed on Earth's surface. The "Balancing Rock" on Long Island, near Tiverton in Nova Scotia, is a spectacular basaltic sea stack. How might it have formed?

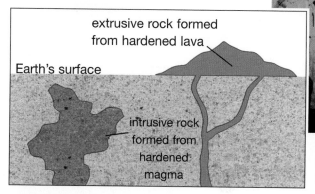

extrusive rock formed from hardened lava

Earth's surface

intrusive rock formed from hardened magma

Figure 5.8 This diagram shows two main types of igneous rock and how they are formed.

Igneous Rock

Igneous rock forms when hot magma or lava cools and solidifies. **Magma** is melted rock found below Earth's crust, where temperatures and pressures are high. Any rock heated at great depths can melt into magma. Under high pressure, the magma can push away or dissolve the surrounding rock, making room for itself. Sometimes fingers of hot magma push up to the surface through cracks in Earth's crust.

Geologists classify igneous rock based on whether it was formed above or below Earth's surface. Magma can cool and harden below the surface. The resulting rock is called **intrusive rock**. Granite is an example of an igneous rock that formed very deep and very slowly in Earth's crust.

When magma breaks through Earth's surface, in the form of a volcanic eruption, it is called **lava**. Rock that forms when lava cools on Earth's surface is called **extrusive rock** (see Figure 5.9).

Magma can contain crystals. The appearance of the crystals in igneous rock samples can differ depending on how fast the rocks cooled. Write a hypothesis about the relationship between speed of cooling and size of crystals. You can test it in the next investigation.

Figure 5.9 Obsidian is an example of extrusive rock that forms when lava cools rapidly.

Cool Crystals, Hot Gems!

Can you turn small crystals into larger, dazzling gemstones? You might, if you could re-create the formation of igneous rocks and, at the same time, control the conditions for crystal growth.

You can use a liquid solution to represent the melted rock. The crystal size and rate of cooling represent igneous rock formation.

Question

How does the rate of cooling affect crystal size?

Hypothesis

Formulate a hypothesis about how the rate of cooling affects crystal size.

Safety Precautions

- Heat is used in this activity. Handle heated items with great care.

- Do not touch copper (II) sulfate. Wash your hands thoroughly if you touch it accidentally.

- Be careful pouring hot liquids.

- Wash your hands after completing each day's activity.

Apparatus

2 test tubes
1 beaker (250 mL)
2 beakers (400 mL each)
100 mL graduated cylinder
stirring rod
hot plate
balance
scoopula
watch glass
hand lens
tongs or hot mitts

Materials

40 g copper (II) sulfate (powder or granules)
ice (crushed or broken)
masking tape

Procedure

Day One

1 Use the masking tape to make labels for two test tubes. On one, write your name and the word "ice." On the other, write your name and the words "warm water." Labels are necessary because the ice will eventually melt. Place the labels near the rims of the test tubes.

2 Pour 50 mL of water into the 250 mL beaker.

3 Add 40 g of copper (II) sulfate to the beaker. Stir carefully.

Skill
FOCUS

To review safety symbols, turn to Skill Focus 1.

4 Place the beaker on the hot plate and gently heat. Do not let the solution boil vigorously. Continue stirring until all of the copper (II) sulfate has dissolved.

5 Use the mitts and carefully decant (pour) some of the solution into each test tube.

6 Place the test tube marked "ice" into a beaker of crushed ice. Place the test tube marked "warm water" into a beaker of warm water.

7 Leave undisturbed for 24 h.

8 If possible, **observe** when the crystals start to grow.

Day Two

9 Using a scoopula, gently pry the crystals loose from the test tubes. Place them on a watch glass.

Skill
F O C U S

To learn how to do scientific and technological drawing, turn to Skill Focus 11.

10 Examine the crystals from each tube, using the hand lens.

11 Make a drawing in your notebook of what you see. Describe the crystals from each test tube.

12 Recycle the crystals and extra solution into an appropriate container supplied by your teacher. Chemicals should never be washed down the sink.

Analyze

1. Which beaker formed larger crystals?

2. Did you observe which beaker took longer to form crystals? If so, which one did?

3. For a fair comparison of crystal size based on rate of cooling, all of the other conditions had to be the same, or controlled. List all of the conditions, or variables, that were controlled for each beaker in this investigation.

4. What was the **manipulated variable** (the feature you changed)?

5. What was the **responding variable** (the feature that changed as a result of the experiment)?

Conclude and Apply

6. How did the rate of cooling affect the size of the crystals?

7. Which sample of crystals could represent extrusive rock? Why?

8. What is more likely to happen to crystal size in intrusive rock?

9. Where might larger gems be found, on the surface of Earth or deep in the ground?

Extend Your Knowledge

10. Repeat the experiment, but divide your crystal solution evenly into *three* beakers. As before, place one beaker in ice and one in hot water. Leave the other beaker at room temperature. After 24 h, **observe** all three. Are the room temperature crystals different from the other two? If so, **explain** (**and draw**) how they are different. If the crystals do not appear to be different, which of the other crystals, the hot or cool ones, do they more closely resemble? The ice water cooled crystals represent crystals found in extrusive rock. The hot water-cooled crystals represent crystals found in intrusive rock. What natural conditions might the room-temperature crystals represent?

Sedimentary Rock

Sedimentary rock makes up about 75 percent of all the rock we can see on Earth's surface. As its name indicates, **sedimentary rock** is made from **sediment** — loose material, such as bits of rock, minerals, and plant and animal remains. These sediments become closely packed in layers and cemented together. This arrangement in visible layers is called **stratification** (see Figure 5.10).

Most often stratification happens in lakes and oceans. The larger, heavier fragments settle first and end up near the bottom. Sometimes wind, ice, or gravity moves sediment to a place where it settles. Sediment slowly settles on top of other sediment, forming layers. How does settled sediment become rock? Each layer of sediment is squeezed together by the weight of other sediment and the water on top of it. This process of squeezing together is called **compaction**.

Figure 5.10 In this gorge, layer upon layer of rock is visible. Rocks that break away from this rock face will also have layers. These layers provide clear evidence of how sedimentary rock forms.

A shale

Figure 5.11A Shale, or mudstone, is sedimentary rock formed from fine grains of clay or mud.

B sandstone

Figure 5.11B A harder, rougher rock called sandstone is formed from larger granules of sand, usually made of quartz.

C conglomerate

Figure 5.11C Rounded pebbles and small stones, cemented together, form a type of rock called conglomerate.

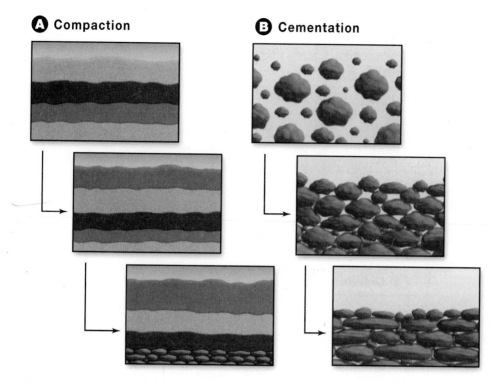

Ⓐ Compaction

Ⓑ Cementation

Figure 5.12 The process of compaction is shown by A. Cementation is shown in B. What similarities can you see between the two processes? What differences can you see?

In some rocks, minerals dissolve as the water soaks into the rock, forming a natural cement that sticks the larger pieces of sediment together. This process is called **cementation**. The appearance of a sedimentary rock can reveal what type of sediment formed it (see Figure 5.13).

Limestone is one of the most common and useful sedimentary rocks. It is also unique because it can include fossils, the remains of plants and animals. For this reason, limestone is in a separate class called organic sedimentary rock. Ocean animals, such as mussels and snails, make their shells mainly from the mineral calcite. When the animals die, their shells accumulate on the ocean floor, where most sedimentary rock is born.

Figure 5.13 In this sedimentary rock, the layers of sediment were formed by both compaction and cementation.

A Granite   **B** Gneiss

Figure 5.14 Pressure is one condition that causes metamorphic rocks to form. When pressure is applied to granite (A), the mineral grains are flattened and aligned. This results in the formation of gneiss (B). It is a long, slow process.

Metamorphic Rock

Once a rock is made, can it change its form? The answer is, yes, it can. Geologists have found rocks that resemble certain igneous and sedimentary rocks but differ from them in significant ways. They know that these rocks must have formed deep inside Earth.

The third family of rock is called **metamorphic** (meaning "changed form") **rock**. Metamorphic rock may be formed below Earth's surface when extremely high pressure and heat cause the original rock, or **parent rock**, to change form. The type of rock formed depends on the amount of pressure applied. Shale, for example, can undergo several changes as pressure and temperature increase over time. This change results in the transformation of shale ⟶ slate ⟶ schist.

Figure 5.14 shows how granite can be changed to form another rock, gneiss. Igneous granite can lie in large bodies, deep below Earth's surface. You can see what can happen to the mineral grains of granite as the pressure of heavy, overlying rock squeezes them closer together. Gneiss, the altered rock in this process, is an example of a metamorphic rock. Slate, schist, and marble are other examples of metamorphic rocks.

Looking Ahead

How could you investigate the processes of rocks changing form? Record your ideas. You may wish to investigate rocks as part of "A Creative Crust" at the end of the unit.

parent rock
sedimentary shale → slate

parent rock
sedimentary limestone → marble

Figure 5.15 Metamorphic rock looks different from its parent rock, but the rocks have common characteristics. What characteristics of shale can you see in slate? Which properties of limestone might you find in marble?

Metamorphic rock can change so completely that it no longer looks like the parent rock. There are enough common characteristics, however, that geologists know the two are related. For example, limestone and marble look different, but both have a hardness value of 3, and both are made of the mineral calcite. Both limestone and marble react with dilute hydrochloric acid.

Figure 5.16 Rock can be a strong and beautiful building material. However, it is heavy as well as durable. A product called Granirex has been developed that is made from crushed granite and is less than 1 cm thick. What uses might this product have?

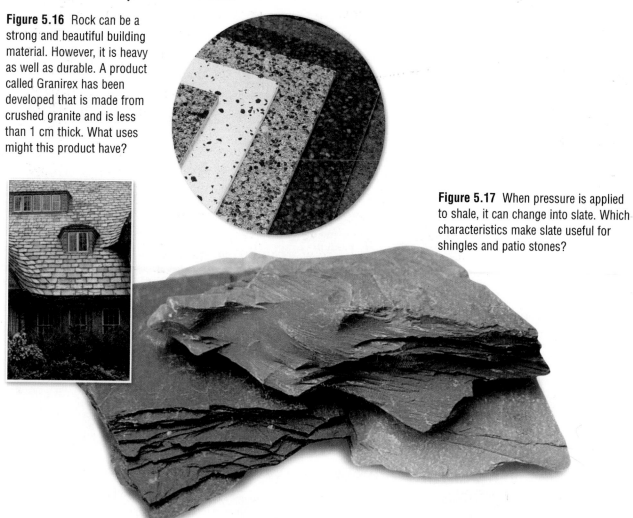

Figure 5.17 When pressure is applied to shale, it can change into slate. Which characteristics make slate useful for shingles and patio stones?

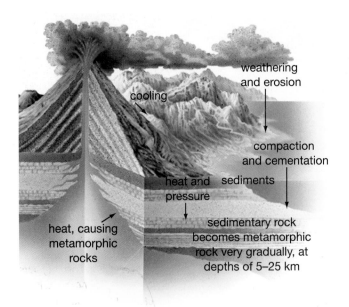

Figure 5.18. This model shows part of the rock cycle. Note that the diagram is not to scale. The production of new magma occurs 25–40 km below Earth's crust.

Labels in figure:
- weathering and erosion
- cooling
- compaction and cementation
- heat and pressure
- sediments
- heat, causing metamorphic rocks
- sedimentary rock becomes metamorphic rock very gradually, at depths of 5–25 km

The Rock Cycle

Much of what you have learned so far in this section suggests that rocks are constantly changing. For example, igneous rock is formed when magma or lava cools. Rock fragments and sediments can be compacted and cemented to form sedimentary rock. Both igneous and sedimentary rock can form metamorphic rock under high pressure and heat (see Figure 5.18).

Do the changes stop there? No, rocks continue to change in an ongoing process called the **rock cycle** (see Figure 5.19). Does the magma ever run out? As rocks sink back into the depths of Earth's crust, the heat and pressure can turn them back into magma. As well, all rocks can be broken down to form smaller rocks, fragments, and sediment. Although human activity is responsible for some of the breakdown process, most of it occurs naturally.

Pause & Reflect

How could you make a model of the rock cycle? You might choose this as an end-of-unit project. Think about different ways you could represent the processes that change rocks.

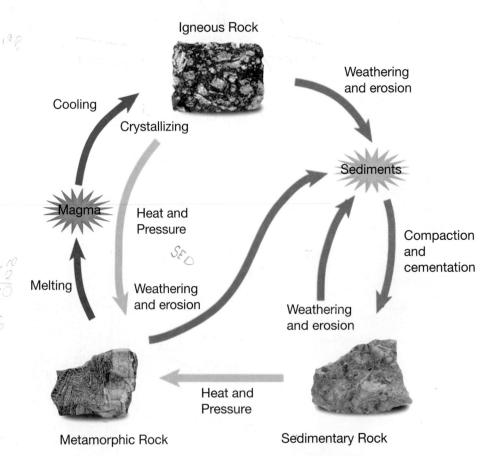

Labels in figure:
- Igneous Rock
- Weathering and erosion
- Cooling
- Crystallizing
- Sediments
- Magma
- Heat and Pressure
- Compaction and cementation
- Melting
- Weathering and erosion
- Weathering and erosion
- Heat and Pressure
- Metamorphic Rock
- Sedimentary Rock

Figure 5.19 There is not a set order to the changes rocks undergo in the rock cycle. Notice the various shortcuts and detours as rocks are weathered, consolidated, buried, melted, and solidified.

Techniques for Identifying Rocks

Rocks can sometimes be identified by appearance. However, if they have been exposed to rain, wind, and extreme temperatures, their colour and appearance may have changed. One step in identifying rocks is to determine from which mineral or combination of minerals they are made. The minerals in many rocks are so fine-grained that they must be observed under a microscope to tell them apart (see Figure 5.20).

DidYou**Know**?

Some rocks come from outer space. Meteorites are pieces of rock and iron that have a fusion crust and smooth pits. They are often strongly magnetic. Billions of tiny meteorites have fallen to Earth. Evidence indicates that Earth, the Moon, and meteorites all formed at the same time, when the solar system formed. Although collisions in space and other processes might have altered the composition of some meteorites, the majority show strong chemical similarities to Earth rock. So, even though some rocks come from outer space, they are related to Earth rock.

Figure 5.20 This basalt is made from magma that contained solidified crystals of minerals. The crystals can be seen clearly when a thin piece of the rock is viewed through a high-powered microscope.

Build Your Own System

Scientists have classified all rocks into three categories: igneous, sedimentary, and metamorphic. These are not categories based on colour or shape, but on how they are formed. What are the characteristics of each type? How can you determine in which category a rock belongs?

Materials

a set of rocks, including rocks from your geographic area

hand lens or binocular microscope

Procedure ✷ Initiating and Planning

Research the three categories of rocks and create your own classification system based on your investigations. The more research you do the easier your task will be. These points may help you:

- Sedimentary rocks are sometimes made of small particles compacted or cemented together.

- Igneous rocks often have small crystals of minerals visible and the minerals appear to be interlocking.

Find Out ACTIVITY

- Metamorphic rocks are created under a great deal of heat and pressure, causing them to have thin, flat layers that are easily visible.

You now have a good start on the classification system. Using the research you have gathered, try to classify each of the rocks into one of the three groups. Do not be discouraged if some rocks are difficult to classify. The system you develop is more important than how accurately you sort the rocks.

What Did You Find Out? ✷ Analyzing and Interpreting

1. Which characteristics did you use to classify igneous rocks?

2. Which characteristics did you use to classify sedimentary rocks?

3. Which characteristics did you use to classify metamorphic rocks?

4. Were there any rocks you were unable to classify? If so, describe their characteristics.

INVESTIGATION 5-C

Hot Rocks

If you've ever built a campfire in a rock pit, you may have noticed how hot the rocks became. How long did they stay warm after the campfire was extinguished? The heat capacity of rocks is often put to use in saunas and gas barbeques. Heat capacity is a measure of how easily a material can be heated or cooled. How can you measure the heat capacity of rocks?

Question

Which variables affect the heat capacity of rocks?

Safety Precautions

• Handle containers of boiling water with care.

Materials

a variety of sizes and types of rocks (fist size and smaller)
hot plate
tongs
large beakers or tin cans
thermometer

Procedure

1. You will be heating rocks, one at a time, in water to the boiling point. Then you will transfer them to a second container of water and measure the temperature rise in the water. **Predict** which rock will cause the greatest increase in temperature. **Explain** why.

2. There are a number of variables that will affect your results, including size and type of rock, how long you boil each rock, the amount of water in your second container, the starting temperature of your second container of water, and so on. **Discuss** the different variables with your group, then write out a step-by-step procedure of what you plan to do.

3. Have your teacher approve your procedure. Obtain the necessary equipment and carry out the investigation. **Record** your results.
   CAUTION Use tongs to carefully handle the hot rocks. Gently lower the rocks into the beakers. If you drop the rocks, the beakers will crack.

Analyze

1. Make a graph of your results, showing the change in temperature for each sample used.

2. **Compare** your group's results with those of other groups. Did all groups have the same results? If not, what could be causing the differences?

Conclude and Apply

3. Summarize the evidence you found. Does it support your prediction? Explain why or why not.

4. Which characteristics of rocks affect their heat capacity?

5. If there were any rocks that could not be used in the experiment, what characteristics made them unsuitable? What would you predict their heat capacity might be?

6. How could you change your experiment to take other characteristics into consideration?

Sediment and Soil

Earlier in this Topic you learned that sediment can be compacted or cemented to form sedimentary rock. The slow process of rock formation takes thousands of years to occur. What happens to sediment in the meantime? Some sediment is carried to the ocean. Other sediment becomes soil.

How does soil form? Earth is covered by a layer of rock and sediment. Plants and animals add organic matter, such as leaves, twigs, and dead worms and insects. The organic matter creates spaces that can be filled with air or water. All of these combine to form soil, a material that can support plants (see Figures 5.21A, B, and C). Climate, the type of rock, and the amount of moisture influence soil formation. Even the slope of the land can influence soil formation.

In addition to these non-living factors, the small living creatures that invade the soil can speed up the process of soil formation. As you saw in Unit 1, soil is a complex ecosystem, where small rodents, worms, insects, algae, fungi, bacteria, and decaying organic matter all live in harmony. Most of the decaying matter is made up of dead plant matter, called **compost**. It mixes with other matter to form the dark-coloured portion of the soil called **humus**.

Humus is rich in nutrients such as nitrogen, phosphorus, potassium, and sulfur. These nutrients dissolve in water in the soil. Plants absorb the nutrient-rich water through their roots. Humus also promotes good soil structure and helps keep the water in the soil. As worms, insects, and rodents burrow throughout the soil, they mix the humus with the fragments of rock. In good-quality soil, there are equal parts humus and broken-down rock.

A **fertile** soil is one that can supply nutrients for plant growth. Soils that develop near rivers are generally fertile. Some soils may be nutrient-poor and have low fertility, such as the eroded, rocky soil of steep cliffs and roadsides.

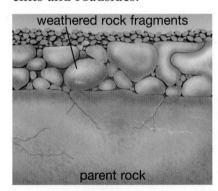

Figure 5.21A: Weathered rock fragments contain many cracks and spaces, providing areas that air and water can fill.

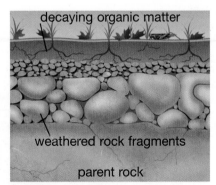

Figure 5.21B: Immature soil can support small hardy plants that attract insects and other small animals. Over time, dead plant and animal material builds up, and bacteria and fungi cause them to decay. The decaying organic matter forms a layer on top of the weathered rock.

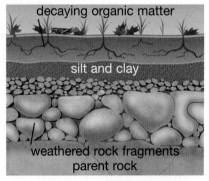

Figure 5.21C: Mature soil contains mineral-rich clay on top of weathered rock. The clay forms when water carries the minerals away from the decaying organic matter and mixes with the weathered rock fragments.

Soil Profiles

Soils can take thousands of years to form. They can range in thickness from 60 m in some areas to just a few centimetres in others. Soil varies in structure and appearance, depending on its depth. Scientists have exposed layers of soil with clear differences in appearance and composition. The layers of soil make up a **soil profile**. The soil profile in Figure 5.22 illustrates how the layers are divided. The layers show different degrees of soil evolution.

Examine Figure 5.22. The top layer (A) is called **topsoil**. It consists of dark-coloured, rich soil that contains humus and small grains of rock. It has undergone the greatest number of changes from the underlying rock layer.

The next layer (B) is generally lighter in colour because there is little or no humus, and it contains minerals that have leached from the top layer. **Leaching** is the removal of soil materials dissolved in water. Water reacts with humus to form an acid. Acid can dissolve elements and minerals from upper layers and carry them through the spaces in the soil to lower layers.

The bottom layer (C) contains partly weathered rock and minerals leached from above. This layer most closely resembles the parent rock below and is at the beginning of the long, slow process of rock evolving into soil.

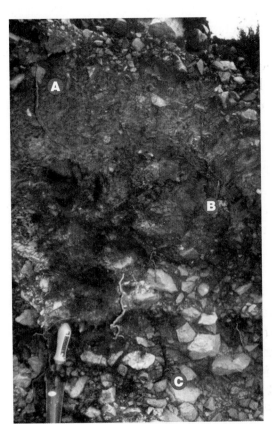

Figure 5.22 Exposed soil profile of an eroded hillside

Pause& Reflect

Imagine trying to grow a flower on a rock. In your Science Log, list and explain the reasons why this would be difficult and why it would be easier if you used soil.

TOPIC 2 Review

1. What is the composition of rocks?

2. Name and describe the three families of rocks. Give an example of each.

3. Describe the rock cycle, and explain how rocks may change with time.

4. **Analyse** How does leaching fit into the rock cycle?

5. **Thinking Critically** A core sample was taken from the bottom of a lake that contained first a layer of sandstone, then a layer of shale, and finally a layer of conglomerate on top. Why could these sediments not have settled at the same time? Explain what you think happened.

6. **Thinking Critically** How could you explain the presence of an igneous rock in a bed of sedimentary rock?

TOPIC 3 Erosion

Erosion is the movement of rock and mineral grains from one place to another. Sediment comes from larger rocks that have broken down or worn away through **weathering**. Rocks can be weathered mechanically, chemically, or biologically.

Mechanical Weathering

Mechanical weathering is the physical break-up or disintegration of rocks. For example, gravity causes rocks to fall down a cliff and break apart. Rocks rolling down a slope or in a fast-moving stream rub and bump against each other, becoming smoother and more rounded.

Temperature change can also cause mechanical weathering. In early spring or during winter warm spells, the days are warm, but night time temperatures still dip below freezing. This time of year is known as the freeze-thaw period, and it can continue for several weeks. During the freeze-thaw period, snow and ice melt in the daytime, allowing water to seep into cracks in rock. At night, when the temperature falls below 0°C, the water freezes and expands, pushing the cracks wider apart. Each day, more water fills up the cracks. Each night, it freezes and pushes the rock pieces farther apart. Finally the rock breaks apart. If a rock has many cracks it can seem to crumble at the end of a freeze-thaw period. This entire process is called **frost wedging** (see Figure 5.24). Materials other than water, such as crystal salts, can wedge rocks apart as well.

Wind and water wear away the surfaces of rocks and carry the pieces to another place, where the pieces build up. Mechanical weathering is the part of the process responsible for "wearing away." **Sedimentation** is the part of the process responsible for "building up."

Figure 5.23 Many thousands of years of rain, wind, and ice have eroded this rock in Alberta's Dinosaur Provincial Park. How do you predict this rock will look in 100 years? in a thousand years? Sketch your ideas in your Science Log.

Water freezing in crack expands, widening crack.

Eventually rock is broken free by progressive fracturing.

Figure 5.24 Frost wedging is caused by water that repeatedly freezes and thaws.

Pause& Reflect

Road repair crews are a common sight each spring. Use your understanding of weathering processes to explain why our roads are in need of repair at this time of year. Write your ideas in your Science Log.

Chemical and Biological Weathering

Chemical reactions can speed up the process of erosion. **Chemical weathering** breaks down minerals through chemical reactions. Some material may be dissolved. Other material may be weakened. Rocks react with water, with other chemicals dissolved in water, or with gases in the air. An example of a chemical weathering is acid rain, which contains dissolved chemicals from air pollution. Acidic rainwater reacts with some rocks, such as limestone and dolomite. The rock material dissolves easily in the acidic water and washes away (see Figure 5.25).

Figure 5.25 Many old and valuable marble statues and buildings in Europe and Asia have suffered the effects of acid rain and have had to be repaired. The Parthenon in Athens, Greece is shown here under reconstruction.

Biological weathering is the physical or chemical breakdown of rock caused by living organisms, such as plants, animals, bacteria, and fungi. Physical breakdown occurs, for example, when a plant root wedges into a rock by forcing its way into a crack. As the root grows and expands, so does the crack, and the rock is pushed apart until it eventually crumbles and breaks. Acidic fluids produced by plant roots, bacteria, fungi, and some insects and small animals can cause chemical reactions. As the rock slowly dissolves and flows away with rainwater, cracks and crevices increase in size until the rock finally breaks apart (see Figure 5.26).

The physical environment includes natural processes such as weathering, earthquakes, and volcanic eruptions. If the physical environment changes, the rocks in it will also change. Mechanical, chemical, and biological weathering work together constantly to change the landscape around us.

Figure 5.26 Tree roots work their way into cracks and, as they grow, eventually break up the rock.

INQUIRY

INVESTIGATION 5-D

SKILLCHECK

Initiating and Planning

☼ Performing and Recording

☼ Analyzing and Interpreting

Communication and Teamwork

Rocks That Fizz

Question

Rain and ground water can be acidic. When acids react with certain rocks, carbonates are dissolved and CO_2 gas is produced. Which rocks are affected by acids?

Hypothesis

Formulate a hypothesis about which rocks would be affected by acid rain or ground water.

Safety Precautions

- Take care handling acids. Wipe all spills immediately with a neutralizer or plenty of water. Wash your hands with cool water. Report spills to your teacher.

Apparatus

watch glass
tongs or tweezers
eye dropper
dropper bottle

Materials

10% hydrochloric acid
small pieces of rock
two unknown rock samples from your geographic area

Procedure

1. **Make an observation chart** like the one shown here.

2. Obtain a few of the specimens to be tested.

3. **Observe** the physical characteristics, such as colour, texture, and other properties under "General observations."

4. Put a specimen on a watch glass.

5. Put on your safety goggles and place a few drops of 10% hydrochloric acid on the specimen. **Observe** the results. **Record** your observations on your chart.

6. Rinse the specimen under the water tap. Dry the specimen and return it to the proper place.

7. Repeat steps 4–6 for the other specimens.

Name	General observations	Hydrochloric acid test
granite		
chalk		
sandstone		
shale		
marble		
limestone		
unknown rock A		
unknown rock B		

Analyze

1. What was the **manipulated variable** (the feature you changed)?

2. What was the **responding variable** (the feature you observed changing)?

Conclude and Apply

3. What can you conclude from your observations about the types of rock that would be most affected by chemical weathering?

4. Which rocks were not affected by chemical weathering?

5. **Predict** the names of the unknown rocks.

Extend Your Skills

6. **Formulate** your own definition of "chemical weathering."

The Changing Surface of Earth

Glaciers, gravity, wind, and water are agents of erosion. Some changes, such as those caused by glaciers, happen very slowly over many thousands of years. These small changes are called gradual change. Changes such as flash floods, landslides, and rock slides are called sudden change.

There are many glaciers in the mountain ranges of Western Canada. Glaciers have been formed by the weight of layers of snow piling up year after year. When glacier ice spreads out over the top of a slope, the force of gravity causes it to flow down the slope. Geologists study the effects of glaciers, to learn more about past periods of glaciation. During the Ice Ages, sheets of ice covered much of the northern hemisphere.

As glaciers pass over land they erode it, changing its features. Rocks frozen in the glaciers scrape across the bedrock, wearing it down and making scratches called striations. Eroded sediments get pushed in front of a glacier and piled up along its sides. These are called moraines. When glaciers begin to melt and retreat, the meltwater forms channels and deposits sediment in new locations. Large rocks called erratics can be left behind, many kilometres from their source.

Figure 5.27 The scrape marks, called striations, indicate the presence of a glacier. Notice the smooth polish.

Figure 5.28 As the glacier advances, rocks, sediments, and trees are pushed along in front of it.

Figure 5.29 The "Big Rock" near Okotoks, Alberta, is an example of an erratic that has been left behind by a glacier. It might be the largest erratic in the world. Which characteristics would you use to determine its original location?

Figure 5.30 These great piles of moraine were pushed aside by a glacier in Banff National Park only a few decades ago. How many decades do you think it will be until weathering creates enough soil for plants to grow here?

Gravity is one of the forces responsible for landslides and rock slides. Some steps can be taken to protect areas where people live from the effects of water erosion, rock slides, and landslides. Retaining walls can be built, drainage can be improved, and dangerous slopes can be monitored. But slope conditions can change suddenly and unexpectedly.

Wind can also erode rock particles. When it blows across dry ground, wind picks up loose sediment, such as clay, silt, and sand. These windblown particles strike rock and wear it down by **abrasion**. Extreme examples of wind erosion include sand deserts. Wind erosion can be slowed or stopped by planting of vegetation, contour farming, and reduced tillage.

Figure 5.31 The most disastrous rock slide in Canadian history was the Frank Slide in 1903 in Alberta's Crowsnest Pass. Over 80 million tonnes of rock crashed down the side of Turtle Mountain, burying part of the town of Frank. More than 70 people died in the disaster. The slide lasted less than 100 s. Scientists are studying the Frank Slide using new technology and sound waves.

Water in Motion

Water in motion is one of the most powerful causes of erosion. Sudden changes can occur as rivers erode their banks and fast-moving flood waters carry away large amounts of soil. Heavy rain can disturb the stability of a slope, detaching solid blocks of rock and causing landslides. Oceans, seas, and large lakes erode their shorelines. When waves hit cliffs and shores, rocks are broken down and land is eroded. In some places this happens quickly. A coastline can lose several metres every year to erosion.

Slower, incremental changes happen as streams and rivers carry rock fragments along in the water. The fragments rub against each other and the riverbed as they are bounced along and they are gradually rounded and worn down. Rivers can cut straight into rock to form canyons or gorges and steep V-shaped valleys (see Figure 5.32). Eventually the sides of the valleys are worn down by weathering. When a river becomes mature, it cannot dig its channel any deeper. Instead it might start to meander, curving its bed from side to side (see Figure 5.33).

Figure 5.32 The Athabasca River near Jasper is gradually deepening the quartzite rock canyon. Where do you think the eroded material will be deposited?

Figure 5.33 A meandering river continually changes the contours of the land. Can you identify where erosion is the fastest? Where are sediments being deposited?

INVESTIGATION 5-E

Nature's Design

Models are useful for investigating some of the processes that take place in Earth's crust. In this investigation, you will design your own model.

Challenge

Design a model to describe the origin and history of a lake or a river valley in your area or an area of your choice in Canada.

Materials

construction materials: wood, plaster of Paris, modelling clay, clay, plastic, plastic bags, rubber, paper, papier mâché, cardboard, wax, sand, stones

other materials: paint, tape, glue, plastic wrap, hardware (such as screws and nails), cotton batting, macaroni, glitter, beads, fabric, yarn

Specifications

A. Your model should be at least 0.5 m × 0.5 m, with clear labels.

B. Use at least two construction media (for example, papier mâché and wood, or plastic and cardboard).

C. Choose a period of time that will be easy to recognize in a model representation of your land formation.

D. Not all models look like the system they represent. Design a new model, for the same land formation and time period, that does not look like the model you have already made.

Plan and Construct

① With your group, plan how you will construct your model.

   (a) Will you need to make a sequence of small models, or will one large one be enough?

   (b) Will your model include moving parts?

   (c) Which materials will you use to best illustrate the aspects of the land formation?

   (d) How will you show your labels?

② Prepare a labelled sketch of your model. Build your model based on your sketch.

③ Demonstrate your model for your classmates.

Evaluate

1. (a) Did your model demonstrate lake or river formation effectively?

   (b) If it contained moving parts, did they work successfully?

2. (a) Compare your work with that of other groups.

   (b) If you were to make another model, how might you improve on your current model?

Extend Your Skills

3. Design Your Own A "working model" is a model that can demonstrate how a sequence of events takes place by making the same events occur in the model itself. For example, a working model of a diverted river might involve dripping water over a cliff. It could demonstrate how dirt would eventually build up along one river bank, changing the river's direction. You could reset the working model by placing the sediment back on the cliff. How would you design a working model for your land formation?

Skill
FOCUS

For tips on using models in science, turn to Skill Focus 12.

Across Canada

When Dr. Charles Yonge joined a caving club at university, he didn't know that he would be spending much of his future life underground. Charles was a physics student, but after he experienced the beauty of cave rock, he was hooked. "Ninety-nine percent of the world's caves are limestone or dolomite," he says, "and they are the most fascinating landscapes you'll see anywhere."

After Charles switched his studies to geology, he worked with moon rocks and began investigating the rocks and minerals in caves. One of his expeditions included exploring Mayan caves with the National Geographic Society. He entered a cave system in Belize, a Central American country, and exited the cave over 50 km later in another country, Guatemala. His studies have also taken him to Vietnam and China with the Leakey Foundation. He has searched for evidence of the extinct Great Asian Ape.

While he explores, Charles conducts research in climate studies, searching for clues about the climate hundreds of thousands of years ago. "A cave might be a few million years old, but the parent rock could be 320 million years old or more. The rock can help us understand cycles of glaciation. It can also tell us about the past rain and snowfall, soil, forest cover, and even solar events."

Dr. Charles Yonge

Back home in the Canadian Rockies, he has been exploring Castleguard and Arctomys caves, Canada's longest and deepest caves, and discovering new cave systems. He guides cave tours with his Canmore-based cave consulting company and works with the University of Calgary. "Alberta's caves are treasure troves of information locked up in the mineral formations and hidden in the sediment deposits," he says. "Caves provide one of the last places on Earth for original exploration."

Figure 5.34 Over a million years of melting glacier water has dissolved deposits of limestone, forming Castleguard Cave. This enormous cave system is more than 18 km long. It is located near the Columbia Icefield in Banff National Park.

TOPIC 3 Review

1. What is erosion?

2. What is mechanical weathering?

3. How are chemical and biological weathering related? How are they different?

4. **Thinking Critically** List as many causes of erosion as possible. For each cause, describe the erosion processes that result.

If you need to check an item, Topic numbers are provided in brackets below.

Key Terms

rock	igneous rock	cementation	leaching
minerals	magma	metamorphic rock	erosion
crust	intrusive rock	parent rock	weathering
element	lava	rock cycle	mechanical weathering
crystals	extrusive rock	compost	frost wedging
lustre	sedimentary rock	humus	sedimentation
streak	sediment	fertile	chemical weathering
cleavage	stratification	soil profile	biological weathering
fracture	compaction	topsoil	abrasion

Reviewing Key Terms

1. Fifteen of the key terms are hidden in the word search. Can you find all fifteen? Do not write in this textbook.

T	N	E	M	I	D	E	S	S	O	R	D
R	S	X	F	K	G	N	I	T	P	L	W
I	B	U	E	O	D	C	A	J	R	I	O
G	R	M	R	D	O	V	Q	O	M	O	H
N	O	I	T	C	A	P	M	O	C	S	F
E	C	N	I	L	W	O	V	R	L	P	B
O	K	E	L	E	M	E	N	T	U	O	G
U	Z	R	E	A	M	E	A	M	S	T	L
S	U	A	E	V	I	S	U	R	T	X	E
W	O	L	L	A	A	H	T	S	R	J	A
F	I	S	D	G	K	L	O	V	E	G	C
F	O	I	T	E	M	P	L	H	A	M	H
G	U	M	A	G	M	A	U	O	K	R	I
V	I	U	S	O	G	D	Z	K	Y	I	N
A	S	D	C	R	Y	S	T	A	L	S	G

4. Explain why a diamond does not leave a streak on a streak plate. (1)

5. What is the source of sediment? (2)

6. Compare magma and lava. (2)

7. Compare the process of compaction and cementation. (2)

8. Examine the following diagram. What family of rock is being described? Explain how the two types of rock shown in the diagram are formed. (2)

9. Describe the different kinds of weathering. (3)

10. How do glaciers contribute to sedimentation? (3)

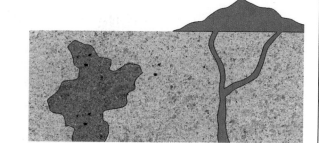

Understanding Key Concepts

If you need to check an item, Topic numbers are provided in brackets below.

2. What is the difference between a mineral that has cleavage and a mineral that has fracture? (1)

3. If a mineral belongs to the hexagonal crystal group, how many sides do its crystals have? (1)

The Moving Crust

Why does Earth's crust move? The mystery of the moving crust has puzzled people for thousands of years. During the past 25 years technology has been developed to provide clues to solve the mystery. Many of those clues come from deep within Earth. If you could travel through Earth's crust into the centre of our planet, what would you find? Figure 5.35 is a model of the layers of Earth.

A. The crust includes the layer you can walk on, and is home to plants, animals, and soil. It also includes deeper areas where minerals are mined and oil and gas are formed. The crust is very thin under the ocean. In some places it extends only 5 km deep. Under some parts of the continents it reaches a depth of 60 km.

B. The **mantle** is found under the crust. It is made of rock material. The upper mantle is solid, and together with the crust forms the lithosphere. The lower mantle is partly melted and has the consistency of taffy. Rock material in the mantle can flow very slowly.

C. The outer core is composed of iron and nickel. The temperature here is over 5500°C. It is so hot, the iron and nickel are liquid.

D. The intense pressure of all the layers forces the inner core into a solid ball. The inner core has a temperature over 6000°C.

Math CONNECT

If you were travelling at 100 km/h, how long would it take you to travel through Earth's crust? How long would it take you to travel through the entire mantle?

Cool Tools

Satellites high above Earth now take pictures of Earth. These pictures are similar to X-rays because they can show what is underneath the crust. They can detect differences in temperature the same way a CAT scan can detect a tumour inside a person's body. Computers are used to interpret the pictures.

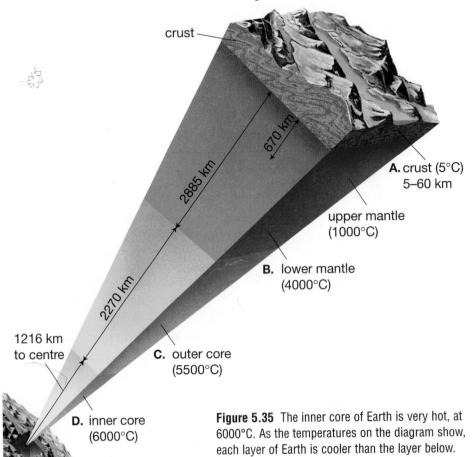

crust

670 km

2885 km

2270 km

1216 km to centre

A. crust (5°C) 5–60 km

upper mantle (1000°C)

B. lower mantle (4000°C)

C. outer core (5500°C)

D. inner core (6000°C)

Figure 5.35 The inner core of Earth is very hot, at 6000°C. As the temperatures on the diagram show, each layer of Earth is cooler than the layer below.

Evidence for Continental Drift

The map of the world is a common sight on classroom walls. Look at Figure 5.36. Can you see where the bulge of South America could fit into the indented side of Africa? Are there other continents that might fit together?

The fit of the continents was a mystery to scientists for a long time. If the continents were fixed in place, why did they look as though they had once been joined? One scientist who wondered about the fit of the continents was Alfred Wegener (1880–1930).

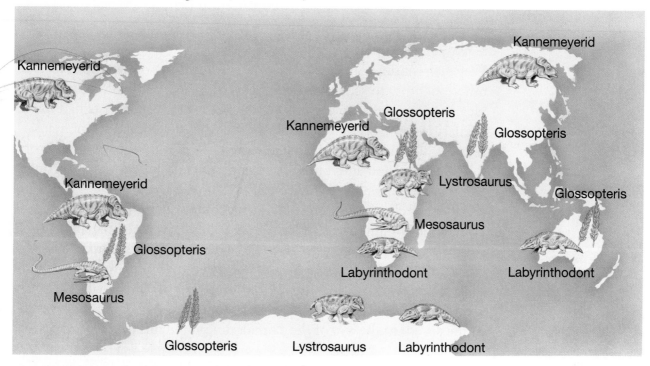

Figure 5.36 The map above shows the location of three kinds of fossils that have been found on many different continents. Notice that fossils of *Glossopteris* have been found on Antarctica, which is totally covered with ice now.

Biological Evidence

In his research, Wegener noticed that several fossils of similar plants and animals (like those in Figure 5.36) had been found on different continents. *Mesosaurus* lived in freshwater lakes, and its fossils have been found in eastern South America and southern Africa. If it was able to swim in salt water, why did it not swim to more locations?

Lystrosaurus could not swim at all, but travelled from South America to Africa. It must have travelled by some sort of land connection.

Several explanations were offered for this biological evidence (evidence from plants and animals). Perhaps a bridge of land between the continents had existed, then disappeared. Maybe trees had fallen into the water, enabling animals to cross the ocean. At one time the ocean might have been lower and islands had existed close enough together to allow the animals to cross.

Wegener studied the fossil evidence and the interlocking shapes of the continents. He concluded the continents had been joined together when the fossil animals and plants had been alive. Over thousands, maybe millions, of years, the continents had gradually moved to their present locations. Wegener called his explanation **continental drift**.

Evidence from Rocks

Wegener continued his research. He examined the observations of other scientists to see if there might be more evidence to support the idea of continental movement. He discovered that geologists had found similarities in rocks on both sides of the Atlantic Ocean. A mountain range, called the Appalachians, in eastern North America was made of the same kind and ages of rock as the mountain range that ran through Britain and Norway (see Figure 5.37).

A further clue came from fossils of trilobites found high up on the Himalayan Mountains in India. These trilobites roamed the ancient seas 250 to 500 million years ago. How did trilobites end up on the "roof" of the world? The evidence suggested that India was once a separate piece of land. Many millions of years ago, India drifted into Eurasia. The collision pushed rocks containing fossils from the bottom of the sea up to the top of the Himalayan mountains (see Figure 5.38).

Figure 5.37 How could mountains formed from the same type of rock occur thousands of kilometres from each other across an ocean?

Geological Evidence of Climate

Coal provided further important information about Earth's history. In order for coal to form, there has to be rich, luxurious plant life in a tropical, swampy environment. The coal beds that exist in North America, Europe, and Antarctica are now in moderate to cold climates. How did tropical plants grow there in the past? Why has the climate changed in so many places?

For Wegener, the clues provided by geological evidence of climatic change raised questions that had no easy answers. Since Wegener was trained as a meteorologist, he was especially interested in these clues. He found evidence of even greater climatic changes in places that had probably been covered by glaciers.

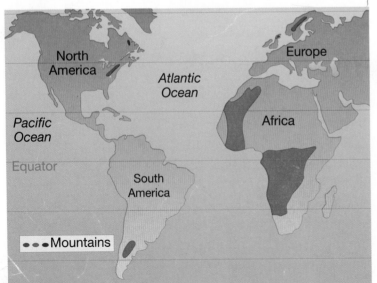

Ancient glacial deposits (200 to 300 million years old) were found spread over the southern hemisphere. Layers of deposits left behind by glaciers were found in southern Africa, South America, India, and Australia. Under the deposits in some places, there were grooves in the bedrock showing the direction in which the glaciers had moved. All of these locations now had very warm climates, much too warm for glaciers. Was the whole world cold, or had these land masses moved to their present warm locations from a place nearer to the South Pole?

INTERNET CONNECT

www.mcgrawhill.ca/links/sciencefocus7

Find out more about Wegener by going to the web site above. Click on **Web Links** to find out where to go next. See if you can locate any drawings from Wegener's book. Find some information about him that you did not learn in this text, and use it to prepare a brief biography.

Response to Wegener

In 1915 Wegener published his findings in a book, written in German, called *The Origin of Continents and Oceans*. In the book, he stated that all of Earth's continents had been joined together in a giant supercontinent called Pangaea. Pangaea started breaking up about 200 million years ago, and the pieces began moving or drifting into their present locations. Wegener wrote, "It is just as if we were to refit the torn pieces of a newspaper by matching their edges and then check whether the lines of print run smoothly across. If they do, there is nothing left but to conclude that the pieces were in fact joined in this way."

To support his hypothesis about drifting continents, Wegener thought about what forces might be causing the movement. He proposed that the Moon might be responsible, but other scientists disagreed with him. Because Wegener could not satisfactorily explain the origin of the force that was moving the continents, the scientific community rejected his ideas on continental drift.

Wegener died in Greenland in 1930, still searching for evidence to support his theory of continental drift. Years later, advances in technology and the work of a Canadian scientist led to a new theory that explained Wegener's observations.

Figure 5.38 Earth may have looked like this 180 million years ago. Try to name the seven biggest land masses on the maps. Can you find India on the map?

Give Me a Clue!

Wegener collected all of the fossil and rock evidence that he could find and put it onto a map of the world. He imagined that all of the continents that we see on Earth today were joined together in one huge supercontinent that he called Pangaea.

Question

What clues do fossils and rocks provide about the ancient world? Can you make the puzzle fit?

Apparatus

coloured pencils
scissors
glue

Materials

world map

blue paper

Procedure

1. **Examine** Figure 5.36. Mark the three fossils shown on your blank world map.

2. Put a legend on your map, telling what each symbol represents.

3. Find other fossil evidence in other sources. Try the Internet or a CD-ROM in your library. Hint: Look for *Cynognathus*!

4. Mark these additional fossil locations on your map. Add the symbols to your legend.

5. **Examine** Figure 5.37. Add the three samples of "rock evidence" to your map. Use four different colours to shade in the locations and

call each colour "same rocks" on the legend. Do not cover up your fossil evidence.

6. On the world map, write the names of the seven continents on the land masses.

7. Colour each continent. Do not cover up any evidence you marked on the world map. Decide if India will be the same colour as Eurasia or a different colour.

8. Cut out the land pieces on the world map around the continental shelf edges. Remember to cut India away from Eurasia along the tops of the Himalayas.

9. Fit the pieces of the world map together to resemble Pangaea. Once the pieces are in place, glue them to a sheet of blue paper.

10. Transfer the legend to the blue paper by cutting it out or copying it.

Analyze

1. What difficulties, if any, did you experience in fitting the pieces of land together?

2. Which pieces were the hardest to fit together? How might these pieces have looked 300 million years ago? How could you test your ideas?

Conclude and Apply

3. Why was Wegener's idea on continental drift a reasonable one? Why did it make sense at the time?

4. As a young child, did you have ideas that you had to change as your knowledge increased? Was it easy or hard to give up your old ideas? How might your experience be compared to the experience of scientists?

Advances in Technology

Important and surprising clues about Earth's crust have been collected from the sea floor using **sonar** (sound wave technology), as shown in Figure 5.39A.

When many sonar tests from Earth's oceans were studied, the results amazed everyone. It was obvious that there were mountains on the sea floor. Moreover, there were long mountain ranges or ridges in some places, just like the mountain ranges that existed on land. Scientists identified a mountain ridge that stretched from north to south along the middle of the Atlantic Ocean. They called this ridge the Mid-Atlantic Ridge (see Figure 5.40).

The features found on the sea floor were similar to the features found on land. What was causing these mountains to form? The answer would come from another technology.

Sonar stands for **So**und **N**avigation **a**nd **R**anging. This technology is used in nature by bats to navigate around objects in the dark. Sonar works by sending out a sound and then recording the time that the sound takes to bounce back. For example, scientists can bounce a sound off the ocean floor and measure the time that it takes to bounce back. Since they know how fast the sound travels, they can calculate the distance to the bottom of the ocean.

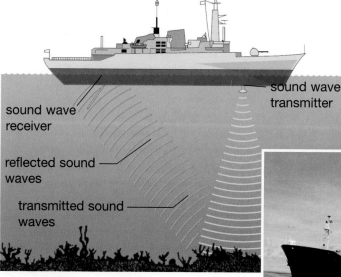

sound wave transmitter

sound wave receiver

reflected sound waves

transmitted sound waves

Figure 5.39A Sonar revealed that the ocean floor was not flat, as was previously believed.

Figure 5.39B The *Glomar Challenger* used oil-drilling technology to help scientists explore beneath the ocean floor.

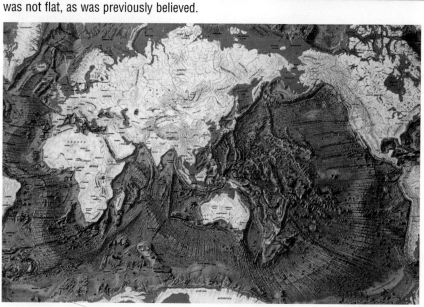

Figure 5.40 This map shows the mid-ocean ridges and the trenches. The long, ridged structures are the mid-ocean ridges.

Figure 5.41 The pattern of magnetic reversals on the sea floor led scientists to the theory of sea floor spreading. As new crust forms, it takes on the magnetic polarity of Earth at the time of formation.

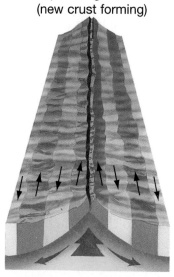

spreading centre
(new crust forming)

↑ ↓ magnetic stripes   ▲ mid-ocean ridge

Ask an Expert

Turn to page 434 to find out how Charlotte Keen studies rock many kilometres below Earth's surface.

Magnetometers are electronic instruments that can detect the direction and strength of a magnetic field. They usually record a magnetic field that points north. However, as the ships that carried them moved across the Atlantic Ocean, sometimes the magnetometers recorded a magnetic field that pointed south. A pattern of magnetic reversals was found travelling parallel to the Mid-Atlantic Ridge. The width and direction of the stripes on both sides of the Ridge were similar (see Figure 5.41). What was causing the reversals?

Igneous rock provided a clue. The magma that forms igneous rock contains iron-bearing minerals such as magnetite. These minerals line themselves up with Earth's magnetic field. As the molten rock hardens at Earth's surface, the mineral particles stay in line with the magnetic field. So the magnetic reversal stripes must have formed at a different time — a time when Earth experienced a reversal of its magnetic field. If the stripes lined up with the ridges, it could mean that the sea floor was spreading. It also meant that new rock was being formed at the mid-ocean ridges. The theory of **sea floor spreading** was formulated.

What Do the Rocks Tell Us?

What information can rocks provide about the ocean floor?

Procedure ✳ **Analyzing and Interpreting**

The graph on the right is a "best fit" graph. The small dots represent samples of rock taken from the magnetic stripes at the bottom of the Atlantic Ocean. Each dot represents a sample of rock.

1. Find the age of the oldest rock and the youngest rock on the graph.

2. State the distance of the oldest rock and the youngest rock from the Mid-Atlantic Ridge.

3. Infer or predict some additional data for the graph.

Find Out ACTIVITY

What Did You Find Out?

What does this evidence suggest was happening to the sea floor? Explain your answer.

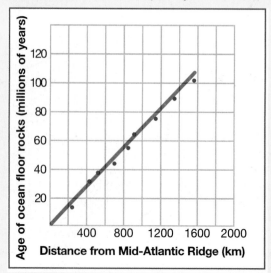

The Spreading Sea Floor

Find Out **ACTIVITY**

When magma rises from the mid-ocean ridge, it produces a new crust which pushes the plates apart. How can you create a model of this process?

Materials

sheet of paper (21 cm × 28 cm)

paints, markers, or coloured pencils

scissors

tape

Procedure

1. Cut the paper in half lengthwise. Tape the ends together to make one long strip.

2. Push two desks or tables together. Fold the long strip of paper in half. Hold the paper vertically under the crack between the desks. Push the open ends of the folded paper upward until the ends are about 5 cm above the desk.

3. Fold the ends and colour a pattern on them.

4. Push up another 5 cm and colour a different pattern.

5. Repeat until all the paper is at the surface.

What Did You Find Out?

1. What does the paper represent in your model?

2. What does the crack between the desks represent?

3. Which pattern on your strip represents the oldest rock? the youngest rock?

Deep Sea Drilling

Scientists confirmed the theory of sea floor spreading when they were able to bring up samples of rock for testing. The ship *Glomar Challenger* (see Figure 5.39B) carried equipment that could drill deep holes into the sea floor. Rock from the holes was brought onto the ship for testing by scientists. Can you imagine the excitement of the scientists who first examined these rock samples, knowing that they were the first people in the history of the world to do so! Tests of the rock samples showed that younger rock was closer to the Mid-Atlantic Ridge and older rock was closer to the continents. Scientists found that the Atlantic Ocean is getting wider by about 2 cm every year — about the same speed that your fingernails grow!

Figure 5.42 Advances in Canadian fibre technology have allowed submersibles to travel even deeper in the ocean. Submersibles like *Alvin* have made it possible for us to see lava coming out of cracks in the sea floor. The lava cools so quickly in the cold water that it is called "pillow lava." Why might it have been given this name?

Cool Tools

Even with scuba (**s**elf-**c**ontained **u**nderwater **b**reathing **a**pparatus) gear, deep-sea divers can go only a few hundred metres down into the ocean because of the tremendous pressure of the water on their bodies. Submersibles allow people to travel deeper into the ocean by protecting them from the pressure of the water. Submersibles are equipped with an air supply and powerful lights.

The Theory of Plate Tectonics

The evidence collected by advanced technology indicated that Earth's crust was moving. The crust was not fixed in place, as most people believed.

A Canadian scientist helped form a new theory to explain how the crust moves. The new theory stated that Earth's crust is broken up into pieces, called **plates**. These plates are always moving on Earth's mantle. Scientists called the new theory **the theory of plate tectonics.**

In Figure 5.43, the major plates are labelled. Can you see that most of the plates are named for the continent that is on the plate? Two plates pushing together are called **converging plates**. Two plates pulling apart are called **diverging plates**.

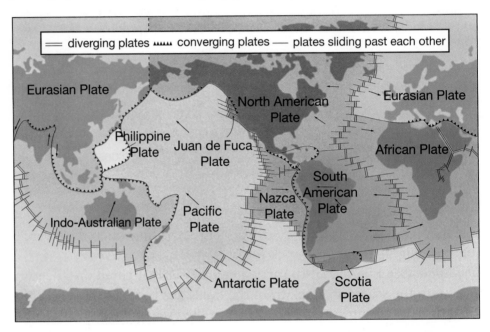

= diverging plates ᴧᴧᴧ converging plates — plates sliding past each other

Eurasian Plate

North American Plate

Eurasian Plate

Philippine Plate

Juan de Fuca Plate

African Plate

South American Plate

Nazca Plate

Indo-Australian Plate

Pacific Plate

Antarctic Plate

Scotia Plate

Figure 5.43 This diagram shows the major plates, their direction of movement, and the type of boundary between them. What is happening to the Juan de Fuca Plate where it meets the North American Plate?

J. Tuzo Wilson, a Canadian scientist, is one of the long line of scientists who have contributed to our understanding of Earth's crust (see Figure 5.44). He made an important addition to scientific observation when he developed the concept of a third kind of movement along plate boundaries. Instead of pushing together or pulling apart, he hypothesized that plates were sliding past each other.

Wilson's idea of sliding plates brought about a rethinking of Earth's crust movement.

Figure 5.44 Tuzo Wilson (1908–1993)

Building a Model of Plate Tectonics

Geologists often have a difficult time duplicating the conditions found in Earth's crust, so they develop models and computer simulations to use in the laboratory. Models help them develop hypotheses about why Earth's crust behaves the way it does. In this investigation you and your partners may collect the same data, but each of you may develop a different hypothesis. Many geologists create different hypotheses based on the data they collect.

Question

What hypothesis about Earth's crust can you form based on your model?

Apparatus
1 large plastic tub
(35 cm x 25 cm x 15 cm) per group

4 petri dishes

measuring container

pieces of puzzles, marbles, building blocks, bingo chips, etc.

Materials
2 boxes (1 kg) of cornstarch per group

water

spoon

disposable gloves (optional)

Procedure

❶ Clean the plastic tub.

❷ Wear disposable gloves or wash your hands before beginning. Only one person's hands should be in the mixture at one time. It is important that the mixture stays clean.

❸ Mix the cornstarch and 500 mL water in the tub. Continue adding water until the mixture is solid when you squeeze it between your fingers and runs through your fingers when you hold it loose in your palm.

❹ **Investigate** the properties of this mixture for several minutes. Then squeeze as much cornstarch as possible

from your hands back into the tub.

❺ Meanwhile, the remaining partners can work with small amounts of the mixture in petri dishes. Use the bingo chips, puzzle pieces, and any other objects approved by the teacher. **Create a model** of plate tectonics in the petri dishes while you wait your turn for the larger tub. Slide the objects slowly across the surface. Create many different types of boundaries between the continental plates. **Form a hypothesis** about Earth's crust based on your observations.

❻ **Record** your observations and hypothesis.

Analyze

1. **Describe** the appearance of a freshly broken piece of cornstarch. **Explain** how this might support your hypothesis on plate movement.

2. Why do some substances float and some sink in the mixture?

Conclude and Apply

3. In what ways does the mixture resemble a liquid?

4. In what ways does the mixture resemble a solid?

5. **Explain** why you think the mixture has these unusual properties.

6. **State your hypothesis**. Support it with evidence from your investigation.

Extend Your Knowledge and Skills

7. How do you think your model helps to explain the concept of plate tectonics?

8. **Draw a diagram** of your model. Use arrows to indicate plate movement.

9. **Design** a new experiment to support your hypothesis.

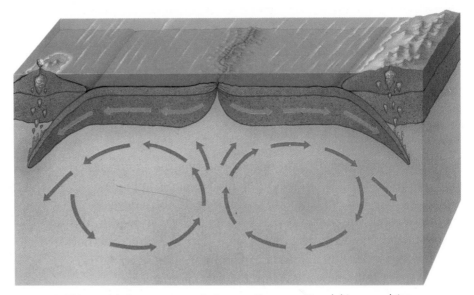

Figure 5.45 This model shows one way that convection currents might move plates.

Convection Currents

Geologists are still not sure what causes Earth's plates to move. One explanation is that convection currents in the mantle under Earth's crust move the plates (see Figure 5.45). A **convection current** is the flow resulting from the rise of warmer materials and the sinking of cooler materials. Many scientists believe convection currents are moving Earth's plates as shown in Figure 5.46 below. Study the diagram.

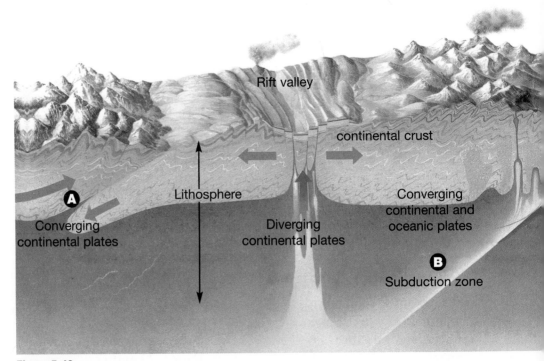

Rift valley

continental crust

Lithosphere

A Converging continental plates

Diverging continental plates

Converging continental and oceanic plates

B Subduction zone

Figure 5.46

A If converging plates are both continental, their leading edges crumple, forming mountains.

B If an oceanic plate slides under the continental plate, melting occurs, forming volcanoes and mountain ranges.

Each plate touches several other plates. Scientists call the places where the two plates collide convergent or collision boundaries. Although they move too slowly for us to notice, each movement affects other plates as shown in Figure 5.46. When two plates collide or converge, one is shoved under the other. These places are called **subduction zones**.

Scientists suggest that subduction zones form where convection currents cool and sink. The same process might be occurring in Earth's mantle, creating the force behind plate tectonics. Hot plastic-like rock in the lower mantle moves upward after it is heated by the intense heat in Earth's core. At the upper part of the mantle, the heated rock moves horizontally under the plate above it. The heated rock moves the plate along as if the plate were on a conveyor belt. When the rock finally cools, it sinks down farther into the mantle. As it does so, it pulls the edge of the plate down with it, forming a deep ocean trench.

The convection currents might be causing the Atlantic Ocean to widen at the Mid-Atlantic Ridge. Does this mean that Earth's crust is getting bigger? No, because while new crust is forming in the middle of the Atlantic Ocean, other crust is being pushed or pulled down into the ocean trenches and recycled back into the mantle as molten rock.

The theory of plate tectonics is called a unifying theory, a single theory that explains different natural events and landforms. The theory is our best explanation for the formation of earthquakes, volcanoes, and mountains. Who knows what further discoveries will be made in your lifetime!

Pause & Reflect

Scientists are using satellites and lasers to measure plate movements. Plates that hold the greatest continental masses move more slowly than plates that hold smaller continental masses. The African, Eurasian, and American Plates move about 20 mm per year. In comparison, the Pacific, Nazca, and Cocos Plates can move up to 130 mm per year. Plate movements are an example of incremental change, which is change that happens slowly. Where might the plates be in a million years? in a billion years? Use library resources to find the answer, or research on the Internet. Find a simulation of plate movements predicted for the next four billion years.

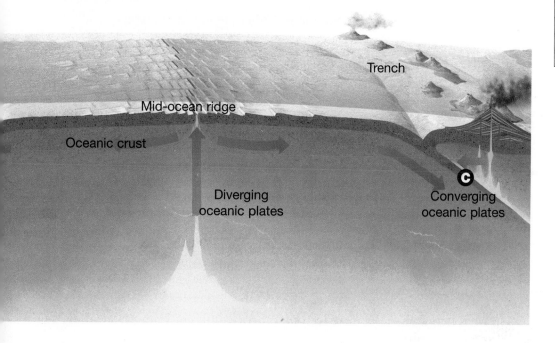

© If the two converging plates are oceanic plates, either plate might subduct, forming island arcs and volcanoes.

Miners of the future may look for gold and other precious metals on the sea floor near volcanic vents called black smokers. Scientists say that the vents act like smelters. The vents dissolve metals from the surrounding rock and send them into the cold water, where they collect outside the vents. Use the Internet or library resources to find out about a fossilized black smoker deposit called Kidd Creek in northern Canada. Write notes about your findings in your Science Log.

Figure 5.47 When submersibles found deep-sea vents called "black smokers," they also found tube worms. The sulfur compounds escaping from the vents provide an energy source for the worms.

Skill
FOCUS

To find out how to use technology tools to research, turn to Skill Focus 9.

TOPIC 4 Review

1. Make a drawing of Earth's interior and label the four main layers.

2. List the three kinds of evidence that Wegener collected to support his idea of continental drift. Give one example for each kind of evidence, and explain why the example suggested that the continents had moved.

3. Thinking Critically

   (a) Why were other scientists unwilling to accept Wegener's ideas?

   (b) Are people generally willing or unwilling to change? What does this suggest to you about scientific progress?

4. What do scientists now think is causing the continents to move?

5. (a) What happens when continental plates collide?

   (b) What happens when a continental plate and an oceanic plate collide?

   (c) What happens when oceanic plates collide?

6. In what two ways is the plate tectonics theory different from the ideas of continental drift?

You are in a class at school, and suddenly a bell starts to ring very loudly. The teacher asks you all to leave the room calmly and walk outside to a safe place for attendance to be taken. You are having a fire drill, just as students in schools do every year. Now imagine yourself sitting in your classroom and hearing the same bell ring. This time the teacher asks everyone to get under the desks as shown in Figure 5.48. You are having an earthquake drill. Students who live in places where earthquakes can happen have earthquake drills as well as fire drills.

How do you know if your school should have earthquake drills as well as fire drills? How do people prepare for earthquakes? Where do earthquakes happen in Canada?

Figure 5.48 These students are crouched under a classroom table during an earthquake drill.

Figure 5.49 Seismologists study earthquakes by reading seismograms.

Cool Tools

The eight dragon heads that are attached to this urn have little balls inside them. Earthquake movement shakes the balls into the toads' open mouths. The direction of the earthquake is determined by which toad swallows the ball.

How accurate was this ancient device? On one occasion long ago, a ball fell from a dragon's mouth but no ground movement was noticed. Several days later, however, a messenger brought news of an earthquake that had happened about 650 km away.

Measuring Earthquakes

Scientists called seismologists use a special machine called a **seismograph** to measure earthquakes (see Figure 5.49). Seismographs must be attached to **bedrock** (the solid rock that lies beneath the soil and looser rocks) in order to feel the vibrations that result from an earthquake. Inside the seismograph, a marking pen hangs over a rotating drum, just touching the drum. The drum is covered with paper to record the vibrations marked by the pen. When an earthquake strikes, it shakes the bedrock, causing the pen to move while the paper drum stays still. The pen point moves against the paper drum, making a jagged line. Most modern seismographs are electronic, but they are based on the same principle.

Seismologists use a method of measurement called the **Richter scale** to describe the magnitude (strength) of an earthquake. The scale starts at zero and can go as high as necessary. The amount of energy released increases greatly as the numbers increase. An earthquake that registered 7 would be about 30 times stronger than one that registered 6, and about 900 times stronger than one that registered 5. Most earthquakes that cause damage and loss of life register between 6 and 8 on the Richter scale; the Kobe earthquake (see Figure 5.50) registered 7.2.

Table 5.3 shows some of the numbers on the Richter scale, the effects of earthquakes of each magnitude, and their frequency.

Table 5.3 Richter Scale

Richter magnitudes	Earthquake effects	Estimated number per year
< 2.0	generally not felt, but recorded	600 000
2.0 – 2.9	felt by few	300 000
3.0 – 3.9	felt by some	49 000
4.0 – 4.9	felt by most	6200
5.0 – 5.9	damaging shocks	800
6.0 – 6.9	destructive in populated regions	266
7.0 – 7.9	major earthquakes, which inflict serious damage	18
≥ 8.0	great earthquakes, which produce total destruction to communities near the source	1.4

SOURCE: Earthquake Information Bulletin

Earthquake Waves

There can be many episodes of ground-shaking movement in an earthquake caused by **seismic waves**. These are the energy waves that travel outward from the source of the earthquake. These **aftershocks** are actually smaller earthquakes, and they can cause damaged buildings to collapse. The Kobe earthquake in Japan produced over 600 aftershocks.

Figure 5.50 In 1995 an earthquake in Kobe, Japan, caused over 5000 deaths and cost many billions of dollars in property damage.

Shake It!

With a partner, design and make your own seismograph.

Procedure ✴ Initiating and Planning

What parts in the diagram might present a challenge? What method could you devise, other than a rotating drum, to record movement? Draw and label your design. Write what you will need to make your seismograph and how you will go about it. If your model differs in any way from your design, draw and label your seismograph. Describe the changes and why you made them.

Demonstrate your seismograph for other students. Compare it with those designed by your classmates. Discuss your comparisons with your partner, and write down what you noticed. How might you improve your seismograph?

Extension

Find out if there is a seismograph located somewhere close to where you live. The best place to start is the university or college closest to your home. If it is close enough to visit, check with your teacher about arranging a field trip for your class to see the seismograph.

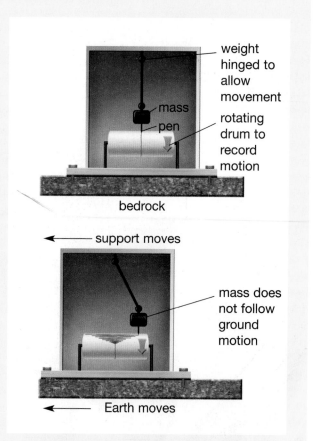

Types of Earthquake Waves

Three kinds of seismic waves occur in an earthquake.

Math CONNECT

Primary waves travel at about 6 km/s through Earth's crust. The distance from Edmonton to Calgary is about 300 km. How long would it take for primary waves to travel between these two cities?

- **Primary** or **P waves** travel the fastest of all three types of waves and can pass through solids, liquids, and gases. They cause a slight vibration (compression) that would rattle dishes on the shelves. These waves warn people in earthquake areas that an earthquake is happening and can give people a few seconds to prepare for the movement to come.

- **Secondary** or **S waves** travel more slowly than P waves and can pass only through solids, not through liquids or gases.

- **Surface waves** are the slowest of the three waves, but their rolling motion breaks up roads and buildings, so they do the most damage. You have probably thrown a small stone into water and watched the ripples spread out from the point where the stone entered the water. Surface waves travel through Earth in just the same way. They cause part of a building to move up while another part moves down. Rigid structures will collapse if the movement is too great.

Examine Figure 5.51. Which type of wave causes the greatest reaction in the seismograph? What does the seismogram tell you about the arrival times of the different waves?

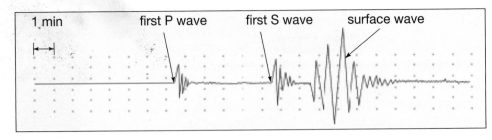

Figure 5.51 The jagged line on this seismogram represents the three different kinds of waves.

Earthquake waves give us some evidence of what might be inside Earth. The earthquake that happened in Kobe, Japan, in 1995, registered on the seismograph at the University of Manitoba because P waves travel right through the centre of Earth. S waves did not register. We know that P waves can travel through liquid and that S waves cannot. Therefore, we can hypothesize that Earth's outer core must be liquid.

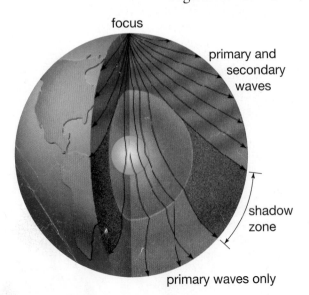

Figure 5.52 Primary waves are bent or refracted as they travel. There is an area where they do not come through on the other side of Earth. This area is called a *shadow zone*.

Locating an Earthquake

During a thunderstorm, you see lightning before you hear thunder. It is possible to estimate how far away the storm is by counting the time that passes between the flash of lightning and the sound of thunder. Light travels many times faster than sound, so you see the lightning flash before you hear the thunder. The more seconds you can count between the lightning and the thunder, the farther away the storm is. If the thunder happens at almost the same time as the lightning, the storm is right above you.

You can use the same idea with earthquake locations. You know that P waves travel faster than S waves. Since this is so, it is possible to determine the location of an earthquake by the interval between the P and S waves. The farther apart the P and S waves are, the farther away the earthquake.

Scientists have a special name for the source of an earthquake. In fact, they use two names. The place deep in the crust where the earthquake begins is called the **focus** of the earthquake. The primary and secondary waves come from the focus of the earthquake. The surface location directly above the focus is called the **epicentre.** Surface waves travel out from the epicentre (see Figure 5.53).

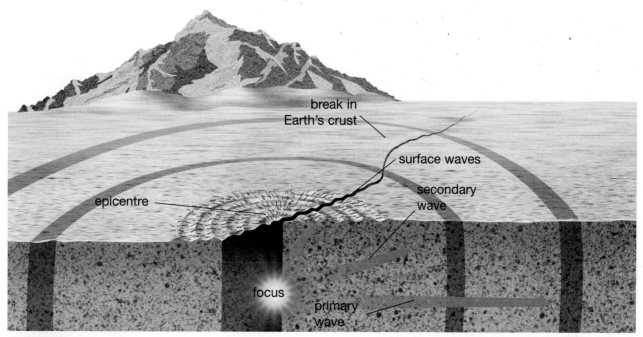

Figure 5.53

A Sudden movement in Earth's crust releases energy that causes an earthquake. The point beneath Earth's surface where the movement occurs is the focus of the earthquake.

B Primary waves and secondary waves originate at the focus and travel outward in all directions. Primary waves travel about twice as fast as secondary waves.

C The place on Earth's surface directly above the focus of the earthquake is called the epicentre. When primary and secondary waves reach the epicentre, they generate the slowest kind of seismic waves, surface waves.

D Surface waves travel outward from the epicentre along Earth's surface much as ripples travel outward from a stone thrown into a pond.

INQUIRY

INVESTIGATION 5-H

SKILLCHECK

Initiating and Planning

✿ Performing and Recording

✿ Analyzing and Interpreting

Communication and Teamwork

Locate the Epicentres

Each year, areas of Canada experience low-intensity earthquakes. In this activity you will plot data to discover the epicentres of two earthquakes.

Question

How can you use the data from seismograph stations to locate the epicentre of earthquakes?

Materials

compass

pencil

map of Canada provided by your teacher, with scale of 1000 km = 2.2 cm

Part 1
Procedure

❶ Copy the data table into your notebook. Use the graph provided to determine the difference in arrival times for primary and secondary waves for each distance in the table. Two differences are already provided.

Data Table

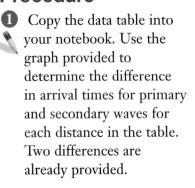

Distance (km)	Difference in arrival time
1500	2 min; 45 s
2250	
2750	
3000	
4000	5 min; 35 s
7000	
9000	

Analyze

1. What happens to the difference in arrival times as the distance from the earthquake increases?

2. Based on your calculations, **make a hypothesis** about how this graph could be used to determine the epicentre of an earthquake.

Part 2
Procedure

❶ Use the Epicentre Location chart to determine the difference in arrival time for the primary and secondary waves at each station. **Develop a chart** to record and organize your data.

❷ Use the Time Travel Graph for P and S Waves to determine the distance in kilometres of each seismograph from the epicentre of the earthquake. **Record** your data in your chart.

❸ Now you know how far each city is from the earthquake. Next you need to draw a circle around each city with the radius of the circle being the time lag distance. Use the scale on the map provided by your teacher. Set your compass radius to the distance Earthquake A is from Edmonton. Draw a circle around St. John's with your compass.

❹ Repeat step 3 above, setting your compass radius for the distance of the epicentre from Iqaluit. Using this new radius, draw another circle on your map with Iqaluit as the centre of your circle.

❺ Repeat step 3 above for all your data.

Epicentre Location Data and Observations

Location of seismograph	Wave	Wave arrival times	
		Earthquake A	Earthquake B
(1) Edmonton	P	2:36:15 p.m.	4:42:10 p.m.
	S	2:38:52 p.m.	4:48:25 p.m.
(2) Iqaluit	P	2:32:35 p.m.	4:50:23 p.m.
	S	2:39:15 p.m.	4:55:03 p.m.
(3) Whitehorse	P	2:25:00 p.m.	7:50:35 p.m.
	S	2:28:50 p.m.	7:58:10 p.m.
(4) Ottawa	P	1:30:00 p.m.	4:30:05 p.m.
	S	1:36:45 p.m.	4:31:40 p.m.
(5) Yellowknife	P	4:22:15 p.m.	4:42:12 p.m.
	S	4:26:25 p.m.	4:48:32 p.m.

Analyze

1. Identify the epicentre of each earthquake. Near which two cities did the earthquakes occur?

2. How is the distance of a seismograph from the earthquake related to the arrival time of the waves?

3. How many seismograph stations were needed to accurately locate each epicentre?

Conclude and Apply

4. What does this method reveal about the intensity of an earthquake?

5. How might seismologists use similar techniques to determine the epicentre of earthquakes?

Time Travel Graph for P and S Waves

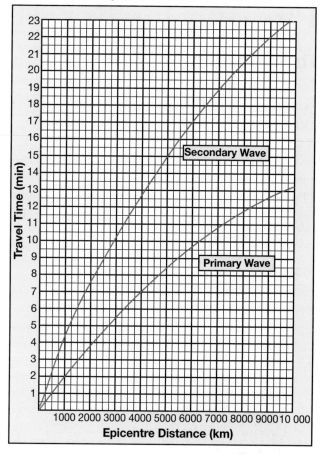

Cool Tools

This system of lasers monitors movement along the San Andreas Fault. A series of 18 reflectors are positioned several kilometres away from the laser station. If a reflector's position changes, the change is measured. Movements of less than 1 mm along the fault can be detected.

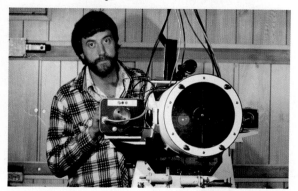

Plotting Earth's Movement

Think About It

Earth scientists use information about earthquake locations to study plate boundaries. Plotting the foci of many earthquakes may indicate the outline of possible plates.

The table below shows the location of 11 earthquake foci that occurred under South America. Thousands of earthquakes have happened in this area. How can earthquake locations tell us how the plates are moving?

Materials

earthquake data   graph paper   pencil

Earthquake	Distance east (km)	Depth (km)
1	400	230
2	80	50
3	450	320
4	220	120
5	10	15
6	480	400
7	250	150
8	500	500
9	150	60
10	300	175
11	600	550

What to Do

1 Make a copy of the graph in your notebook or on a sheet of graph paper.

2 Using the table, plot the 11 earthquake foci on the graph. Note that all data are plotted east of the 0 line.

3 You have only plotted the foci of a few of the earthquakes that have occurred over the years. Therefore, instead of connecting data, you are going to make a "best fit" line graph. Draw a smooth or curved line that illustrates the pattern of data.

Analyze

1. Predict where you think future earthquake foci might occur along this plate boundary. Using the symbol of a triangle, draw in four new foci on the graph.

2. Draw a large arrow on your graph to indicate the motion of one of the plates.

3. What other features besides earthquakes might occur at this location?

4. Which type of plate boundary does this look like to you (convergent, divergent, transform)?

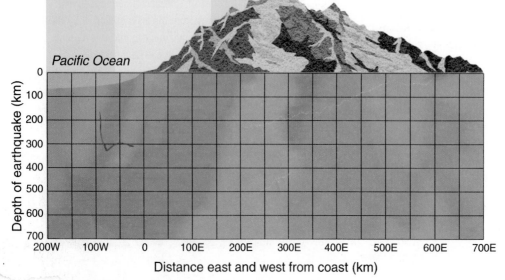

Pacific Ocean

Depth of earthquake (km)

0 — 100 — 200 — 300 — 400 — 500 — 600 — 700

200W   100W   0   100E   200E   300E   400E   500E   600E   700E

Distance east and west from coast (km)

Earthquake Zones

Since 1900, more than 4600 sizable (greater than 3.0 magnitude) earthquakes have been recorded in Canada, the United States, and Mexico. Only 17 of these earthquakes have been magnitude 8 or greater. One of these was off Canada's west coast, eight were in Mexico, and eight were in Alaska. Why might it be important to know when an earthquake has happened elsewhere?

Types of Rock Movement in Earthquakes

The rock in Earth's crust is under pressure all the time from tremendous forces. These stresses can cause the rock to bend and stretch. But when the pressure is too great, the rock breaks suddenly, creating a **fault**. Movement along a fault can spread more than a kilometre in a second. Fault zones exist where tectonic plates meet. Three types of faults are examined below in Figure 5.54.

You could compare the inside structure of Earth to an egg. The crust is the eggshell. The mantle is the white of the egg. The inner and outer cores are represented by the egg yolk. The cracks you make in the shell of a hard-boiled egg could be the faults in the rocks that cause earthquakes to happen!

Figure 5.54

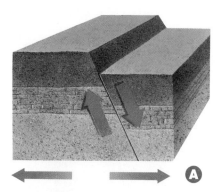
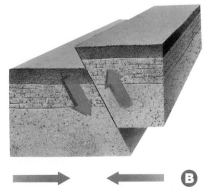
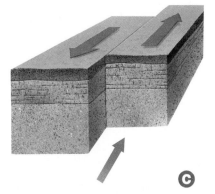

Normal Faults Tension is the force that causes stretching. In places where plates are moving apart, the tension can pull rocks apart and create a normal fault. In this type of fault, rock above the fault moves downward.

Earthquakes that are caused by rock surfaces pulling apart are very shallow. Most of these types happen on the sea floor and cause very little damage. The island of Iceland in the North Atlantic Ocean experiences many shallow earthquakes. It has huge cracks on its surface where the rocks have pulled apart.

Reverse Faults Compression is a force or stress that squeezes or compresses. In places where the rock is squeezed by the movement of the plates, the compression can cause rocks to bend and break. In this type of fault, rock above the fault is forced up and over rock below the fault.

Scientists can tell what kind of rock movement is occurring in an area by measuring the depth and focus of each earthquake. The deepest earthquakes are usually caused by rocks that have been pushed together, forming a subduction zone. One of the deepest subduction zones in the world is in the Pacific Ocean, in the Marianas Trench off the coast of Japan.

Strike-Slip or Transform Faults Shear is a force that causes slipping. In places where plates are moving sideways past each other, the rock along the edges has many bumps and bulges in it. The surfaces get caught on the rock spots and the rock is twisted and strained. As the plates keep trying to move, the forces build up until the rocks break and an earthquake occurs.

The Pacific Plate carries the Pacific Ocean floor, its islands, and a narrow strip of California. It touches seven other plates and has a lot of action on its boundaries where it slides past other plates.

Share Your Faults

Can you build your own working models of faulting?

Materials

Styrofoam™ blocks, cardboard boxes, or blocks of wood, the larger the better (approximately 20 cm × 10 cm × 5 cm)

Procedure ✳ **Communication and Teamwork**

Brainstorm with your group how you could build models of faulting. Do some research about faults on the Internet or at the library. You might even be able to download some 3-D diagrams to help you. Using the supplies approved by your teacher, create working models of different types of faults. If you use wood be sure to have an adult help you with sawing. Colour your models. Work collaboratively and divide up the responsibilities. Compare your models with other students' models. Make any changes that would improve your models.

Skill
F O C U S

For tips on using the Internet, turn to Skill Focus 9.

Preparing for Earthquakes

People who live in earthquake zones learn how to prepare for earthquakes. In many homes, people attach the furniture to the walls so that it won't shift or fall over during an earthquake. They store heavier items on shelves that are nearer the floor.

Buildings and roads are constructed differently in areas that experience many earthquakes. Engineers try to make them earthquake-resistant — able to withstand the shaking of the ground that occurs during an earthquake. Rigid structures made of bricks or solid concrete break during an earthquake because they have very little flexibility. Buildings made of steel, wood, and reinforced concrete can bend a little without breaking.

Figure 5.55 This office building in Vancouver is specially built so that it will not collapse in an earthquake. The floors are suspended from the central core of the building by huge cables that are visible at the top. What do you think will happen to this building when the ground moves in an earthquake?

Be Prepared!

Think about how you might prepare for an earthquake.

Procedure ✳ **Initiating and Planning**

Consider what changes might be necessary in your bedroom to prevent you from being injured if an earthquake happened while you were sleeping. For example, are there shelves with heavy objects at the top?

Think about the items you might need in an emergency kit after an earthquake. How long might you need them? Where could you store your emergency kit?

Make a list of changes to your bedroom and another list of items for your emergency kit. Compare your lists with another student's lists, and make any changes that you feel would improve your own work.

Figure 5.56 Tsunamis are common along Japan's coastline. This painting by artist Katsushika Hokusai shows a huge ocean wave near Japan, with Mount Fuji in the background. Tsunami is a Japanese word meaning "harbour wave."

Other Effects of Earthquakes

Some earthquakes happen under the sea. The water displaced by an earthquake can become huge waves called tsunamis (see Figure 5.56). Tsunamis can travel across oceans and cause great damage when they break on the shore. In mountains, earthquakes can trigger avalanches or rock slides. One of the most damaging earthquakes happened about 350 km east of Mexico City in 1985. When the shock waves reached the city, their size was increased by the soft sediments of the ancient lake bed on which the city is built. The sandy base turned into quicksand, and many buildings fell over. The process of changing into a liquid-like substance such as quicksand is called liquefaction. The official number of deaths caused by this earthquake was over 5000.

INTERNET CONNECT

www.mcgrawhill.ca/links/sciencefocus7

Find out about the tsunami that struck Port Alberni, B.C., in March 1964 by going to the above web site. Click on **Web Links** to find out where to go next. Write a short story, a poem such as a haiku, or a script, as though you were one of the people whose account you have just read.

TOPIC 5 Review

1. Name the instrument that measures earthquakes, and explain how it works.

2. Explain why three seismographs are required to locate an epicentre.

3. Where do earthquakes usually occur in Canada?

4. **(a)** Explain the rock movement in a normal fault.
   (b) Explain the rock movement in a reverse fault.
   (c) Explain the rock movement in a strike-slip or transform fault.

5. Imagine waking up in the middle of the night to find an earthquake occurring. When the shaking stops, you get out of bed to check on the rest of your family. Everyone is fine, but you notice cracks in the walls of your home. Should you stay inside or leave? Explain.

6. **Thinking Critically** What kinds of structures might suffer the least damage during an earthquake? Write your ideas, and then share them with a classmate. Check your ideas by looking at books or using the Internet.

Volcanoes

What would it be like to watch a huge volcano erupt? Imagine the terrific heat, the choking ash, and the streams of molten lava. A volcano is an opening in Earth's crust that releases lava, steam, and ash when it erupts (becomes active). The openings are called **vents**. When volcanoes are not active, they are described as **dormant**. Scientists try to predict when volcanoes will erupt so that the people living near them can avoid injury or death.

Figure 5.57 The most active volcano on Earth is Kilauea in Hawaii. It has been continuously erupting since 1983. The lava has flowed into residential areas, causing many millions of dollars of damage.

Like earthquakes, volcanoes can be formed when rock surfaces beneath Earth's crust push against one another. The part of the crust that is pushed downward reaches very hot areas where it melts and becomes magma. Eventually there is so much magma, it is forced up through openings, and erupts.

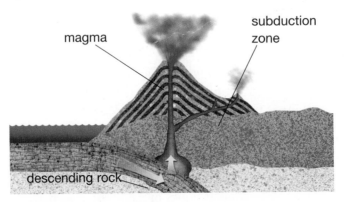

Figure 5.58 In a subduction zone, the descending rock moves deeper and deeper until it melts into magma. This magma rises up through cracks in the rock until it exerts enough pressure to cause the volcano above to erupt.

Famous Volcanoes

Mount St. Helens, in Washington, is an example of a major volcanic eruption. The rock on one side of the mountain began to bulge out in the days before the eruption that occurred in 1980. Scientists knew that an eruption would happen soon, so they had time to warn people to stay away from the area. The eruption literally blew away the side of the mountain. Figure 5.59 shows how magma built up inside the volcano to cause the eruption.

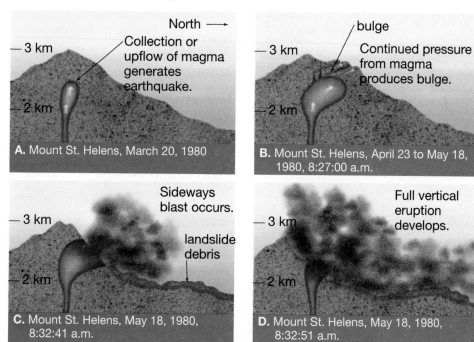

North →
Collection or upflow of magma generates earthquake.
— 3 km
— 2 km
A. Mount St. Helens, March 20, 1980

bulge
Continued pressure from magma produces bulge.
— 3 km
— 2 km
B. Mount St. Helens, April 23 to May 18, 1980, 8:27:00 a.m.

Sideways blast occurs.
— 3 km
landslide debris
— 2 km
C. Mount St. Helens, May 18, 1980, 8:32:41 a.m.

Full vertical eruption develops.
— 3 km
— 2 km
D. Mount St. Helens, May 18, 1980, 8:32:51 a.m.

Figure 5.59 Volcanoes erupt in stages, over a period of several weeks, months, or even years.

One of the most famous volcanoes is Mount Vesuvius in southern Italy. Many scientists believe that Vesuvius, dormant since 1944, is due for a large eruption. A huge area beneath the peak is filling with magma. The situation is even more dangerous because the opening at the peak is sealed by a rock "plug." Scientists have produced computer simulations to show that, when pressure forces the rock "plug" out, a cloud of molten rock, ash, and gas will blast about 1.5 km upwards. Plans are being made for emergency measures if such an event occurs.

Figure 5.60 This photograph shows a plaster cast of a body buried in the eruption of Vesuvius in 79 C.E.

Figure 5.61 After the body decayed, plaster was poured into the cavity it left. When the plaster cast hardened, the surrounding ash was removed.

INQUIRY

INVESTIGATION **5-J**

SKILLCHECK

Initiating and Planning
☼ Performing and Recording
☼ Analyzing and Interpreting
Communication and Teamwork

Patterns in Earthquake and Volcano Locations

One way to predict earthquakes and volcanic eruptions is to look for patterns in their occurrence. In this investigation, you will plot earthquake and volcano locations, and plate boundaries on a map using lines of latitude and longitude. You may recognize a pattern of earthquake and volcano activity which suggests that something unusual occurs in Earth's crust in certain areas.

Question

Is there an observable pattern in the occurrence of earthquakes, volcanoes, and plate boundaries?

Apparatus

world map with latitude and longitude lines

Table: Earthquakes Around the World

Table: Volcanoes Around the World

coloured pencils or markers

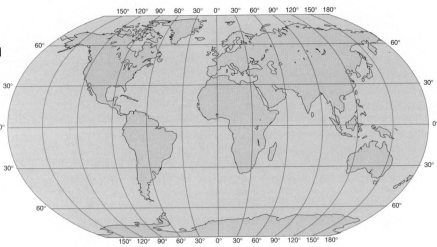

Procedure

1. Use the tables on page 409, or obtain your own earthquake/volcano list from the Internet.

2. Decide on a symbol that you will use to indicate earthquake locations and another symbol that you will use to indicate volcano locations. Use red to mark volcanoes, blue for earthquakes, and purple for plate boundaries.

Put your symbols and colours on your map under the title "Legend," indicating what each symbol represents.

3. Mark the locations on the map. Use the Internet or an atlas in your research.

4. Keep your map in a safe place so that you can use it later in this chapter.

Skill
FOCUS

For tips on using the Internet, turn to Skill Focus 9.

Earthquakes Around the World

Longitude	Latitude	Location	Year
122°W	37°N	San Francisco, California	1906
72°W	33°S	Valparaiso, Chile	1906
78°E	44°N	Tien Shan, China	1911
105°E	36°N	Kansu, China	1920
140°E	36°N	Tokyo, Japan	1923
102°E	37°N	Nan Shan, China	1927
85°E	28°N	Bihar, India	1934
39°E	35°N	Erzincan, Turkey	1939
136°E	36°N	Fukui, Japan	1948
133°W	54°N	near Queen Charlotte Islands	1949
97°E	29°N	Assam, India	1950
3°E	35°N	Agadir, Morocco	1960
48°E	38°N	Northwestern Iran	1962
147°W	61°N	Seward, Alaska	1964
57°E	30°N	Southern Iran	1972
87°W	12°N	Managua, Nicaragua	1972
92°W	15°N	Central Guatemala	1976
118°E	39°N	Tangshan, China	1976
40°E	40°N	Eastern Turkey	1976
68°W	25°S	Northwestern Argentina	1977
78°W	1°N	Ecuador-Colombia border	1979
137°E	37°N	Honshu, Japan	1983
102°W	18°N	Western Mexico	1985
45°E	41°N	Northwestern Armenia	1988
122°W	37°N	San Francisco, California	1989

Volcanoes Around the World

Longitude	Latitude	Location
122°W	46°N	Mount St. Helens, Washington
123°W	50°N	Garibaldi, British Columbia
130°E	32°N	Unzen, Japan
25°W	39°N	Fayal, Azores
29°E	1°S	Nyiragongo, Zaire
152°W	60°N	Redoubt, Alaska
102°W	19°N	Paricutin, Mexico
156°W	19°N	Mauna Loa, Hawaii
140°E	36°S	Tarwera, Australia
20°W	63°N	Heimaey, Iceland
14°E	41°N	Vesuvius, Italy
78°W	1°S	Cotopaxi, Ecuador
25°E	36°N	Santorini, Greece
123°E	13°N	Mayon, Philippines
93°W	17°N	Fuego, Mexico
105°E	6°S	Krakatoa, Indonesia
132°W	57°N	Edziza, British Columbia
74°W	41°S	Osorno, Chile
138°E	35°N	Fujiyama, Japan
15°E	38°N	Etna, Sicily
168°W	54°N	Bogoslov, Alaska
121°W	40°N	Lassen Peak, California
60°W	15°N	Mount Pelée, Martinique
70°W	16°S	El Misti, Peru
90°W	12°N	Coseguina, Nicaragua
122°W	49°N	Mount Baker, Washington State
121°E	15°N	Mount Pinatubo, Philippines

Analyze

1. Are most of the earthquakes located near volcanoes, or are their locations unrelated?

2. Describe the pattern of earthquakes, volcanoes, and plate boundaries in or around the Pacific Ocean.

3. Does the pattern around the Atlantic Ocean look similar to or different from the Pacific Ocean pattern?

4. Where do most earthquakes in North America occur?

5. Describe any other places in the world that appear to have a large number of earthquakes and volcanoes.

Conclude and Apply

6. What conclusion can you reach about earthquake and volcano locations, based on your observations?

7. If you were a scientist, what might you hypothesize about Earth's crust in these areas?

Extend Your Knowledge

8. Look on the Internet for a map of worldwide earthquake activity prepared by the Geological Survey of Canada and the United States Geological Survey. How does the pattern of earthquake and volcano activity on this map compare with the pattern on the map you prepared?

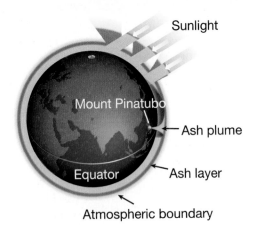

Sunlight

Mount Pinatubo

Ash plume

Equator

Ash layer

Atmospheric boundary

Figure 5.62 Mount Pinatubo erupted in the Philippines in 1991. The huge amount of ash blown out of the volcano formed an ash layer within the atmosphere that circled the globe and cooled temperatures around the world.

Look again at the volcano map you made. Run your finger around the edge of the Pacific Ocean, from New Zealand north to Asia and then down the west coast of North America and South America. Can you see all of the volcanoes in this circle? These volcanoes around the Pacific Ocean make up the **Ring of Fire**. The name comes from the circle of volcanoes that pour out red hot lava, fire, and steam. Mount St. Helens and Mount Pinatubo are part of this Ring of Fire. Most volcanoes in the Ring of Fire occur at subduction zones.

Figure 5.63 Ash from the eruption of Mount Pinatubo blocked the sunlight and buried fields and roads. Torrential rains caused mudflows that destroyed villages and left thousands of people homeless.

Myths Retold

Find Out **ACTIVITY**

The mythologies of Greeks, Romans, Indonesians, Japanese, Icelanders, and Hawaiians all contain accounts of gods or goddesses whose anger resulted in a volcanic eruption. For example, Hawaiians believed that the Fire Goddess Pele, whose image is shown in the photograph, lived inside the volcano Kilauea. They believed that the volcano erupted when she became angry.

Procedure

Look for myths about volcanoes in library books and on the Internet. Choose one of the myths. Tell it in your own words and illustrate it.

DidYouKnow?
A new volcano is forming under the ocean, right beside the main island of Hawaii. It has already been named Loihi. It will continue to grow until it is another island in the middle of the Pacific Ocean. Perhaps your descendants will visit Loihi in the future!

Figure 5.64 These active volcanoes were photographed on Io, one of Jupiter's moons. Volcanoes on Mars and our Moon have been extinct for millions of years, but it may be that Venus's volcanoes are still erupting.

Figure 5.65 The largest volcano yet found in the solar system is the extinct Olympus Mons on Mars. It is 600 km across and 25 km tall!

TOPIC 6 Review

1. How can volcanoes form?

2. What similarities are there between the causes of earthquakes and the causes of volcanoes?

3. Where is the Ring of Fire, and how did it get its name?

4. Where might you find volcanoes in Canada?

Cool Tools

How did we find out about Io's volcanoes? Vidicon, a type of TV camera mounted on the Voyager spacecraft, collected images as it travelled past Jupiter. The camera used an electron gun and a photoconductor, then transmitted the data to Earth in the form of signals. The data were processed and coloured to create the simulated photo.

TOPIC 7 Mountains

"You're really growing, aren't you?" How many times has someone made a comment like this to you? Have you ever thought that the same kind of comment could be applied to a mountain? How do mountains form? Which ones are still growing? Why do they stop growing? These are the kinds of questions that scientists ask as they try to solve some of the mysteries related to Earth's crust.

In Topic 2, you learned how sedimentary rock is formed. Some sedimentary rocks formed at the bottom of ancient oceans from shells of marine creatures. These shells gradually settled to the bottom and, over many, many years, are compressed into layers. Other sedimentary rock is made of sand, gravel, and mud.

How does sedimentary rock turn into mountains? Use the Find Out Activity "Make a Mountain!" to help you visualize the process.

Figure 5.66 Trace the sedimentary layers of this mountain with your finger. Which forces can bend and fold a mountain?

Mountain Formation and Distribution

Mountain building takes many years, and it creates some of the most beautiful scenery in the world. The Canadian Rockies, the American Rockies, and the mountains in Alaska are all part of the Western Cordillera of North America. The name *cordillera* is Spanish for mountain range. Each mountain range has a distinctive and fascinating geological history due to plate tectonics.

Most mountains are large areas that have been uplifted due to the movement or heating of plates. As you learned in Topic 4, the plates can converge, diverge, or slide past each other. The movement along these boundaries can create great heat and pressure. The pressure can cause the rocks to fold and fault, creating mountains. Sometimes the heat can melt the rock and cause it to rise to form volcanoes.

Find Out ACTIVITY

Make a Mountain!

How do layers of sedimentary rock form into mountains?

Materials

3 sheets of flexible, spongy Styrofoam™ of different colours

Procedure

Pile the Styrofoam™ sheets on top of each other. Put your hands on each side of the stack and push together. What happens to the layers?

Sedimentary rocks that are placed under slow, gradual pressure can either fold or break. Geologists explain that rocks can fold if they are hot enough to act like bendable plastic. The soft rock may bend into curves. Some of the sedimentary rock can be changed to metamorphic rock during the process of folding.

The upward or top part of the folded rock is called the **anticline**. The bottom of the fold is called the **syncline**. Over time, both of these can erode, but the folded layers still indicate what has happened.

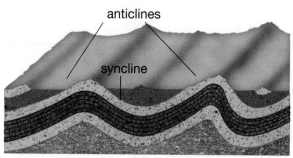

Looking Ahead

How could you make a model that shows different types of mountain building? How could you investigate mountain building processes? You may wish to use your ideas for "A Creative Crust" at the end of the unit.

anticlines

syncline

Figure 5.67 These are the main types of folding action in mountain formation.

Sometimes the rocks in Earth's crust are too brittle to fold. When pressure is exerted on them, they break, forming a fault. A fault can be the result of squeezing or stretching of Earth's crust. When sedimentary rock is squeezed from the sides, it can form into slabs that move up and over each other like shingles on a roof. This process is called **thrust faulting**. When tectonic forces stretch Earth's crust, fault blocks can tilt or slide down. The older rock may end up on top of the younger rock. These huge amounts of rock can form mountains called **fault block mountains**.

Rock movement along a fault can be vertical or horizontal. The amount of movement along a fault may be traced by matching rock on opposite sides. One major fault follows the Rocky Mountain Trench west of the Rocky Mountains. Some rocks along this fault have been moved over 400 km.

Push the skin on the back of your hand. Do you see the wrinkles that are formed as the skin slides? A similar process is at work in the Canadian Rockies where the sedimentary rock has come loose and slides on the "basement" rock beneath it. Farther south, in the American Rockies, the basement rock has broken along faults. Large areas of the crust have been shoved on top of each other, raising the underlying metamorphic and igneous rock up high (see Figure 5.68).

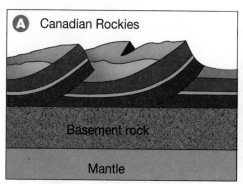

A Canadian Rockies

Basement rock

Mantle

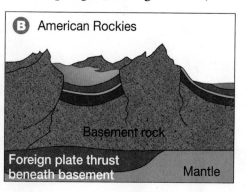

B American Rockies

Basement rock

Foreign plate thrust beneath basement

Mantle

Figure 5.68 In the Canadian Rockies (A), sedimentary rock is seen at the surface. In the American Rockies (B), "basement" rock is at the surface.

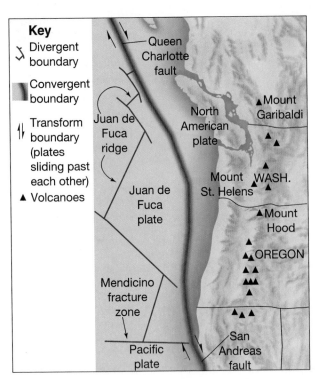

Key

- ↘ Divergent boundary
- ▮ Convergent boundary
- ↕ Transform boundary (plates sliding past each other)
- ▲ Volcanoes

Queen Charlotte fault

Juan de Fuca ridge

North American plate

▲ Mount Garibaldi

Juan de Fuca plate

Mount St. Helens

WASH.

▲ Mount Hood

OREGON

Mendicino fracture zone

Pacific plate

San Andreas fault

Figure 5.69 The subduction of the Juan de Fuca plate off the west coast of North America has caused a variety of features. The sedimentary rocks have been uplifted, folded, and faulted. Magma bodies have also been created that rise in the crust, forming volcanoes.

Mountains can be formed by the convergence of continental plates and oceanic plates. The continental plate is lighter and rides over the oceanic plate. Melted rock wells up under the edge of the overriding plate, pushing up mountains. The melted rock can break through the surface and erupt as volcanoes.

Usually more than one of these processes occurs. A combination of different processes creates **complex mountains**.

Ages of Mountains

What does a "young" mountain look like? What does an "old" mountain look like? Mountains that are jagged at the top are young; mountains that are more rounded are older. Think back to the rock cycle in Topic 2 and try to identify another difference in appearance between a young and an old mountain range.

Would you describe the Rockies as an old or a young mountain range? Some of the peaks in the Rockies are so high that they are snow-covered all year. The Rockies are one of many younger mountain ranges in the world, with the Himalayas in India being the youngest and highest. The top of Mount Everest in the Himalayas, like you, is still growing taller! The Laurentian Mountains in Québec are not as high as the Rockies. They are an older mountain range that is in the process of being worn down.

Mountain Ranges

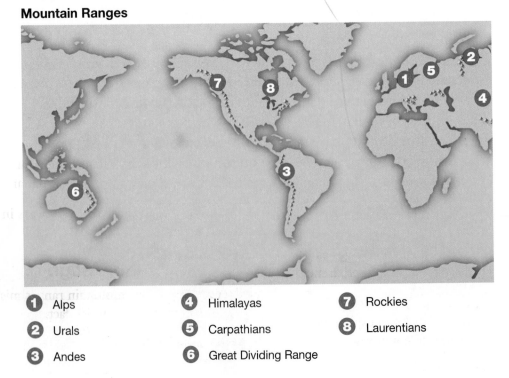

Figure 5.70 Compare this map of mountain ranges with your map of earthquakes and volcanoes. Most of the western coastline of North and South America are areas where rock surfaces are pushing against each other.

① Alps   ④ Himalayas   ⑦ Rockies

② Urals   ⑤ Carpathians   ⑧ Laurentians

③ Andes   ⑥ Great Dividing Range

Building a Mountain-Building Theory

What is a mountain? The term mountain has no simple definition because there are so many different ways mountains can be built. In this investigation you are going to investigate the location of many of Earth's mountain ranges. You will create a legend to distinguish mountains from each other based on how they were formed. As well, you will expand on an existing theory or develop a theory of your own to explain mountain distribution.

Question

Where are the major mountains found on Earth's surface and what has created them?

Apparatus

transparency provided by your teacher

water soluble transparency pens (3 colours)

atlas or other source of mountain locations

Procedure

❶ **Research** the location of Earth's major mountain ranges. Be sure to include the mountain ranges under the oceans.

❷ **Classify** the mountains based on how they were formed.

❸ Choose a separate colour for each type of mountain category. Use the transparency and the special transparency pens.

❹ **Record** the location of as many mountain ranges as you can on the transparency.

❺ Add a legend to your transparency to explain your system of colouring.

❻ You probably found mountains for which you could not explain the origin.

Form a hypothesis about how these mountains might have developed or expand one of the ideas in the textbook.

Analyze

1. What categories did you create to classify your mountains? Why?

2. Where do most of the mountains on Earth's crust occur?

3. Put the transparency you made for this investigation on your map of volcanoes and earthquakes from Inquiry Investigation 5-J, Patterns in Earthquake and Volcano Locations. What similarities can you **observe** between the location of mountain ranges and that of volcanoes?

Conclude and Apply

4. How do the locations of mountain ranges compare with the locations of plate boundaries? What are the exceptions?

5. **Describe** at least three different ways in which mountains can be created.

Extend Your Knowledge

6. **Predict** where new mountain ranges might occur in the next 3 to 4 million years. On which facts do you base your prediction?

7. **Write a definition** of the word "mountain."

Figure 5.71 Mount Rundle, near Banff, Alberta, has been uplifted and then tilted.

Figure 5.72 Castle Mountain is located between Banff and Jasper. Can you see the almost horizontal layers of sedimentary rock uplifted?

Career CONNECT

Room at the Top

Scenic mountainous areas have long been popular vacation spots. In a small group, brainstorm what sorts of businesses would likely be found in mountainous areas.

What sort of business might you be interested in starting in this type of area? Write a description of your business, explaining what service it would provide, who its clients would be, and why you think it could be successful. With the help of an adult, try to arrange an interview with someone who runs a similar type of business in your own community.

Before the interview, prepare questions such as these:

- How did you plan your business before you actually started?

- How has your business grown?

- What have you learned from having your own business?

TOPIC 7 Review

1. How are folded mountains formed?

2. What are two actions of Earth's crust that can create a fault?

3. How is a fault block mountain formed?

4. How are complex mountains formed?

5. What is an anticline? What is a syncline? What does each indicate to a geologist?

6. Thinking Critically Why do you think the Himalayas are getting taller and the Laurentians are getting smaller?

7. Thinking Critically Explain how the Olympic Mountains were formed, using Figure 5.73 as a guide.

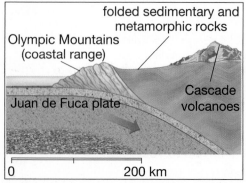

folded sedimentary and metamorphic rocks
Olympic Mountains (coastal range)
Cascade volcanoes
Juan de Fuca plate
0   200 km

Figure 5.73 The convergent plate boundary just off the coast of British Columbia.

If you need to check an item, Topic numbers are provided in brackets below.

Key Terms

mantle	convection current	secondary (S) waves	anticline
continental drift	subduction zones	surface waves	syncline
sonar	seismograph	focus	thrust faulting
sea floor spreading	bedrock	epicentre	fault block mountains
converging plates	Richter scale	fault	complex mountains
diverging plates	seismic waves	vents	
plates	aftershocks	dormant	
theory of plate tectonics	primary (P) waves	Ring of Fire	

Reviewing Key Terms

1. In your notebook, match the description in column A with the correct term in column B. There will be some terms left over. Do not write in this book!

A
• fastest travelling earthquake wave
• surface location of an earthquake
• second type of earthquake wave generated
• bottom portion of a rock fold
• person who studies earthquakes
• scale used to measure earthquake magnitude
• wave that causes the most damage
• upward portion of a rock fold
• rock break location under the ground
• huge ocean wave caused by earthquake

B
• epicentre (5)
• focus (5)
• P wave (5)
• anticline (7)
• vents (6)
• seismologist (5)
• tsunami (5)
• Richter scale (5)
• surface wave (5)
• syncline (7)
• S wave (5)
• dormant (6)
• Ring of Fire (6)
• aftershocks (5)

Understanding Key Concepts

2. Name the layers beneath Earth's crust. Which layer is thickest? Which layer is hottest? (4)

3. How does technology help us to understand whether the layers of Earth are solid or liquid? (6)

4. Explain the theory of plate tectonics. (4)

5. Describe the three kinds of rock movement that can cause earthquakes. (5)

6. Explain two main processes of mountain building. (7)

Figure 5.74 Trilobites are one of the most famous groups of fossils. They date from a time before the dinosaurs, about 200 to 400 million years ago. Trilobites lived in warm ocean water and are now extinct.

What evidence do we have of ancient life more than 10 000 years old? Fossils provide clues about when life began, and when plants and animals first lived on land. We can study fossils to learn when certain organisms, such as the dinosaurs, flourished and disappeared.

Fossils tell us not only when and where organisms once lived, but also how they lived and behaved. Understanding the evidence can be challenging however. For example, when bones of the dinosaur *Oviraptor* were found with a clutch of eggs, it was thought that *Oviraptor* was an egg stealer. Recent finds in the Gobi desert in China reveal *Oviraptor* was more likely an attentive parent that protected its eggs and young.

Fossils are useful in determining the history and dates of the rock layers and may reveal information about the environment and climate. We know Antarctica's climate was once very different than it is today because fossils of leaves have been found there.

Types of Fossils

Usually the remains of dead plants and animals quickly decay and are destroyed. When the remains are protected from scavengers and micro-organisms, however, they can become fossilized.

If a carcass is in water and sinks to the bottom, the body can be buried by sediment. Soft parts, such as skin, muscle, or organs decay rapidly and are rarely found as fossils. The hard parts (bones, shells, or teeth) may be altered to become fossilized remains. When water penetrates the bones of a dead animal, the water dissolves the calcium carbonate in the bones. A deposit of another very hard mineral, silica (quartz) remains, turning the bones into a **petrified** (rock-like) substance.

When an organism is buried under many layers of sediment, pressure and heat may build up, leaving a thin film of carbon residue on rock surfaces. The residue forms an outline of the organism. The outline is called a **carbonaceous film**.

Pause&Reflect

Draw a sketch in your Science Log of how you think the dinosaur at the right would look when it hatched. Compare your sketch with those drawn by classmates. Are there some common characteristics? What might account for the differences in designs? How might scientists draw conclusions about how dinosaurs looked?

Figure 5.75 This is a reconstructed model of a dinosaur egg found at Devil's Coulee, Alberta.

Figure 5.76 Over 20 sets of fossilized dinosaur tracks have been found in Alberta. What information do you think a footprint provides about the animal that made it?

Figure 5.77 The Marrella is the most abundant of the Burgess Shale fossil animals. It may be a distant relative of crustaceans. What similarities to a crab or lobster can you see in the Marrella?

Figure 5.78 This fossilized patch of dinosaur skin was discovered near the Milk River Reservoir in southern Alberta in 1997. Although it shows the pattern of the skin, it does not preserve the colour. What colour and pattern do you imagine this skin would have been? Why?

Figure 5.79 This insect lived million of years ago. It was trapped in resin, which turned to amber. How is it similar to, and different from, common insects today?

Figure 5.80 Coiled ammonites are common fossils in Alberta. Hundreds of ammonites are sometimes found clustered together. Why do you think so many ammonites have been preserved as fossils?

Sometimes the actual organism or part of it may be preserved as a fossil. These are called **original remains**. Animals and plants have been found preserved in peat bogs, tar pits, and amber. Woolly mammoths have been found in the Yukon preserved in the ice.

Trace fossils are evidence of an animal activity. Worm holes, burrows, and footprints can be fossilized. They provide a fascinating glimpse of ancient life on Earth.

Figure 5.81 Fossilized ammonites are found worldwide. However, only those near Lethbridge display the beautiful gemstone ammolite. Millions of years of pressure and heat have turned these shells into rare and colourful mosaics.

Fossil Mould and Cast Formation

Sometimes an organism falls into soft sediment, like mud. As more sediment falls, the original sediment gradually turns into rock. Water and air pass through pores in the rock, reaching the organism. Its hard parts dissolve, leaving a cavity in the rock called a **mould**. Other sediments or minerals may fill the hole, hardening into rock and producing a **cast** of the original object.

  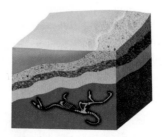 

A An ancient animal dies. Its remains sink into the mud. The soft parts of the remains decay rapidly.

B The animal's hard parts are buried by sediment. Millions of years pass. The sediment slowly turns to rock.

C The skeleton gradually dissolves, leaving a mould in the rock. Other sediments fill the mould, forming a cast.

D The surface rock is eroded. The fossil is exposed.

Find Out ACTIVITY

Mystery Fossils

In this activity, you will make a mould of an object. Will your classmates be able to guess its identity?

Materials

small object (shell, ring, ornament, etc.)

plaster of Paris

sturdy spoon

2 Styrofoam™ plates

petroleum jelly

wax paper

Procedure

Day One

1. Place a thin layer of petroleum jelly on your object and the surface of a Styrofoam™ plate.

2. Mix water with the plaster of Paris to make 250 mL of the mixture.

3. Quickly spread the plaster of Paris on the greased plate.

4. Press your object in the plaster until it is almost buried.

5. Cover your specimen with wax paper to hide the object.

Day Two

6. Gently pry your object loose from the plaster.

7. Display your mould. Try to identify the moulds made by your classmates.

What Did You Find Out? ✴ Analyzing and Interpreting

1. Which objects make the best moulds? Why?

2. The filling in a mould is known as a cast of the object. Most fossils found on Earth are actually casts of living things. How could you make a cast of your object?

3. What uncertainties do scientists face when they investigate fossil evidence? Why do they need to investigate a variety of fossil evidence before making conclusions?

INQUIRY

INVESTIGATION (5-L)

SKILLCHECK
☼ Initiating and Planning
☼ Performing and Recording
☼ Analyzing and Interpreting
Communication and Teamwork

Make a Lasting Impression

Certain conditions need to be present in order for fossils to form. In this investigation you will make and test a hypothesis about the type of materials that work best.

Question

What are the best conditions for making a fossil mould and cast?

Hypothesis

Read the procedure carefully. Then make a hypothesis about which mixture will make the best mould.

Apparatus
5 Styrofoam™ bowls
spoons
shells or plastic animals
graduated cylinder

Materials
plaster of Paris
sand
clay
pebbles
water

Procedure

1 Label four of the bowls A, B, C, and D.

2 In bowl A mix 250 mL of clay and 30 mL of water.

3 In bowl B mix 250 mL sand and 30 mL of water.

4 In bowl C mix equal parts pebbles and sand.

5 In bowl D make a mixture of equal parts of sand, clay, and pebbles. Add 30 mL of water and mix.

6 Choose the object you will use to make imprints.

7 Gently press the object into each of the four bowls. Remove the object after 30 s in each mixture. Clean the object between pressings.

8 **Observe** and **make notes** about the impressions left behind in each bowl. These impressions are called moulds.

9 Choose the best two moulds.

10 Mix approximately 100 mL of plaster of Paris with 10 mL of water in the fifth bowl. Continue adding water to

the plaster until you get a thick but soupy mixture.

11 Gently spoon the plaster into your two best moulds. Fill the entire impression *but do not press so hard that you destroy the mould.*

12 Let the plaster dry overnight.

13 After the plaster is dry, remove your cast from the mould. **Observe** the details of the cast.

Analyze

1. What was the **manipulated variable**? What was the **responding variable**?

2. Which of the mixtures created the best moulds? Why? Which of the mixtures created the poorest moulds? Why?

3. What happened to each of the mixtures as they dried overnight?

Conclude and Apply

4. What would have happened if the object and the mixture had been added at the same time?

Many myths and folk tales have been created about fossils. For example, we now know that these fossil belemnites (A) are the shells of extinct squid-like animals. But ancient people thought they were darts flung to Earth during thunderstorms. They thought belemnites had medicinal powers and sometimes added them to burial mounds. Pictured below is horn coral (B), a common fossil of Alberta. Develop and write a myth about horn coral or another fossil choice. Consider what its shape might represent and how finding it might be significant to your story.

Belemnites

Horn Coral

Across Canada

Imagine having a job searching for and examining fossils! Paleontology is the study of the history of life on Earth as reflected in the fossil record. A paleontologist needs to know about many fields — physics, chemistry, biology, geology, and astronomy. Dr. Phil Currie has used all these subjects — and others — in his career as a paleontologist.

Currie's fascination with dinosaurs began with finding a plastic dinosaur in a box of cereal. He still has the plastic dinosaur, but in his years as a paleontologist, he has gotten to know the remains of many hundreds of real dinosaurs. Fieldwork has taken Currie to the Arctic, Argentina, and China, but his main focus is western North America. He is especially interested in dinosaur behaviour and migrations, and the origin of birds. As well as finding dinosaurs, Dr. Currie writes books and articles, gives lectures, and teaches students. He is Head of the Research Program and Curator of Dinosaurs and Birds at the Royal Tyrrell Museum near Drumheller. You can visit the museum's web site and read about the latest field research done by Dr. Currie and his team.

TOPIC 8 Review

1. What type of clues can fossils provide about Earth's history?

2. What conditions are necessary for fossils to form?

3. Name five types of fossils and describe how each is formed.

4. **Analyze** What parts of a living thing are most likely to be preserved as a fossil? Why?

5. **Thinking Critically** Identify each fossil type shown in the photographs on pages 418 and 419. Explain how you decided.

Geologic Time

Suppose that on a Tuesday, you want to find an article in the newspaper from last Saturday. You probably find Tuesday's paper on the top of the pile in the recycling bin. Underneath is Monday's paper, then Sunday's, and finally Saturday's at the bottom. You knew that you would probably find the older newspaper under the more recent ones. Geologists have used this principle to infer the relative ages of different layers of rock. It is called the **principle of superposition** (see Figure 5.82).

The principle of superposition states that in undisturbed layers of rock, the oldest layers are always on the bottom and the youngest layers are on the top. As you learned in Topic 2, sediments deposited at the bottom of bodies of water eventually form sedimentary rocks. Additional new layers of sediment continue to form over the previous layers. Unless something happens to move these layers, they stay in their original positions, like the newspapers in the pile. Another term for these sedimentary layers of rock is **strata.**

Geologists use a similar technique, called **relative dating,** to find the order in which events occurred. Scientists determine the relative age of rocks by examining their position in the strata. If a crack or a fault runs through a layer, it must have happened after the layer was in place, so the rock is older than the fault. Some fossils can be used to determine the age of the layer of rock in which they are found. If the creature that became fossilized was on Earth for only a short period of time and it was widespread, it can give accurate information about the age of the rock in which it is found. A fossil used to determine the relative age of the layer of rock is called an **index fossil**.

Figure 5.82 Geologists can use the principle of superposition to determine the relative ages of these layers of rock. The top layer is the youngest, and the bottom layer is the oldest.

Which Rock Is the Oldest?

Find Out  ACTIVITY

Procedure

1. **(a)** Examine the illustration below. The legend will help you to interpret the layers.

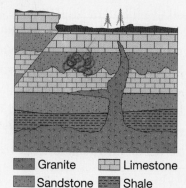

☐ Granite   ☐ Limestone
☐ Sandstone   ☐ Shale

(b) Discuss the relative ages of the rock layers and events based on what you see.

2. **(a)** Make a sketch similar to the illustration.

(b) Label the relative age of each rock layer on your sketch. The bottom layer is the oldest, so mark it with a 1. Mark the next oldest layer with a 2, and so on.

What Did You Find Out?

1. Where is the fault line in the rocks?

2. How do you know that this is an old fault line, which has not moved for some time?

Clues from Technology

You can easily use the dates printed on newspapers to put them in order. Unlike newspapers, rocks are not dated, so how can geologists establish their age?

The amounts of certain elements in a rock can tell geologists a great deal about the rock's age. Over billions of years, some elements can change into others. For example, over a period of 4.5 billion years, half of the uranium in a rock will turn into lead. The lead will then undergo no further change. This time period is called the **half-life** of uranium. The uranium is called the parent element. Once half of the parent element has changed, only half of the remaining element continues to change over a similar period of time.

So, in another 4.5 billion years, half of the remaining uranium will change into lead. The process will continue until such a small amount of uranium remains, it may not be measurable, as shown in Figure 5.84.

By measuring the amounts of such elements in a rock, and by knowing the half life of the parent, a geologist can calculate the absolute age of the rock. This process is called **radiometric dating**.

Figure 5.83 Scientists have determined that the oldest rocks on Earth's surface may be the Acasta Gneiss, found in the Northwest Territories. These rocks are 4.03 billion years old.

Math **CONNECT**

How old is a fossil that contains $\frac{1}{4}$ of its original carbon-14?

DidYou**Know**?

It is very difficult for us to comprehend the vast expanse of 4.5 billion years. If we compare this period of time to a 24 h day, for example, humans have been here for only the last second, and the ancient civilizations in Egypt, Greece, and Rome took place in less than 1/s! (It has taken you much more than a second just to read the last three sentences.) Keep these ideas in mind as you read about geologic time scale.

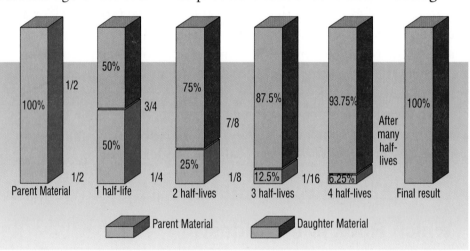

Figure 5.84 After each half-life, only one half of the parent material remains. Eventually almost all of the parent material will be gone.

Scientists also use **radiocarbon dating**, a type of radiometric dating, to find out when recent events in Earth's history occurred. Radiocarbon dating uses carbon-14, a rare form of carbon, as its parent material. This method is used to find the age of fossils, bones, and wood that are up to 50 000 years old. After 50 000 years, the amount of carbon-14 left in the sample is too small to measure. All living things take carbon-14 out of the environment to build cells and tissues. When they die, the carbon-14 changes into nitrogen gas in a half-life of 5730 years. The amount of carbon-14 left in the tissue allows scientists to determine the age of the remains.

Tell-Tale Layers

What can fossils tell us about Earth's age?

Procedure

1. Examine the cross-section at the right. It shows three layers of sedimentary rock with the fossils found in each layer.

2. The chart below identifies each fossil. The vertical arrows indicate the time span in which the animal lived.

3. Study the cross-section and the chart carefully. Identify the time range in which each layer might have been formed.

4. Make an inference from the fossil evidence about when the middle layer of rock might have been formed.

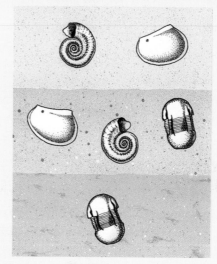

Millions of years ago	Euomphalus	Illaenus	Leperditia
286			
320			
360			
408			
438			
505			

Geologic Time Scale

The geologic time scale is a division of Earth's history into smaller units based on the appearances of different life forms. It starts 4.5 billion years ago when Earth was formed. The largest divisions in the scale are called **eons**. Eons are divided into **eras** and eras are divided into **periods**. Examine the time scale on page 426 to locate eras and periods.

For the first 4 billion years, there is little fossil evidence. This vast expanse of time is called the **Precambrian**. Scientists think the earliest supercontinent, **Rodinia**, formed during this time, about 1.1 billion years ago. Rodinia split apart 750 million years ago, forming the ocean basins. There is evidence that simple forms of life, such as bacteria, algae, fungi, and worms, lived on Earth during the Precambrian. Because the bodies of these creatures were soft, they left little fossil evidence. The three eras that are rich in fossil evidence began 570 million years ago: the **Paleozoic Era** (ancient life), the **Mesozoic Era** (middle life), and the **Cenozoic Era** (recent life).

Pangaea, the second supercontinent to form, came together during the Paleozoic Era about 350 million years ago, and broke up about 180 million years ago during the Mesozoic Era. The dinosaurs dominated Earth in the Jurassic Period, which was 200 million years ago during the Mesozoic Era. The fossil evidence indicates that Pangaea first split into a northern portion called **Laurasia** and a southern portion called **Gondwanaland** (see Figure 5.86).

Figure 5.85 Is this how the supercontinent Rodinia looked about 750 million years ago?

Figure 5.86 Present day North America was once part of Laurasia. The split into Laurasia and Gondwanaland was the first break-up of Pangaea.

Geologic Time Scale

Era	Period	Million years ago	Major life events	Representative organisms
Cenozoic	Quaternary	5	First human-like organisms	
Cenozoic	Tertiary		First placental mammals	
		65		
Mesozoic	Cretaceous		Flowering plants dominant	
		144		
Mesozoic	Jurassic		First birds / First mammals / First flowering plants	
		213		
Mesozoic	Triassic		First dinosaurs	
		248		
Paleozoic	Permian		Cone-bearing plants dominant	
		286	First reptiles	
Paleozoic	Carboniferous		Great coal deposits form	
		320	First seed plants	
		360		
Paleozoic	Devonian		First amphibians	
		408	First land plants / First jawed fish	
Paleozoic	Silurian			
		438		
Paleozoic	Ordovician		Algae dominant / First animals with backbones	
		505		
Paleozoic	Cambrian		Simple animals without backbones	
		590		
	Precambrian		Life diversifies	
			Bacteria-like organisms	
			First life forms	
		4500		

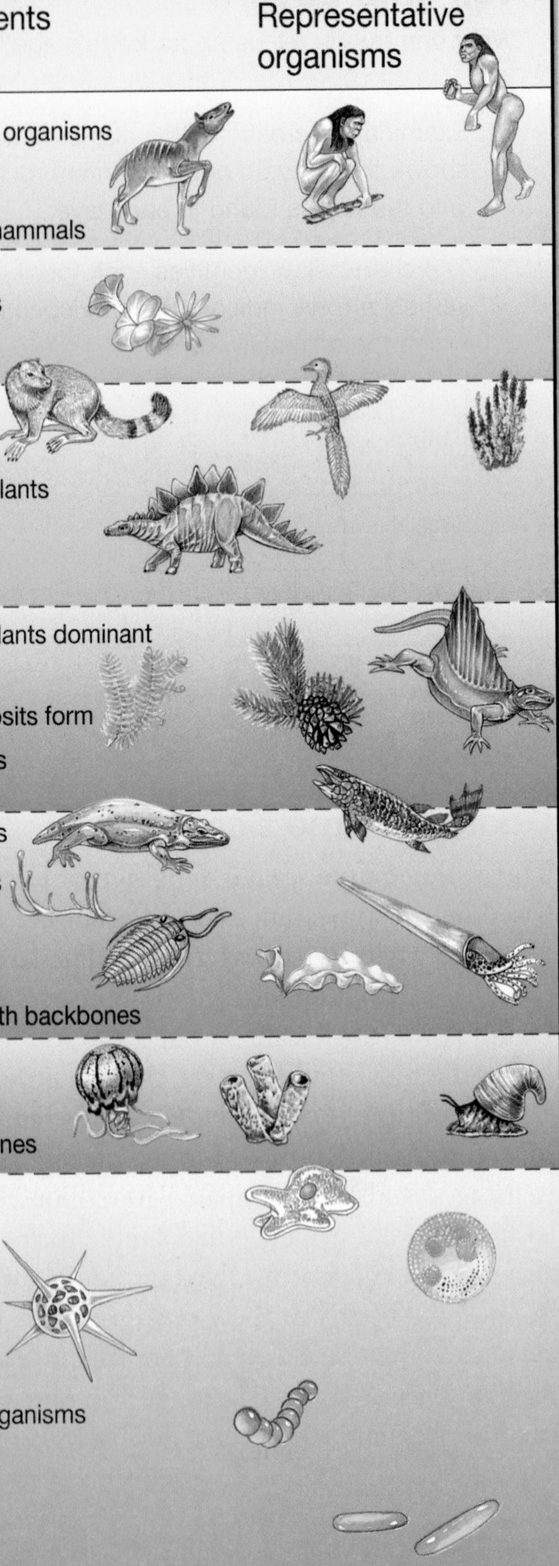

Figure 5.87 This geologic time scale provides even greater detail about geological events than you have just studied. It divides eras into periods. The scale shows the approximate dates that scientists now have for the first appearance of each general group of organisms on Earth.

Call That Old?

You are a geologist. You must organize the information you have about the history of Earth's crust and construct an informative time line.

Materials

scissors, adding machine tape, metre stick or ruler, pencil, set of coloured pencils

Procedure ✴ Initiating and Planning

1. Look back over Topics 1 to 9. Note when various events in Earth's history occurred and when various ideas about Earth's history were suggested. Decide which events you want to include on your time line. If you have time, you might want to research other events you could also include.

2. Decide how long a piece of adding machine tape you need for your time line. Use a scale of 1 m of tape = 1 billion years. If you have ideas about other materials you might use to construct a time line, have them approved by your teacher. For example, you might do this activity using the computer.

3. Decide how you will indicate events on your time line.

4. Complete your time line.

What Did You Find Out?

1. Where on the time line do most events occur? Why might they occur here?

2. Compare your time line with your classmates' time lines. Did your classmates include any events that you feel you should have included in your time line?

3. If you were to do it again, how might you improve your time line?

Extension

4. Choose a period of time on your time line, and research it. Try to find out about other major events that you could add to your time line.

Career CONNECT

Digging out the Facts

Take a look at the following occupations:

mineralogist	oil rig operator	paleontologist	geologist	paleobotanist
museum curator	miner	archaeologist	surveyor	geochronologist

With your group, produce a booklet or multimedia presentation about one of the occupations. Make sure that you describe what it has to do with the study of Earth's crust. You can use photographs and illustrations from magazines or from the Internet. If possible, interview someone working in the occupation and include your interview as an article.

TOPIC 9 Review

1. What is the principle of superposition? How does it help geologists to determine the ages of rocks?

2. Compare radiometric dating with relative dating. What do they indicate?

3. What does "half-life" mean? Give one example.

4. How old is Earth? Describe Pangaea, Laurasia, and Gondwanaland. When did they exist, and what evidence do we have about them?

Figure 5.89 The most productive oil and gas area in Canada is the Western Canada Sedimentary basin, which includes most of Alberta. However, reserves of fossil fuels are limited. Their use as a fuel is a major source of pollution. Alternative sources of energy, such as solar and wind energy, are being developed.

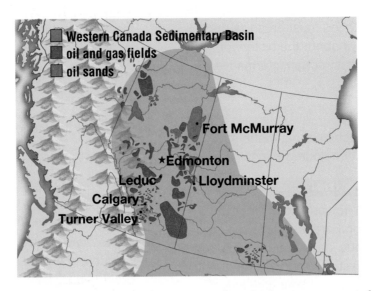

- Western Canada Sedimentary Basin
- oil and gas fields
- oil sands

Fort McMurray

★Edmonton

Leduc Lloydminster

Calgary

Turner Valley

Figure 5.88 Each of these giant trucks carries more than 300 t of oil sand. To support the weight they need tires that are 3 m wide! These trucks operate 24 h a day, 365 days of the year, at the oil sands mining projects near Fort McMurray.

Did you know that the energy that fuels your car might have come from ancient plants and animals? The source of most of the fuels used today is petroleum. How did it form? Where is it found?

Petroleum is a naturally occurring mixture of hydrocarbons, such as bitumen, coal, oil, and gas. Petroleum is most often found in sedimentary rock basins. These basins were formed from the sediments of tiny plants and animals deposited in the mud and silt. The basins were under heat and pressure for millions of years. It is thought that during that time, the soft parts of the plants and animals were transformed into solid, liquid, or gas hydrocarbons called **fossil fuels**. Coal is usually formed from plants that grew on the land. Oil is usually formed from water-based plants and animals. Natural gas can be formed from either land-based or water-based plants and animals.

Another theory about fossil fuels suggests that hydrocarbons may have been trapped inside Earth during the planet's formation. Since then, oil and natural gas have been slowly rising to the surface.

Oil and natural gas can move long distances through the strata and sometimes escape at the surface. Sometimes the lighter compounds are removed by the air or water, leaving heavier types of oil behind.

Finding and Mining Fossil Fuels

How do earth scientists know where to find oil and gas? They study surface rocks and samples from deep within the ground to identify traps where oil and gas have accumulated within rock formations. Pictured in Figure 5.91 are just three ways that oil and natural gas can be trapped.

Bitumen is a heavy, almost solid form of petroleum. Some bitumen deposits are found near the surface and can be mined. The sands are scooped up by electrically powered shovels and loaded into trucks. Hot water is used to separate the bitumen from the sand at the processing plant. In other places, the bitumen is too deep for mining to be economical. The underground oil sands reservoir is heated with steam and the melted bitumen is pumped to the surface.

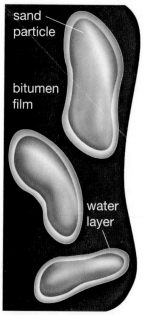

Figure 5.90 Each particle of oil sand is coated with a layer of water and a film of bitumen.

Figure 5.91

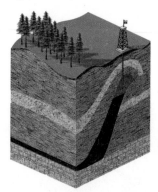

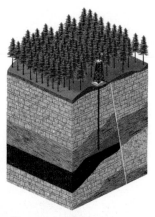

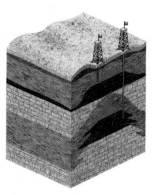

A **Thrust Fault** The original limestone layer was first folded then thrust-faulted. An example is the Turner Valley oil and gas field in south-western Alberta.

B **Normal Fault** The Dunvegan gas field in north-western Alberta is an example of a normal fault trap.

C **Reef** An ancient coral reef has been folded to form several traps, such as at the Leduc oil and gas field.

Figure 5.92 Seismic crews use modern technology to help locate oil and gas. A satellite-based global positioning system identifies the location. Large vibroseis trucks send energy waves into Earth's crust to create seismic waves. The waves are analyzed using computer software.

Cool Tools

Drilling is called "making hole." A revolving steel bit grinds a hole through the rock layers. Industrial diamonds or tungsten carbide can be used on the drill bit to reduce wear and help penetrate harder rock formations.

Where Shall We Drill?

Drilling for oil and gas can be very expensive. Just because your neighbours have a working well on their property does not mean that your land will provide an oil- or gas-producing well. In this activity you are going to make a three-dimensional model of the farm you just inherited from your grandfather in the foothills of Alberta. You are curious as to whether there could be a deposit of oil and gas under the land. However, you have only enough money to drill one hole and you do not want to make a mistake. Therefore you have hired a geologist to research the area and make a block diagram for you. Now all you have to do is interpret the diagram and tell your crew where to drill.

Question

Where will you drill for oil?

Prediction

Make a prediction about which areas are likely to contain oil.

Materials

coloured pencils, glue, scissors

block diagram (provided by your teacher)

Although advanced technology is used to find likely places for gas and oil, there is no guarantee. Drilling is always a gamble. Sometimes nothing is found, and sometimes there is greater-than-expected success.

Procedure

❶ Colour the block diagram on the sheet provided by the teacher. Be sure to follow the legend on the sheet and make the colours dark.

❷ Cut, fold, and glue the diagram according to the instructions on the sheet.

❸ You have just created a geologic map and four cross-sections.

❹ Study the block diagram carefully.

Analyze

1. At which location (A, B, or C) would you drill for oil? Why?

2. Are there any other locations where you would expect to find oil?

3. What is the name of the oldest rock in the area? How do you know?

4. What type of fault occurred. Why is the glacial till not faulted?

Conclude and Apply

5. Write a brief history of the area starting with the formation of the oldest bed.

6. Make another block diagram from the cross-section A, B, or C shown on page 431.

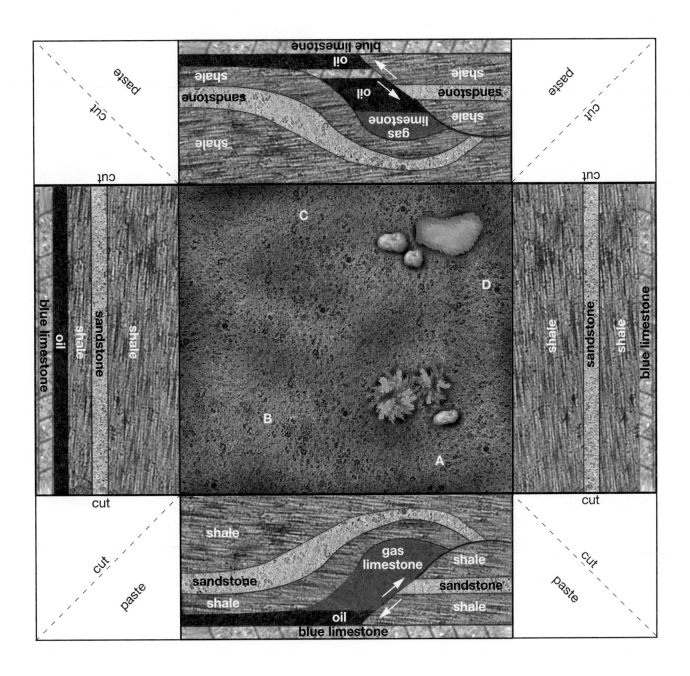

INTERNET CONNECT

www.school.mcgrawhill.ca/resources/

Where is petroleum found on Earth? Why is it sometimes found under the ocean? Learn more about this energy resource by going to the web site above. Go to **Science Resources**, then to **SCIENCEFOCUS 7** to find out where to go next. Prepare a brief report of your findings.

Figure 5.93 Sometimes core samples are drilled at potential well sites. The cores are stored in government laboratories, and information about them is added to a data base. What type of data do you think core samples provide about rock? Which type of data base would you use?

Career CONNECT

"Oil" in a Day's Work

Petroleum companies hire people like Jennifer Dunn to help them find the best places to dig for oil and natural gas. Jennifer is a petroleum geologist. She uses what she knows about Earth's crust to figure out where these petroleum products may be, far below the surface.

To decide if a spot may yield oil or natural gas, Jennifer needs to find out what kinds of rock are deep underground. She visits the area and examines the rocks on the surface. Then she and her co-workers use a special drill to bring up a "core sample," a thin cylinder of rock, from far under the ground. By studying the core sample, she can see the types of rock it contains and how they were formed. After additional tests, she makes maps explaining what the whole area is like and decides if there is a good chance of finding oil or natural gas there.

What kind of education do you think Jennifer needed for this job? Find out about the geology courses or programs offered by a university, college, or technical school near you. Try to find out what careers these courses or programs could lead to by talking to someone at that school or to a guidance counsellor in your own school.

TOPIC 10 Review

1. What is petroleum?

2. How are coal, oil, and natural gas formed?

3. How do geologists decide where to drill for oil and gas?

4. What are some common products that come from fossil fuels?

If you need to check an item, Topic numbers are provided in brackets below.

Key Terms

petrified	strata	eras	Pangaea
carbonaceous film	relative dating	periods	Laurasia
mould	index fossil	Precambrian	Gondwanaland
cast	half-life	Rodinia	petroleum
original remains	radiometric dating	Paleozoic Era	fossil fuels
trace fossil	radiocarbon dating	Mesozoic Era	bitumen
principle of superposition	eons	Cenozoic Era	

Reviewing Key Terms

1. Fill in the blanks with key terms, then find the terms in the word search. Words can be written backwards, forwards, or diagonally. Do not write in this book.

   (a) On the geologic time scale, Cenozoic is an _____ and Cambrian is a _____. (9)

   (b) _____ fuels include oil, natural gas, and coal. (10)

   (c) The earliest supercontinent was called _____. (9)

   (d) An _____ fossil can be used to determine the relative age of strata. (9)

   (e) A _____ is a cavity in rock left when hard parts of an organism dissolve. A _____ is produced when sediments fill in the cavity. (8)

   (f) A woolly mammoth found preserved in the ice is an example of _____ remains. (8)

   (g) Layers of rock are also called _____. (10)

   (h) A dinosaur footprint is an example of a _____ fossil. (8)

   (i) Relative, radiometric, and radiocarbon _____ provide information about the age of the strata. (10)

Understanding Key Concepts

2. Make a series of labelled diagrams showing the formation of a mould and cast fossil. (8)

3. Explain why we do not have fossil evidence of all the species that once lived. (8)

4. How do we know how old Earth's crust is? (9)

5. Explain two ways that fossil fuels may have formed. (10)

```
M K H Q E N I M E R S C
U V E N G Z Q C O T B A
O R I G I N A L R U S S
A N M G P R G A U R L T
E U W E T L T A H O V D
M H S G S A N S E D G U
G L R Y V O J W E I N V
D O I R E P Z I G N I G
V V K S B I H O R I T N
G N D V S M V N I A A E
I N D E X O H F H C D K
E Y E Q Y I F X A E R D
```

Ask an Expert

Is it possible to study rock that is many kilometres below Earth's surface? Charlotte Keen would answer with a resounding "Yes!" Charlotte is a senior research scientist with the Bedford Institute of Oceanography and the Geological Survey of Canada. For 28 years, she has been studying the rock under the ocean floor. In 1995, she won the J. Tuzo Wilson Medal for her outstanding contributions to geophysics in Canada.

Q What exactly is a geophysicist?

A A geophysicist is a scientist who uses knowledge of physics — the interactions of matter and energy — to study parts of Earth that are beneath its surface.

Q What part of Earth do you study?

A I look at the continental margin off the east coast of Canada that runs from Baffin Bay right down to south of Nova Scotia. This is the area where the North American continent, of which Canada is part, once separated from neighbouring continental plates. Continental margins can tell us a lot about how Earth is changing, and the rock underneath them holds great potential for natural resources: oil, gas, and valuable minerals. I study the rock that lies up to 40 or 50 km below that margin.

Q How can you study rock so far below Earth's surface?

A I look at the way vibrations from sound waves travel through that rock. My colleagues and I plan experiments for the area we want to study. We assemble a team of nearly 100 people, gather the necessary equipment, and then head out to sea. We lower very sensitive recording devices onto the ocean floor of the area we will study. After that, the ship travels away from the devices firing an air gun, which makes a very loud sound. The sound waves go down through the water and into the rock.

Some waves bounce up off layers of rock, others go deeper before they bounce back. When each sound wave reaches the device, it is recorded.

Q How the sound is recorded tells you something about the rock?

A Yes. Sound waves travel through different types of materials at different speeds. The amount of time it takes for each sound wave to be recorded helps me figure out what kind of rock the sound wave may have passed through. We keep firing the air gun from many different distances, keeping track of exactly where we were and the time at which it was fired. Usually, we are at sea for two to four weeks to record everything that we need. Once we're back on land, I analyze the data from the recording devices to figure out what type of rock exists in each place and how thick the layers of rock are.

Q Why did you decide to study the rock under the ocean, rather than somewhere else?

A When I graduated from physics at Dalhousie University in Halifax, research in oceanography was expanding in Canada. It was an exciting time. I think my love of the sea had a lot to do with my decision too. I was born in Halifax and my whole family enjoyed sailing.

An air gun is fired from the ship, making a loud sound.

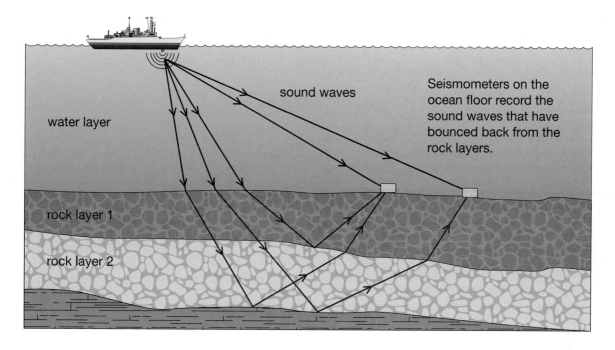

sound waves

water layer

rock layer 1

rock layer 2

Seismometers on the ocean floor record the sound waves that have bounced back from the rock layers.

Q What can the rock under the ocean tell you that other rocks cannot?

A Rock under the ocean provides information about ocean floor spreading. This is something we have been investigating since technology developed during World War II became available to us.

Q Does the fact that the sea floor is spreading mean that Earth is getting bigger?

A No, it doesn't. As new crust is produced in one area, it disappears in another. There are deep trenches in certain parts of Earth's oceans. At these trenches, a plate will slip past another one, down into the mantle, where it melts and turns back into magma. This is a continuing process.

Q Why is the study of rock under the ocean "special"?

A The technology is fairly recent, and the latest theories about what is occurring on and beneath Earth's crust are still quite new. The theory of sea floor spreading was only developed in the 1960s. It is exciting to be able to explore areas where new observations can be made. Who knows what the ocean floor still has to tell us about Earth's crust?

EXPLORING Further

The Speed of Sound

Geophysicists like Charlotte Keen study how vibrations travel through different materials. Try this experiment to compare how sound vibrations travel through wood, glass, and metal.

Hold a ticking watch by its band and place the back of the watch against a large glass window. Put one ear on the window 1 m away from the watch and cover your other ear with your hand. Can you hear the ticking? Now, try the same thing with the watch 1 m from your ear on:

• a metal vacuum cleaner hose or water pipe

• a wooden table or board.

How did the sounds compare? Which materials transferred the ticking sound best?

INVESTIGATION

A Creative Crust

Think About it

Unit 5 has shown how Earth's crust is always moving and changing. Some changes are incremental and may take many millions of years. Other changes are sudden and occur in minutes or hours. In whatever way they occur, the changes in Earth's crust result in events such as the following:

• Minerals form when magma cools.

• Rocks form in various ways and are classified as igneous, sedimentary, or metamorphic.

• Weathering causes rock to erode and sediment to form.

• Mountain formation is caused by convection currents under Earth's tectonic plates.

• Earthquakes occur when pressure at fault lines becomes too great.

• Volcanoes erupt when magma pushes upward, usually due to plate movement.

• Fossils indicate when various strata in Earth's crust formed.

• Fossil fuels are created over millions of years.

Your task is to think of a question to investigate about one of the processes that have shaped Earth's crust. Formulate your question based on information you have learned in this unit. For example, you could ask how the pressure at a fault line might vary before an earthquake occurs. You might ask how weathering by pure water or acidic water affects a substance such as chalk. Develop an experiment that will help you to answer your question.

Materials

Brainstorm a list of the materials that will be most appropriate in answering your question. You may also need electronic resources, art materials, or construction materials.

Safety Precautions

• Do not mix chemicals without your teacher's knowledge and approval.

• List additional safety precautions as you design your experiment.

Initiate and Plan

1 With your group, decide on an experimental question to investigate. You might need to do some further research in order to decide on the question.

2 Formulate a hypothesis or a prediction that will answer your question. Base your hypothesis on previous knowledge and on inferences that you can make as a result of that knowledge.

Skill
FOCUS

For tips on how to set up a controlled experiment, turn to Skill Focus 6.

For tips on using technology tools to present your results, turn to Skill Focus 9.

Analyze and Interpret
(Draw Conclusions)

6 Draw conclusions based on the results of your experiment. Discuss your conclusions with your group.

7 Did your findings support your hypothesis? Explain.

8 Write up your findings in a laboratory report. Be sure to include the following:
- Introduction
- Hypothesis or Prediction
- Procedure (step by step), including a diagram
- Data/Observations in the form of words combined with graphs, tables, etc.
- Conclusions

3 Design an experiment to test your hypothesis or prediction. Use words and diagrams to explain your design. Think about the order in which you could carry out the steps in your procedure. Decide on the feature you will change (the manipulated variable) and the feature you will observe changing (the responding variable). Decide what your control will be. You might find it helpful to refer to the Experimental Design Checklist.

Perform and Record
(Test Your Hypothesis)

4 Set up and perform your experiment. If necessary, carry out second and third trials. Make any modification to your experiment, if necessary.

5 Gather and record data and observations as you conduct your experiment. Decide how to record and present your data in a clear format (table, graph, diagram, etc.).

Experimental Design Checklist

1. Have you clearly stated the purpose of your experiment, the question you want to answer?

2. Have you written your best guess (hypothesis) about what you expect the answer will be?

3. Have you written a step-by-step procedure?

4. Have you obtained all the information you need from a variety of sources?

5. Did you make a complete list of all the materials you need?

6. Have you identified all of the variables in your experiment?

7. Identify all sources of error that you can think of in your design.

8. Did you repeat your experiment several times? How many?

Unit at a Glance

- Minerals are made from one or more elements. Minerals can be identified by properties, such as hardness, lustre, colour, streak, cleavage, and fracture.

- The three main rock families are igneous, sedimentary, and metamorphic. The rock cycle is the process through which rocks continue to change.

- Earth's surface is constantly being worn down and carried away through the forces of erosion. Some types of erosion, such as glaciers, bring slow, incremental change. Other types of erosion, such as flash floods, bring sudden change.

- Mechanical, chemical, and biological weathering wear away Earth's crust. Sedimentation builds up Earth's crust.

- The theory of plate tectonics describes the movement of the crust on Earth's mantle. Biological, geological, and meteorological evidence show that the continents have drifted over time.

- Earthquakes are caused by sudden movements in Earth's crust where tectonic plates meet.

- A volcano is an opening in Earth's crust that releases lava, steam, and ash when it erupts.

- Most mountains are formed by tectonic plates converging or diverging.

- Evidence suggests that Earth is about 4.5 billion years old.

- Fossils are evidence of ancient life. Fossils provide clues about the history and past climates of Earth, and about the plants and animals that lived long ago. Fossil fuels may have been created from the soft parts of ancient plants and animals.

Understanding Key Concepts

1. In your notebook, copy and complete the concept map below:

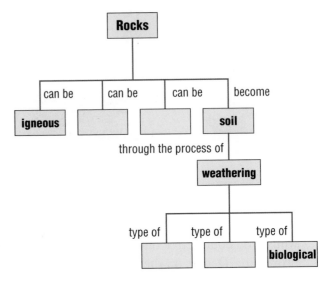

2. What hardness does a mineral have if it cannot be scratched by glass, but it can scratch an iron nail?

3. Use cardboard to make three-dimensional models of each major crystal shape.

4. Here are four answers to four different questions:

   Alfred Wegener

   J. Tuzo Wilson

   plate tectonics

   convection currents

   Write a question for each answer.

5. In your notebook, copy and complete the following concept map about Earth's crust.

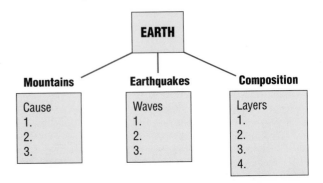

Developing Skills

6. Examine the rocks in your neighbourhood. Are they mostly from one rock family, or are all three families represented? What might be the reasons for finding more of one type than another?

7. Investigate the effects of erosion and sedimentation in your geographic area. Find examples of all three types of weathering. Describe the effects of glaciation.

8. Describe how convection currents have changed the surface of Earth.

9. What information might a geologist discover by examining strata? How does the principle of superposition help a geologist understand rock layers?

10. Carbon-14 has a half-life of 5730 years. In a fossil which had 40 g of parent material, 5 g of the carbon-14 is left. About how old is the fossil? Explain how you got your answer.

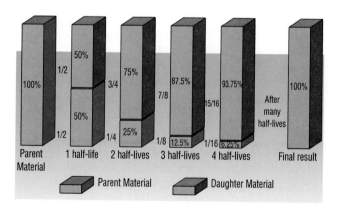

11. Give two examples of gradual change. Explain their causes. Give two examples of sudden change. Explain their causes.

Problem Solving/Applying

12. Could you find a fossil in an igneous rock? Why or why not?

13. If all you had to use was a piece of paper, a steel knife, and a glass bottle, how could you tell the difference between calcite and quartz? What other test would help you identify calcite?

14. Use the rock cycle to explain why pieces of granite and slate can be found in the same piece of conglomerate.

15. Suppose you were given two rocks to classify. Rock A was formed deep underground and was found at the surface. Rock B was found in an underground mine but was formed at the surface. Write a paragraph about each rock. Identify the family to which each belongs. Speculate how each might have been formed and moved to its new location.

16. Draw a sketch of a meandering river. Imagine you are planning to build three hotels in the river valley. Where would you place them? Mark their locations on your sketch, then show where you think the river will be in 50 years and in 100 years.

17. Read the newspaper excerpt below, and answer these questions:

(a) What inaccuracy does this article contain?

(b) Aside from its greater strength, why do you think the Kobe earthquake killed thousands of people, while the earthquake described in this article killed only about 60 people?

Adapted from *Winnipeg Free Press*, May 23, 1998

About 60 people were killed, many as they slept, during an earthquake in central Bolivia yesterday. A 5.9 magnitude quake struck, followed by a second one, 13 min later, with a magnitude of 6.8. The epicentre was 89 km below Earth's surface. Repeated aftershocks—up to 150 in the first 12 h alone—sent panicked residents fleeing any buildings left standing. About 30 000 people, mostly farmers, live in the area hit by the quakes. Eighty percent of houses in the community where the earthquake struck were destroyed, the hospital roof caved in, and a landslide blocked access to the town. Reports indicate that the town was almost wiped out. People gathered in main plazas after the jolts, fearing the aftershocks would bring down more buildings. Streets were cleared of rubble by tractors so that workers could assist the injured and homeless.

18. You have just discovered a fossil common to your province in the ground at a construction site. How will you find out how old the fossil is? What does the age tell you about the ground where it was found? What can you infer about the ancient climate and environment of the province?

19. Suppose you were studying fossils from a specific location and era. You notice that all the creatures had shells. Could you conclude that there were no worms living at that time and place? Explain your answer.

20. Copy this chart in your notebook. For each topic choose one question that you would like to investigate. Write each question next to its topic.

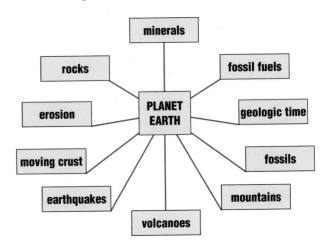

Critical Thinking

21. Why do you think some igneous rocks have holes or air spaces? Do you think such rocks are likely to be intrusive or extrusive? Explain why.

22. How can water be a factor in both mechanical and chemical weathering?

23. Laser beams are used to measure plate movement. How would they need to be set up and monitored?

24. What is the relationship between the locations of earthquakes, volcanoes, and mountain ranges? Which parts of the world have all three?

25. Research in newspapers, magazines, or on the Internet to find an article about an earthquake or volcano. Write a summary of the article to share with the class. Identify three questions that the article did not answer.

26. Imagine that you are designing a display showing dinosaurs in their environment. Why would you not include any models of humans in the display? How would you explain this to the museum staff?

27. Many trilobite fossils are found in Alberta. What does this tell you about Alberta's past?

28. What are three questions that scientists have not yet been able to answer about Earth's past? Why is each question difficult to answer? Predict the answer for each question. Support your predictions with evidence.

29. Reverse crossword puzzle. This is a completed crossword puzzle about Earth's crust. Your challenge is to write the clues. Remember to classify your clues as "Across" and "Down" and to number each.

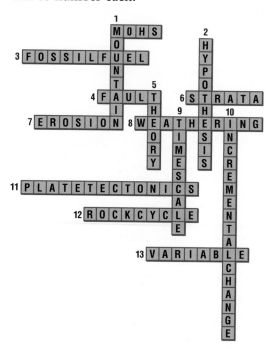

30. Like water wells, oil wells use pumps to bring the underground liquid up to the surface. Pumping petroleum is not as easy as pumping water because the oil is a very thick liquid. It is found in small, sponge-like pores of underground rock. The diagram below shows how petroleum is brought up to the surface.

Examine the diagram and answer the following questions

(a) How many pumps are lifting oil up to the surface?

(b) Which pump is lifting oil up to the surface?

(c) What is the other pump doing? Explain how it helps to separate the oil from the rock.

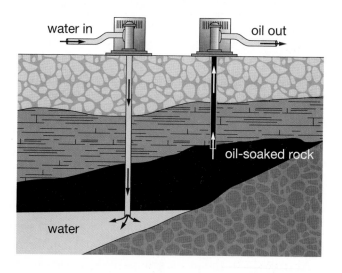

Pause&
Reflect

Look back to the Focussing Questions at the beginning of Planet Earth on page 352. Record your answers to the three questions in your Science Log. How does the new information you've learned in this unit connect with your previous understanding? What new questions do you now have about Earth's Crust? How could you find the answers?

Classifying Living Things

Over 2000 years ago, the Greek philosopher Aristotle developed a system of classification that grouped organisms according to whether they were plant or animal. Scientists used Aristotle's system for hundreds of years. As they discovered more and more living things, the system did not work well because it did not show probable relationships between similar organisms.

In 1735, Carolus Linnaeus produced a new system that also classified all organisms as plant or animal. This new system was, however, very different in other ways from Aristotle's system.

Linnaeus' system gives a two-word name to each type of organism. This system of naming organisms is still in use today. The two-word name is called the organism's scientific name, and it is given in Latin, a language that is no longer spoken. The first word of the organism's name is its genus, and the second word is its specific name. A **genus** is a group of species that are related. A **species** is the smaller, more limiting classification grouping. A species name includes both the genus name and specific name. For example, the bobcat shown above on the left and the Canada lynx shown on the right are members of the same genus, *Lynx*. The bobcat, however, is the species *Lynx rufus*, whereas the lynx is the species *Lynx canadensis*.

By the 1900s, scientists had discovered a great diversity of organisms on Earth. Separating organisms into only two main groups or **kingdoms**, plant and animal, began to seem inadequate. For example, bacteria are just too different from either plants or animals to be grouped with either. Similarly, fungi such as bread mould, yeast, and the many kinds of mushrooms are very different from plants and animals. In 1969, Robert Whittaker proposed a system that classifies organisms into five different kingdoms. The illustrated table on the next page shows the major groups of organisms and their kingdoms.

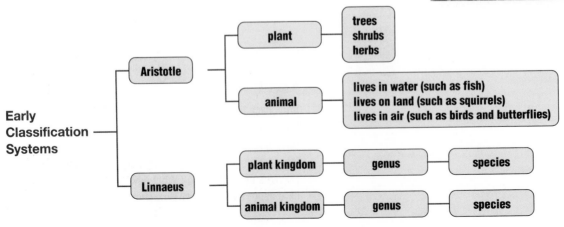

All Living Things

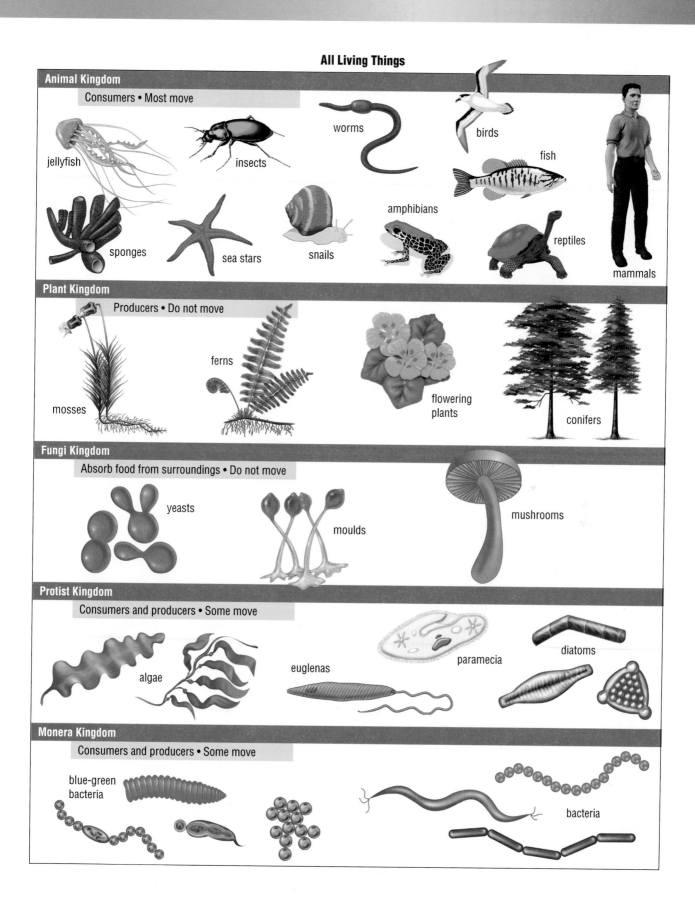

Animal Kingdom

Consumers • Most move

jellyfish
insects
worms
birds
fish
sponges
sea stars
snails
amphibians
reptiles
mammals

Plant Kingdom

Producers • Do not move

mosses
ferns
flowering plants
conifers

Fungi Kingdom

Absorb food from surroundings • Do not move

yeasts
moulds
mushrooms

Protist Kingdom

Consumers and producers • Some move

algae
euglenas
paramecia
diatoms

Monera Kingdom

Consumers and producers • Some move

blue-green bacteria
bacteria

Science Skills Guide

SAFETY SYMBOLS

The following safety symbols are used in the **SCIENCEFOCUS** 7 program to alert you to possible dangers. Be sure that you understand each symbol you see in an activity or investigation before you begin.

	Disposal Alert This symbol appears when care must be taken to dispose of materials properly.
	Fire Safety This symbol appears when care should be taken around open flames.
	Thermal Safety This symbol appears as a reminder to use caution when handling hot objects.
	Sharp Object Safety This symbol appears when a danger of cuts or punctures caused by the use of sharp objects exists.
	Electrical Safety This symbol appears when care should be taken when using electrical equipment.
	Skin Protection Safety This symbol appears when use of caustic chemicals might irritate the skin or when contact with micro-organisms might transmit infection.
	Clothing Protection Safety A lab apron should be worn when this symbol appears.
	Eye Safety This symbol appears when a danger to the eyes exists. Safety goggles should be worn when this symbol appears.
	Poison Safety This symbol appears when poisonous substances are used.
	Chemical Safety This symbol appears when chemicals that are used can cause burns or are poisonous if absorbed through the skin.
	Animal Safety This symbol appears whenever live animals are studied, and the safety of the animals and the students must be ensured.

WHMIS (Workplace Hazardous Materials Information System)

Look carefully at the WHMIS (Workplace Hazardous Materials Information System) safety symbols that are shown below. The WHMIS symbols are used throughout Canada to identify the dangerous materials that are found in all workplaces, including schools. Make sure that you understand what these symbols mean. When you see these symbols on containers in your classroom, at home, or in a workplace, use safety precautions.

Compressed Gas	Flammable and Combustible Material
Oxidizing Material	Corrosive Material
Poisonous and Infectious Material Causing Immediate and Serious Toxic Effects	Poisonous and Infectious Material Causing Other Toxic Effects
Biohazardous Infectious	Dangerously Reactive

Instant Practice

1. Find four of the **SCIENCEFOCUS** 7 safety symbols in activities or investigations in this textbook. Record the page number and title of the investigation or activity in which you found each symbol. What possible dangers that relate to the symbol are in the activity or investigation?

2. Find two of the WHMIS symbols on containers in your school, or ask your parent or guardian to look for two WHMIS symbols in a workplace. Record the name of the substance on each container and the place where you, or your parent or guardian, saw the container stored. What dangers are associated with the substance in each container?

USING YOUR TEXTBOOK AS A STUDY TOOL

SCIENCEFOCUS 7 contains a lot of useful information. It can help you to add to what you already know and to identify areas of inquiry that you might like to learn more about. How can you read your textbook effectively in order to help you accomplish these goals? This *Skill Focus* will give you some ideas that will help you better remember what you read.

Organizing the Information in Your Textbook

Read all of the suggestions presented here. Use the learning methods that work for you, but try others as well.

1. When you are starting a new unit, read the *Unit Contents*, the *Focussing Questions*, and the Topic cluster descriptions beside each photograph on the Unit Preview page. Think about how the ideas fit into the "big picture" or main theme of the unit. Try to predict some ideas you might learn about in each Topic cluster. Write some of your own questions about each Topic.

2. Try rewriting the Topic headings and subheadings as questions. Then look for the answer to each question as you read.

3. Think about what you are reading, and write brief notes to help you remember the information in each paragraph.

4. Look at the sample page shown above. It provides an example of how you can arrange your own notes as you work through the text.

Using Your Textbook Visuals

As you read, look at any photographs, illustrations, or graphs that appear on the page. Think about the information each visual provides, and note how it helps you to understand the ideas presented in the text. Visuals often help clarify

Unit 5: Planet Earth

Unit Introduction: Main Idea
Scientists have observed and developed theories about the forces beneath Earth's crust and mantle that have changed and shaped the crust over millions of years.

Topic Titles:
Topic 1 Minerals
Topic 2 Rocks and the Rock Cycle
Topic 3 Erosion
Topic 4 The Moving Crust
Topic 5 Earthquakes
Topic 6 Volcanoes
Topic 7 Mountains
Topic 8 Fossils
Topic 9 Geologic Time
Topic 10 Fossil Fuels

Topic 1, introduction

Main Idea
Rock is made of minerals, most of which are rare.

Other Ideas
- Quartz and mica are common
- A mineral an be an element or a compound.
- Properties of minerals help us to identify them.
- Friedrich Mohs developed the Mohs hardness scale. It can be used to compare objects according to hardness value.
- Other properties, such as crystal structure, also help to identify minerals.

Heading: The Mohs Hardness Scale

A substance's "scratchability" can be used to identify it.

Heading: Other Clues to Mineral Identification

Lustre is a way of identifying minerals.

- Minerals can be shiny or dull.

or provide examples of these ideas. For example, look closely at the illustration below. What information does it give you?

Also look at any terms that are in bold (dark, heavy) type. You will find it helpful to pay special attention to these terms. They provide important definitions that you will need in order to understand and write about the information in the chapter. Each boldfaced term appears in the *Glossary* at the back of this book.

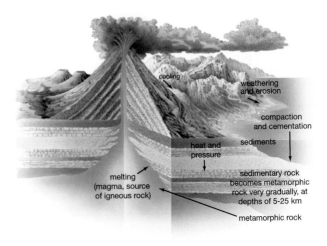

The rock cycle

Making Sure You Understand

At the end of every Topic and every Topic cluster, you will find review questions. These questions are designed to help you reinforce your learning of the main ideas. If you are unable to answer them, reread the text to find the answers.

Instant Practice

1. Go to the unit your teacher has told you that you will be studying, and try method number 1, on page 446.

2. In the first Topic of the unit, try method number 2.

3. Look for boldfaced terms in the first section of the first Topic of the unit. Record the terms and their meanings.

Graphic Organizers

A good way to organize the information you are learning is to use a **graphic organizer**. One kind of graphic organizer that you will find useful is a **concept map**. A concept map is a diagram that represents visually how ideas and terms are related. It can help you to clarify the meanings of the ideas and terms, and better understand what you are studying.

The following concept map is known as a **network tree**. Notice how some words are enclosed while others are written on connecting lines. The enclosed words are the main ideas or concepts. The lines in the map link related concepts, and the words that are written on the lines describe relationships between the concepts.

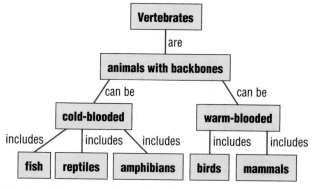

A network tree concept map showing the groups of animals with backbones.

As you learn more about a Topic, your concept map will grow and change. Concept maps are just another tool for you to use. There is no single "correct" concept map. Your map is a record of your thinking and it shows the connections that make sense to you. Make your map as neat and clear as possible, and be sure that you have good reasons for suggesting the connections between concepts.

Although your map may contain many of the same concepts as other students' maps, the concepts on your map may be recorded and linked differently. You can use your map for study and review. You can refer to it when you want to recall concepts and relationships. At a later date, you can use your map to see what you have learned and how your ideas have changed.

An **events chain concept map** describes ideas in order. In science, an events chain can be used to describe a sequence of events, the steps in a procedure, or the stages of a process. When making an events chain, you first need to find the one event that starts the chain. This event is called the initiating event. Then you find the next event in the chain and continue until you reach an outcome or final result. Here is an events chain concept map that shows the events you might go through in a typical morning.

An events chain map of a typical morning routine

A **cycle concept map** is a special type of events chain concept map. In a cycle concept map, the series of events does not produce a final outcome. A cycle concept map has no beginning and no end. To construct a cycle map, you first decide on a starting point, and then you list each important event in order. Since there is no outcome and the last event relates back to the first event, the cycle repeats itself. Look at the cycle concept map showing the stages of life that a frog goes through.

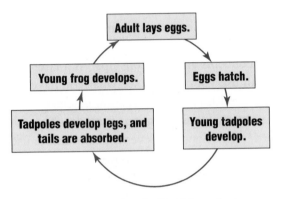

A cycle concept map showing the life history of a frog

A **spider map** is a concept map that can be useful for brainstorming. You may have a central idea and several associated concepts, but they may not be directly related to each other. By placing these associated ideas outside the main concept, you can begin to group these ideas so that their relationships become easier to understand. Examine the following spider map showing what happens when light strikes an object.

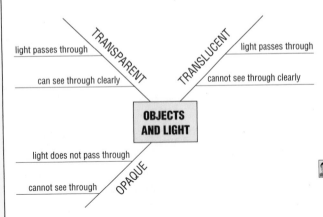

A spider concept map showing what happens when light strikes three different objects

Comparing and contrasting is another way to help solidify your learning. When you compare, you look for similarities between two things. When you contrast, you look for differences. Thus you can compare and contrast by listing ways in which two things are similar and ways in which they are different. You can also use a graphic organizer called a **Venn diagram**, as shown below.

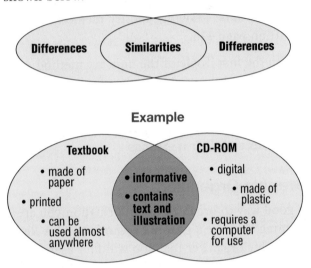

A Venn diagram is a useful tool to help you show similarities and differences.

Instant Practice

1. The following words are out of order: hockey, team sports, ice, diamond, field, bat, puck, hardball, cleats, ice skates, baseball, cleats, soccer ball, stick, soccer, feet. Use these words to produce a network tree concept map.

2. Produce an events chain concept map that starts with lunch and ends with your return home from school.

3. Produce a cycle concept map using the following words: summer, winter, fall, spring.

4. Make a Venn diagram to compare and contrast a CD and a cassette tape.

5. In a group, create a spider map based on one of the following topics:

   (a) food and nutrition
   (b) music
   (c) scientific discoveries
   (d) communication

HOW TO USE A SCIENCE LOG/SCIENCE JOURNAL

Scientists keep logs — detailed records — of their observations, new data, and new ideas. You can keep a *Science Log* (or *Science Journal*) to help you organize your thinking.

In it, you can record what you already know about a Topic and add to this information as you learn more. Your teacher might ask you to keep a *Science Log* or *Science Journal* as a special booklet or as a marked-off section of your science notebook. Whichever approach your teacher takes, you will find that writing about new ideas as you learn them will help you understand them better.

It is useful to consider what you already know about a new subject area. You may be surprised to find out that you know more than you realized. On the other hand, you may realize that new material needs special attention because you do not know very much about it. The value of a *Science Log* or *Science Journal* is that you find out for yourself how clear (or unclear) your understanding is. You do not have to wait until your teacher assesses your understanding through a formal test or examination.

SCIENCEFOCUS 7 makes sure that you can add to your *Science Log* effectively. For example, each unit begins with a set of *Focussing Questions*.

- How do you use energy every day?

- What happens to materials when they are heated?

- How can we reduce the amount of energy we use?

Can you answer any of these questions from your previous studies? You can write your answers, draw a sketch, or use whatever ways you

find best to explain what you know. Also, feel free to record that you know very little about any of these questions. This will help you focus on some of the things you need to learn as you read through the unit.

Pause & Reflect

Imagine that you have been chosen to be interviewed by the education reporter for a local newspaper or radio station. The reporter wants an explanation, in your own words, of what your class has been studying in science for the past few weeks, and why this knowledge is useful in everyday life. There is space for a paragraph of about 150 words. In your Science Log, write what you would say.

Throughout each unit, *Pause & Reflect* features keep you thinking about what you have learned. These features are designed to help you make connections between ideas and organize your thoughts. Your teacher may ask you to use all these features regularly to record your new knowledge. On the other hand, your teacher may leave it up to you to decide how often you want to use them.

The final item in each Unit Review is a *Pause & Reflect* feature that asks you to look at your original answers to the *Focussing Questions* at the beginning of the unit, and to write new answers to these questions. You may be amazed at how much your answers have changed, based on what you have learned by studying the unit.

Here are some entries that you might want to include in your *Science Log/Science Journal*.

- questions that you would like to be able to answer

- sketches and notes about models and processes in science
- graphic organizers (see Skill Focus 2 for a few examples)
- your thoughts on what is difficult for you, and your ideas on what you can do to overcome any barriers you have when learning new information
- notes about interesting items in the news that involve a Topic and that spark more questions or new answers to existing questions
- profiles of leading Canadian scientists or technologists that you learn about in the media
- profiles of careers related to science and technology that you find interesting
- connections among science and other subject areas that occur to you in the course of your learning

Your *Science Log/Science Journal* will help you become a better learner, so take the time to make entries on a regular basis.

Instant Practice

1. A balloon filled with helium will rise in the air, but a balloon that you blow up yourself will sink. Scientific investigation can help answer why one balloon rises and the other sinks. Think about some of the questions you would need to ask to help you find out about the way the balloons behave. Record your questions and then exchange your set of questions with a classmate so that each of you can start your own *Science Log/Science Journal* using these questions.

2. Find and read a newspaper article that deals with technology. Write a short summary of the article in your *Science Log/Science Journal*. After you have done this, record why the subject of the article makes you think the article is about technology. Is science involved, as well? If so, record how it is connected to technology.

3. What area of science or technology are you most interested in? Record why you might like to pursue a career in this scientific or technological field. Write down three issues or problems facing society that you could help deal with by following such a career. For each issue, record how your chosen field can contribute to a solution or improvement.

UNITS OF MEASUREMENT

Throughout history, groups of people have developed their own systems of numbering and units. When different groups of people began to communicate with each other, they discovered that their units of measurement were not the same, which caused confusion. For example, imagine trying to report your height in ells and your weight in scruples, or going out to "buy a hogshead of strawberries!" Even the "foot" as a measurement took a long time to standardize.

For consistency, scientists throughout the world have agreed to use the same system of measurement, the metric system of numbers and units. The metric system is also the official system of measurement in Canada.

The Metric System

The word "metric" comes from the Greek word, *metron*, which means "measure." The **metric system** is based on multiples of ten. For example, the basic unit of length is the metre. All larger units of length are expressed in units based on metres multiplied by 10, 100, 1000, or more. Smaller units of length are expressed in units based on metres divided by 10, 100, 1000, or more. Each multiple of ten has its own prefix (a word joined to the beginning of another word). For example, *kilo-* means multiplied by 1000. Thus, one kilometre is one thousand metres.

$$1 \text{ km} = 1000 \text{ m}$$

The prefix *centi-* means divided by 100. Thus, one centimetre is one one-hundredth of a metre.

$$1 \text{ cm} = \frac{1}{100} \text{ m}$$

The prefix *milli-* means divided by one thousand. Thus, one millimetre is one one-thousandth of a metre.

$$1 \text{ mm} = \frac{1}{1000} \text{ m}$$

In the metric system, the same prefixes are used for nearly all types of measure, such as mass, weight, area, and energy. The following table lists the most commonly used metric prefixes.

Commonly Used Metric Prefixes

Prefixes	Symbol	Relationship to the base unit
giga-	G	1 000 000 000
mega-	M	1 000 000
kilo-	k	1 000
hecto-	h	100
deca-	da	10
–	–	1
deci-	d	0.1
centi-	c	0.01
milli-	m	0.001
micro-	μ	0.000 001
nano-	n	0.000 000 001

(**Note:** Time does not have a metric form of measure. Time is still measured in seconds, minutes, and hours. There are 60 s in 1 min, 60 min in 1 h, and 24 h in 1 d.)

Example 1

The length of Canada's longest river, the Mackenzie River, is 4241 km. How many metres is this distance?

Solution

$$4241 \text{ km} = ? \text{ m}$$
$$1 \text{ km} = 1000 \text{ m}$$
$$4241 \times \frac{1000 \text{ m}}{1} = 4\ 241\ 000 \text{ m}$$

Example 2

There are 250 g of rice in a package. Express this mass in kilograms.

Solution

$$1 \text{ kg} = 1000 \text{ g}$$
$$250 \times \frac{1 \text{ kg}}{1000} = 0.250 \text{ kg}$$

You are probably most familiar with the units for length and mass. As you continue in your science courses, you will learn about other quantities of measurement. The following table lists most of the frequently used metric quantities that you will encounter in this course.

Frequently Used Metric Quantities, Units, and Symbols		
Quantity	**Unit**	**Symbol**
length	nanometre	nm
	micrometre	μm
	millimetre	mm
	centimetre	cm
	metre	m
	kilometre	km
mass	gram	g
	kilogram	kg
	tonne	t
area	square centimetre	cm^2
	square metre	m^2
	hectare	ha
volume	cubic centimetre	cm^3
	cubic metre	m^3
	millilitre	mL
	litre	L
time	second	s
temperature	degree Celsius	°C
force	newton	N
energy	joule	J
	kilojoule	kJ

Instant Practice

1. A can contains 0.355 L of pop. How many millilitres does the can contain?

2. The height of a table is 0.75 m. How high is the table in centimetres?

3. A package of chocolate-chip cookies has a mass of 396 g. What is the mass of the cookies in milligrams?

4. One cup of water contains 250 mL. What is the volume of one cup of water in litres?

5. The distance from your kitchen to the front door is 6000 mm. How far is the front door in metres?

6. A student added 0.0025 L of lemon juice to water. How much lemon juice did the student add in millilitres?

SI Units

In science classes, you will often be asked to report your measurements in **SI** units. The term SI is taken from the French name *Le Système international d'unités*. In SI, the base unit of mass is the kilogram, the base unit of length is the metre, and the base unit of time is the second.

Example 1

Convert 426 cm to the SI base unit.

Solution

The SI base unit of length is the metre.

$$1 \text{ m} = 100 \text{ cm}$$
$$426 \times \frac{1 \text{ m}}{100} = 0.426 \text{ m}$$

Example 2

Convert 1.7 h to the SI base unit.

Solution

The SI base unit of time is the second.

1 min = 60 s
1 h = 60 min
Therefore, $1.7 \times 60 \times 60 \text{ s} = 6120 \text{ s}$

Instant Practice

Convert the following quantities to the SI base unit.

1. 7.02 g

2. 32 min

3. 8.13 km

4. 25 961 mm

5. 223 625 cm

6. 3.25 h

ESTIMATING AND MEASURING

Estimating

How long is your pen or pencil? How much time does it take you to return home from school? What is the width of your desk? You could probably answer all of these questions fairly quickly by estimating — making an informed judgment about a measurement. The estimate gives you an idea of the measure, but it is not totally accurate. Scientists also make estimates of measurements when exact numbers are not essential.

It is useful to be able to estimate as accurately as possible. For example, suppose that you want to know how many words are in your textbook. Counting every word on every page would be very time-consuming and unnecessary. Instead, you can count the number of words on one page of your textbook. Then you multiply this number by the total number of pages to find an estimate of the total number of words in the book.

Instant Practice

1. An African elephant has a mass of about 7500 kg. Students in your class have an average mass of about 45 kg. Estimate the number of students it will take to equal the elephant in mass. Calculate the exact number to see how close your estimate was.

2. The greatest distance across Canada is 5514 km. A jet airliner flies about 600 km per hour. Estimate how long it takes for the jet to fly across Canada. Calculate the time to see how close your estimate was.

3. A 1000 mL (1 L) jar is filled with candies. How can you make a good estimate of the number of candies in the jar?
   (a) Decide how you can use a 100 mL container and a small amount of candies to estimate the number of candies in the larger jar.
   (b) Carry out your plan.
   (c) Compare your results with those of two or three classmates.
   (d) About how many candies will a 0.5 L container hold? About how many will a 2 L container hold?

Measuring Length

You can use a metre stick or ruler to measure short distances. Metre sticks and rulers are usually marked off in millimetres and/or centimetres. You place the zero mark of the metre stick or ruler at one end of the distance to be measured and read the length at the other end.

Instant Practice

Use a ruler to measure the distance between the following points: A and D; C and E; B and F.

A •   • B

        • C   • E   • D

                • F

Measuring Area

Area refers to the amount of surface of an object. For example, you may want to know the area of a piece of paper, a rock, or even a shirt. Area is reported in square units, such as cm². When you want to calculate an area, you can use length measurements. For a square or a rectangle, you find the area by multiplying the length by the width.

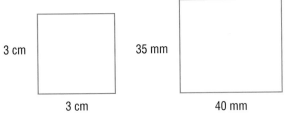

3 cm

3 cm

35 mm

40 mm

Area of square is 3 cm × 3 cm = 9 cm².
Area of rectangle is 35 mm × 40 mm = 1400 mm².

Instant Practice

Imagine that you are in charge of an art project that will transform one wall of your classroom into a large mural to show a diversity of materials. You may use as many different kinds of materials as you like, but each piece must be a 30 cm × 30 cm square. How many squares will you need to make your mural?

1. First decide what unit of measurement will be most practical for the area of the mural. Why would you not choose to measure the area in mm²?

2. Measure the height and the width of the wall you will cover.

3. Calculate the area of the wall in the measurement you have selected.

4. Calculate how many 30 cm × 30 cm squares you will need to fill 1 m².

5. Multiply this number by the area of the wall in m².

Make sure that you always use the same units — if you mix centimetres and metres, your calculations will be wrong. Remember to ask yourself if your answer is reasonable. (You could make an estimate to check it.)

Measuring Volume

The **volume** of an object is the amount of space that the object occupies. Why would you want to know volume? Think of an example, from your own experience, when knowing the volume of an object is useful. Did cooking or baking come to mind?

There are several ways of measuring volume, depending on the kind of object you want to measure. A cubic metre is the space occupied by a cube 1 m × 1 m × 1 m. This unit of volume is used to measure large quantities, such as the volume of concrete in a building. In this course, you are more likely to use cubic centimetres (cm³) or cubic millimetres (mm³) to record the volume of a solid object. You can calculate the volume of a cube by multiplying the length of its sides. For example:

Volume = 1 cm × 1 cm × 1 cm = 1 cm³

You can calculate the volume of a rectangular solid if you know its length, width, and height.

Volume = length × width × height

The units that are used to measure the volume of a solid are called **cubic units**. If all the sides are measured in millimetres (mm), the volume will be in cubic millimetres (mm³). If all the sides are measured in centimetres (cm), the volume will be in cubic centimetres (cm³).

The units that are used to measure the volume of a liquid are called **capacity units**. The basic unit of volume for liquids is the litre (L). In this course, you also measure volume using millilitres (mL). Recall that 1 L = 1000 mL. You have probably seen the capacity of juice, milk, and soft drink containers given in litres and millilitres.

Cubic units and capacity units are interchangeable. For example:
$1 \text{ cm}^3 = 1 \text{ mL}$
$1 \text{ dm}^3 = 1 \text{ L}$
$1 \text{ m}^3 = 1 \text{ kL}$

As you can see in the diagrams below, the volume of a regularly shaped solid object can be measured directly.

$3 \text{ cm} \times 3 \text{ cm} \times 3 \text{ cm} = 27 \text{ cm}^3$ $4 \text{ cm} \times 6 \text{ cm} \times 2 \text{ cm} = 48 \text{ cm}^3$

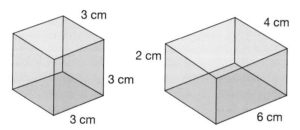

Measuring the volume of regularly shaped solids

The volume of a liquid can also be measured directly with a graduated cylinder, as shown below. Make sure that you measure to the bottom of the **meniscus**: the slight curve where the liquid touches the sides of the container. To measure accurately, make sure that your eye is at the same level as the bottom of the meniscus.

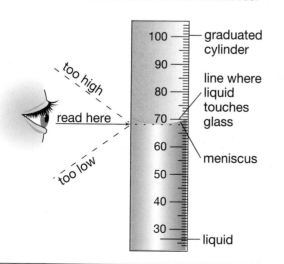

The volume of an irregularly shaped solid object must be measured indirectly. You need to find out the volume of liquid that the object will displace. As shown here, the volume of liquid that is displaced is equal to the volume of the object.

1 Record the volume of the liquid.

2 Carefully lower the object into the cylinder containing the liquid. Record the volume again.

The volume of the object is equal to the difference between the two volumes, e.g.:

Volume of object = Volume of water with object – Original volume of water
= 85 mL – 60 mL
= 25 mL

3

Measuring the volume of an irregularly shaped solid

Take a reading from the bottom of the meniscus with your line of sight at the level of the meniscus.

Instant Practice

1. Write an explanation of how to find the volume of an irregularly shaped solid.

2. Read the volume indicated by each graduated cylinder below.

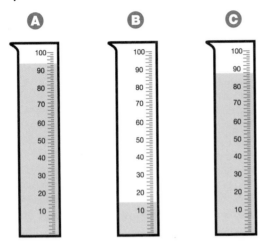

3. Determine the volume of a series of objects using the method of water displacement. Try to use objects that are different in shape and made of different materials, such as a pebble, a marble, and a coin.

Measuring Mass

Is your backpack heavier than your friend's backpack? This can be difficult to check by holding a backpack in each hand. You need a way to measure mass accurately. The **mass** of an object is the measure of the amount of material that makes up the object. Mass is measured in milligrams, grams, kilograms, and tonnes.

A balance is used for measuring mass. A triple beam balance, such as the one shown here, is commonly used. To measure the mass of a solid object, follow these steps:

1. Set the balance to zero. Do this by sliding all three riders back to their zero points. Using the adjusting screw, make sure that the pointer swings an equal amount above and below the zero point at the far end of the balance.

2. Place the object on the pan. Observe what happens to the pointer.

3. Slide the largest rider along until the pointer is just below zero. Then move the rider back one notch.

4. Repeat with the middle rider and then with the smallest rider. Adjust the smallest rider until the pointer swings equally above and below zero again.

5. Add the readings on the three scales to find the mass.

What if you add a quantity of a substance, such as sugar, to a beaker? How would you know the mass of the substance? First you find out the mass of the beaker, as shown. Then you pour the sugar into the beaker and measure the mass of the beaker and sugar together. Subtract the mass of the beaker from the mass of the beaker and sugar together. This gives you the mass of the sugar.

Mass of sugar = Mass of sugar and beaker together – Mass of beaker

The mass of the empty beaker is 61.5 g.

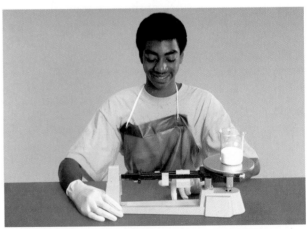

The mass of the sugar and beaker together is 161.5 g.
The mass of the sugar equals the mass of the sugar and beaker together minus the mass of the beaker (161.5 g – 61.5 g = 100 g).

Instant Practice

1. Which takes more "muscle" to carry, your favourite paperback book or a calculator? Find out by using a balance to compare their masses.

2. Write the steps you would take to find the mass of the contents of a glass of pop.

Measuring Temperature

"Temperature" is a measure of the thermal energy of the particles of a substance. In the very simplest terms, you can think of temperature as a measure of how hot or how cold something is. The temperature of a material is measured with a thermometer.

For most scientific work, temperature is measured on the Celsius scale. On this scale, the freezing point of water is zero degrees (0°C), and the boiling point of water is one hundred degrees (100°C). Between these points, the scale is divided into 100 equal divisions. Each division represents 1 degree Celsius. On the Celsius scale, average human body temperature is 37°C, and a typical room temperature may be between 20°C and 25°C.

The SI unit of temperature is the Kelvin (K). Zero on the Kelvin scale (0 K) is the coldest possible temperature. This temperature is also known as absolute zero. It is equivalent to –273°C, which is 273 degrees below the freezing point of water. Notice that degree symbols are not used with the Kelvin scale.

Most laboratory thermometers are marked only with the Celsius scale. Because the divisions on the two scales are the same size, the Kelvin temperature can be found by adding 273 to the Celsius reading. Thus, on the Kelvin scale, water freezes at 273 K and boils at 373 K.

Tips for Using a Thermometer

When using a thermometer to measure the temperature of a substance, here are three important tips to remember:

- Handle the thermometer extremely carefully. It is made of glass and can break easily.
- Do not use the thermometer as a stirring rod.
- Do not let the bulb of the thermometer touch the walls of the container.

Celsius thermometer

Instant Practice

Your teacher will supply your class with three large containers of water, each at a different temperature.

1. Twelve students will each be provided with a thermometer. When your teacher says "now," the students will take temperature readings of the water in the different containers. Four students will be asked to take a temperature reading of the water in one container. Four others will take the temperature reading of the water in the second container, and four others will take a reading of the water in the third container. Each student should keep the temperature reading a secret until putting it on a class chart.

2. Make a class chart on the chalkboard to record each of the students' temperature readings. The three columns will be:

Container 1 Temperature Reading (°C)	Container 2 Temperature Reading (°C)	Container 3 Temperature Reading (°C)

3. Each student will record the temperature reading of the water in the container used.

4. Did each person get the same temperature reading of the water in the same container? If the temperature readings were not all the same, explain why you think this might be so.

SCIENTIFIC INQUIRY

"What happened to that puddle of water that was here a while ago?" You could probably quickly answer that question, but for an early scientist, it might have been more difficult. If you were that early scientist, how might you go about answering that question?

First, you might **observe** what happens to some other puddles. You would watch them closely until they disappeared and **record** what you observed.

One observation you might make is, "The puddle is almost all gone." If you did, you would be making a **qualitative observation**, an observation in which numbers are not used. A little later, you might also say, "It took five hours for the puddle to disappear completely." You have made a **quantitative observation**, an observation that uses numbers.

Instant Practice

In your notebook, copy the observations below. Beside each, write "Qual" if you think it's a qualitative observation and "Quan" if you think it's a quantitative observation.

(a) an armful of flowers

12 carnations

(b) 40 L of gasoline

a tankful of gas

(c) It took all afternoon to do the investigation.

The investigation took 2 h and 45 min.

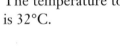

(d) It's so hot today.

The temperature today is 32°C.

(e) The mass of the books is 5 kg.

These books are really heavy.

(f) The park is 12 000 m².

We have a large park near our school.

As you made your observations, you might have noticed something interesting about the disappearance of the two puddles. (As a twenty-first-century science student, you already know that evaporation is the reason that the puddles are disappearing, but there are still lots of questions you can ask about evaporation.) Although the two puddles were the same size, one evaporated much more quickly than the other one did. Your quantitative observations tell you that one evaporated in 4 h, whereas the other one took 5 h. Your qualitative observations tell you that the one that evaporated more quickly was in the Sun. The one that evaporated more slowly was in the shade. You make the same observations about another pair of puddles. You now have a **question** to ask that you can investigate: Does water always evaporate more quickly in the Sun than in the shade? Now you are ready to make a **hypothesis**, a statement about an idea that you can test, based on your observations. Your test will involve comparing two things to find the relationship between them. You know that the Sun is a source of thermal energy, so you might use that knowledge to make this hypothesis: Evaporation from natural pools of water is faster for pools in sunlight than for pools in shade. (You will be comparing the effect of Sun and shade.)

As you prepare to make your observations, you can make a **prediction**, a forecast about what you expect to observe. In this case, you might predict that pools A, B, and C will dry up more quickly than pools X, Y, and Z.

"But wait a minute," you think, as you look again at your recorded observations. "There was a strong breeze blowing today. What effect might that have had?" This could become confusing, couldn't it? The breeze is one factor that could affect evaporation. The Sun is another factor that could affect evaporation. Scientists think about every possible factor that could affect tests they conduct. These factors are called **variables**. It is always important to test only one variable at a time. If you consider more than one variable in a test, you are not conducting a **fair test** (one that is valid and unbiased). Your results won't tell you anything useful. You won't know whether the breeze or the Sun made the water evaporate.

So, you need to control your variables. This means that you change only one at a time. The variable that you change is called the **manipulated variable**. In this case, the manipulated variable is the condition under which you observe the puddle (one variable would be adding thermal energy; another would be moving air across it).

According to your hypothesis, adding thermal energy will change the time it takes for the puddle to evaporate. The time in this case is called the **responding variable**. Often, experiments have a control. This is a test that you carry out with no variables, so that you can observe whether your manipulated variable does indeed cause a change. Look at the illustration on page 460 to see some examples of variables.

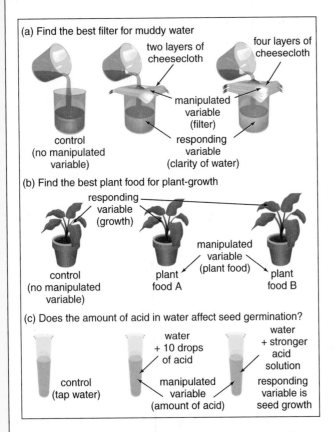

(a) Find the best filter for muddy water

two layers of cheesecloth

four layers of cheesecloth

manipulated variable (filter)

responding variable (clarity of water)

control (no manipulated variable)

(b) Find the best plant food for plant-growth

responding variable (growth)

manipulated variable (plant food)

control (no manipulated variable)

plant food A

plant food B

(c) Does the amount of acid in water affect seed germination?

water + 10 drops of acid

water + stronger acid solution

control (tap water)

manipulated variable (amount of acid)

responding variable is seed growth

As you have been reading, a question may have occurred to you: How is it possible to do a fair test on puddles? How can you be sure that they are the same size? In situations such as these, scientists often use **models**. A model can be a mental picture, a diagram, a working model, or even a mathematical expression. To make sure your test is fair, you can prepare model "puddles" that you know are all exactly the same.

Instant Practice

With a partner, examine the following illustration. In your notebook, write the letters of the "puddles" you would *not* use to set up a fair test. Explain why you would not use them.

Now, you can carry out your experiment. How many times will you do it, in order to be sure that you have truly tested your hypothesis? The test you are conducting is a simple one, but you still need to carry it out more than once.

Instant Practice

What kinds of errors can creep into a test such as the one described above? Use your sense of humour, and work with a partner to draw some sketches that illustrate some errors. Make sure they are errors that could actually occur!

Many investigations are much more complex than the one described here, and there are many more possibilities for error. That's why it's so important to keep careful qualitative and quantitative observations. After you have collected all your data, you are ready to analyze it and draw a **conclusion**. A conclusion is a statement that indicates whether your results support or do not support your hypothesis. If you had hypothesized that the addition of thermal energy would have no effect on the evaporation of water, your results would not support your hypothesis. A hypothesis gives you a place to start and helps you design your experiment. If your results do not support your hypothesis, you use what you have learned in the experiment to come up with a new hypothesis to test. Scientists often set up experiments without knowing what will happen. Sometimes they deliberately set out to prove that something will *not* happen.

Eventually, when a hypothesis has been thoroughly tested and nearly all scientists agree that the results support the hypothesis, it becomes a **theory**.

Whenever you have a task to do, it always helps if you can follow a process. If you look back over the boldface terms in these pages, you will see that you now have a process for designing investigations to try to find answers to scientific questions. Imagine comparing the speed at which moisture from two paper towels evaporates. The process you might follow can be seen in the student notes shown here:

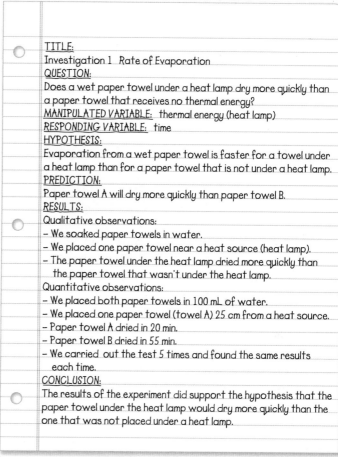

TITLE:
Investigation 1 Rate of Evaporation
QUESTION:
Does a wet paper towel under a heat lamp dry more quickly than a paper towel that receives no thermal energy?
MANIPULATED VARIABLE: thermal energy (heat lamp)
RESPONDING VARIABLE: time
HYPOTHESIS:
Evaporation from a wet paper towel is faster for a towel under a heat lamp than for a paper towel that is not under a heat lamp.
PREDICTION:
Paper towel A will dry more quickly than paper towel B.
RESULTS:
Qualitative observations:
- We soaked paper towels in water.
- We placed one paper towel near a heat source (heat lamp).
- The paper towel under the heat lamp dried more quickly than the paper towel that wasn't under the heat lamp.
Quantitative observations:
- We placed both paper towels in 100 mL of water.
- We placed one paper towel (towel A) 25 cm from a heat source.
- Paper towel A dried in 20 min.
- Paper towel B dried in 55 min.
- We carried out the test 5 times and found the same results each time.
CONCLUSION:
The results of the experiment did support the hypothesis that the paper towel under the heat lamp would dry more quickly than the one that was not placed under a heat lamp.

EVERY TIME WE HAVE ADDED THERMAL ENERGY TO WATER, IT HAS EVAPORATED MORE QUICKLY THAN WATER WITH NO THERMAL ENERGY ADDED.

I PROPOSE A THEORY THAT THE ADDITION OF THERMAL ENERGY INCREASES THE SPEED OF EVAPORATION OF WATER.

Now, try using this process to set up your own investigation.

Observing Glider Characteristics

In this investigation, you will use the concepts you have just learned about the process of science inquiry. You will identify and test the variables that affect the motion of a device called a "ring-wing glider." The steps in making a ring-wing glider are shown in the photographs below.

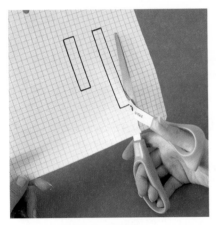

A Cut two strips of paper of different lengths from graph paper.

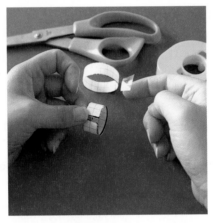

B Roll the strips of paper into loops and tape the ends together.

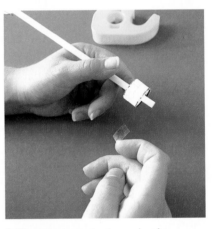

C Tape the loops to the ends of a drinking straw.

You have probably made many paper airplanes, but you may never have seen one that looked like a ring-wing glider. Find out what characteristics affect the motion of this type of glider. For example, how far apart should you position the small ring and the large ring? How does the width of the rings affect the flight? Does the glider fly better if the large ring or the small ring is in the front when you launch it? Should the straw be held at the top or the bottom when you fly the glider? Should you launch the glider rapidly or gently?

Question

How do changes in two different characteristics (variables) of the ring-wing glider affect its flight patterns?

Safety Precautions

Be careful when using sharp objects such as scissors.

Apparatus
pencil
scissors
ruler

Materials
non-bendable drinking straws
graph paper
transparent tape

Procedure

1. To collect some general information about the ring-wing glider, each member of the group can make his or her own glider. Choose a size and shape for your glider and assemble it.

2. The whole group should observe the flight of each glider to gather information. Hold the gliders in different positions to find out if one way of launching them works better than another.

3. As a group, choose two different characteristics (manipulated variables) to test. For each variable, formulate and write down a prediction about the effect of the variable on the flight of the glider. For example, "We predict that placing the rings closer together will make the glider fly farther."

4. For each of the two variables you selected, decide on a basic design for all the glider characteristics except the one you are going to test. (Remember, to carry out a fair test, you must change only one variable at a time.) For example, if you decided to test the diameter of the rings, then the width of the rings and the distance between the rings must remain constant (the same). As well, you must hold the gliders in the same position and launch them with the same speed and amount of force when testing their flight patterns.

5. For each variable you have chosen, build at least four gliders that have differences in the variable you are testing.

6. Fly your gliders. To make good comparisons, test each glider several times. Have several different group members test each glider. Observe the flight characteristics carefully. Write down qualitative data (descriptions of flight patterns) for each of the two variables you have tested.

Analyze

1. Was there a relationship between either of the variables that you tested and the distance that the glider flew? If so, describe the relationship in writing.

2. Was there a relationship between either of the variables that you tested and the smoothness of the flight pattern of the glider? If so, describe the relationship in writing.

Conclude and Apply

3. For each of the two characteristics that you tested, did your results support your hypothesis or not? Explain.

4. Write a summary statement that describes any relationships that you observed between the characteristics you tested and the flight patterns of the ring-wing glider. Submit your summary to your teacher.

SCIENTIFIC PROBLEM SOLVING

"Technology" — what does that word make you think of? Do you think of complicated electronic equipment? Do you think of the latest-model cars? Do you think of space exploration? Well, all of those have to do with technology, but think about this: Have you ever used a pencil to flip something out of a tight spot where your fingers couldn't reach? Have you ever used a stone to hammer "bases" or "goal posts" into the ground?

These, too, are examples of technology. **Technology** is the use of scientific knowledge, as well as everyday experience, to solve practical problems. You may not know why your pencil works as a lever or the physics behind levers, but your everyday experiences tell you how to use a lever successfully. Often, science has a part in technology, but not always.

When you used that pencil to move the small item you couldn't reach, you did so because you needed to move that item. In other words, you had identified a problem that needed to be solved. Clearly identifying a problem is a good first step in finding a solution. In the case of the lever, the solution was right before your eyes, but finding a solution isn't always quite so simple.

Think about the following problem.

Your school is soon to close for a 16-day winter holiday. You and other members of your science class have been experimenting with some cactus plants. They must stay in their present location. They need to be watered, but the soil must become dry between waterings or the roots will rot. What kinds of devices could you invent to solve this problem?

First, you need to identify the exact nature of the problem you have to solve. You could state it as follows:

Plants in their present location must receive water on a regular basis so that they stay alive over a certain period of time and do not become overwatered.

Now, how will you be able to assess how well your device works? You can't invent a device successfully unless you know what criteria (standards) it must meet. In other words, you must know the design specifications.

In this case, you could use the following as your criteria:

1. Device must water the plants in their present location.

2. Plants must be thriving at the end of the 16-day period.

3. Plants must be watered only when the soil is dry.

On your own, you might not come up with such a device. If you work with a team, however, each of you will have useful ideas to contribute.

You'll probably come up with something great! Like all other scientists, though, you will want to make use of information and devices that others have developed. Do some research and share your findings with your group. Can you modify someone else's idea? With your group, brainstorm some possible designs. How would they work? What materials would they require? How many parts are there that could stop working during the 16-day period? Make a clear, labelled drawing of each design, with an explanation of how it would work.

Examine all of your suggested designs carefully. Which do you think would work best? Why? Be prepared to share your choice and your reasons with your group. Listen carefully to what others have to say. When the group votes on the design that will be built, be prepared to co-operate fully, even if the group's choice is not your choice.

Get your teacher's approval of the drawing of the design your group wants to build. Then gather your materials and build a **prototype** (a model) of your design. Experiment with your design to answer some questions you might have about it. For example, your invention might require some tubing. Until you try it out, you may be unsure of the best kind of tubing to use. Would a drinking straw work? Would flexible plastic tubing work? Would glass tubing be the best choice? Keep careful, objective records of each of your tests and of any changes you make to your design.

You might find, too, that your invention always seems to fail in a particular way. Perhaps it always leaks at a certain point where two parts are joined. Perhaps the spout always floods your plants. Make adjustments and test them so that your device works in the best and most efficient way possible.

When you are satisfied with your device, you can demonstrate it and observe those constructed by other groups. Evaluate each design in terms of how well it meets criteria. Think about the ideas other groups used and why they work better than (or not as well as) yours. What would you do differently if you were to redesign this device?

Now, not only have you made a successful (if only imaginary) model, you have also used a process for solving problems. The problem-solving model you have just used is shown here.

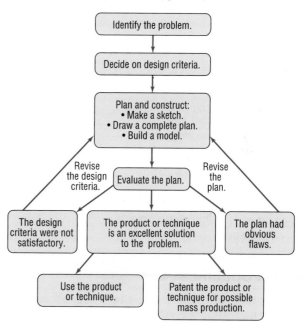

Solving a Technological Problem

This is the kind of step-by-step model that engineers, architects, technologists, and designers use to help them solve problems.

In your investigation of glider characteristics, you saw that strange-looking objects such as the ring-wing glider can actually fly. Now see if you can use the problem-solving process discussed here to solve a technological problem involving gliders.

Going the Distance

Imagine that you and your teammates are engineers for an airplane design company. You know that many pilots have had to land a plane that has lost all power. However, you also know that the farther the airplane can glide, the greater the chance that the pilot will find a good place to land. As well, the more smoothly the airplane glides, the more easily the pilot will land it. Therefore, you and your teammates are working on designs for aircraft that glide as far as possible and that land as smoothly as possible. You have heard that some scientists are testing the gliding characteristics of a new ring-wing glider. You have decided to obtain as much information about those experiments as possible, to see if this glider might have the characteristics that your company requires.

Challenge

Design and construct a ring-wing glider that will glide for as long a distance as possible and that will land as smoothly as possible.

Apparatus

graph paper, pencil, scissors, ruler, long measuring tape

Materials

non-bendable drinking straws, transparent tape, masking tape

Safety Precautions

Be careful when using sharp objects such as scissors.

Design Specifications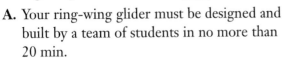

A. Your ring-wing glider must be designed and built by a team of students in no more than 20 min.

B. Your ring-wing glider must withstand five flights.

C. Your ring-wing glider must be no longer than two drinking straws.

D. You must draw and clearly label a sketch, with dimensions, before you begin constructing your ring-wing glider. Have your teacher approve the sketch.

Plan and Construct

1 Your teacher will give you a summary of all the class data on the relationships between the variables of the ring-wing glider and the flight patterns. As a group, study the summary of the scientific data. Discuss the class data, your own experience with the ring-wing glider, and the design criteria.

2 Choose a specific design for your ring-wing glider. Draw the plan to scale. Study your design and discuss any possible changes you wish to make. Agree on a final design and show it to your teacher.

❸ Assemble your ring-wing glider.

❹ Test your ring-wing glider.

   (a) Use masking tape to mark a spot for the "pilot" to stand when launching the glider.

   (b) Launch the glider five times. Each team member may launch the glider or the team may elect a pilot.

   (c) Using the measuring tape, measure and record the distance that the glider travelled during each trial.

❺ Calculate the average distance that your glider travelled.

❻ Post the class results and display the gliders.

Evaluate

1. Examine each of the gliders and their gliding distances. Evaluate your own design. If your glider did not travel the greatest distance, how did it differ from the glider that did? If your glider travelled the farthest, what characteristics do you think account for its success?

2. After considering all of the gliders, how would you revise yours to make it travel farther? If you have time, build and test your revised plan.

SOCIETAL DECISION MAKING

Suppose you are part of an enthusiastic mixed hockey team that practises at an arena belonging to a town a few kilometres away. The town council is in the middle of budget discussions, and one of the items under discussion is the salting of roads. The council is prepared to expand the salting program so that roads in your area will be salted in winter. You and your teammates are delighted. This will make your trip to the arena easier — and always possible. There are days now when you just can't get there because the roads are too icy.

Soon after hearing the news about the road-salting, you go to your friend's house. You find your friend sitting in front of the computer, composing a letter to the town council. In it, your friend is asking that the salting program not be expanded to your area. You can't believe your eyes, but as you begin discussing the letter, you start to see your friend's point of view.

"What do you mean, damage the environment?" you ask. "Surely it's important that it makes our roads safer."

"It is," answers your friend, "but is there some way we can make the roads safer without doing so much harm to the plants at roadsides and to the drinking water in springs and wells? I was going to check the Internet to find information about these questions I've written down."

"Whew," you say. "There's an awful lot to think about here. Let's see what we can find out from the Internet."

"Well, we found a lot of information, but I'm still not completely convinced that salting the roads causes that much damage," you say. "What sorts of things do we need to find out in order to answer that question?"

"We could do an investigation," your friend suggests. "Then I could use the results in my letter to the town council."

```
TITLE:
Investigation STS 1  Effect of Salt on Living Things
QUESTION:
How much salt can be added to a plant's water before
the plant is harmed?
MANIPULATED VARIABLE:
- amount of salt
RESPONDING VARIABLE:
- plant health
HYPOTHESIS:
Plants that are fed salty water suffer more damage
than plants that are fed plain water.
PREDICTION:
If we add varying quantities of salt to water, the amount
of damage to a plant will increase as the quantity of
salt increases.
PROCEDURE:
1.
```

"I guess salt does damage living things," you admit after completing your investigation. "But we did only look at one type of plant. I wonder if other plants would be affected in the same way. Let's do some more research in the library and on the Internet, and see if we can find out about the effects of salt on various types of plants. Maybe we can also see what kinds of alternatives there are. We could look for something about using less salt on the roads — or even no salt."

Instant Practice

How would you go about finding the above information on the Internet? Work with a partner to come up with some ideas. You have probably done research on the Internet. You may have looked for something that you thought would be easy to find. Instead, you became lost in a lengthy list of highly technical sites that you couldn't understand. How creative can you be in coming up with terms that you could use to find the information you want? If you can, try your terms out to see how successful you are.

In some cases, the information you want might not yet exist. Think about what you might do then.

When you have all of the data that your scientific studies can provide, your decision will still involve some human and personal elements. People have strong feelings about the societal and environmental issues that affect them. Something that seems obvious to you might not be so obvious to another person. Even your scientific data might not change that person's mind. If you are going to encourage a group to make what you consider a good decision, you have to find ways to persuade the group to think as you do.

Instant Practice

Think of something that's "good for you" that you dislike doing. Develop a series of arguments, a cartoon, a poster, a video — whatever you feel would persuade someone to do that "good for you" thing.

After all the data are in, after all the persuading is done, it's time to take some action. The seemingly small actions done by you and your friends can have a snowball effect. You are very keen to show your sense of responsibility and community spirit by getting your ideas across to town council when one of your friends makes you stop and think. "I've noticed you putting a lot of salt out on your sidewalk," says your friend. "You could use a bit of time and muscle power to chip away the ice, but that isn't the choice you make." You realize your friend is right — it isn't up to the town council or any other group to act responsibly and start that snowball effect; it's up to you and your friends. How easy is it for you to give up an undemanding way of doing a task in order to make an environmentally responsible decision?

Issues rarely have easy answers. Those who are affected have differing, valid points of view. It is easier for you to act as an individual, but if you can persuade a group to act, you will have greater influence. In the issue discussed here, you might write a letter to town council. As a compromise, you might suggest a combination of salt and sand on the roads. Your scientific study can provide you with appropriate statistics. As a group, you could attend a town council meeting or sign a petition to make your views known.

Over time, you can assess the effects of your actions: Are there fewer accidents on the salted/sanded roads? Are there fewer negative effects on the plant life near the roads than there are when more salt is used?

As you reached your decision, you went through various stages. Now you can think about how well each stage worked and how well you feel you completed each stage. If you look back over these pages, you will see that we have indeed developed a process that can be used for decision making. Examine the flowchart below.

Developing Decision-Making Skills

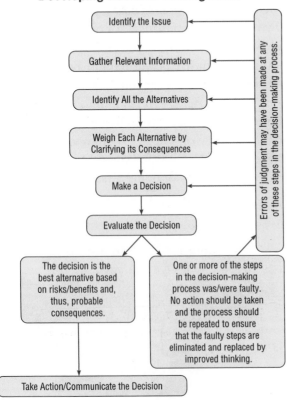

You can see that you used every step in this process. As with science inquiry and problem solving, having a process to use helps you to focus your thinking and stay on track.

Instant Practice

1. Read the following brief news clipping:

> British Columbia could soon become the first province to regulate the use of cellphones by drivers in order to cut automobile accidents. In a policy shift yesterday, B.C.'s attorney general said he will reconsider his opposition to such regulation, which has been strongly endorsed by the B.C. Medical Association. Ujjal Dosanjh said he was reacting to a tide of public support for such regulation, building since B.C.'s doctors called for a law at their annual meeting in June.

2. With a partner, work through the flowchart above, using the news clipping as a basis. First, write what you think the issue is in the news clipping.

3. Instead of gathering relevant information, write notes about the kind of information you would need to gather in order to come to a decision.

4. Follow through the rest of the chart. Be ready to share your decision with the rest of the class and to back up your decision and explain the alternatives you considered.

USING TECHNOLOGY IN SCIENCE

Technology includes the designing and use of devices, processes, and materials to solve practical problems.

The computer is an important technological advance. In your science lab you may also be able to use other advances in technology, such as electronic balances, scientific calculators, electronic probes, and other electronic tools. Your teacher can explain their use to you.

Technology tools can be used to make more accurate measurements, collect and store information, and display the data in a colourful and exciting manner. These tools can also make the sharing of data easier between partners. However, the advances in technology can be expensive, can reduce the need for human input, and can destroy natural resources. Science and technology must work together to create a balance between human needs and the needs of a sustainable environment.

Using a Word Processor

Word processing software allows you to write, change, store, and print information. You may already be familiar with editing functions, such as cut and paste, find and replace, and copy. Formatting features let you change the font, style, size, and alignment of print. The word processor can also be used to create tables and columns, insert art, add page numbers, and check spelling and grammar. Remember that the spell check does not catch those words that are spelled correctly but that are the wrong words

(such as "date" instead of "data"). If you are uncertain about how to use certain features, check the Help menu for instructions.

Instant Practice
Using a Word Processor

1. Using a word processor, write an answer to the following question: How many students in your class are male and how many are female?

2. Add a picture to the answer you wrote for question 1 by inserting a graphic.

3. Add a chart that shows the data you used to answer question 1. Use the chart to make a graph.

4. Number the pages in your document and complete a spell check. Proofread the document for grammatical errors and then print.

Using a Database

How do you keep track of all the information you gather for a project? A good tool to use is the database. You can think of a database as being a file cabinet within your computer that can sort information into a variety of categories. If you use shortcuts, such as tabbing between entry fields and utilizing your software's automatic formatting, the task becomes even faster. When you search for information within your database, use "and," "or," and "not" to narrow your search.

Instant Practice
Using a Database

1. Collect information from five books. Include the title, publisher, publication date, and number of pages.

2. Enter the information you collected on the books into a database and sort, based on publication date.

Using Graphics Software

Have you discovered your computer's graphics software? You can use it to arrange clip-art, change scanned images, create illustrations, and integrate text into your diagrams. You might find it easier to start by studying and manipulating existing drawings. The more you practise using graphics software, the easier it will be to make your own illustrations. Keep in mind that your final product should effectively represent your message. Consider the balance of text and visuals, and the use of colour, style, and font. Avoid cluttering your final product with too many elements.

Instant Practice
Using Graphics Software

1. Import an image into a graphics software program. Play with the image (resize, crop, etc.), and add text to relay a message.

2. Use a scanner or pieces of clip art to create a message. Add text to the graphic you created to improve the message.

Developing Multimedia Presentations

A multimedia presentation can make your information come alive for your audience. You might integrate visuals, such as posters, charts, slides, or photographs, with sound. Or you might produce a video and represent information from an Internet site. Software programs, such as PowerPoint™ and HyperStudio™ can help you create your multimedia presentation. Consider what medium will best communicate the information you want to share. Whatever your choices, make sure you know how to use the equipment. Practise your presentation several times and ask for feedback from friends or family.

Instant Practice
Developing Multimedia Presentations

1. Use multimedia software such as Powerpoint™ or Hyperstudio™ to create a short presentation about yourself. Include graphics and text in your presentation. Make a section about your personal information (age, where you live, etc.) and a section about your interests.

Using E-mail

If you want to correspond with a scientist, contact a relative who might be able to help you with your project, or send your homework to your teacher, an electronic mail system can quickly get your message on its way. Before sending an e-mail message, remember to check it carefully for both spelling and grammar. Make sure you have correctly entered the e-mail address. If you receive frequent e-mail messages, keep them organized. Delete messages you no longer need, and save others in folders.

Instant Practice
Using E-mail

1. Find a short, interesting article in the newspaper, in a magazine, or an interesting portion of a book you are reading. Key the information into your computer, and e-mail it to friends, relatives, and/or teachers you think might be interested. Ask for their comments.

Using an Electronic Spreadsheet

Electronic spreadsheets can be used to keep track of, and make calculations with, scientific data. Information is entered in both rows and columns. Calculations can be made with any combination of numbers. For instance, you might enter the time and distance various fluids travelled in an investigation. To calculate the speed of each, you could enter the formula *speed = distance ÷ time*. Once the calculations are complete, the results can be graphed.

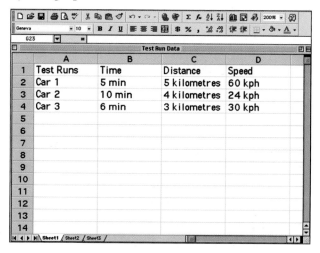

Instant Practice
Using an Electronic Spreadsheet

1. Gather information on the number of boys and the number of girls in your school at each grade level. Using spreadsheet software, create a spreadsheet that displays this information.

2. Use calculations in the spreadsheet to determine the total number of students in each grade level at your school.

3. Create a graph from the information in the spreadsheet you created.

Using a CD-ROM

When you are researching information for a science project or just wanting to know more about a topic, consider using a CD-ROM. A CD-ROM is a form of compact disc that stores information as well as sounds and videos. Encyclopedias, atlases, and other valuable references are available as CD-ROMs. Some science CD-ROMs include interactive tutorials so that you can learn about volcanoes by watching them explode, or discover deep sea vents by viewing them in action. Be sure to include a reference to the CD-ROM in your bibliography if you are preparing a research project.

Instant Practice
Using a CD-ROM

Use an encyclopedia CD-ROM to find out information about mammals. Find out how many mammal species there are.

Using the Internet

The Internet can be an invaluable research tool for homework, investigations, and research projects. You can find sites that offer virtual tours of museums and the very latest information about a subject — sometimes just a few hours old! However, you can also find incorrect and outdated information. Always be sure to verify the origin of the site and check your facts with several sources. Take a few minutes to think about key words before you begin your search. Make a list of several possibilities for key words. Limit your search with terms such as "and," "or," and "not." If you place an "and" between two words in your search, the database will look for any entries that have both the words. If you place an "or" between the two words, the database will show entries that have at least one of the words. If you place a "not" between two words, the database will look for entries that have the first word but do not have the second word.

Always record the information that identifies any material you use. You will need to let your audience know where you obtained your information, and you may need to go back to it. Make sure that you record

- the author's name (or the name of the group that provided the information)
- the name of the resource
- the name of the publisher or information source
- the city where the resource was published
- the publishing date
- the URL, if the information is from an Internet site

Gue, David et al.
SCIENCEFOCUS 7:
Science, Technology, Society.
McGraw-Hill Ryerson Limited,
Toronto, 2001.

At the end of every research project, record each source of information you used. Here is an example of the proper way to list a source in a bibliography. List your sources by author's last name, in alphabetical order.

Most of this information can be found on the copyright page at the beginning of a book. The URL can be found in the address bar at the top of an Internet page. (Some URLs are very long and complex. Get a partner's help to make sure that you have copied the URL correctly.)

Above is an example of how to cite your source. (NOTE: et al. means "and others.")

Instant Practice
Using the Internet

1. Use an Internet search engine to locate information on the population of Alberta.

2. Narrow your search to determine the population for your city or town.

Using Probeware

Some scientific investigations involve taking measurements over a long period of time. The task of collecting and storing the data is made easier by using probeware. In many cases, the probeware provides more accurate quantitative measurements than non-electronic methods. Measurements such as temperature, pressure, motion, and pH can be taken by a probe hooked to the computer. Once all the measurements have been collected, the probeware can be used to graph and analyse the data. When using probes, be sure all cables are solidly connected. Consider doing many trials in your investigation to strengthen your data.

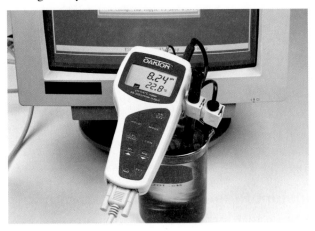

Instant Practice
Using Probeware

1. Fill a glass with cold tap water. Use probeware to determine the temperature of the water over a 1 h period.

2. Use probeware to determine the pH of the water.

INTERNET CONNECT

www.mcgrawhill.ca/links/sciencefocus7

You have looked at animal adaptations, and the photographs here show some plant adaptations. Find out about the special adaptations of cacti for their dry environments by going to the web site above. Click on **Web Links** to know where to go next. Write and sketch your findings.

This recurring feature in *SCIENCEFOCUS 7* will take you to interesting web sites.

ORGANIZING AND COMMUNICATING SCIENTIFIC RESULTS

If you skim through the pages of this textbook, you will find many tables and graphs. Textbooks present scientific information in tables and graphs because they are easy to read and understand. Scientists also present their data in tables and graphs to communicate with other scientists. To learn more about making and using tables and graphs, study the following examples and then practise what you have learned.

Making a Table

When you do investigations in your science courses, you will often be asked to record and present your own data in the form of a table. A data table is an efficient way to organize data. To learn how a data table is set up, read through the following example. Then read "Drawing Data Tables by Hand" to learn the steps to follow in preparing a data table.

Example

Read the following paragraph, then examine the table to see how the data are organized.

White rats have an average mass of 0.15 kg and a resting heart rate of about 350 beats per minute. An average 12.0 kg dog has a resting heart rate of about 100 beats per minute. Adult humans have an average mass of about 70 kg and a heart rate of about 72 beats per minute. An elephant with a mass of 4000 kg has a heart rate of about 30 beats per minute.

1. Note that there are three categories: animal, mass, and heart rate. Thus, the table needs three columns with the headings "Animal," "Mass," and "Heart rate."

2. There are four items: white rats, dogs, humans, and elephants. There should be one row for headings, and four rows for the different types of animals.

Table 1 Heart Rates and Masses of Four Animals

Animal	Mass (kilograms)	Heart rate (beats per min)
white rat	0.15	350
dog	12.0	100
human	70.0	72
elephant	4000	30

Drawing Data Tables by Hand

Much of the time, you will probably be preparing data tables on a computer (see Skill Focus 9). However, you do need to know how to put such tables together by hand. Read the following steps in the process. Refer to Table 1 above to see how the steps were followed. Then try making your own table.

1. Use a ruler and pencil.

2. Print all letters and words.

3. Express all numbers as numbers (e.g., 1, 2, 3), not as words (e.g., one).

4. Give the table a title. (In the title, you can express small numbers as words.)

   (a) Some data tables simply organize observations. The title gives a brief description of what was being observed (for example, Heart Rates and Masses of Four Animals).

   (b) Other data tables give the results of an experiment. The variables in the experiment can become the title of the data table (for example, The Effects of Amount of Light on Plant Growth).

5. Draw a box around the data. Place the title outside the box.

6. Print headings at the top of each column.

7. Include the units for the data with the headings, not in the columns.

8. Draw a line separating the headings from the data.

9. Record the data in columns below the headings.

10. Separate the columns of data with lines.

Instant Practice

Make a table from the data in the following paragraph:

Half a cup of cooked pasta has about 15 g of carbohydrate, 3 g of protein, and no fat. A small piece (32 g) of beef has no carbohydrate, 7 g of protein, and about 5 g of fat. Half a banana has 15 g of carbohydrate, no protein, and no fat. One cup of milk has 12 g of carbohydrate, 8 g of protein, and about 3 g of fat. One large tomato has about 5 g of carbohydrate, 2 g of protein, and no fat.

Graphing

A graph is a very good way to display data. A graph can help you to see patterns and relation-ships among the numbers. Throughout your science courses, you will be using many types of graphs, such as line graphs, bar graphs, histograms, and circle graphs (pie charts). Here are some examples to help you use and understand graphs.

Graphing Terms You Need to Know

1. *x-and-y Axis*: The *x*-axis is the horizontal line on a graph. The *y*-axis is the vertical line.

2. *Origin*: The point at which the *x* and *y* axes meet. The origin is often (but not always) the point, 0, on a graph.

3. *Data*: Information plotted on a graph

4. *Plotting*: Drawing a point or line on a graph that represents data.

5. *Scale*: Equal divisions marked on the *x* and *y* axes so that they can be used for measuring. Numbers of a scale must increase as you move away from the origin.

6. *Interval*: The distance or divisions between units marked on a scale (e.g., 0, 1, 2, 3 … or 0, 5, 10, 15 …). The spaces between the numbers must be equal in size.

7. *Range*: The difference between the largest and smallest of a series of numbers (e.g., the range in a set of data).

8. *Key (Legend)*: A small table that explains or identifies symbols on a graph. The legend should be placed close to the graph.

Drawing a Line Graph by Hand

Line graphs make it easy to see relationships between two sets of numbers. You can use a line graph to predict events that are not even on the graph. The following example demonstrates how to create a line graph from a data table.

Example

The following data give the number of species that became extinct between 1600 and 1900. To learn how to make a line graph from these data, examine the graph as you read the steps.

| Table 2 Species Extinction Over Time ||
Year	Number of extinct species
1600	10
1700	11
1800	28
1900	70

1. With a ruler and pencil, draw an *x*-axis and a *y*-axis on a piece of graph paper. (Hint: The first point above tells you which axis is horizontal and which is vertical.)

2. Label the axes. Write the years along the *x*-axis and "Number of extinct species" along the *y*-axis.

3. Decide on a scale to use. Your *x*-axis will have only four years on it. For your *y*-axis, you will need to go from 10 to 70. You can start from 0, and you will want to end at a number past 70, as you do not want your final number to be right at the top of your graph. You could go from 0 to 80, dividing the scale into intervals of 10. Use a tick mark at major intervals on your scale, as shown below.

4. To plot the first point, 10, carefully move a pencil up the *y*-axis until you reach the 10. Now move right until you are at the line that represents the year 1600. Make a dot at this point. Repeat this procedure until you have plotted all the data points in the table.

5. If it is possible, draw a line that connects all of the points on your graph. This might not be possible. Scientific investigations often involve quantities that change smoothly. On a graph, this means that you should draw a smooth curve (or straight line) that has the general shape outlined by the points. This is called a **line of best fit**. Such a "best fit" line often passes through many of the points, but sometimes it goes between them. Think of the dots on your graph as "clues" about where the perfect smooth curve (or straight line) should go.

   A line of best fit shows the trend of the data. It can be extended beyond the first and last points to indicate what might happen.

6. Give your graph a title.

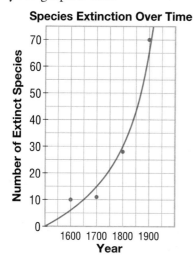

Species Extinction Over Time

Instant Practice

Make a line graph using the following data on the development of baby teeth in infants and children. Put age on the *x*-axis and number of teeth on the *y*-axis. Be sure to include units in your labels.

Table 3 Number of Teeth and Baby's Age	
Age (months)	**Average number of teeth**
8	5
10	9
13	12
16	18
20	25
28	28

Drawing a Bar Graph

A bar graph helps you to compare the number of items in one category with the number of items in other categories. The height of the bar represents the number of items in the category. Study the example, and then make your own bar graph.

Example

Make a bar graph from the data listed in the table on boiling water. Use only the data on time — lower table. As you read the steps, examine the completed graph to see how the steps were followed.

Table 4 Time and Cost to Boil 900 mL of Water		
Method	**Time (min)**	**Cost (cents)**
electric kettle	4.5	0.71
electric stove	8.0	1.25
gas stove	6.0	0.32
camp stove	7.0	11.1

1. Draw an *x*-axis and a *y*-axis on a sheet of graph paper. Label the *x*-axis with the names of the heating methods. Label the *y*-axis with the title "Time (min)."

2. Look at the data carefully in order to select an appropriate scale. The values in this case are fairly close together, so you can number from 0 to 9. Write the numbers on your *y*-axis scale.

3. Decide on a width for the bars in the graph. They should be large and easy to read.

4. Mark the width of the bars on the *x*-axis. Leave the same amount of space between each bar.

5. To draw the bar for the electric kettle, go to the centre of the bar on the *x*-axis, then go up until you are halfway between 4 and 5. Make a mark to represent 4.5 min. Use a pencil and a ruler to draw in the first bar.

6. Repeat the procedure for the other heating methods.

7. When you have drawn all the bars, colour them so that each one is different. If you had no colours, you could use techniques such as cross-hatching, dots, or diagonal lines to distinguish among the bars. If you are comparing two or more manipulated variables that you have plotted on the *x*-axis, you will need to make a legend or key to explain the meanings of each bar.

8. Give your graph a title.

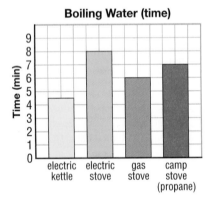
Boiling Water (time)

Instant Practice

A science teacher asked her students what kind of pet they had or would like to have. She planned to have her students research the proper care and feeding of each pet. The responses are shown in the following table. Make a bar graph using the data.

Table 5 Pets Chosen by Students	
Pet	**Number of students choosing pet**
cat	16
gerbil	11
hamster	13
goldfish	3
mice	7
guinea pig	10
dog	14
hedgehog	10

Constructing a Histogram

The graph on page 479 is called a histogram. It is another type of bar graph. Compare the histogram to the graph on this page. How are they similar? How are they different? You probably noticed that there is no space between the bars in a histogram but there is space between the bars in the graph on this page. The reason for the space is that each bar represents a different item. In a histogram, the *x*-axis represents one continuous item, divided into size categories. In the histogram, notice that the *x*-axis represents temperature, divided into two-degree categories. Thus the *x*-axis is quantitative, meaning that it contains numerical values. In a typical bar graph, the *x*-axis is qualitative and cannot be described with numbers. Follow the steps in the example that follows to see how to make a histogram.

Example

A group of students conducted a test on plant growth. They placed plants in rooms with different temperature ranges and observed the effects on the plants. Table 6, called a frequency table, shows how many plants were placed in each location. Make a histogram to display these data. As you read the steps, examine the completed histogram.

Table 6 Temperature of Rooms	
Temperature (°C)	Frequency (number of plants)
10–12	1
13–15	3
16–18	3
19–21	2
22–24	3
25–27	5
28–30	5
31–33	3

1. On a piece of graph paper, draw an *x*-axis and a *y*-axis. Label the *x*-axis "Temperature (°C)" and the *y*-axis, "Frequency (number of plants)."

2. Separate the *x*-axis into eight equal segments. Label the segments using the temperatures listed in the frequency table.

3. Make a scale on the *y*-axis that goes to 5.

4. Move your pencil up the *y*-axis to 1, and make a light mark. Then, using a ruler, make a bar that is the width of the 10–12 temperature range.

5. Repeat this procedure for each temperature range and corresponding number of plants.

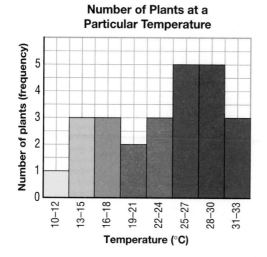

Number of Plants at a Particular Temperature

Instant Practice

The following frequency table gives the number of launches of the space shuttle in two-year intervals. Make a histogram using the data.

Table 7 Launches of the Space Shuttle	
Years	Number of launches
1981–1982	5
1983–1984	9
1985–1986	11
1987–1988	2
1989–1990	11
1991–1992	14
1993–1994	14
1995–1996	14
1997–1998	13
1999–2000 (planned)	10

Drawing a Circle Graph

A circle graph (also called a pie chart) is a very good way to present data as percentages of a total. To learn how to make a circle graph, study the following example.

Example

The table below lists the energy use by cows. Make a circle graph from these data.

Table 8 Energy Use by Cows		
Use of Energy	Energy (%)	Degrees in "piece of pie"
Building and repairing body tissues	4	14.4
Breathing, mooing, pumping blood	33	118.8
Waste	63	226.8

1. Copy the first two columns of Table 8 into your notebook. Add a third column to your table. Label it "Degrees in piece of pie."

2. Determine the number of degrees in the "piece of pie" that represents the percentage of energy use, using the following formula:

Degrees for "piece of pie" =
$$\frac{\text{Percent for energy use}}{100\%} \times 360°$$

For example, the calculation for the "piece of pie" representing the building and repairing of body tissues is

$$\frac{4\%}{100\%} \times 360° = 14.4°$$

Write the number of degrees in the third column of the table.

3. Use a compass to make a large circle on a sheet of paper. Put a dot in the centre of the circle.

4. Draw a straight line from the centre of the circle to the edge. Place a protractor on this line and make a mark almost halfway between 14° and 15°. Draw a line from the centre of the circle, through the mark, to the circumference of the circle. This is the "slice of pie" that represents the percentage of the total energy that is used to build and repair the cow's tissues.

5. To draw the next "piece of pie," representing breathing, mooing, and pumping blood, use the line that ended the first "piece of pie" as the starting place.

6. Repeat the procedure for the final piece, waste.

Energy Use by Cows

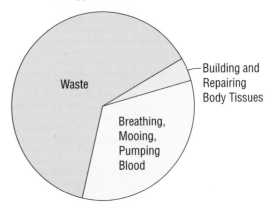

Instant Practice

1. Make a circle graph using the data in Table 9, "Percent of Buildings in an Area Using Each of a Variety of Heating Fuels." You may wish to compare your graph with what you learn about heating methods in your part of Alberta during your study of "Heat and Temperature."

Table 9 Percent of Buildings in an Area Using Each of a Variety of Heating Fuels		
Fuel	**Percent of total area**	**Degrees in "piece of pie"**
Gas	50	
Water (steam)	25	
Electric	10	
Coal	10	
Other	5	

Graphing on a Computer

Computers are a great tool for graph preparation for the following reasons:

1. Data need only be entered once. As many graphs as you need can then be prepared without any more data entry.

2. Once the data are entered, you can get the computer to manipulate them. You can change the scale, zoom in on important parts of the graph, graph different parts of the data in different ways, and so on — all without doing any calculations!

3. Computers prepare graphs far more quickly than people working carefully.

4. Computers can be hooked up to sensors (thermometers, timers, and probes) so you don't need to read instruments and enter data by hand, with all the resulting possibilities for error. The computer can display the readings on a graph as data are collected (in "real" time) so you can quickly get a picture of how your experiment is going.

5. Errors can be corrected much more easily when working with a computer. Just change the incorrect number and print again. Imagine the time and effort involved if you had to redo your graph by hand.

6. Computer graphs can be easily inserted into written lab reports, magazine articles, or Internet pages. It is possible to scan hand-drawn graphs into a computer, but it isn't easy to do it well, and the resulting files are very large.

7. Once data have been entered into a computer, the computer can determine a "best-fit" line *and* a mathematical equation that describes the line. This helps scientists to discover patterns in their data and make predictions to test their inferences in a very precise manner.

As you decide which type of graph you are going to create, remember your graph's purpose, its audience, and the amount of time you want the audience to spend on the graph. You might be tempted by the wealth of varieties of available graphs. Take care that you do not present your information in a cluttered manner. Scientific data should always be presented in a relevant, clear, easy-to-read manner.

Instant Practice

Take any of the graphs you have constructed by hand. Input the data into the computer, and produce a graph. Try different types of graphs and select the one that most clearly presents your data.

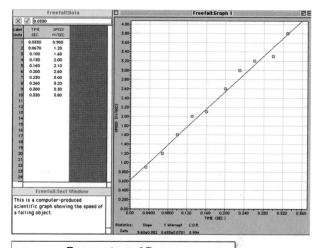

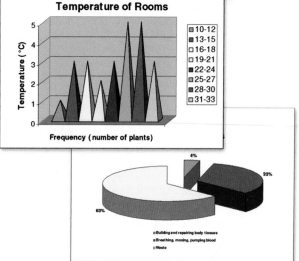

SCIENTIFIC AND TECHNOLOGICAL DRAWING

Have you ever heard the expression "a picture is worth a thousand words"? This expression means that a difficult idea can often be explained more easily by using a visual, such as a picture or a diagram. Have you ever used a drawing to explain something that was too difficult to explain in words? Perhaps you have sketched a map when giving directions to a friend. Think of an example, from your own experience, when a drawing helped you get an idea across to someone else or clarified a difficult idea for you.

A clear drawing can often assist or replace words in a scientific explanation. In science, drawings are especially important for explaining difficult concepts or describing something that contains a lot of detail. It is important that you make your drawings clear, neat, and accurate.

Example

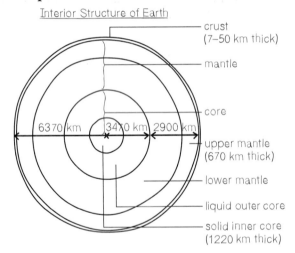

Interior Structure of Earth

Examine the drawing shown here. It is taken from a Grade 7 student's notebook and summarizes the internal structure of Earth. The student's verbal description of Earth's interior included an explanation of how the various layers are arranged and gave the thickness of each layer. As you can see, a clear diagram can support or even take the place of many words of explanation. While the drawing itself is important, labelling it clearly is also important. If you are comparing and contrasting two objects, label each object, as well as the points of comparison between them.

Making a Scientific Drawing

Follow these steps to make a good scientific drawing.

1. Use unlined paper and a sharp pencil with an eraser.

2. Give yourself plenty of space on the paper. You need to make sure that your drawing will be large enough to show all the necessary details. You also need to allow space for labels. Labels identify parts of the object you are drawing. Place all of your labels to the right of your drawing, unless there are so many labels that your drawing looks cluttered.

3. Carefully study the object that you will be drawing. Make sure that you know what you need to include.

4. Draw only what you see, and keep your drawing simple. Do not try to indicate parts of the object that are not visible from the angle you are observing. If you think that you need to show other parts of the object, do a second drawing. On each drawing, indicate the view that is shown.

5. Shading or colouring is not generally used in scientific drawings. If you want to indicate a darker area, you can use stippling (a series of dots). Note the stippling in the illustrations of the hand-held drill. You can use double lines to indicate thick parts of the object.

6. If you do use colour, try to be as accurate as you can. Choose colours that are as close as possible to the colours in the object you are observing.

7. Label your drawing carefully and completely, using lower-case (small) letters. Pretend that you know nothing about the object you have just observed, and think about what you would need to know if you were looking at it for the first time. Place all your labels (if possible) to the right of the drawing. Make sure your labels line up, as shown. Use a

ruler to draw a horizontal line from each label to the part you are identifying. Make sure that none of your label lines cross. All of the label lines should be parallel.

8. Give your drawing a title.

FRONT AND SIDE VIEWS OF A HAND–HELD DRILL

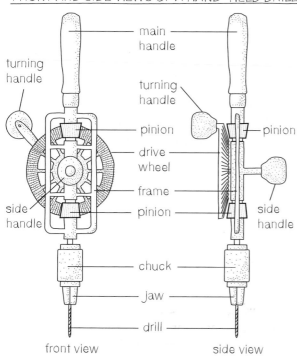

front view

side view

Tips on Technological Drawing

You will find that well laid-out drawings are a valuable learning tool. Ask the advice of specialist teachers, engineers, or technology experts about technological drawings.

Instant Practice

1. Draw an object in your classroom. Use stippling as a technique to give it three dimensions.

2. Exchange drawings with a classmate to see if each of you can identify the other's "object." As well, give each other feedback on how you think the drawing could be improved for greater clarity.

3. Draw a spherical object. Use stippling to give the impression of curvature.

4. Select any mechanical system in your classroom or at home, such as a window blind or a door hinge. Show two different views of the system to help someone else understand how the system works.

USING MODELS IN SCIENCE

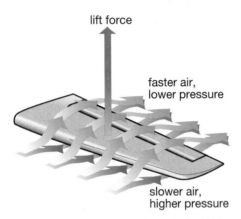

lift force

faster air,
lower pressure

slower air,
higher pressure

When the wing of an airplane cuts through the air, it pushes up the air above the wing. This causes the air above the wing to move faster than the air below the wing. As a result of the wing's shape, there is less air pressure above the wing than below it. The difference in air pressure creates the "lift" that allows an extremely heavy airplane to rise up into the sky.

Cut a strip of paper 2 cm wide and 20 cm long. To make a tab, fold back one end of the strip 1 cm. Holding the paper by the tab, put it just below your lips. Blow smoothly. What happens to the paper?

When engineers design a new airplane, they build a scale model and test it in a wind tunnel. Huge fans blow air toward the model. Streamers of smoke make the flow of the air visible. These smoke patterns allow the engineers to test their predictions about the lift that the wings will provide.

Compare the photographs and the illustrations at the left. How are they similar? Each photograph or illustration models the scientific principles of flight. A scientific model is anything that helps you understand, communicate, or test an idea.

Textbooks use illustrations, diagrams, charts, and graphs to model scientific concepts. When you visualize or create a picture of an idea, the idea is often easier to understand. The first illustration shows how the air moves above and below an airplane wing. You may remember, from previous science studies, that air pressure under a wing creates lift.

Many people understand a concept better when they make a model that demonstrates the concept. Activities and investigations are learning tools. The student in the photograph is using a strip of paper to model an airplane wing. When the student blows over the top of the paper, the air above the "wing" moves faster than the air below it, just as the first illustration shows. Watching the paper lift up helps the student better understand the concept of "lift."

Scientists build models to test hypotheses or to find possible answers to questions. Engineers use models to test new designs. In the second photograph, aircraft engineers are testing the design of an airplane in a wind tunnel. Not only can they see how the air flows around the wings, they can also detect turbulence, or uneven flow of air, around all the parts of the model. Turbulence causes drag, which slows an airplane.

Examples

As you can see, models help scientists and students in many ways. Look at the photographs on the next page to find more reasons for using models.

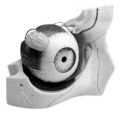

Sometimes important structures are hidden from view. Models allow you to see how these structures work. You can use this model of the human eye to learn how your own eyes focus on near and distant objects. As well, you can learn why some people are near sighted and others are far sighted. You can even see how glasses or contact lenses help to correct these vision problems.

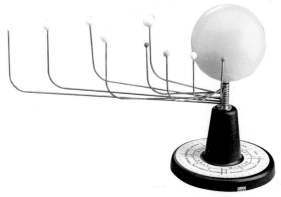

From Earth, you cannot see all the planets in the solar system at the same time. Therefore, you cannot see how the planets are arranged. This model helps you see how the planets orbit the sun and how the solar system is arranged. Distances, however, are not to scale.

Instant Practice

Build a model of a lake and of dry land to learn how they affect climate.

You will need a pencil, a piece of paper, two baking dishes, potting soil (or dirt), water, two identical lamps with identical light bulbs (or direct sunlight), and two thermometers.

Safety Precautions

Be careful when handling the thermometers. They are fragile and can break easily.

1. Fill one baking dish with water and the other with potting soil. Press down gently on the soil until it is fairly firm. The water and the soil should both be about 4–5 cm deep.

2. Place a strong lamp about 20 cm above each dish, or place the dishes in direct sunlight. Be sure that both dishes are getting the same amount of light.

3. Place a thermometer in each dish. The bulb of the thermometer should be just below the surface of the soil.

4. Read and record the temperature of the soil and the water as soon as you put the thermometers into the dishes. Then read and record the temperature about every 15 min for 1 h.

5. Examine the temperature readings. What would you infer about the climate near a very large body of water? What would you infer about the climate on land, a large distance from a lake or an ocean?

6. Wash your hands after completing this activity.

Glossary

How to Use This Glossary

This Glossary provides the definitions of the key terms that are shown in **boldface** type in the textbook (instructional boldfaced words such as "observe," and "gather," used in investigations are not included). Other terms that are not critical to your understanding, but that you may wish to know, are also included in the Glossary. The Glossary entries also show the page number where you can find the boldfaced words. The pronunciations of terms that are difficult to say appear in square brackets after the terms. Use the following pronunciation key to read them:

a = mask, back
ae = same, day
air = stare, where
e = met, less
ee = leaf, clean

ih = ice, life
i = simple, this
o = stop, thought
oh = home, loan
oo = food, boot

uh = Sun, caption
uhr = insert, turn
yoo = cute, human

A

abiotic [AE-bih-o-tik] a term applied to non-living things in the environment; for example, air, water, and soil are abiotic (38)

abrasion the wearing down of rocks by wind, ice, waves, and running water (377)

acid rain rain that contains higher than normal levels of acid; caused by waste gases released into the atmosphere by industries and automobiles; damaging to the environment (52)

active of a volcano, the stage when materials such as lava, smoke, and ash are released into the environment

active solar heating a type of heating that uses mechanical devices like fans to distribute stored thermal energy

adapted well-suited (10)

adaptation an inherited characteristic that helps an organism survive in its environment (10)

adhesive a sticky substance, such as glue or epoxy cement, that is used to hold objects or materials together (292)

aesthetics [e-STHE-tiks] a branch of philosophy that studies the principles of beauty; the properties of an object that make it pleasing to the senses (284)

aftershocks smaller ground movements caused by seismic waves moving outward from an earthquake's focus (396)

anther the tip of a stamen (male reproductive organ of a plant) (122)

anticline an upfold of rock layers

area the amount of surface; measured in square units such as cm²

asexual (vegetative) reproduction a type of reproduction that occurs when a "parent" plant grows new plants from its roots, stems, or leaves (118)

ash-and-cinder cone the smallest of the three main types of volcanoes, having steep sides formed by layers of ash and rock

atmosphere the air surrounding the earth

B

balance a device to measure mass; many balances work by using the force of gravity (299)

balance refers to the condition of a stable structure, in which external and internal forces are balanced

bar graph a diagram consisting of horizontal or vertical bars that represent (often numerical) data

baseline data information gathered by scientists to be used as a starting point to compare changes in the environment (74)

bedrock unweathered rock beneath the soil (396)

bending force a combination of push (compression) and pull (tension) forces that results in a temporary curving change in the shape of some structures (308)

bioacculumation movement of pollutants through levels of a food chain so that greater quantities are retained with movement up the food chain (54, 170)

biological community *see* community

biological control a method of controlling insect pests using their natural enemies (61, 173)

biological evidence the type of evidence obtained from living or non-living organisms

biological population
see population

biological weathering the break-up or disintegration of rocks through the physical or chemical effects of living organisms (374)

biomass the total mass of living matter; often expressed in terms of dry weight per unit area (43)

biome a region of land that contains certain kinds of organisms, particularly plants; determined by climate; examples are desert, grassland, and forest

biosphere the thin area around Earth that can sustain life; made up of the atmosphere, the hydrosphere, and the lithosphere

biotic [bih-O-tik] a term applied to living things in the environment, such as humans, plants, birds, animals, and insects (38)

bitumen a heavy, almost solid form of petroleum: some bitumen deposits are found near the surface of Earth and can be mined or heated and pumped to the surface (428)

boiling rapid vaporization occurring at a specific temperature called the boiling point

boiling point the temperature at which a liquid begins to boil and change into a gas or a vapour

brace a device used to add strength to a structure, usually by forming a rigid triangle at the point where pieces come together at a right angle

bromthymol blue [BROM-thih-mol] a chemical indicator that changes colour (from blue to green to yellow) when carbon dioxide is present

buckle of a material, to fold under a compressive force (316)

buttress a slanted brace that supports part of a structure, transferring its thrust line to the ground along an angle

 C

cantilever a horizontal board or other span supported at one end only, by a very strong column (e.g., a diving board)

capacity the largest amount that can be held by a container (usually measured in litres or millilitres)

capacity unit unit used to measure the volume of liquids; an example is the litre (L)

carbon cycle the cycle in which carbon is used and reused through the ecosystem (49)

carbonaceous film [car-bon-AE-shuhss] a type of fossil found in sedimentary rock when organic material is compressed, leaving a thin carbon film (418)

carnivore an animal that eats other animals; examples are lynx, wolf, hawk

cast a type of fossil in which sediments or minerals have filled a mould and hardened into rock (420)

Celsius (C) scale the most common scale for measuring temperature; on the Celsius scale, water at sea level boils at 100° and freezes below 0° (194)

cementation a process by which particles are held together by another material (365)

Cenozoic Era [sen-oh-ZOH-ik E-ruh] the fourth and current era on the geologic time scale; the era in which humans evolved (425)

centre of gravity the point at which all of the gravitational force of an object may be considered to act (332)

chemical control the use of herbicides, insecticides, and fungicides to control weeds, insects, and fungi

chemical weathering the break-up or disintegration of rocks through the effects of chemical reactions upon them (374)

chlorophyll a pigment in plants that makes leaves green (110)

circle graph a circle divided into sections (like pieces of a pie) to represent data; also called a pie chart

classification (or biological key) a list of alternatives (e.g., backbone or no backbone) used by scientists as an aid in identifying an unknown plant or animal

clear-cut removing all of the trees from a particular area

cleavage of a mineral, the characteristic of splitting along smooth, flat planes (357)

cogeneration [coh-jen-uhr-AE-shuhn] a method of energy conservation by which waste heat or energy from one industry is used by another industry (247)

cold-blooded of an organism, having a body temperature that varies with the temperature of its environment

commensalism a symbiotic relationship between two different types of organisms in which one partner benefits and the other neither benefits nor loses (15)

community an association of different populations of organisms in a particular environment or geographic area

compaction the process by which sedimentary rock is formed from sediment, through the weight and pressure of water and other sediment

complex mountains mountains that are formed by the combined processes of folding and faulting (414)

composite of materials, made up of several different materials, with different properties, to fulfil a specific purpose (286)

compost the part of soil composed of dead plant matter (371)

compression force a force that compacts or squeezes a material (307)

compressive strength a measure of the largest compression force that a material can withstand before changing shape or breaking apart (307)

concept map a diagram comprising words or phrases in circles or boxes and connecting lines; used to show various relationships among concepts; can also contain references to events, objects, laws, themes, classroom activities, or other items or patterns related to the concepts

condense change from a gas or vapour into a liquid (220)

condensation the process of changing from a gas or vapour to a liquid; clouds, fog, and dew are examples of condensation (51)

condensation point the temperature at which a gas or vapour begins to change into a liquid; the condensation point of a gas is the same temperature as the boiling point of the material in its liquid state

conifers types of softwood (e.g., hemlock and fir) which have needles and cones

conservation of energy the law stating that the amount of energy within a system always remains the same if the system is left undisturbed

consumers organisms that eat the food made by producers; can be either herbivores, carnivores, or omnivores (40)

continental drift a theory about Earth's structure; according to this theory, the continents have slowly changed their positions over time; the slow movement of continents (384)

contract of substances, to shrink or decrease in volume (210)

control in a scientific experiment, a standard to which the results are compared; often necessary in order to draw a valid conclusion; ensures a fair test

controlled variable in an experiment, a condition that is not allowed to change

convection a process by which a warm fluid moves from place to place carrying thermal energy (230)

convection current a flow resulting from the rising of warm materials and the sinking of cooler denser materials (392)

converging plates two or more plates colliding (390)

convergent boundary an area on Earth's crust where two plates are pushing against each other

co-ordinate graph a grid that has data points named as ordered pairs of numbers; for example (4, 3)

core the innermost part of Earth; made of iron and nickel in solid and liquid form

criteria a set of standards or expectations; specifications for a design

crop rotation a practice whereby crops are rotated annually through various fields, so that each crop is grown in a different field and pests have little opportunity to establish themselves

cross pollination a process whereby the eggs of one plant are fertilized by sperm from another plant of the same species

crust the thin, outermost layer of Earth (354)

crystal the building block of minerals; crystals occur naturally and have straight edges, flat sides, and regular angles (355)

cubic units the units used to report the volume of a substance; for example, cm^3

cuttings a process used in plant reproduction whereby small sections of leaf and stem are cut from a parent plant and grow into new plants

cycle concept map an events chain map in which a series of events does not produce a final outcome; this type of concept map has no beginning and no end

data facts or information

database an organized or sorted list of facts or information, usually generated by computer

dead load the weight of a structure upon itself (306)

decomposers organisms that break down the cells of dead or waste materials and absorb their nutrients; many bacteria and fungi are decomposers (45)

deformation the change in a structure when a force is acting on it; deformation is an indicator that the materials are stressed (305)

desalination [dee-sal-i-NAE-shuhn] a process for removing the salt from salt water

desertification [de-zuhrt-i-fi-KAE-shuhn] the process in which deserts are formed through the erosion of nutrient-rich topsoil; after desertification the soil is no longer able to support plant life

design the shape and size of a structure and the materials of which is it composed (272)

differentially permeable cells that allow some materials to pass through (e.g., water and nutrients) while keeping others out (107)

diffusion tendency of particles in gas or liquid to become evenly distributed by moving from areas of greater concentration to areas of lesser concentration (107)

dilute to weaken the strength of a solution by increasing the amount of solvent

dilute solution a solution that contains relatively little solute

dispersal the transport of seeds away from the parent plant

dissolving mixing a solute completely with a solvent to form a solution; the distinct properties of each of the materials combine into one set of properties

distillation a process for separating the parts of a liquid solution; the solvent is heated to change it into a gas, then converted back to a liquid state through condensation

divergent boundary an area of Earth's crust where two plates are pulling apart from each other

diverging plates two or more plates moving away from each other (390)

diversity a measure of how many different species live in an ecosystem; an ecosystem with many species has greater diversity than an ecosystem with only a few species

dormant of a volcano, a stage when no eruption is occurring (406)

ecological footprint a calculation of the total area of land and water needed to supply all of the materials and energy a human uses, as well as absorb the waste produced (30)

ecologist [ee-KOL-oh-jist] a scientist who studies interactions between the abiotic and biotic parts of the environment (6)

ecology the study of how organisms interact with each other and their environment (6)

ecosystem all the interacting parts of a biological community and its environment (13)

ecosystem (environmental) monitoring a method of checking the condition of an ecosystem by comparing investigation results done at different times (68)

electromagnetic radiation (EMR) energy that is transferred in the form of electromagnetic waves; examples of EMR include radio waves, X-rays, and microwaves (226)

element a type of pure substance (made of one type of particle or atom) that cannot be broken down into simpler parts by chemical means and that has a unique set of properties (354)

embryo a tiny living plant inside a seed (125)

energy the ability to do work and to cause change (chemical or physical)

energy flow the movement of energy, which originally comes from the Sun, from one organism to another (42)

energy source an object or material that can transfer energy to other objects (226)

Environmental Impact Assessment (EIA) a report that outlines how an activity will affect the environment (74)

eon the largest division of time on the geological scale (425)

epicentre [E-pi-sen-tuhr] the area on the surface of Earth that is directly above the focus, or source, of an earthquake

era one of the four longest subdivisions in the history of Earth (425)

erosion movement of rock and mineral grains from one place to another (373)

ethanol a type of liquid fuel made from a process in which microorganisms convert the sugar in plants such as sugar cane, corn, and grain, into fuel that can be burned

evaporation the process by which a liquid, such as water, changes into a gas or a vapour (51, 220)

evaporative cooling a process in which the faster-moving particles on the surface of a liquid evaporate and escape into the air; the slower-moving particles, which are left behind, have lower kinetic energy, decreasing the temperature of the remaining liquid and the surface on which it is resting

events chain map a concept map used to describe a sequence of events, the steps in a procedure, or the stages of a process

expand of substances, to increase in volume (210)

external force stresses that act on a structure from outside (305)

extinct of a species, no longer existing (64)

extrusive rock the type of igneous rock formed when magma (lava) cools and solidifies above Earth's crust (361)

fair test an investigation (experiment) carried out under strictly controlled conditions to ensure accuracy and reliability of results. In a fair test, all variables are controlled except the one variable under investigation.

fault a fracture in the bedrock along which rock have moved (403)

fault block mountain mountains formed by the process of thrust faulting (413)

feedback information that is gained from outside a particular system and returned to it for the purposes of modifying a behaviour or a process

fertile of soil, containing the nutrients needed for plant growth (371)

fibres thread-like materials that make up plant and animal tissue, and some manufactured materials

fibre the tissue of plants from the stem, leaves, seeds, or roots

fibre roots a shallow system of similar-sized roots than can quickly soak up moisture

filament the stalk of a stamen (male reproductive organ of a plant) (122)

fixed-continent model a theory about Earth's structure; according to this theory, the continents and the oceans have always occupied the same positions

fluids materials that lack a definite shape and can flow from one place to another (230)

food chain a sequence of feeding relationships among living organisms, as they pass on food energy (42)

food web the network of feeding relationships among organisms (43)

footing a base for a wall in the foundation of a structure; a footing is wider than the wall to spread the weight over a larger area (337)

force a push or pull, or anything that causes a change in the motion of an object (270, 299)

force diagram a drawing that uses arrows to represent the direction and strength of one or more forces (304)

force meter a scientific device used to measure force; also called a spring scale (300)

fossil any trace or remains of once-living organisms

fossil fuels solid, liquid, or gas hydrocarbons formed from the soft parts of plants and animals over millions of years and/or trapped inside the Earth during the planet's formation (426)

foundation the solid base of a structure

fractional distillation a process in which a solution is vaporized and condensed into several different products; for example, petroleum is vaporized and condensed to produce gasoline, diesel fuel, and kerosene

fracture the property of some minerals to break with rough or jagged surfaces (357)

frame structure a type of structure in which a skeleton of materials supports the weight of the other parts (274)

freeze change from a liquid to a solid (220)

freezing point *see* melting point

friction a force that resists, or works against the movement of two surfaces rubbing together (326)

frost wedging a process of mechanical weathering that occurs when water goes through a cycle of freezing and thawing; the water expands and contracts in the cracks of a rock, eventually breaking the rock apart (373)

fruit the growing ovary of a plant that swells and protects the developing seeds until they are ripe

fulcrum the part of a lever that does not move (315)

function of a structure or object, its main purpose (270)

 G

gas one of the phases or states of matter; a gas has no particular shape or size and can be compressed; a gas is sometimes known as a vapour

genes the parts of a cell that control the organism's characteristics

genus a group of related species

geothermal energy energy generated in the interior of Earth (240)

germination the development of a seed into a new plant (128)

global warming the gradual increase in the temperature of Earth's atmosphere; some scientists think that global warming results from a surplus of greenhouse gases in the environment and that it may have harmful effects on life on Earth

Gondwanaland the southern part of the supercontinent Pangaea, which split off approximately 200 million years ago (425)

grafting a process used in plant reproduction whereby a branch is taken from one tree and attached to another tree

graphic organizer a visual learning tool that helps clarify the relationship between a central concept and related ideas or terms

gravitational force the force exerted by gravity on an object; measured in newtons (N); the preferred scientific term for the everyday term "weight" (300)

greenhouse gases gases, such as carbon dioxide, that result from the burning of fossil fuels or wood; greenhouse gases prevent heat from leaving the atmosphere, increasing the temperature of the atmosphere (245)

ground water the water contained in the lithosphere or Earth's crust (51)

gyroscope [JIH-roh-skohp] a circular device with a heavy outer rim that spins at a very fast rate, stabilizing the axis so that the axis always points in the same direction (340)

 H

habitat the location where an organism lives (8)

half-life the amount of time that a given amount of radioactive substance takes to be reduced by one-half (424)

hardiness a plant's ability to withstand certain environmental conditions

hard water water that contains a high proportion of dissolved materials

heat thermal energy transferred from one object or substance to another because of a temperature difference

heat capacity the thermal energy needed to raise the temperature of 1 kg of a substance, such as water, by 1°C

heat insulators materials that slow the transfer or conduction of thermal energy from one object to another; examples of heat insulators include fibreglass and Styrofoam™ cups (229)

herbivore an animal that eats only plant material; examples are grasshopper, beaver, and moose (40)

heterogeneous [het-uhr-oh-JEEN-ee-uhs] of a mixture, made up of parts that retain their own properties, even if these properties are not visible to the unaided eye

histogram a type of bar graph in which each bar represents a range of values and in which the data are continuous

homogeneous [hoh-moh-JEEN-ee-uhs] of materials, having only one set of properties

horizons the layers in a cross section of soil (150)

host the organism that a parasite lives and feeds on (14)

hot spot an area under Earth's crust where the temperature is much hotter than normal, forcing magma toward the surface

humus [HYOO-muhs] the dark-coloured part of soil that is rich in nutrients, such as nitrogen, phosphorus, potassium, and sulphur (150, 371)

hydroponics a technique for growing plants without soil

hydrosphere all water found on the Earth including lakes, oceans, rivers and ground water

igneous rock [IG-nee-uhs] the type of rock that is formed by the solidification of hot magma; it is defined as either intrusive or extrusive (361)

incremental change small changes that happen gradually over many thousands of years

index fossil a type of fossil that can be used to determine the age of the material in which it is found (423)

indicator species plant or animal species that help to indicate environmental change (69)

individual a single organism

infrared radiation (or heat radiation) a type of electromagnetic radiation that has a wavelength just greater than the red end of the visible light spectrum

input the materials or forms of energy that are used by a system to do work or to produce new materials (output)

insoluble of a substance, meaning not able to be dissolved in a particular solvent

internal force a force that acts on an object from the inside (305)

introduced species species which are introduced into an environment where they are not naturally found (62)

intrusive rock the type of igneous rock formed when magma cools and solidifies below Earth's crust (361)

irrigate the use of a system of large pipes and sprinklers to water crops

joint a fastening that holds parts of structures together. Joints can allow movement (mobile joint) or prevent movement (rigid joint)

joule (J) the standard SI unit for measuring energy

Kelvin scale a scale used for measuring temperatures in scientific experiments; on the Kelvin scale, pure water freezes at 273 K and boils at 373 K; the coldest possible temperature (also known as absolute zero) is 0 K (195)

kilogram the primary measurement of mass in SI, equal to 1000 g; 1 kg is the primary standard for mass (298)

kinetic energy [kin-E-tic] energy that is released or transferred by the motion of an object or its particles

kingdom one of five main groupings for classifying living things on Earth; the five kingdoms are: animal, plant, fungus, protist, and monera

lamination a process in which a layer of material is pressed or glued onto other layers (286)

landfill site an area where garbage is deposited and eventually buried

Laurasia the northern part of the supercontinent Pangaea, which split off approximately 200 million years ago (425)

lava the term used for magma when it breaks through Earth's crust, as in a volcanic eruption (361)

law in science, a statement of a pattern, action, or condition that has been observed so consistently that scientists are convinced it will always happen

layering a process used in plant reproduction whereby plants reproduce from stems

leaching the process by which materials from soil are dissolved and carried away by water (372)

lever a device used to change the amount of force needed to move an object (315)

line graph a diagram that shows how one value depends on or changes according to another value; produced by drawing a line that connects data points plotted in relation to a *y*-axis (vertical axis) and an *x*-axis (horizontal axis)

liquefaction [lik-we-FAK-shuhn] the process of changing solid material into a liquid-like substance, such as quicksand

liquid one of the states or phases of matter; in the liquid state, a material has a specific size or volume but not a specific shape

lithosphere a hard outer layer of the Earth consisting of the crust and upper level of the mantle

live load the force or forces that act in or on a structure but are not part of the structure; examples of a live load include the wind, the weight of people, and a collision (306)

load the weight carried or supported by a structure (270)

loam a type of soil that is good for plant growth; made up of sand, silt, and clay

lubricants substances that can be made from plants to oil machinery parts to avoid heat buildup from friction

lustre the light-reflecting properties, or "shininess," of minerals (356)

magma melted rock, formed under Earth's crust by high temperature and pressure; magma occasionally escapes to Earth's surface as lava (361)

magnetometer [mag-net-O-met-uhr] a device that detects the direction and strength of a magnetic field

manipulated variable in an experiment, a condition that is selected or adjusted to see what effect the change will have on the responding variable

mantle the middle layer of Earth, located between the crust and the core, and made of rock

manufactured structure an object or a structure that is made by humans (271)

margin of safety the need for something built or manufactured to perform as expected for a long time, so that people's safety and health are not at risk. In a structure, a margin of safety would ensure that the structure has extra strength to support more load than normal (285)

mass the amount of matter in a substance; often measured with a balance (298)

mass structure a structure, natural or manufactured, that is made by the piling up of materials; examples of a mass structure include a pyramid and a snow fort (272)

matter anything that takes up space, has mass, and is made up of particles

mechanical energy the energy in a moving object or in moving parts of an object

mechanical mixture a substance made of more than one kind of material, in which the different materials can be easily identified

mechanical weathering of rocks, the break-up or disintegration by the actions of physical forces such as wind, water, and gravity (373)

melt to change from a solid to a liquid (220)

melting point (or freezing point) the temperature at which solid matter begins to change to liquid

Mesozoic Era [mes-oh-ZOH-ik E-ruh] the third era on the geologic time scale; the era in which dinosaurs were the dominant life form on Earth (425)

metal fatigue a weakening of metal due to stress, resulting in an accumulation of small cracks (318)

metallic ores rocks that contain a high proportion of metals and metal oxides

metamorphic rock a type of rock made when high pressure and heat act on another type of rock and change it into a new form (366)

meteorological evidence the type of evidence that is obtained by studying climate change

methanol a type of liquid fuel that is made from wood by a similar process to the one used in producing ethanol

metric system a system of measurement based on multiples of ten and in which the basic unit of length is the metre

micro-organisms organisms that are too small to be seen by the human eye without the aid of a microscope

mineral an inorganic, naturally occurring solid material; minerals can be either elements (pure substances) or compounds (two or more substances combined) (354)

mixture a material made up of several different types of materials; in a mixture, each material retains its own properties

mobile joint a joint that is designed to allow movement; examples of a mobile joint include a door hinge and an elbow (290)

model a verbal, mathematical, or visual representation of a scientific structure or process, which allows scientists to construct and test inferences and theories (e.g., the particle theory of matter)

Mohs hardness scale in geology, a scale that compares the hardness of ten minerals; talc has a hardness value of 1 (the softest) and diamond has a hardness value of 10 (the hardest) (355)

monoculture the limiting of a crop to one particular type in an area in order to use energy and equipment efficiently

mould a type of fossil in which the hard parts of the organism have dissolved, leaving a cavity in the rock (420)

mountain a large, naturally occurring formation of Earth's surface that rises sharply above the surrounding area

mutualism [MYOO-choo-al-is-uhm] a symbiotic relationship between two different types of organisms that is beneficial to both organisms (14)

natural resources the materials and products found in nature (18)

natural structure an object or structure not made by people (270)

network tree a concept map in which some terms are circles while other terms are written on connecting lines

newton (N) the standard unit of force in the *Système international d' unitès* (SI) (299)

niche [NEESH] the role or characteristic activity that is undertaken by an organism in an ecosystem; one organism may fill several different niches (40)

non-renewable resources resources that take millions of years to form

non-target organisms organisms that are affected negatively by chemical controls

normal fault a type of fault in which rock above the fault moves downward

nuclear energy the energy released when the smallest particles (called atoms) of a substance break apart or fuse together; also known as atomic energy

omnivore an animal that eats other animals and plant material; examples are bear, raccoon, people (40)

organic sedimentary rock that is largely made up of once-living matter; limestone is an example (172)

organic food food that is grown without the use of chemical fertilizers and chemical pesticides

organic sedimentary rock sedimentary rock made from remains of plant and animals (365)

organism any type of living creature

original remains a type of fossil in which all or part of the original organism has been preserved (419)

osmosis the diffusion of water through a differentially permeable membrane (107)

output the final materials and energy forms that a system produces by applying energy to raw materials (input)

ovary a tiny chamber containing the plant's ovules (122)

ovule eggs produced by the female species (120)

Paleozoic Era [pae-lee-oh-ZOH-ik E-ruh] the second era on the geologic time scale; the era in which the first plants and animals appeared (425)

Pangaea [pan-JEE-uh] the name of the second supercontinent thought to have existed approximately 350 million years ago; Pangaea included all the present continents (425)

parasite an organism that lives on or in another organism (the host) and feeds on it (14)

parasitism a symbiotic relationship between two different types of organisms in which one of the partners is harmed and the other benefits (14)

parent material the mineral (non-organic) matter (rock, soil, clay) from which the soil developed (150)

parent rock the original rock that was acted on by high pressure and heat to form a metamorphic rock (366)

particle size of soil, the average size of the particles of various materials of which the soil is made

particle model of matter a scientific model of the structure of matter; according to the particle theory, all matter is made up of extremely tiny particles, and each pure substance has its own kind of particle, different from the particles of other pure substances (203)

passive solar heating a type of heating that uses materials in a structure to absorb, store, and release solar energy (241)

period on the geologic time scale, a subdivision of an era (425)

permanent plots study areas (74)

permeate of water, to drain through soil

pesticide a substance used to control insects or other organisms that are harmful to plants or animals

petals brightly coloured parts of a flower that help to attract bees to its nectar (122)

petrified a rock-like substance formed when water penetrated dead organic matter, and deposits dissolved mineral matter (418)

petrochemical a product that is produced from petroleum; there are over 500 000 different petrochemicals

petroleum naturally occurring mixture of hydrocarbons such as bitumen, coal, oil and gas (423)

pH a symbol used to express acid or alkaline content (52)

phases of matter the different forms (solid, liquid, or gas) that matter can take; also known as states of matter

photosynthesis [foh-toh-SIN-the-sis] the process by which plants make their own food using sunlight (110)

phytoplankton [fih-toh-PLANK-ton] plankton that use photosynthesis to make their own food

piling a large, cylindrical structure used to carry the weight of a structure to a solid foundation material (337)

pistil female part of a flower (122)

plankton the general name for microscopic plants, algae, and other organisms that float in oceans and other bodies of water

plate one of the large sections into which Earth's crust is divided (390)

plate tectonics a theory about Earth's structure; according to this theory, Earth's crust is made up of very large pieces, called plates, that are always moving very slowly on Earth's mantle (390)

plateau on a graph, a flat, horizontal region where data remain constant

pollen grains the tiny particles of pollen containing sperm

pollination process by which pollen, containing sperm, travels to the female cone (120)

pollutants substances that cause pollution (52)

pollution a collective term for the different types of harmful materials that are released into the environment through human activities (52)

population a group of organisms of the same species found in a particular geographic area

potential energy stored energy

Precambrian Era the first of the four eras on the geologic time scale (425)

precipitation the water (in its liquid or solid state) that falls to Earth; rain, snow, sleet, hail, etc. (51)

predator an organism that catches and eats other organisms of a different species (40)

prey an organism that is caught and eaten by another organism of a different species (40)

primary succession the gradual growth of organisms in an area that was previously bare (57)

primary standard the name given to a small cylinder of metal on which the kilogram (kg) is based; equivalent to 1 kg (298)

primary (P) waves the fastest moving of the three types of seismic waves that are produced by an earthquake, originating from its focus; can pass through solids, liquids, and gases (398)

principle of superposition a geological theory; according to this theory, in undisturbed layers of rock, the oldest layers will be on the bottom and the youngest layers will be on the top (423)

producers plants that use energy from the Sun to make nutrients they need to survive; includes some bacteria that transfer energy from particles (40)

properties the characteristics of materials; every material has its own unique set of properties; examples of properties include colour, odour, and density (286)

protozoa [proh-toh-ZOH-uh] one-celled, animal-like organisms that live in or on other organisms

pure substance a material that is composed of only one type of particle; examples of a pure substance include gold, oxygen, and water

pyramid of numbers the number of individual organisms at each level of a food chain; the number of organisms decreases with each level higher in the food chain (there is a greater number of organisms at the bottom of the food chain than at the top) (43)

quadrat a small square area, marked out for study (76)

qualitative data information gathered by observations in which no measurements take place

qualitative property a characteristic of a substance that can be described but not measured

quantitative data data that consist of numbers and/or units of measurement; obtained through measurement and through mathematical calculations

quantitative property a characteristic of a substance that can be measured

radiant energy energy that is transmitted via electromagnetic waves; radiant energy can be absorbed and reflected by objects, and it moves through empty space at 300 000 km/s (226)

radiation the transfer of energy in the form of electromagnetic waves (226)

radiocarbon dating a method used to determine the age of organic remains by measuring the relative amount of radioactive carbon found in the remains (424)

radiometric dating the process of determining the age of a geological specimen by measuring the relative amounts of radioactive particles that are present in the specimen (424)

rate of dissolving the speed at which a solute dissolves in a solvent

recycling the process of using the same item over again; recycling can either use the item as it was originally used or find new uses for it, perhaps by changing its composition

refrigerants liquids that evaporate easily at low temperatures (252)

refining the processing of petroleum to separate it into its parts, such as asphalt or kerosene

relative dating determining the order in which geological events occurred and the relative age of rocks by their positions in rock layers (423)

renewable resources energy resources that can be recycled or replaced by natural processes in less than 100 years (245)

residues chemicals that have washed off plants. These remain in the soil and water (170)

resistant able to withstand certain effects; insects become resistant to pesticides

respiration in the cells of living things, the process in which oxygen is used to get energy from food and is converted into carbon dioxide (111)

responder a pointer, light, or other mechanism that uses the signal in some way (199)

responding variable in an experiment, a condition that is changed as a result of changes to manipulated variable

reverse fault a type of fault in which rock below the fault is forced upward over rock below the fault (403)

Richter scale [RIK-tuhr] a scale on which the magnitude, or strength, of an earthquake is measured (396)

rigid joint a device designed to fix an object into place; a joint that allows no movement; examples of a rigid joint include a nail and a screw (290)

Ring of Fire an area of volcanoes around the Pacific Ocean (410)

rock a natural material composed of one or more minerals (354)

rock cycle the naturally occurring process in which rocks continue to change form over long periods of time (368)

Rodinia the name of the earliest supercontinent thought to have broken apart approximately 750 million years ago; Rodinia included all the large land masses (425)

root hairs tiny hairs that cover the small roots coming out of a tap root. They increase the plant's ability to absorb water and nutrients (105)

run-off water that runs off the ground into lakes, rivers, or streams (51)

salinization salt that has collected on the surface of soil (156)

sampling in population studies, a method used to estimate population size in ecosystems by finding out the number of individuals in a portion (that is, the sample) of the population and then calculating the total number for the population as a whole

saturated solution a solution in which no more of a solute is able to be dissolved at a particular temperature

scale a series of equally divided sections that are marked and numbered for use in measurement (e.g., centimetres, litres, or grams) (194)

scavenger an organism that eats dead or decaying plant or animal matter; a carrion beetle is an example of a scavenger (44)

science a body of facts or knowledge about the natural world, but also a way of thinking and asking questions about nature and the universe

science inquiry the orderly process of asking concise and well-focussed questions and designing experiments that will give clear answers to those questions

scientific investigation an investigation that involves the systematic application of concepts and procedures (e.g., experimentation and research, observation and measurement, analysis and sharing of data)

sea floor spreading the process in which an ocean floor slowly increases in size over time because of the formation of new igneous rock along a fault (388)

secondary succession the gradual growth of organisms in an area that was formerly home to many different species; the regeneration of a burned forest is an example (57)

secondary (S) waves the second fastest moving of the three types of seismic waves that are produced by an earthquake, originating from its focus; can pass through solids but not liquids or gases (398)

sediment loose material such as bits of rock, minerals, and plant and animal remains (364)

sedimentary rock the most common type of rock on Earth's surface; formed by the compacting of sediment (loose materials, such as minerals and organic remains) (364)

sedimentation the process in which eroded material is deposited and built up (373)

seismic waves [SIHZ-mik] the energy waves (either primary, secondary, or surface) that are released by an earthquake and travel outward from its focus (396)

seismograph [SIHZ-moh-graf] a sensitive machine that is attached to bedrock in order to measure the strength of earthquakes (396)

seismologists [sihz-MOL-oh-jists] scientists who study earthquakes

selective breeding a process that involves choosing specific plants with particular characteristics and encouraging these plants to reproduce (115)

selective harvest removing specific trees from a specific area

sensor a material that is affected by change in some feature of the environment, such as temperature (199)

sepals enclose tightly bound petals of a bud and protect the flower before it opens (122)

sexual reproduction a process that involves the production of seeds and fruits from the specialized reproductive cells of two individuals (118)

shadow zone an area on Earth's surface that is not reached by primary waves after an earthquake, due to the bending of P waves as they pass through Earth

shear of a section of compressed material, to slide over another section along a weak point (315)

shear force a force that bends or tears a material by pushing parts of it in opposite directions (307)

shear strength measures the largest shear force a material can stand before ripping apart (307)

shelterbelt a row of trees planted along the edge of a field to protect crops (159)

shield volcano the largest of the three main types of volcanoes; formed above an area, called a hot spot, where the temperature under the crust is much hotter than elsewhere, causing lava to be forced upward through vents

shell structure a type of structure that obtains its strength from a thin, carefully shaped outer layer of material and that requires no internal frame; examples of a shell structure include an igloo and an egg (278)

shrinking apple theory a nineteenth-century theory about Earth's structure; according to this theory, Earth was once a hot mass, which cooled and shrank over time; the theory compared Earth to an apple that dried up, causing wrinkles

(mountains) and valleys between the wrinkles (oceans and lakes)

SI (from the French *Le Système international d'unités*) the international system of measurement units, including such terms as kilogram, metre, and second

signal information about temperature, such as an electrical current (199)

society a group of people united by common goals and interests

softwood a type of tree, usually used in construction because it has straight grain, is low in cost, and widely available

soft water water that contains few dissolved minerals

soil a mixture of weathered rock, organic matter, mineral fragments, water, and air

soil profile a description of the characteristics of the different layers that make up a particular soil (372)

solar energy energy from the Sun (241)

solar collectors mechanical systems and devices, usually containing water, or air, used in active solar heating systems (243)

soldering [SO-duhr-ing] a process in which a melted material is applied to a different type of material; the melted material hardens when it cools, forming a rigid joint that holds the other material in place (292)

solid one of the states or phases of matter; in the solid phase, materials keep a specific shape and size

solidification change from a liquid to a solid

solubility the limit to how concentrated a solution can become, before it becomes a saturated solution at a particular temperature; for example, no more than 35 to 37 g of salt will dissolve in 100 g of cold (0°C) water

soluble of a substance, able to be dissolved in a particular solvent; something that is soluble is called a solute

solute a substance that can be dissolved in a solvent; for example, salt is a solute that dissolves in water

solution a homogeneous mixture of two or more substances; the distinct properties of the different substances that make up the solution are combined into one set of properties

solvent a substance into which a solute may be dissolved; for example, water is a solvent that dissolves sugar

sonar (sound **n**avigation **a**nd **r**anging**)** a technology that bounces sound waves off an object to determine its distance from the source of the waves (387)

species a narrow classification grouping for organisms; e.g., a wolf is the species *Canis lupus*, while a dog is the species *Canis familiaris*

specific heat capacity of a material, the energy change that is required to warm or cool a standard amount of the material (1 g or 1 kg) by 1°C

specifications a set of standards or expectations; criteria

spider map a concept map used to organize a central idea and a jumble of associated ideas that are not necessarily related to each other

spin stabilization the tendency of an object that is spinning on its axis to move in a predictable manner; an example of spin stabilization is the motion of a bicycle wheel (340)

stable of a structure, tending to maintain its shape and position

stamen male part of a flower (122)

states of matter the different forms (solid, liquid, or gas) that matter can take; also known as phases of matter

stigma sticky tip of a pistil (122)

strata layers of sedimentary rock (423)

stratification the arrangement of sedimentary rock in visible layers (364)

streak the colour of a mineral in powdered form; a property useful in the identification of minerals (357)

stress an internal or external force that acts on an object, perhaps causing it to move or change shape

structure an object with a definite size and shape, which serves a purpose or function. The parts of a structure have a specific arrangement that remains the same (270)

STS an abbreviation for the interrelationships among science, technology, and societal issues

style tube connecting the stigma and ovary (122)

subduction zone a place on Earth's crust where high pressure pushes one very large piece of rock below another; earthquakes are often formed in subduction zones (393)

sublimation a change in state when a gas changes directly to a solid or a solid changes directly to a gas (220)

succession the process by which new species gradually replace old species in an ecosystem (56)

summer fallow the practice of cultivating land to control weeds but planting no crops

supersaturated solution a solution that contains more solute than would normally dissolve at a particular temperature

surface area the amount of surface of an object; measured in square units such as cm²

surface waves the slowest moving of the three types of seismic waves that are produced by an earthquake, originating from its epicentre; surface waves do the most damage of the three types of waves (398)

sustainability resources of nature are being renewed at least as quickly as they are being used, and all wastes are able to be completely absorbed (29)

sustainability in the study of plants, being able to grow food and fibre while keeping our natural systems healthy for the long term (132)

symbiosis [sim-bih-OH-sis] an interaction between organisms of different species living in close proximity to each other in a relationship that lasts over time (14)

syncline a downfold of a rock layer (413)

system I. a set of things that are organized and interact with each other to such an extent that they may be described as a single unit II. in biology, a group of organs that work together to perform a major function (e.g., respiratory system, root system)

table an orderly arrangement of facts set out for easy reference; for example, an arrangement of numerical values in rows or columns

taproot a single, prominent root with numerous small roots coming out of it (105)

technology the design and construction of devices, processes, and materials to solve practical problems and to satisfy human needs and wants

temperature a relative measure of how hot or cold something is, measured on a scale; the average kinetic energy of the particles in a substance (204)

tensile strength a measure of the largest tension force that a material can withstand before changing shape or breaking apart (307)

tension force a force that pulls on a material and stretches it apart (307)

texture of soil, how it feels to the touch; texture is affected by the size of the particles in the soil

theory an explanation of an event that has been supported by consistent, repeated experimental results and has therefore been accepted by many scientists

theory of plate tectonics theory suggesting the lithosphere is divided into plates that interact with each other (390)

thermal conduction the direct transfer of thermal energy from one particle or object to another through contact or collision (229)

thermal energy the energy generated by the movement or vibration of particles; the total kinetic energy of all the particles in a substance (205)

thermal pollution a warming of the environment that results from human activities, such as the burning of fossil fuels (247)

thermogenic [THUR-moh-jen-ik] of plants or animals, able to raise their own temperature

thermograph a thermometer that records temperature

thermometer a device used to measure temperature (193)

thrust faulting low angle faulting of rock (413)

thrust line the line that runs downward from an object's centre of gravity, through which force is transferred

tie a device used to add strength to a structure, usually by forming a rigid triangle at the point where the pieces come together in a right angle; a type of rigid joint, such as a piece of rope, that is used to pull objects or materials together and hold them in place

topsoil the topmost layer of soil, which is dark-coloured and rich in humus (150, 372)

torsion force a force that acts on a material by twisting its ends in opposite directions (307)

torsion strength a measure of the largest torsion force that a material can withstand and still be able to return to its original shape (307)

trace fossil a type of fossil in which evidence of animal activities have been preserved (419)

transform boundary an area of Earth's crust where plates are sliding past each other

transformation the changing of a substance or material with a particular set of properties into a new substance (or substances); a change in the characteristics of something

transpiration the process in which water that is taken in by a plant or an animal evaporates from the organism (51)

tubers the swollen, underground stems of potatoes

twist of a material, to change shape through the application of torsion forces

unifying theory a single theory that explains many different natural phenomena, events, objects, or processes

unsaturated solution a solution in which more of a solute can be dissolved at a particular temperature

variable a condition or factor that can influence the outcome of an experiment

vegetative (asexual) reproduction a type of reproduction that occurs when a "parent" plant grows new plants from its roots, stems, or leaves (118)

Venn diagram a graphic organizer consisting of overlapping circles; used to compare and contrast two concepts or objects

vent an opening in Earth's crust through which magma can escape, forming lava (406)

vertical fault a fault in which rock moves up or down

volcano an opening in Earth's crust that can release materials such as lava, smoke, and ash; volcanoes can be either active (releasing materials) or dormant (not releasing materials)

volume the measurement of the amount of space occupied by a substance; measured in litres or cubic units such as cubic centimetres (cm^3)

warm-blooded of an organism, maintaining a relatively consistent body temperature regardless of the environment; all mammals are warm-blooded

waste heat energy that is transferred outside the system in which it is generated, without doing any useful work

water cycle the continuous movement of water through the biosphere; the water cycle consists of evaporation, transpiration, condensation, and precipitation (51)

water-holding capacity the ability of a soil to retain water; soils with low water-holding capacity allow a great deal of water to permeate through them

weathering the process in which rocks are broken down and sediment is formed by mechanical, chemical, or biological means (373)

weed a plant that grows where it is not wanted

weight the force of gravity exerted on a mass (300)

welding a process in which pieces of metal or plastic are fused together by the application of heat (292)

WHMIS an acronym that stands for Workplace Hazardous Materials Information System

Index

The page numbers in **boldface** type indicate the pages where the terms are defined. Terms that occur in investigations (*inv.*) and activities (*act.*) are also indicated.

Photo Credits

Illustration Credits